P9-DDK-301

191
P353c
v.7,8

DISCARD
Phillips Library
Bethany College

DISCARD

BETHANY
COLLEGE
LIBRARY

COLLECTED PAPERS OF
CHARLES SANDERS PEIRCE

COLLECTED PAPERS OF
CHARLES SANDERS PEIRCE

VOLUME VII
SCIENCE AND PHILOSOPHY

AND

VOLUME VIII
REVIEWS, CORRESPONDENCE,
AND BIBLIOGRAPHY

EDITED BY
ARTHUR W. BURKS

TWO VOLUMES IN ONE

THE BELKNAP PRESS OF
HARVARD UNIVERSITY PRESS

CAMBRIDGE, MASSACHUSETTS

1966

© COPYRIGHT 1958 BY THE PRESIDENT
AND FELLOWS OF HARVARD COLLEGE

Second Printing

Volumes I–VIII of the *Collected Papers of Charles Sanders Peirce* are now published by the Belknap Press of Harvard University Press, but responsibility for the content of these volumes and for the care of the entire corpus of Peirce Papers remains with the Department of Philosophy of Harvard University. The present volumes are reproduced by offset lithography from the first edition. Lists of errata are included.

DISTRIBUTED IN GREAT BRITAIN BY
OXFORD UNIVERSITY PRESS, LONDON

LIBRARY OF CONGRESS CATALOG CARD NUMBER 60–9172
PRINTED IN THE UNITED STATES OF AMERICA

Volume VII

SCIENCE AND PHILOSOPHY

191
P353c
v. 7, 8

PREFACE

When the first volume of the *Collected Papers* of Charles Peirce was published in 1931, its Introduction predicted some ten volumes in the series, those beyond the sixth being expected to contain Peirce's "writings on physics and psychology, as well as his reviews, letters, and biography." Footnotes to the subsequent text even cited some of those last volumes. Nevertheless, it was only of the six volumes that the Introduction spoke in the present tense, and these, under the editorship of Drs. Charles Hartshorne and Paul Weiss, appeared as promised, ending with Volume VI in 1935. Selection, preparation, and publication of further material was at that time impractical, and for the next twenty years the remaining papers in Harvard's custody were accessible only to such scholars as could consult them in Cambridge. In 1954, however, the Harvard Department of Philosophy was able to renew the enterprise. The Rockefeller Foundation granted to the University a subvention for the costs of further editing, and the Department was fortunate to enlist Professor Arthur W. Burks, of the University of Michigan, to perform that peculiarly exacting task. The Department is glad of this occasion to acknowledge its debt, and that of the scholarly community in general, both to the Foundation and to Professor Burks, and to remind the reader that since the expense of the further actual book-making is defrayed from royalties from the earlier volumes, which were subsidized by gifts of the late Professor James H. Woods and anonymous friends, we are still their beneficiaries too.

The present publication comprises two volumes instead of the four of the old estimate. Mr. Burks's Introduction, which follows on page xi, indicates how nearly he is completing the original plan. A substantial addition is his extraordinarily searching bibliography, with its introduction comparing the sum of published material with what still remains only in manuscript.

Besides joining in the editor's acknowledgements of those who assisted him, the Department and Publishers thank the

Houghton Library for permission to print previously unpublished correspondence between Peirce and James, Edith Davidson Harris and the Hoose Library of Philosophy at the University of Southern California for permission to print a letter from Peirce to William T. Harris, and the following for the use of copyrighted material as indicated: Helen G. Baldwin, definitions from James Mark Baldwin's *Dictionary of Philosophy and Psychology*, Vol. II; *The Nation*, several reviews; *Popular Science Monthly*, Peirce's review of Pearson's *Grammar of Science*; Whitlock's, Inc., parts of two letters reprinted from Irwin C. Lieb's *Charles S. Peirce's Letters to Lady Welby*; William James, correspondence from Peirce to his father, William James, and quotations from a Peirce manuscript, "Questions on William James's Principles of Psychology," previously printed in Ralph Barton Perry's *Thought and Character of William James*.

Harvard University
August, 1957

CONTENTS

INTRODUCTION

The first six volumes of the series, *Collected Papers of Charles Sanders Peirce*, included Peirce's main writings in general philosophy, logic (deductive, inductive, and symbolic), pragmatism, and metaphysics. The present two volumes are a continuation of this series. Volume VII is organized in three books containing papers on experimental science, scientific method, and philosophy of mind, respectively. Volume VIII contains selections from Peirce's reviews and correspondence and a bibliography of his published works.

Since Book I of Volume VII, "Experimental Science," is the only book in the series not on philosophy, its inclusion may require special comment. Much of Peirce's life was devoted to experimental science. In fact, the only permanent position Peirce held was with the United States Coast Survey, where he was employed to do research in astronomy and geodetics. Though this position allowed him considerable time for philosophy, it is nevertheless true that for more than half of his mature life his main responsibility was to conduct scientific investigation.[1] His efforts in the physical sciences resulted in a large number of published papers, several of considerable length, as well as his only published book, *Photometric Researches*, 1878.[2] Moreover, Peirce's experimental work had an important influence on his philosophy. His pragmatic theory of meaning is a generalization from scientific practice, his laboratory experience having influenced his discovery of that theory (see

[1] He was employed by the Coast Survey from September 21, 1859, to June 1, 1860, and from July 1, 1861, to December 31, 1891.

[2] See the Bibliography in Vol. VIII, especially the years 1872 through 1886; Peirce produced little in the way of results for the Coast Survey after he moved to Milford, Pa., in the spring of 1887.

5.411–412). His indeterminism was connected with his work for the Coast Survey on precise measurement.[3] And his empirical investigations in psychology (see 7.21–35) influenced his theory of mind. Thus Peirce's scientific work played an important role in his life and in the formation of his philosophy, and it is for these reasons that we have reprinted his only published article in experimental psychology and two short pieces on gravity. We have limited ourselves to this small sample of his work in physical science because, though his astronomical researches showed originality and his gravimetric work was well respected by eminent men in geodetics, Peirce remained a minor figure in these fields.

The editors of the earlier volumes made some introductory remarks about the Peirce manuscripts and their policies in editing them (Vol. I, p. iv ff.). The present editor has continued their practice of publishing only parts of some of the works, omitting large portions altogether. He has also continued the policy of selecting or compiling a draft for publication whenever there were several drafts available. The justification for these procedures is to be found in certain aspects of the Peirce manuscripts. Many of the manuscripts are internally variable in quality: one frequently finds publishable sections in the midst of material which either is of little contemporary interest or presents ideas better treated in other manuscripts. Moreover, there are often alternative and sometimes incomplete versions of the same work to choose from; and in some cases no final version is discernible. The editor must then make selections and, if necessary, piece together drafts from the hodgepodge of partial drafts. These characteristics are so typical that any satisfactory edition of Peirce's papers must contain a great deal of fragmentary material.

The present editor has also continued the plan of organization pursued in the previous volumes, breaking up manuscripts, books, and series of articles, and arranging the resultant ma-

---

[3] Cf. 6.44, 6.46. Peirce's most original contribution to geodetics was the discovery of a new source of error in gravity measurement; this is described at 7.1–12. Peirce also did research for the Coast Survey on standards of measurement.

terials primarily by subject matter rather than chronologically. Though this plan tends to bring together under one heading passages on a given topic, it makes Peirce's writings appear to be more disorganized than they actually are. To mitigate this shortcoming, there is included in Volume VIII as complete a bibliography of Peirce's published works as the editor could compile. This bibliography is arranged for the most part chronologically, with a connected series of articles, parts of a single manuscript, or a series of lectures grouped together under one listing. The bibliography will also assist the reader in locating any published works not reprinted in this series.

The chapter and section headings have been chosen by the editor; when these are the same as Peirce's, the footnotes so indicate. Editorial alterations are enclosed in brackets, and the editor's footnotes are indicated by "(Ed.)." Peirce's punctuation, spelling, and underlining for emphasis have, in general, been retained. Obvious errors, however, have been corrected; and where clarity of presentation has required them, minor changes have been made in format, capitalization, abbreviations, italicizing of titles, etc., without any indication. Likewise, questions of manuscript interpretation which made no significant difference in the meaning have been settled without any indication.

The editor wishes to thank the Rockefeller Foundation and the Department of Philosophy of Harvard University for their aid in the preparation and publication of these two volumes. While giving him the kindest and fullest assistance, both left him completely free in his work and have no responsibility for any shortcomings in it. The editor is also grateful for a grant for editorial assistance from the Horace H. Rackham School of Graduate Studies of the University of Michigan.

For assistance in locating and evaluating various Peirce materials, the editor is personally indebted to William Alston, Jackson Cope, Carolyn Eisele, Mrs. E. L. C. Hales, Murray Murphey, W. E. Schlaretzki, James F. Sheridan, Manley Thompson, and Philip Wiener; to the previous editors, Charles Hartshorne and Paul Wiess; and especially to Max Fisch, who also read the manuscript and made many valuable suggestions. In all cases the final decision as to what materials were to be included was made by the editor, and the responsibility for the choices is his alone.

The editor expresses his deep thanks to Grace L. Wood, who assisted greatly in the preparation of the bibliography and did much of the editorial work for the volumes, and to his wife, Alice, for her helpful advice.

Arthur W. Burks

Ann Arbor, Michigan

Book I

EXPERIMENTAL SCIENCE

CHAPTER 1

MEASUREMENT OF THE FORCE OF GRAVITY

§1. A SOURCE OF ERROR IN PENDULUM MEASUREMENTS [1]

1. The fact that the rate of a pendulum might be largely influenced by the elastic yielding of its support was first pointed out by Dr. Thomas Young in his article on Tides in the Encyclopædia Britannica, where he gave a correct mathematical analysis of the problem. Kater made use of the *noddy*, or inverted pendulum of Hardy, to assure himself that its support was sufficiently steady.

2. Hardy's noddy is a pendulum turning with a reed spring and provided with an adjustable bob. It differs from an ordinary pendulum, first, in being upside down, that is, having its center of mass above its point of support; and second, in having a spring so strong as to act a little more strongly than gravity. The force tending to bring the pendulum to the vertical is then the excess of the force of the spring over the moment of gravity. In this way the noddy is easily adjusted so as to have the same period of oscillation as the pendulum used to determine gravity, while its moment of inertia is very small. In a note at the end of this paper I give the mathematical analysis of this state of things, from which it will be seen that Kater might have constructed his noddy in such a manner as to detect any amount of flexure sufficient to have a serious effect upon the period of his pendulum.

[1] (Ed.) From pp. 359–361 of Appendix 14, "On the Flexure of Pendulum Supports," [CS 1881] 1883, pp. 359–441.

This gives a succinct account, in Peirce's own words, of his most original work in the field of pendulum measurements.

3

3.   Bessel, at the end of §3 of his great memoir on the length of the second's pendulum at Königsberg, states that he also used Hardy's noddy, and that he swung his pendulum again after stiffening the support. He adds that the effect on the period would probably be the same for his long pendulum as for his short one — a very just remark — which made it less necessary for him to attend to the rigidity of the stand.

4.   The construction of English pendulum supports, that of Bassevi, for example, shows that in that country this source of error was never overlooked. It is noticed even in brief accounts in English of the process of measuring gravity. Thus, a writer in the Encyclopædia Britannica proposed to make use of two different reversible pendulums of the same form but of different weights, in order to take account of the flexure, an idea lately borrowed by M. Cellerier.

5.   When the reversible pendulum came into use the study of the writings of the older observers seems to have been neglected,[2] and the grave errors due to flexure were never suspected until Albrecht found a value of gravity at Berlin differing by nearly 2 millimeters from that of Bessel. So little was the true cause of this discrepancy at first suspected that it was paradoxically attributed to the neglect of a buoyancy correction.

6.   In 1875, however, General Baeyer gravely suspected that the period of a pendulum swinging upon a Repsold tripod was affected by the oscillation of the latter, and in a circular addressed to the members of the committee on the pendulum of the International Geodetic Congress, he wrote: "The necessity of suspending the pendulum from a stand is a source of error, since a pendulum swinging on a stand sets the latter into oscillation and so influences the rate of the former. The effect could be diminished by the use of a shorter pendulum and smaller stand; but whether it would be rendered entirely insensible is open to question."

7.   It was at this time that I first received the Repsold apparatus from the makers, of whom it had been ordered two years before, on the occasion of my first being charged with the pendulum operations of the Coast Survey. Becoming ac-

[2] Thus, Bessel's idea of directly measuring the position of the center of mass was supposed by the Swiss *savans* to belong to M. Cellerier.

4

quainted with General Baeyer's doubts, I determined to settle the question by measuring the flexibility of the Repsold tripod at the earliest opportunity. This I did at Geneva, where, though I only made a rough measurement, I found that the flexure was fully sufficient to account for the discrepancy between the determinations of Bessel and of Albrecht.

8. On September 25 of the same year I communicated my result to the standing committee of the Geodetical Congress.[3] At the same sitting the reports of the different members of the pendulum committee were read. Dr. Bruhns said: "The question whether the stand is set into oscillation, and whether the rate of the pendulum is influenced thereby is, in my opinion, well worth investigation. But I should suppose that the stand could be made so stiff as to eliminate this source of error for a pendulum used only as a relative instrument." The views of M. Hirsch, who is so much occupied with the going of timekeepers, are interesting. He said: "The fear that the tripod of suspension may also enter into oscillation, unless it be a fact established by direct observations, seems to me unfounded. Indeed, it cannot be supposed that there are any true oscillations of a body of such a form resting on three points. Besides, the movement of the pendulum whose mechanical moment (*moment mécanique*) is slight on account of its small velocity, could only be communicated to the tripod by the friction of the knife on the supporting plane. Now, this friction is insignificant, as the slowness of the decrement of the amplitude shows, this being almost entirely due to the resistance of the air." It may be observed that the rolling friction of the knife edge is, in truth, very slight, but the amount of the sliding friction is sufficient to hold the knife in place on the supporting plane. Dr. von Oppolzer, the designer of the Repsold tripod in its definitive form, said that the construction of the stand rendered any serious flexure *a priori* improbable; but he did not support this opinion by any calculations.

9.   During the spring of 1876, having already measured the flexibility of the tripod in Paris, I remeasured it in Berlin,

---

[3] (Ed.) [Bibliography] G-1875-5. The quotations from the circular by Baeyer, given in 7.6, and from the reports, given in this paragraph, are in [International Geodetic Comm., Paris, 1875] 1875, pp. 90–91, 93, and 96.

where my experiments were witnessed by General Baeyer and
a party of gentlemen attached to the Prussian Survey.

10.   In October, 1876, at the meeting of the standing committee of the International Geodetical Union at Brussels, the
result of my experiments was announced by General Baeyer.[4]
M. Hirsch described certain experimental researches undertaken by him to ascertain whether there was any such flexure
in the case of the Swiss tripod. He had, in the first place,
employed an extremely sensitive level, which had not entered
into oscillation while the pendulum was swinging upon it. It
is not clear why M. Hirsch employed a very sensitive level, the
natural time of oscillation of which would differ much more from
the period of the pendulum than that of a less sensitive level
would do. He also used an artificial horizon in the same way. M.
Hirsch's conclusion is that "there remains no doubt that the
Swiss stand is free from every trace of such oscillations." Dr.
von Oppolzer entirely agreed with the views of M. Hirsch.

11.   In the following summer I addressed to M. Plantamour
a paper upon the subject, to be submitted to the next meeting
of the Geodetical Congress.[5] In this note, which is reprinted
at the end of the present report, I first give a mathematical
analysis of the problem. I next show experimentally that the
motion of the knife-edge support is not a translation, but is a
rotation, so that different parts of the head of the tripod, only
a few centimeters distant from one another, move through
very different distances. Consequently, measures of the flexure
made anywhere except at the center of the knife-edge plane
require an important correction before they can be used to
correct the periods. This is confirmed by experiments with a
mirror while the pendulum is in motion. I next give a brief
résumé of my statical measures of the flexure. I then give
measures of the actual flexure under the oscillation of the
pendulum, and show that the statical and dynamical flexibili-
ties are approximately equal. Finally, I swing the same pendulum upon the Repsold support and upon another having seven

---

[4] (Ed.) See [Bibliography] G-1875–5. The quotation in this paragraph from
Hirsch is in [International Geodetic Comm., Brussels, 1876] 1877, p. 18.
   [5] (Ed.)   [Bibliography] G-1877–3.

times the rigidity of that one, and I show that the difference of the periods of oscillation agrees with the theory.

12. Immediately upon the reception of my manuscript, MM. Hirsch and Plantamour commenced new researches, designed to form an "étude approfondie de ce phénomène." These were embodied in a paper by M. Plantamour, which was read to the Geodetical Congress, and which has since been expanded into a memoir entitled "Recherches expérimentales sur le mouvement simultané d'un pendule et de ses supports." [6] M. Plantamour finds fault with me, first, for having measured the flexure with a force five or ten times that of the deflecting force of the pendulum; and second, for measuring the elasticity statically instead of dynamically. The reply to the first objection is that the properties of metals are known to a great extent, that elasticity is not "une force capricieuse," and that no fact is better established than that an elastic strain is proportional to the stress up to near the limit of elasticity, which limit was not approached in the author's experiments. As to the second objection, I had shown by experiment that the statical and dynamical flexures are nearly equal; and I am willing to leave it to time to show whether this will not be assumed in future measures of the flexure of future pendulum supports. M. Plantamour caused a fine point fixed into the head of the tripod to press against a little mirror, mounted on an axis; and then observed the reflection of a scale in a telescope. The length of the path of light from the scale to the telescope divided by the distance of the bearing point from the axis of the mirror he calls the *grossissement*; so that had he used a fixed star in place of his scale, the *grossissement* would have been virtually infinite. From the given length of the lever it would appear that a movement of $0^\mu.03$ in the point would turn the mirror $4''$. The aperture of the mirror is not stated, but it cannot be supposed that the error of observation would be less than this. It does not seem to me that the use of this mode of measurement, which magnifies the motion but little more than my method, is conducive to accuracy, especially in investigating the difference between statical and dynamical flexure. A

[6] (Ed.) See [Bibliography] G-1877-3.

certain finite force presses together the point and the lever. Dividing this force by the minute area of pressure, we find the pressure upon the metal is very great, approaching the crushing pressure. Now, the behavior of metals under great pressure is greatly influenced by the time. But my objection is not merely theoretical; I have myself made experiments upon this method, and, making them as skillfully as I could, I still found great uncertainty in the results.

§2. SIX REASONS FOR THE PROSECUTION OF PENDULUM EXPERIMENTS [7]

13.   [Reason 1.]   The first scientific object of a geodetical survey is unquestionably the determination of the earth's figure. Now, it appears probable that pendulum experiments afford the best method of determining the amount of oblateness of the spheroid of the earth; for the calculated probable error in the determination of the quantity in question from the pendulum work already executed does not exceed that of the best determination from triangulation and latitude observations, and the former determination will shortly be considerably improved. Besides, the measurements of astronomical arcs upon the surface of the earth cover only limited districts, and the oblateness deduced from them is necessarily largely affected, as Mr. Schott has remarked, by the old arc of Peru, the real error of which no doubt greatly exceeds that which the calculation attributes to it, so that we cannot really hold it probable that the error of this method is so small as it is calculated by least squares to be. On the other hand, the pendulum determinations are subject to no great errors of a kind which least squares cannot ascertain; they are widely scattered over the surface of the earth; they are very numerous; they are combined to obtain the ellipticity by a simple arithmetical process; and, all things considered, the calculated

[7] (Ed.) "Six Reasons for the Prosecution of Pendulum Experiments," pp. 506–508 of Appendix 22, "Report of a Conference on Gravity Determinations, Held in Washington, in May, 1882," [CS 1882] 1883, as corrected from a reprint marked "Copy read by C. S. Peirce," Widener IC2c.

This is reprinted here because it is a good statement by Peirce of what he thought the value of his pendulum work to be.

probable error of the oblateness deduced from them is worthy of unusual confidence. In this connection it is very significant, as pointed out by Colonel Clarke (*Geodesy*, p. vi), that while the value derived from pendulum work has for a long time remained nearly constant, that derived from measurements of arcs has altered as more data have been accumulated, and the change has continually been in the direction of accord with the other method. It is needless to say that the comparison of the expense of the two methods of obtaining this important quantity is immensely in favor of pendulum work.

14.   [Reason 2.]   Recent investigations also lead us to attach increased importance to experiments with the pendulum in their connection with metrology. The plan of preserving and transmitting to posterity an exact knowledge of the length of the yard after the metallic bar itself should have undergone such changes as the vicissitudes of time bring to all material objects, was at one time adopted by the British Government. It was afterwards abandoned because pendulum operations had fallen into desuetude, and because doubts had been thrown upon the accuracy of Kater's original measure of the length of the second's pendulum. Yet I do not hesitate to say that this plan should now be revived, for the following reasons.

15.   First, because measurements of the length of the second's pendulum, although formerly subject to grave uncertainties, are now secure against all but very small errors. Indeed, we now know that the determinations by Kater and his contemporaries, after receiving certain necessary corrections, are by no means so inaccurate as they were formerly suspected to be. Secondly, metallic bars have now been proved, by the investigations of Professor Hilgard [8] and others, to undergo unexpected spontaneous alterations of their length, so that some check upon these must be resorted to. To this end the late Henri Ste. Claire Deville and Mascart constructed for the International Geodetical Association a metre ruled upon a sort of bottle of platin-iridium, with the idea that the cubic contents of this bottle should be determined from time to time, so as to ascertain whether its dimensions had undergone any change.

[8] (Ed.) J. E. Hilgard was Superintendent of the United States Coast and Geodetic Survey at this time.

I am myself charged with, and have nearly completed, a very exact comparison of the length of a metre bar with that of a wave of light, for the same purpose.[9] Neither of these two methods is infallible, however, for the platin-iridium bottle may change its three dimensions unequally, and the solar system may move into a region of space in which the luminiferous ether may have a slightly different density (or elasticity), so that the wave length of the ray of light used would be different. These two methods should therefore be supplemented by the comparatively simple and easy one of accurately comparing the length of the second's pendulum with the metre or yard bar. Thirdly, I do not think it can be gainsaid by any one who examines the facts that the measurements of the length of the second's pendulum by Borda and by Biot in Paris and by Bessel in Berlin do, as a matter of fact, afford us a better and more secure knowledge of the length of their standard bars than we can attain in any other way. So also I have more confidence in the value of the ratio of the yard to the metre obtained by the comparison of the measurements of the length of the second's pendulum at the Kew observatory by Heaviside in terms of the yard and by myself in terms of the metre than I have in all the elaborate and laborious comparisons of bars which have been directed to the same end. I will even go so far as to say that a physicist in any remote station could ascertain the length of the metre accurately to a one hundred thousandth part more safely and easily by experiments with an invariable reversible pendulum than by the transportation of an ordinary metallic bar.

16. A new application of the pendulum to metrology is now being put into practice by me. Namely, I am to oscillate simultaneously a yard reversible pendulum and a metre reversible pendulum. I shall thus ascertain with great precision the ratio of their lengths without any of those multiform comparisons which would be necessary if this were done by the usual method. These two pendulums will be swung, the yard one in the office of the Survey, at a temperature above 62°F., which is the standard temperature of the yard, the other nearly at 0°C., which is the standard temperature of the metre; and thus we

[9] (Ed.) Cf. [Bibliography] G-1879-1, G-1881-5, G-1882-12.

shall have two bars compared at widely different temperatures, which, according to ordinary processes, is a matter of great difficulty. The knife-edges of the pendulums will be interchanged and the experiments repeated. Finally, the yard pendulum will be compared with a yard bar and the metre pendulum with a metre bar, and last of all the yard pendulum with its yard bar will be sent to England, the metre pendulum with its metre bar to France, for comparison with the primary standards; and thus it is believed the ratio of yard to metre will be ascertained with the highest present attainable exactitude.

17. [Reason 3.] Geologists affirm that from the values of gravity at different points useful inferences can be drawn in regard to the geological constitution of the underlying strata. For instance, it has been found that when the gravity upon high lands and mountains is corrected for difference of centrifugal force and distance from the earth's centre, it is very little greater than at the sea-level. Consequently it cannot be that there is an amount of extra matter under these elevated stations equal to the amount of rock which projects above the sea-level; and the inference is that the elevations have been mainly produced by vertical and not by horizontal displacements of material. On the other hand, Mendenhall has found that gravity on Fujisan, the well-known volcanic cone of Japan, which is about 12,000 feet high, and which is said to have been upheaved in a single night, about 300 B.C., is as much less than that in Tokio as if the mountain had been wholly produced by horizontal transfer. This conclusion, if correct, must plainly have a decisive bearing upon certain theories of volcanic action. Again, it has long been known that gravity is in excess upon islands, and I have shown that this excess is fully equal to the attraction of the sea-water. This shows that the interior of the earth is not so liquid and incompressible that the weight of the sea has pressed away to the sides the underlying matter. But in certain seas gravity is even more in excess than can be due to the attraction of the ocean, as if they had been receptacles of additional matter washed down from the land. It is evident that only the paucity of existing data prevents inferences like these from being carried much further. On the two sides of the great fault in the Rocky Mountains gravity

11

must be very different, and if we knew how great this difference was we should learn something more about the geology of this region; and many such examples might be cited.

18. [Reason 4.] Gravity is extensively employed as a unit in the measurement of forces. Thus, the pressure of the atmosphere is, in the barometer, balanced against the weight of a measured column of mercury; the mechanical equivalent of heat is measured in foot-pounds, etc. All such measurements refer to a standard which is different in different localities, and it becomes more and more important to determine the amounts of these differences as the exactitude of measurement is improved.

19. [Reason 5.] It may be hoped that as our knowledge of the constitution of the earth's crust becomes, by the aid of the pendulum investigations, more perfected, we shall be able to establish methods by which we can securely infer from the vertical attractions of mountains, etc., what their horizontal attractions and the resulting deflections of the plumb-line must be.

20. [Reason 6.] Although in laying out the plan of a geodetical survey the relative utility of the knowledge of different quantities ought to be taken into account, and such account must be favorable to pendulum work, yet it is also true that nothing appertaining to such a survey ought to be neglected, and that too great stress ought not to be put upon the demands of the practically useful. The knowledge of the force of gravity is not a mere matter of utility alone, it is also one of the fundamental kinds of quantity which it is the business of a geodetical survey to measure. Astronomical latitudes and longitudes are determinations of the direction of gravity; pendulum experiments determine its amount. The force of gravity is related in the same way to the latitude and longitude as the intensity of magnetic force is related to magnetical declination and inclination; and as a magnetical survey would be held to be imperfect in which measurements of intensity were omitted, to the same extent must a geodetical survey be held to be imperfect in which the determinations of gravity had been omitted; and such would be the universal judgment of the scientific world.

12

CHAPTER 2

SMALL DIFFERENCES OF SENSATION

§1. ORIGINAL PAPER [1]

21.   The physiological psychologists assume that two nerve excitations alike in quality will only produce distinguishable sensations provided they differ in intensity by an amount greater than a fixed ratio. The least perceptible difference of the excitations divided by half their sum is what they call the *Unterschiedsschwelle*. Fechner [2] gives an experiment to prove the fact assumed, namely: He finds that two very dim lights placed nearly in line with the edge of an opaque body show but one shadow of the edge. It will be found, however, that this phenomenon is not a clearly marked one, unless the lights are nearly in range. If the experiment is performed with lateral shifting of one of the lights, and with a knowledge of the effects of a telescope upon the appearance of terrestrial objects at night, it will be found very far from conclusive.

22.   The conception of the psychologists is certainly a diffi-

[1] (Ed.) "On Small Differences of Sensation," *Memoirs of the National Academy of Sciences* 3, Part I (1884) 73–83, with corrections from a reprint marked, "Prof. John W. Langley, With the regards of C. S. Peirce," Widener IC1a.

The article was written with Joseph Jastrow, a student of Peirce at Johns Hopkins University. In *The Nation* 98 (14 May 1914) 571 Jastrow says of it: "It was Mr. Peirce who introduced me to the possibility of an experimental study of a psychological problem. He provided the problem, the instruments which I set up in my room, the method, and the mode of reaching the results; these were printed over our joint names." See also Joseph Jastrow, "Charles S. Peirce as a Teacher," *The Journal of Philosophy, Psychology, and Scientific Method* 13 (21 Dec. 1916) 724.

Edwin G. Boring, in his *A History of Experimental Psychology*, p. 529, refers to "On Small Differences of Sensation" as "an important paper on the method of determining the differential limen . . ."

[2] Elemente der Psychophysik, I, p. 242.

cult one to seize. According to their own doctrine, in which the
observed facts seem fully to bear them out, the intensity of the
sensation increases continuously with the excitation, so that
the least increase of the latter must produce a corresponding
increase of the former. And, indeed, the hypothesis that a
continuous increase of the excitation would be accompanied by
successive discrete increments of the sensation, gratuitous as
it would be, would not be sufficient to account for a constant
Unterschiedsschwelle. We are therefore forced to conclude
that if there be such a phenomenon, it has its origin, not in the
faculty of sensation, but in that of comparing sensations. In
short, if the phenomenon were established, we should be forced
to say that there was a least perceptible difference of sensation
— a difference which, though existing in sensation, could not
be brought into consciousness by any effort of attention. But
the errors of our judgments in comparing our sensations seem
sufficiently accounted for by the slow and doubtless complicated
process by which the impression is conveyed from the periphery
to the brain; for this must be liable to more or less accidental
derangement at every step of its progress. Accordingly we find
that the frequencies of errors of different magnitudes follow the
probability curve, which is the law of an effect brought about
by the sum of an infinite number of infinitesimal causes. This
theory, however, does not admit of an *Unterschiedsschwelle*.
On the contrary, it leads to the method of least squares, according to which the multiplication of observations will indefinitely reduce the error of their mean, so that if of two excitations one were ever so little the more intense, in the long run
it would be judged to be the more intense the majority of
times. It is true that the astronomers themselves have not
usually supposed that this would be the case, because (apart
from constant errors, which have no relevancy to the present
question) they have supposed this extreme result to be contrary to common sense. But it has seemed to us that the most
satisfactory course would be to subject the question to the test
of direct experiment. If there be a least perceptible difference,
then when two excitations differing by less than this are presented to us, and we are asked to judge which is the greater,
we ought to answer wrong as often as right in the long run.

14

Whereas, if the theory of least squares is correct, we not only ought to answer right oftener than wrong, but we ought to do so in a predictable ratio of cases.[3]

23.   We have experimented with the pressure sense, observing the proportion of errors among judgments as to which is the greater of two pressures, when it is known that the two are two stated pressures, and the question presented for the decision of the observer is, which is which? From the probability, thus ascertained, of committing an error of a given magnitude, the probable error of a judgment can be calculated according to the mathematical theory of errors. If, now, we find that when the ratio of the two pressures is smaller than a certain ratio, the erroneous judgments number one-half of the whole, while the mathematical theory requires them to be sensibly fewer, then this theory is plainly disproved, and the maximum ratio at which this phenomenon is observed the so-called *Unterschiedsschwelle*. If, on the other hand, the values obtained for the probable error are the same for errors varying from three times to one-fourth of the probable error (the smallest for which it is easy to collect sufficient observations), then the theory of the method of least squares is shown to hold good within those limits, the presumption will be that it extends

---

[3] The rule for finding this ratio is as follows: Divide the logarithm of the ratio of excitations by the probable error and multiply the quotient by 0.477. Call this product t. Enter it in the table of the integral θt, given in most works on probabilities; θt is the proportion of cases in which the error will be less than the difference between the given excitations. In all these cases, of course, we shall answer correctly, and also by chance in one-half of the remaining cases. The proportion of erroneous answers is therefore $(1-\theta t) \div 2$. In the following table the first column gives the quotient of the logarithm of the ratio of excitation, divided by the probable error, and the second column shows the proportion of erroneous judgments:

0.0	0.50
0.05	0.49
0.1	0.47
0.25	0.43
0.5	0.37
1.0	0.25

To guess the correct card out of a pack of fifty-two once in eleven times it would be necessary to have a sensation amounting to 0.37 of the probable error. This would be a sensation of which we should probably never become aware, as will appear below.

still further, and it is possible that it holds for the smallest differences of excitation. But, further, if this law is shown to hold good for difference so slight that the observer is not conscious of being able to discriminate between the sensations at all, all reason for believing in an *Unterschiedsschwelle* is destroyed. The mathematical theory has the advantage of yielding conceptions of greater definiteness than that of the physiologists, and will thus tend to improve methods of observation. Moreover, it affords a ready method for determining the sensibility or fineness of perception and allows of a comparison of one observer's results with the results of others; for, knowing the number of errors in a certain number of experiments, and accepting the conclusions of this paper, the calculated ratio to the total excitation of that variation of excitation, in judging which we should err one time out of four, measures the sensibility. Incidentally our experiments will afford additional information upon the value of the normal average sensibility for the pressure sense, which they seem to make a finer sense than it has hitherto been believed to be. But in this regard two things have to be noted: (1) Our value relates to the probable error or the value for the point at which an error is committed half the time; (2) in our experiments there were two opportunities for judging, for the initial weight was either first increased and then diminished, or *vice versa*, the subject having to say which of these two double changes was made. It would seem at first blush that the value thus obtained ought to be multiplied by $\sqrt{2}(1.414)$ to get the error of a single judgment. Yet this would hardly be correct, because the judgment, in point of fact, depended almost exclusively on the sensation of increase of pressure, the decrease being felt very much less. The ratio $\sqrt{2}(1.414)$ would therefore be too great, and 1.2 would perhaps be about correct. The advantage of having two changes in one experiment consists in this: If only one change were employed, then some of the experiments would have an increase of excitation only and the others a decrease only; and since the former would yield a far greater amount of sensation than the latter, the nature of the results would be greatly complicated; but when each experiment embraces a double change this difference in the amount of sensation caused by an in-

16

crease and decrease of pressure affects every experiment alike, and the liability to error is constant.[4]

24.   Throughout our observations we noted the degree of confidence with which the observer gave his judgment upon a scale of four degrees, as follows:

0 denoted absence of any preference for one answer over its opposite, so that it seemed nonsensical to answer at all.

1 denoted a distinct leaning to one alternative.

2 denoted some little confidence of being right.

3 denoted as strong a confidence as one would have about such sensations.

We do not mean to say that when zero was the recorded confidence, there was absolutely no sensation of preference for the answer given. We only mean that there was no sensation that the observer noticed when attending to his feelings of this sort as closely as he conveniently could, namely, closely enough to mark them on this scale. The scale of confidence fluctuated considerably. Thus, when Mr. Jastrow passed from experiments upon differences of weight of 60, 30, and 15 on the thousand to differences of 20, 10, and 5 on the thousand, although the accuracy of his judgments was decidedly improved, his confidence fell off very greatly, owing to his no longer having the sensation produced by a difference of 60 present to his memory. The estimations of confidence were also rough, and might be improved in future work. The average marks seem to conform to the formula —

$$m = c \, \log \frac{p}{1-p}$$

where m denotes the degree of confidence on the scale, p denotes the probability of the answer being right, and c is a constant which may be called the index of confidence.

25.   To show that this formula approximates to the truth, we compare it with the average marks assigned to estimates of differences for which more than a hundred experiments were made. Mr. Jastrow's experiments are separated into groups, which will be explained below.

[4] The number of errors, when an increase of weight was followed by a decrease, was slightly less than when the first change was a decrease of pressure.

17

Ratio of pressures.	Peirce, observer. $c=1.25.$		Jastrow, observer.			
			First group. $c=1.5.$		Second group. $c=0.0.$	
	Mean confidence.		Mean confidence.		Mean confidence.	
	Observed.	Calculated.	Observed.	Calculated.	Observed.	Calculated.
1.015...	0.14	0.10	0.30	0.2	0.34	0.2
1.030...	0.30	0.35	0.40	0.42	0.55	0.56
1.060...	0.70	0.70	0.85	0.87	1.02	1.22

Ratio of pressures.	Jastrow, observer.			
	Third group. $c=0.25.$		Fourth group. $c=0.4.$	
	Mean confidence.		Mean confidence.	
	Observed.	Calculated.	Observed.	Calculated.
1.005...........	0.00	0.03	0.00	0.06
1.010...........	0.07	0.06	0.05	0.12
1.020...........	0.12	0.12	0.50	0.39

26. The judgments enunciated with any given degree of confidence were more likely to be right with greater differences than with smaller differences. To show this, we give the frequency of the different marks in Mr. Jastrow's second, third, and fourth groups.[5]

27. The apparatus used was an adaptation of a "Fairbanks" post-office scale; upon the end of the beam of which was fixed a square enlargement (about one-half inch square), with a flat top, which served to convey the pressure to the finger in a manner to be presently described. This was tightly

[5] The result of our observations on the confidence connected with the judgments is as follows:

[Subject, Mr. Peirce.]		
Variations.	Average confidence.	Number of sets of 50.
Grams.		
60	.67	7
30	.28	6
15	.15	5

covered with an India-rubber cap, to prevent sensations of
cold, etc., from contact with the metal. A kilogram placed in
the pan of the balance brought a pressure of one-fourth of
its weight upon the finger. The differential pressure was produced by lowering upon the pan of the balance a smaller pan
into which the proper weights could be firmly fixed; this little
pan had its bottom of cork, and was placed upon a piece of
flannel which constantly remained in the pan of the balance.

[Subject, Mr. Jastrow.]		
60	.90	13
30	.51	12
15	.30	12
20	.11	12
10	.06	12
5	.00	10

In 1,125 experiments (subject, Mr. Peirce) — variations 15, 30, and 60 grams
— there occurred confidence of 3, 35 times (3 per cent.); of 2, 102 times (9
per cent.); of 1, 282 times (25 per cent.); of 0, 706 times (63 per cent.). In
these experiments there were 332 (29 per cent.) errors committed, of which
1 (0.3 per cent.) was made in connection with a confidence 3; 10 (3 per cent.)
with a confidence 2; 51 (15 per cent.) with a confidence 1; 270 (81 per cent.)
with a confidence 0. From which we find that in connection with a confidence
of 3 there occurred 1 error in 35 cases (3 per cent.); with a confidence of 2,
10 errors in 102 cases (10 per cent.); with a confidence of 1, 51 errors in 282
cases (18 per cent.); with a confidence of 0, 270 errors in 706 cases (38 per
cent.).

In 1,975 experiments (subject, Mr. Jastrow) — variations 15, 30, and 60
grams — there occurred confidence of 3, 62 times (3 per cent.); of 2, 196 times
(10 per cent.); of 1, 594 times (30 per cent.); of 0, 1,123 times (57 per cent.).
In these experiments there were 451 (23 per cent.) errors committed, of which
2 (0.4 per cent.) were made in connection with a confidence of 3; 12 (3 per
cent.) with a confidence of 2; 97 (22 per cent.) with a confidence of 1; 340
(75 per cent.) with a confidence of 0. Again, in connection with a confidence
of 3, errors occurred twice in 62 cases (3 per cent.); with a confidence of 2,
12 times in 196 cases (6 per cent.); with a confidence of 1, 97 times in 504
cases (16 per cent.); with a confidence of 0, 340 times in 1,123 cases (30
per cent.).

In 1,675 experiments (subject, Mr. Jastrow) — variations 5, 10, and 20
grams — there occurred confidences of 3, none; of 2, none; of 1, 115 times
(7 per cent.); of 0, 1,560 times (93 per cent.). In these experiments there were
538 (32 per cent.) errors committed, of which 16 (3 per cent.) occurred in
connection with a confidence of 1; 522 (97 per cent.) with a confidence of 0.
Again, in connection with a confidence of 1, errors occurred 16 times in 115
cases (14 per cent.); with a confidence of 0, 522 times in 1,560 cases (34 per
cent.).

19

It was lifted off and on by means of a fine India-rubber thread, which was so much stretched by the weight as certainly to avoid any noise or jar from the momentum of the descending pan. A sufficient weight could also be hung on the beam of the balance, so as to take off the entire pressure from the finger at the end of each experiment. This weight could be applied or removed by means of a cam acting upon a lever; and its bearings upon the beam were guarded by India-rubber. It was found that the use of this arrangement, which removed all annoying irregularities of sensation connected with the removal and replacement of the greater (initial) pressure, rendered the results more uniform and diminished the probable error. It also shortened the time necessary for performing the experiments, so that a series of 25 experiments was concluded before the effects of fatigue were noticeable. It may be mentioned that certain causes tended to the constant decrease of the probable error as the experiments went on, these mainly being an increased skill on the part of the *operator* and an education of the sensibility of the *subject*. The finger was supported in such a way as to be lightly but firmly held in position, all the muscles of the arm being relaxed; and the India-

Second group.

Ratio of weights.	Mark 0.	Mark 1.	Mark 2.	Mark 3.
1.015........	110 right 66 wrong	51 right 17 wrong	3 right 2 wrong	1 right 0 wrong
1.030........	106 right 35 wrong	72 right 11 wrong	23 right 1 wrong	2 right 0 wrong
1.060........	86 right 8 wrong	75 right 1 wrong	54 right 2 wrong	24 right 0 wrong

Third and fourth groups.
[Marks 2 and 3 do not occur.]

Ratio of weights.	Mark 0.	Mark 1.
1.005.................	294 right 203 wrong	2 right 1 wrong
1.010.................	366 right 192 wrong	32 right 30 wrong
1.020.................	395 right 131 wrong	68 right 6 wrong

rubber top of the brass enlargement at the end of the beam of the balance was never actually separated from the finger. The projecting arm of a filter-stand (the height of which could be adjusted) with some attachments not necessary to detail, gently prevented the finger from moving upwards under the pressure exerted by the weight in the pan. In the case of Mr. Peirce as subject (it may be noted that Mr. Peirce is left-handed, while Mr. Jastrow is strongly right-handed) the tip of forefinger, and in the case of Mr. Jastrow of the middle finger, of the left hand were used. In addition, a screen served to prevent the subject from having any indications whatever of the movements of the operator. It is hardly necessary to say that we were fully on guard against unconsciously received indications.

28.   The observations were conducted in the following manner: At each sitting three differential weights were employed. At first we always began and ended with the heaviest, but at a later period the plan was to begin on alternate days with the lightest and heaviest. When we began with the heaviest 25 observations [6] were made with that; then 25 with the middle one, and then 25 with the lightest; this constituted one-half of the sitting. It was completed by three more sets of 25, the order of the weights being reversed. When we began with the lightest the heaviest was used for the third and fourth sets. In this way 150 experiments on each of us were taken at one sitting of two hours.

29.   A pack of 25 cards were taken, 12 red and 13 black, or *vice versa*, so that in the 50 experiments made at one sitting with a given differential weight, 25 red and 25 black cards should be used. These cards were cut exactly square and their corners were distinguished by holes punched in them so as to indicate the scale of numbers (0, 1, 2, 3) used to designate the degree of confidence of the judgment. The backs of these cards were distinguished from their faces. They were, in fact, made of ordinary playing-cards. At the beginning of a set of 25, the pack was well shuffled, and, the operator and subject having taken their places, the operator was governed by the

---

[6] At first a short pause was made in the set of 25, at the option of the subject; later this was dispensed with.

color of the successive cards in choosing whether he should first diminish the weight and then increase it, or *vice versa*. If the weight was to be first increased and then diminished the operator brought the pressure exerted by the kilogram alone upon the finger of the subject by means of the lever and cam mentioned above, and when the subject said "change" he gently lowered the differential weight, resting in the small pan, upon the pan of the balance. The subject, having appreciated the sensation, again said "change," whereupon the operator removed the differential weight. If, on the other hand, the color of the card directed the weight to be first diminished and then increased, the operator had the differential weight already on the pan of the balance before the pressure was brought to bear on the finger, and made the reverse changes at the command of the subject. The subject then stated his judgment and also his degree of confidence, whereupon the total pressure was at once removed by the cam, and the card that had been used to direct the change was placed face down or face up according as the answer was right or wrong, and with corner indicating the degree of confidence in a determinate position. By means of these trifling devices the important object of rapidity was secured, and any possible psychological guessing of what change the operator was likely to select was avoided. A slight disadvantage in this mode of proceeding arises from the long runs of one particular kind of change, which would occasionally be produced by chance and would tend to confuse the mind of the subject. But it seems clear that this disadvantage was less than that which would have been occasioned by his knowing that there would be no such long runs if any means had been taken to prevent them. At the end of each set the results were of course entered into a book.[7]

---

[7] In the experiments of December, 1883, and January, 1884, the method as above described was not fully perfected, the most important fault being that the total weight instead of being removed and replaced by a mechanical device, was taken off by the operator pressing with his finger upon the beam of the balance.

30. The following tables show the results of the observations for each day:

Date.	1.100	1.080	1.060	1.050	1.040	1.030	1.015
				Ratios of pressures. [Subject: Mr. Peirce.]			
December 10	2 errors	......	......	13 errors	......	......	......
December 13	......	4 errors	8 errors	......	15 errors	......	......
December 17	......	......	11	......	......	20 errors	......
December 20	......	......	7	......	......	16	21 errors
January 3	......	......	14	......	......	20	28
January 15	......	......	15	......	......	29	17
January 22	......	......	12	......	......	16	20
January 24	......	......	6	......	......	15	22
Means	2	4	10.4 ± 1.0	13	15	19.3 ± 1.4	21.6 ± 1.1
Calculated from probable error $= 0.051$	4.6 ± 1.0	7.2 ± 1.6	10.7 ± 0.8	12.7 ± 2.1	14.9 ± 2.2	17.2 ± 0.9	21.0 ± 1.1
Average confidence.							
Observed	1.9	0.9	0.7	0.8	0.3	0.3	0.2
Calculated	1.3	1.0	0.7	0.6	0.5	0.3	0.2

The numbers in the columns show the number of errors in fifty experiments. With the average number of errors in a set of fifty we compare the theoretical value of this average as calculated by the method of least squares. The number .051 thus obtained in this case best satisfies the mean number of errors. The numbers affixed with a sign denote, in the upper row the observed (*a posteriori*) probable error of the mean value as given, in the lower row the calculated (*a priori*) probable error. The last two lines give the average confidence observed and calculated with each variation of the ratios of pressure. It will be seen that the correspondence between the real and theoretical numbers is close, and closest when the number of sets is large. The probable errors also closely correspond, the observed being, as is natural, slightly larger than the calculated probable errors.

23

31. The following is a similar table for Mr. Jastrow as subject:

| Date. | \multicolumn{10}{c}{Ratios of pressures.} | | | | | | | | | |
	1.100	1.080	1.060	1.050	1.040	1.030	1.020	1.015	1.010	1.005
December 10	5	....	....	19	....	....	....	....	....	....
December 13	....	9	15	....	15	....	....	....	....	....
December 17	....	....	14	....	....	23	....	....	....	....
December 20	....	....	10	....	....	17	....	25	....	....
January 3	....	....	8	....	....	14	....	24	....	....
January 10	....	....	7	....	....	13	....	17	....	....
January 15	....	....	12	....	....	6	....	22	....	....
January 22	....	....	11	....	....	10	....	16	....	....
January 24	....	....	4	....	....	11	....	18	....	....
February 11	....	....	1	....	....	7	....	18	....	....
February 17	....	....	2	....	....	10	....	17	....	....
February 18	....	....	2	....	....	11	....	17	....	....
February 24	....	....	2	....	....	8	....	15	....	....
March 4	....	....	....	....	....	....	13	....	16	....
March 5	....	....	....	....	....	....	13	....	17	....
March 18	....	....	....	....	....	....	14	....	19	29
March 19	....	....	....	....	....	....	11	....	21	18
March 23	....	....	....	....	....	....	14	....	17	18
March 25	....	....	....	....	....	....	12	....	16	18
March 30	....	....	....	....	....	....	11	....	16	21
March 31	....	....	....	....	....	....	10	....	15	21
April 2	....	....	....	....	....	....	11	....	17	21
April 3	....	....	....	....	....	....	9	....	18	20
April 6	....	....	....	....	....	....	12	....	15	21
April 7	....	....	0	....	....	5	7	14	15	17
Means	5	9	6.6	19	15.0	11.6	11.4	18.9	16.8	20.5

32. It would obviously be unfair to compare these numbers with any set of theoretical numbers, since the probable error is on the decrease throughout, owing to effects of practice, etc. For various reasons we can conveniently group these experiments into four groups. The first will include the experiments from December 10 to January 22, inclusive; the second from January 24 to February 24, inclusive; the third from March 4 to March 25, inclusive; the fourth from March 30 to the end of the work.

33. The mean results for the different groups are exhibited in the following tables:

24

First group.

[Probable error = 0.05.]

Ratios of pressures.	Number of sets of 50.	Average number of errors.		Average confidence.	
		Observed.	Calculated from probable error.	Observed.	Calculated.
1.100	1	5	4.4±1.4	0.9	1.5
1.080	1	9	7.0±1.7	0.9	1.2
1.060	7	11.0±0.7	10.4±0.7	0.85	0.9
1.050	1	19	12.5±2.1	0.35	0.7
1.040	1	15	14.7±2.2	0.3	0.6
1.030	6	13.8±1.5	17.0±0.9	0.5	0.4
1.015	5	20.8±1.1	21.0±1.1	0.3	0.2

Second group.

[Probable error = 0.0235.]

1.060	5	2.2±0.3	2.1±0.4	1.0	1.2
1.030	5	9.4±0.6	9.6±0.8	0.55	0.6
1.015	5	17.0±0.3	16.6±1.0	0.3	0.3

Third group.

[Probable error = 0.02.]

Ratios of pressures.	Number of sets of 50.	Average number of errors.		Average confidence.	
		Observed.	Calculated from probable error.	Observed.	Calculated.
1.020	6	12.8±0.3	12.5±0.8	0.12	0.12
1.010	6	17.7±0.6	18.3±0.9	0.07	0.06
1.005	4	20.7±1.7	21.6±1.2	0.00	0.03

Fourth group.

[Probable error = 0.0155.]

1.060	1	0	0.8±0.6	1.6	....
1.030	1	5	4.8±1.4	0.5	0.4
1.020	6	10.0±0.5	9.6±0.8	0.1	0.2
1.015	1	14	12.8±2.1	0.1	0.13
1.010	6	16.0±0.3	16.5±0.9	0.05	0.12
1.005	6	20.8±0.4	20.6±1.0	0.00	0.06

34.   The tables show that the numbers of errors follow, as far as we can conveniently trace them, the numbers assigned by the probability curve,[8] and therefore destroy all presumption in favor of an *Unterschiedsschwelle.* The introduction and retention of this false notion can only confuse thought, while the conception of the mathematician must exercise a favorable influence on psychological experimentation.[9]

[8] In the tables of the third and fourth groups, there is a marked divergence between the *a priori* and *a posteriori* probable error, for the average number of errors in 50, making the observed probable error too small. This can only be partly accounted for by the fact that the subject formed the unconscious habit of retaining the number of each kind of experiment in a set and answering according to that knowledge. In point of fact the plus errors and minus errors separately do not exhibit the singular uniformity of their sums, for which we are quite unable to account. Thus in the fourth group we have:

Number of + and − errors.

Date.	1.020	1.010	1.005
March 30	−4,+ 7	−6,+10	−13,+ 8
March 31	−7,+ 3	−5,+10	− 6,+15
April 2	−1,+10	−8,+ 9	− 8,+13
April 3	−4,+ 5	−4,+14	−10,+10
April 6	−6,+ 6	−8,+ 7	−10,+11
April 7	−5,+ 9	−8,+ 7	− 8,+ 9

[9] The conclusions of this paper are strengthened by the results of a series of experiments on the color sense, made with the use of a photometer by Mr. Jastrow. The object was to determine the number of errors of a given magnitude, and compare the numbers thus ascertained with the theoretical numbers given by the probability curve. A thousand experiments were made. Dividing the magnitude of the errors from 0 to the largest error, made into 5 parts, the number of errors, as observed and calculated, that occur in each part are as follows:

Observed	199	181	217	213	190
Calculated	213	197	209	181	200

These numbers would be in closer accordance if the probable error were

35. The quantity which we have called the degree of confidence was probably the secondary sensation of a difference between the primary sensations compared. The evidence of our experiments seems clearly to be that this sensation has no *Schwelle*, and vanishes only when the difference to which it refers vanishes. At the same time we found the subject often overlooked this element of his field of sensation, although his attention was directed with a certain strength toward it, so that he marked his confidence as *zero*. This happened in cases where the judgments were so much affected by the difference of pressures as to be correct three times out of five. The general fact has highly important practical bearings, since it gives new reason for believing that we gather what is passing in one another's minds in large measure from sensations so faint that we are not fairly aware of having them, and can give no account of how we reach our conclusions about such matters.[10] The insight of females as well as certain "telepathic" phenomena may be explained in this way.[11] Such faint sensations ought to be fully studied by the psychologist and assiduously cultivated by every man.

§2. LATER REFLECTIONS [12]

36. Our knowledge of any subject never goes beyond collecting observations and forming some half-conscious expectations, until we find ourselves confronted with some experience contrary to those expectations.[13] That at once rouses us to

---

the same throughout, as it is not owing to the effects of practice, etc. Moreover, the experiments were made on different colors — 300 on white and 100 each on yellow, blue, dove, pink, green, orange, and brown. These experiments were not continuous.

[10] (Ed.) See the following section of the present chapter.

[11] (Ed.) Cf. [Bibliography]G–1887–3, p. 194.

[12] (Ed.) From a manuscript, "Guessing," with a quotation in 36n13 from a fragmentary alternative draft. These manuscripts are in Widener IB2–12, and are dated c.1907 on the basis of internal references and statements in the letter referred to in 44n17.

The manuscript, "Guessing," was published in *The Hound and Horn* 2 (April–June 1929) 267–282.

In the passages reprinted here Peirce gives a non-technical summary of the previous paper and discusses some philosophical implications of it.

[13] (Ed.) The fragmentary manuscript (see 36n12) begins: "All our knowl-

consciousness: we turn over our recollections of observed facts; we endeavour so to rearrange them, to view them in such new perspective that the unexpected experience shall no longer appear surprising. This is what we call explaining it, which always consists in supposing that the surprising facts that we have observed are only one part of a larger system of facts, of which the other part has not come within the field of our experience, which larger system, taken in its entirety, would present a certain character of reasonableness, that inclines us to accept the surmise as true, or likely. For example, let a person entering a large room for the first time, see upon a wall projecting from behind a large map that has been pinned up there, three-quarters of an admirably executed copy in fresco of one of Rafael's most familiar cartoons. In this instance the explanation flashes so naturally upon the mind and is so fully accepted, that the spectator quite forgets how surprising those facts are which alone are presented to his view; namely, that so exquisite a reproduction of one of Rafael's grandest compositions should omit one-quarter of it. He guesses that that quarter is there, though hidden by the map; and six months later he will, maybe, be ready to swear that he saw the whole. This will be a case under a logico-psychical law of great importance, to which we may find occasion to revert soon, that a fully accepted, simple, and interesting inference tends to obliterate all recognition of the uninteresting and complex premises from which it was derived. The brighter the observer's intelligence (unless some circumstance has raised a doubt), the more confident he will soon be that he saw the entire composition. Yet, in fact, the idea of the whole's being on that wall will be merely evolved from his *Ichheit:* it will be a surmise, conjecture, or guess.

37. We may be aided by previous knowledge in forming our hypotheses. In that case they will not be pure guesses but will be compounds of deductions from general rules we already know, applied to the facts under observation, for one ingredi-

---

edge starts from perception, and consequently perception ought never to be doubted, and indeed never *can* be doubted. That is to say, that we cannot doubt that that really *seems* which *seems to seem*" and then the manuscript proceeds very much like the version printed above. Cf. 5.157.

ent, and pure guess for the other ingredient. Thus, suppose the surprising facts which puzzle us are the actions of a certain man on a certain occasion; and our conjecture relates to the state of belief that caused such conduct. If we have no previous knowledge of the man, any one state of belief that would account for his conduct might be as good a guess as any other; but if we know that he is particularly inclined, or particularly disinclined, to extravagant beliefs or to any other special kind of belief, we still have to guess; only we shall select our guess from a smaller number of possible hypotheses.

38.   In the evolution of science, guessing plays the same part that variations in reproduction take in the evolution of biological forms, according to the Darwinian theory.[14] For just as, according to that theory, the whole tremendous gulf, or ocean rather, between the moner and man has been spanned by a succession of infinitesimal fortuitous variations at birth, so the whole noble organism of science has been built up out of propositions which were originally simple guesses. For my part I refuse to believe that either the one or the other were *fortuitous*; and indeed I gravely doubt whether there be any tenable meaning in calling them so. As to the biological variations, I will spare the reader my reasons for not believing them fortuitous. For it would only lead us away from our subject. But as to the first guesses out of which science has been developed, I will say a word or two. It is well within bounds to reckon that there are a billion (i.e., a million million) hypotheses that a fantastic being might guess would account for any given phenomenon. For this phenomenon would certainly be more or less connected in the mind of such a being with a million other phenomena (for he would not be restricted to contemporaneous events) and it might be supposed that the special determination of each was connected with the special determinations of each of the others in order to produce the observed phenomenon. I will not carry out this idea further: it suffices to show that according to the doctrine of chances it would be practically impossible for any being, by pure chance, to guess the cause of any phenomenon.

39.   There are, indeed, puzzles, and one might well say

[14] (Ed.) Cf. 2.638, 2.753, 2.755.

mysteries, connected with the mental operation of guessing; —
yes; more than one. There can, I think, be no reasonable
doubt that man's mind, having been developed under the influence of the laws of nature, for that reason naturally thinks
somewhat after nature's pattern. This vague explanation is
but a surmise; but there is no room to believe that it was merely
by luck that Galileo and other masters of science reached the
true theories after so few wrong guesses as they did. This
power of divining the truths of physics, — for such it is, although it is somewhat imperfect, — is certainly an aid to the
instinct for obtaining food, an instinct whose wonders throughout the animal kingdom are exceeded only by that of producing
and rearing offspring.

40.   This latter function requires all the higher animals to
have some insight into what is passing in the minds of their
fellows. Man shows a remarkable faculty for guessing at that.
Its full powers are only brought out under critical circumstances. . . .[15]

41.   All the above, be it understood is sober truth, sedulously freed from all exaggeration and colour. If any reader should
incline to deem the narrative apocryphal, it will certainly not
be the psycholist, equally versed in the the theory of his science
and skilled in the application of it; for to him the incidents
will present no extraordinary features. I suppose almost everybody has had similar experiences. But however frequently
such facts may be encountered, there is certainly something
a little mysterious in them; they demand explanation. That
explanation must itself be conjectural, and must remain so until exact investigation has tested its sufficiency; and unless
some new school of psychology should make its appearance,
I do not believe that scientific testing of the theory is likely to
be performed in our time.

42.   I am going to point out a *vera causa* — a known agency

---

[15] (Ed.) Peirce here recounts a personal anecdote, concerning the theft of
his coat and a valuable watch from his stateroom on a Boston to New York
boat. He says that he made all the waiters stand in a row and after talking
briefly with each, but without consciously getting any clue, he made a guess
as to which one was guilty. The upshot of the story is that after many difficulties, and by making more successful guesses, he proved that his original guess
had been correct.

which tends to produce effects like the facts to be explained. But whether it would, under the circumstances described, be sufficient to produce the somewhat surprising facts, or whether it was aided by some other agency that has not suggested itself to my mind, I will not presume to opine.

43.   My surmise is that at the bottom of the little mystery is buried a principle often enough asserted but never, I believe, supported by scientific observation, until Professor Joseph Jastrow and I carried through, at the Johns Hopkins University, a certain series of experiments.[16] These experiments were mainly designed for quite another purpose, namely, in order to test Fechner's hypothesis of the "Differenzschwelle," which in no wise concerns us now. I proceed to describe, in outline, the essentials of the experiments. Of the two persons engaged in them, the one acted as experimenter and recorder, while the other, who could neither see nor hear the former, was the "subject" or victim of the experimentation. The latter said, "Ready." Thereupon an automatic arrangement, namely, by exposing a card from a well shuffled pack, indicated to the experimenter what pressure he was to bring to bear upon the finger of the subject, who carefully observed the degree of his feeling of pressure. When he was satisfied, perhaps after from five to twenty seconds, he said "Change." Thereupon by an exceedingly delicate contrivance (to avoid any sudden change or shock), the experimenter, according to an automatic operation of chance, either increased or diminished the pressure by less than one *per cent* of itself. The subject observed the new feeling of pressure, and again said "Change," whereupon the first pressure was brought back. These experiments were interspersed (by the automatic chance arrangement which was intended, of course, to exclude, as far as possible, mental action on the part of the experimenter), by others in which the changes of pressure were somewhat more considerable. The subject having observed the three states of feeling of pressure (of which the first and last were equal), first pronounced one or another of the four numerals, Naught, One, Two, Three. "Three" would mean that he was sure, or almost sure, of being able to say whether the middle pressure was greater or less than the

[16] (Ed.) See the first section of this chapter.

31

other two. "Two" would mean that he was by no means sure, yet inclined to think he could tell. "One" would mean that he did not think he really perceived any difference; yet suspected that he perhaps might. "Naught" would mean that he was sure he could not perceive the slightest variation of pressure. Having thus indicated the degree of his confidence, he was *obliged to say* whether the middle pressure was greater or less than the others. In case his confidence was zero, this declaration would be (to his own consciousness) a purely random one, though he would avoid any particular regularity in his declarations, or any great preponderance of either "greater" or "lesser." Of course he never received the slightest intimation of whether he was right or wrong.

44. When our course of experiments had been carried on two hours daily (with such precautions against fatigue as the imperfect psychology of twenty-five years ago prescribed), and for about a month it was found that of the answers supposed to be given at random, which were a good half of the whole number and must, I think (I have not before me the record, which is given in Vol. III of the Memoirs of the U. S. National Academy of Sciences),[17] have approached a thousand in number, about three out of every five were correct. That is to say, among all those cases in which the subject, after carefully searching his consciousness, felt quite sure he had experienced no variation of the sense of pressure, though a change and reverse change had really been made; and had accordingly said, quite at random, as he thought, that the middle pressure was greater or less than the first and last, what he so said agreed with the real fact half as often again as it disagreed. A reader inexpert in dealing with probabilities may think that so small a preponderance of true answers might have come about by chance. But in truth it is among the most certain things that we know that this was not so. So much is demonstrated truth, quite unquestionable. But if you go on to ask me upon what principle I would explain the fact that a person who, after the

[17] (Ed.) Reprinted as the first section of this chapter.

Peirce says in a letter to William James of 16 July 1907 (Houghton Library) that there were 3389 guesses given with a confidence of "Naught" and about two thirds of these were correct (see 26n5).

closest scrutiny of his consciousness, had pronounced that
there was no trace of perceptible difference between two sensations of pressure, should in the very next breath have correctly said which of them was the greater, in three cases out
of every five, my confidence largely evaporates. I can, indeed,
mention a cause which undoubtedly exists and which must
have acted toward producing that indubitable fact; but I cannot say whether that cause would or would not have been sufficient, by itself, for that result.

45. Everybody knows how self-consciousness makes one
awkward and may even quite paralyze the mind. Nobody can
have failed to remark that mental performances that are gone
through with lightly are apt to be more adroit than those in
which every little detail is studied while the action is proceeding, nor how a great effort — say to write a particularly witty
letter — or even to recall a word or name that has slipped
one's memory may spoil one's success. Perhaps it is because
in trying very hard we are thinking about our effort instead
of about the problem in hand. At any rate my own experience
is that self-consciousness, and especially conscious effort, are
apt to carry me to the verge of idiocy and that those things
that I have done spontaneously were the best done. Now, in
the experiments I have described, the so-called "subject," the
victim of the experimentation, would not seldom sit in the
darkened and silent room, straining with all his might for two
or three minutes, to detect the slightest difference between two
pressures. Finding himself unable to do so he would utter his
"zero" that this inability might be recorded. Thereupon all
straining ceased; for all it then remained for him to do was
mention at random which one of the pressures he would mark
as the heavier — and here his perfect unconsciousness greatly
increased his power of discrimination — a discrimination below the surface of consciousness, and not recognized as a real
judgment, yet in very truth a genuine discrimination, as the
statistical results showed. The circumstances of my talking
with the waiters on the boat were almost identical. While I
was going through the row, chatting a little with each, I held
myself in as passive and receptive a state as I could. When I
had gone through the row I made a great effort to detect in

33

my consciousness some symptoms of the thief, and this effort, I suppose, prevented my success. But then finding I could detect nothing I said to myself, "Well, anyway, I *must* fasten on someone, though it be but a random choice," and instantly I *knew* which of the men it was. . . .

46.   I could tell many other true tales of successful guessings; but I have mentioned here two principles which I have been led to conjecture furnish at least a partial explanation of the mystery that overhangs this singular guessing instinct. I infer in the first place that man divines something of the secret principles of the universe because his mind has developed as a part of the universe and under the influence of these same secret principles; and secondly, that we often derive from observation strong intimations of truth, without being able to specify what were the circumstances we had observed which conveyed those intimations.

47.   It is a chapter of the art of inquiry.

48.   Our faculty of guessing corresponds to a bird's musical and aeronautic powers; that is, it is to us, as those are to them, the loftiest of our merely instinctive powers. I suppose that if one were sure of being able to discriminate between the intimations of this instinct and the self-flatteries of personal desire, one would always trust to the former. For I should not rate high either the wisdom or the courage of a fledgling bird, if, when the proper time had come, the little agnostic should hesitate long to take his leap from the nest on account of doubts about the theory of aerodynamics.

BOOK II

SCIENTIFIC METHOD

CHAPTER 1

SCIENTIFIC METHOD

§1. SCIENCE [1]

49. What is Science? We cannot define the word with the precision and concison with which we define *Circle*, or *Equation*, any more than we can so define *Money*, *Government*, *Stone*, *Life*. The idea, like these, and more than some of them, is too vastly complex and diversified. It embodies the epitome of man's intellectual development. We can only single out some leading properties of it, and different people will select these differently. To most men, including all who are outside of the world of science, the term means a particular kind of knowledge. Wherein lies the essential peculiarity of this knowledge? Some thinkers agree with the ancient Greeks in making it consist in the *Method* of knowing, the manner in which the truth is laid hold on. But the majority of modern writers regard the Systematic character of the doctrine itself as more characteristic. Both marks of scientific knowledge are exceedingly important; but the former is deeper cut, and because it is at present less noticed, more needs to be emphasized. Plato is quite right in saying that a true belief is not necessarily knowledge. A man may be willing to stake his life upon the truth of a doctrine which was instilled into his mind before his earliest memories without knowing at all why it is worthy of credence; and while such a faith might just as easily be

---

[1] (Ed.) Paragraphs 49–52 are from manuscript L, undated (but cf. 59n4), Widener IB2–9.

Paragraphs 53–58 are from "Of the Classification of the Sciences. Second Paper. Of the Practical Sciences," Widener II. Paragraphs 53–57, 381n19 and 58 come from the manuscript in that order. This manuscript is dated c.1902 on the basis of references in it.

attached to a gross superstition as to a noble truth, it may, by good luck, happen to be perfectly true. But can he be said to *know* it? By no means: to render the word knowledge applicable to his belief, he must not only believe it, but must know, — I will not say, with the ancients, the rationale of the real fact, as a reality, — but must know what justifies the belief, and just WHY and HOW the justification is sufficient. I beg that the reader will turn this over in his mind and satisfy himself as to how far what I am saying is true. For it is not a very simple point but is one that I intend to insist upon.

50.   Before knowledge of any subject can be put to any extensive use, it is almost indispensable that it should be made as thorough and complete as possible, until every detail and feature of the matter is spread out as in a German handbook. But if I am asked to what the wonderful success of modern science is due, I shall suggest that to gain the secret of that, it is necessary to consider science as living, and therefore not as knowledge already acquired but as the concrete life of the men who are working to find out the truth. Given a body of men devoting the sum of their energies to refuting their present errors, doing away with their present ignorance, and that not so much for themselves as for future generations, and all other requisites for the ascertainment of truth are insured by that one. Strictly speaking, one need not ask for so much as that. Given the oxygen, hydrogen, carbon, nitrogen, sulphur, phosphorus, etc., in sufficient quantities and under proper radiations, and living protoplasm will be produced, will develop, will gain power of self-control, and the scientific passion is sure to be generated. Such is my guess. Science was preordained, perhaps, on the Sunday of the *Fiat lux*.

51.   Coming down to the more immediate and more pertinent causes of the triumph of modern science, the considerable numbers of the workers, and the singleness of heart with which, — (we may forget that there are a few selfseekers who succeed in gaining the power to make themselves more despised than they naturally would be; they are so few,) — they cast their whole being into the service of science lead, of course, to their unreserved discussions with one another, to each being fully informed about the work of his neighbour, and availing

himself of that neighbour's results; and thus in storming the stronghold of truth one mounts upon the shoulders of another who has to ordinary apprehension failed, but has in truth succeeded by virtue of the lessons of his failure. This is the veritable essence of science. It is in the memory of these concrete living gests that we gain the speaking portraiture of true science in all her life and beauty.

52.   The point of view just explained enables us to perceive that a particular branch of science, such as Physical Chemistry or Mediterranean Archeology, is no mere word, manufactured by the arbitrary definition of some academic pedant, but is a real object, being the very concrete life of a social group constituted by real facts of inter-relation, — as real an object as a human carcase, which is made one by the inter-relations of its millions of cells. Any two of these groups (and with them the sciences, which are their lives,) may be related, as to the matter of the groups in either of the three modes of relationship of material wholes; that is, either by *Inclusion*, one being a part of another; or by *Intersection*, when each has one part in common with the other, and another part foreign to the other; or by *Exclusion*, when the two have no part in common. But of greater importance are the dynamical relations between the different sciences, by which I mean that one often acts upon another, not by bringing forward any reason or principle, but as it were with a compulsive quality of action. Thus one group may stimulate another by demanding the solution of some problem. In this way, the practical sciences incessantly egg on researches into theory. For considerable parts of chemical discovery we have to thank the desire to find a substitute for quinine or to make quinine itself synthetically, to obtain novel and brilliant dye-stuffs, and the like. The mechanical theory of heat grew out of the difficulties of steam navigation. For it was first broached by Rankine while he was studying how best to design marine engines. Then again, one group of scientists sometimes urges some overlooked phenomenon upon the attention of another group. It was a botanist who called van't Hoff's attention to the dependence of the pressure of sap in plants upon the strength of the solution, and thus almost instantaneously gave a tremendous

impulse to physical chemistry. In 1820, Kästner, a manufacturer of cream of tartar in Mulhouse, called the attention of chemists to the occasional, though rare, occurrence in the wine casks of a modification of tartaric acid, since named racemic acid; and from the impulse so given has resulted a most important doctrine of chemistry, that of the unsymmetric carbon atom, as well as the chief discoveries of Pasteur, with their far-reaching blessings to the human species.

53. It is now time to explain the classification of this chapter, what it aims to be, by what means that aim has been pursued, and how nearly it seems to have been attained. Two questions have to be answered at the outset: What is here meant by *science*? And what is meant by *a* science, one of the unit species out of which the system is built up? The spirit of this book is always to look upon those aspects of things which exhibit whatever of living and active there is in them.

54. The prevalent definition of a science, the definition of Coleridge, which influenced all Europe through the Encyclopaedia Metropolitana, that science is systematized knowledge, is an improvement upon a statement of Kant (Metaphysische Anfangsgründe der Naturwissenschaft: 1786): "Eine jede Lehre, wenn sie ein System, dass ist, ein nach Principien geordnetes Ganzes der Erkenntniss sein soll, heisst Wissenschaft."[2] Yet it is to be noted that knowledge may be systematic or "organized," without being organized by means of general principles. Kant's definition, however, is only a modification of the ancient view that science is the knowledge of a thing through its causes, — the comprehension of it, as we might say, — as being the only perfect knowledge of it. In short, the Coleridgian definition is nothing but the last development of that sort of philosophy that strives to draw knowledge out of the depths of the *Ich-heit*. If, on the other hand, one opens the works of Francis Bacon, one remarks that, with all the astounding *greenness* and inexperience of his views of science, in some respects he is really a scientific man himself. He met his death as the

---

[2] (Ed.) This statement appears on page 3 in the edition edited by Alois Höfler, published by C. E. M. Pfeffer, Leipzig, 1900.

consequence of an experiment. True, it was rather a foolish one; but what a monument to the genuineness of his intelligence, that he, a great legal light, should, at the age of sixty-six, have perished from his zeal in performing disagreeable and dangerous laboratory work that he thought might go toward teaching him something of the nature of true science! For him man is nature's interpreter; and in spite of the crudity of some anticipations, the idea of science is, in his mind, inseparably bound up with that of a life devoted to singleminded inquiry. That is also the way in which every scientific man thinks of science. That is the sense in which the word is to be understood in this chapter. Science is to mean for us a mode of life whose single animating purpose is to find out the real truth, which pursues this purpose by a well-considered method, founded on thorough acquaintance with such scientific results already ascertained by others as may be available, and which seeks coöperation in the hope that the truth may be found, if not by any of the actual inquirers, yet ultimately by those who come after them and who shall make use of their results. It makes no difference how imperfect a man's knowledge may be, how mixed with error and prejudice; from the moment that he engages in an inquiry in the spirit described, that which occupies him is *science*, as the word will here be used.

55. By *a* specific science will be meant a group of connected inquiries of sufficient scope and affinity fitly to occupy a number of independent inquirers for life, but not capable of being broken up into smaller coexclusive groups of this description. For since we are to consider science in general as a mode of life, it is proper to take as the unit science the scientific mode of life fit for an individual person. But science being essentially a mode of life that seeks coöperation, the unit science must, apparently, be fit to be pursued by a number of inquirers.

56. It seems plain that, with these definitions, the classification cannot be concerned with all possible sciences, but must be confined to actually realized sciences. If, however, this limitation is to be maintained, the question will arise, To what date or stage of scientific development is the classification to relate? According to the general spirit of this book, which values everything in its relation to Life, knowledge which is

altogether inapplicable to the future is nugatory. Consequently, our classification ought to have reference to the science of the future, so far as we are now able to foresee what the future of science is to be. It will therefore be upon the soil of the near future of science that we shall endeavor to plant our flag. If it be objected that we cannot know enough of the science of the future to classify it accurately, the reply would be that even if all faults of classification could be eliminated by remaining on the threshold of the future, it would still be necessary to advance further. For all the applicability of any writing, though it be not (like this,) the fruit of near half a century of study, must evidently be subsequent to its composition, and all its significance for that time has reference to a time still later. But when the objector comes to see the various imperfections that will have to be confessed in that part of the classification which concerns the present state of science, he will probably be disposed himself to acknowledge that its standard will not be much lowered by the danger of mistake about what is likely soon to be discovered.

57.   Meantime, let it not be understood that the classification is to ignore the scientific discoveries of the past. For the memoirs of that work are not so poor as not to merit being read critically, precisely as we shall read the memoirs of tomorrow. Such reading is, therefore, of the nature of scientific inquiry. True, it is not original research; but there is original research still to be done in the same specific science. For none of the sciences of the past is finished. If it be one of the positive sciences that is in question, there is not a single conclusion belonging to it which has in the past been made sufficiently precise or sufficiently indubitable. If it be a branch of mathematics, its propositions require to be further generalized, as well as to be more accurately limited. For these reasons all the old science that still stands is to be retained in the classification, but in its most modern forms.

---

58.   The only remaining instinct on our list is the Gnostic Instinct, or curiosity. In one sense, the sciences that are practically ministrant to this are the Theoretical Sciences; but this

remark leads us to signalize a distinction the neglect of which is the source of several of the most fatal errors into which philosophers have fallen. It is quite true that the Gnostic Instinct is the cause of all purely theoretical inquiry, and that every discovery of science is a gratification of curiosity. But it is not true that pure science is or can be successfully pursued *for the sake* of gratifying this instinct. Indeed, if it were so pursued, it would not be true that this instinct was the cause of it. Its motive would then be the Gust-Instinct, or love of pleasure. One wish may be that another wish should be gratified; but no wish can be that that very wish should be gratified. For in that case, the wish would not have any object at all, and having no object it would not be a wish. The case is precisely like that of an assertion which should have no other subject than itself. For a wish is a sort of proposition. To long for anything is to judge it to be good and urgently good. No doubt every assertion implies that it is itself true;[3] but it cannot consist of that alone; and so every wish that is reflective wishes itself gratified; but it must wish something else, besides. Hence, the hedonist, who opines that man can wish for nothing but pleasure, has fallen into a damnable error from a mere confusion of thought. We should commit the same error if we supposed the gratification of curiosity were the sole, or the principal, object of theoretical science. Curiosity is their motive; but the gratification of curiosity is not their aim.

§2. LOGIC AND SCIENTIFIC METHOD [4]

59. It might be supposed that logic taught that much was to be accomplished by mere rumination, though every one knows that experiment, observation, comparison, active scrutiny of facts, are what is wanted, and that mere *thinking* will ac-

[3] (Ed.) Cf. 5.340.
[4] (Ed.) Paragraphs 59–76 are "Introductory Lecture on the Study of Logic," [JHUC] 2(Nov 1882)11–12, with two preliminary paragraphs omitted.

Paragraphs 77–78 are from manuscript N, Widener IB2–9, undated, but the manuscript contains results from the census of 1900. This manuscript and manuscript L (cf. 49n1) are probably parts of the same work.

complish nothing even in mathematics. Logic had certainly been defined as the "art of thinking," and as the "science of the normative laws of thought." But those are not true definitions. *"Dyalectica,"* says the logical text-book of the middle ages, *"est ars artium et scientia scientiarum, ad omnium aliarum scientiarum methodorum principia viam habens,"* [5] and although the logic of our day must naturally be utterly different from that of the Plantagenet epoch, yet this general conception that it is the *art of devising methods of research*, — the *method of methods*, — is the true and worthy idea of the science. Logic will not undertake to inform you what kind of experiments you ought to make in order best to determine the acceleration of gravity, or the value of the Ohm; but it will tell you how to proceed to form a plan of experimentation.

60. It is impossible to maintain that the superiority of the science of the moderns over that of the ancients is due to anything but a better *logic*. No one can think that the Greeks were inferior to any modern people whatever in natural aptitude for science. We may grant that their opportunities for research were less; and it may be said that ancient astronomy could make no progress beyond the Ptolemaic system until sufficient time had elapsed to prove the insufficiency of Ptolemy's tables. The ancients could have no dynamics so long as no important dynamical problem had presented itself; they could have no theory of heat without the steam-engine, etc. Of course, these causes had their influence, and of course they were not the main reason of the defects of the ancient civilization. Ten years' astronomical observations with instruments such as the ancients could have constructed would have sufficed to overthrow the old astronomy. The great mechanical discoveries of Galileo were made with no apparatus to speak of. If, in any direction whatever, the ancients had once commenced research by right methods, opportunities for new advances would have been brought along in the train of those that went before. But read the logical treatise of Philodemus; see how he strenuously argues that inductive reasoning is not utterly without value, and you see where the fault lay. When such

[5] (Ed.) Orbellis (Nicholaus de), *Expositio super textu Petri Hispani, Super libro Peryhermenias*, Venice, 1500, fol. a3v.

an elementary point as that needed serious argumentation it is clear that the conception of scientific method was almost entirely wanting.

61.   Modern methods have created modern science; and this century, and especially the last twenty-five years, have done more to create new methods than any former equal period. We live in the very age of methods. Even mathematics and astronomy have put on new faces. Chemistry and physics are on completely new tracks. Linguistics, history, mythology, sociology, biology, are all getting studied in new ways. Jurisprudence and law have begun to feel the impulse, and must in the future be more and more rapidly influenced by it.

62.   This is the age of methods; and the university which is to be the exponent of the living condition of the human mind, must be the university of methods.

63.   Now I grant you that to say that this is the age of the development of new methods of research is so far from saying that it is the age of the theory of methods, that it is almost to say the reverse. Unfortunately practice generally precedes theory, and it is the usual fate of mankind to get things done in some boggling way first, and find out afterward how they could have been done much more easily and perfectly. And it must be confessed that we students of the science of modern methods are as yet but a voice crying in the wilderness, and saying prepare ye the way for this lord of the sciences which is to come.

64.   Yet even now we can do a little more than that. The theory of any act in no wise aids the doing of it, so long as what is to be done is of a narrow description, so that it can be governed by the unconscious part of our organism. For such purposes, rules of thumb or no rules at all are the best. You cannot play billiards by analytical mechanics nor keep shop by political economy. But when new paths have to be struck out, a spinal cord is not enough; a brain is needed, and that brain an organ of mind, and that mind perfected by a liberal education. And a liberal education — so far as its relation to the understanding goes — means *logic*. That is indispensable to it, and no other one thing is.

65.   I do not need to be told that science consists of special-

ties. I know all that, for I belong to the guild of science, have learned one of its trades and am saturated with its current notions.[6] But in my judgment there are scientific men, all whose training has only served to belittle them, and I do not see that a mere scientific specialist stands intellectually much higher than an artisan. I am quite sure that a young man who spends his time exclusively in the laboratory of physics or chemistry or biology, is in danger of profiting but little more from his work than if he were an apprentice in a machine shop.

66. The scientific specialists — pendulum swingers [7] and the like — are doing a great and useful work; each one very little, but altogether something vast. But the higher places in science in the coming years are for those who succeed in adapting the methods of one science to the investigation of another. That is what the greatest progress of the passing generation has consisted in. Darwin adapted to biology the methods of Malthus and the economists; Maxwell adapted to the theory of gases the methods of the doctrine of chances, and to electricity the methods of hydrodynamics. Wundt adapts to psychology the methods of physiology;[8] Galton adapts to the same study the methods of the theory of errors; Morgan adapted to history a method from biology; Cournot adapted to political economy the calculus of variations. The philologists have adapted to their science the methods of the decipherers of dispatches. The astronomers have learned the methods of chemistry; radiant heat is investigated with an ear trumpet; the mental temperament is read off on a vernier.

67. Now although a man needs not the theory of a method in order to apply it as it has been applied already, yet in order to adapt to his own science the method of another with which he is less familiar, and to properly modify it so as to suit it to its new use, an acquaintance with the principles upon which it depends will be of the greatest benefit. For that sort of work a man needs to be more than a mere specialist; he needs such a general training of his mind, and such knowledge as shall

---

[6] (Ed.) See Book I of the present volume.

[7] (Ed.) Peirce's main task in the United States Coast Survey was to measure the force of gravity by swinging a pendulum.

[8] (Ed.) See the review of Wundt's book in [CP] VIII, Book I, Review 14.

show him how to make his powers most effective in a new direction. That knowledge is logic.

68.   In short, if my view is the true one, a young man wants a physical education and an aesthetic education, an education in the ways of the world and a moral education, and with all these logic has nothing in particular to do; but so far as he wants an intellectual education, it is precisely logic that he wants; and whether he be in one lecture-room or another, his ultimate purpose is to improve his logical power and his knowledge of methods. To this great end a young man's attention ought to be directed when he first comes to the university; he ought to keep it steadily in view during the whole period of his studies; and finally, he will do well to review his whole work in the light which an education in logic throws upon it.

69.   I should be the very first to insist that logic can never be learned from logic-books or logic lectures. The material of positive science must form its basis and its vehicle. Only relatively little could be done by the lecturer on method even were he master of the whole circle of the sciences. Nevertheless, I do think that I can impart to you something of real utility, and that the theory of method will shed much light on all your other studies.

70.   The impression is rife that success in logic requires a mathematical head. But this is not true. The habit of looking at questions in a mathematical way is, I must say, of great advantage, and thus a turn for mathematics is of more or less service in any science, physical or moral. But no brilliant talent for mathematics is at all necessary for the study of logic.

71.   The course which I am to give this year begins with some necessary preliminaries upon the theory of cognition.[9] For it is requisite to form a clear idea at the outset of what knowledge consists of, and to consider a little what are the operations of the mind by which it is produced. But I abridge this part of the course as much as possible, partly because it will be treated by other instructors, and partly because I desire to push on to my main subject, the method of science.

72.   I next take up syllogism, the lowest and most rudimentary of all forms of reasoning, but very fundamental be-

[9] (Ed.) See [CP] V.

cause it is rudimentary.[10] I treat this after the general style of
De Morgan, with references to the old traditional doctrine.
Next comes the logical algebra of Boole, a subject in itself extremely easy, but very useful both from a theoretical point of
view and also as giving a method of solving certain rather frequently occurring and puzzling problems. From this subject,
I am naturally led to the consideration of relative terms. The
logic of relatives, so far as it has been investigated, is clear and
easy, and at the same time it furnishes the key to many of the
difficulties of logic, and has already served as the instrument
of some discoveries in mathematics. An easy application of
this branch of logic is to the doctrine of breadth and depth or
the relations between objects and characters. I next introduce
the conception of number, and after showing how to treat
certain statistical problems, I take up the doctrine of chances.
A very simple and elegant mathematical method of treating
equations of finite differences puts the student into possession
of a powerful instrument for the solution of all problems of
probability that do not import difficulties extraneous to the
theory of probability itself.

73. We thus arrive at the study of that kind of probable
inference that is really distinctive; that is to say, Induction
in its broadest sense — Scientific Reasoning. The general theory
of the subject is carefully worked out with the aid of real
examples in great variety, and rules for the performance of the
operation are given. These rules have not been picked up by
hazard, nor are they merely such as experience recommends;
they are deduced methodically from the general theory.

74. Finally, it is desirable to illustrate a long concatenation
of scientific inferences. For this purpose we take up Kepler's
great work, *De Motu Stellae Martis*, the greatest piece of inductive reasoning ever produced. Owing to the admirable and
exceptional manner in which the work is written, it is possible
to follow Kepler's whole course of investigation from beginning to end, and to show the application of all the maxims of
induction already laid down.

75. In order to illustrate the method of reasoning about

[10] (Ed.) See the rest of the present book and [CP] II for discussions of most
of the topics mentioned in this and the following paragraphs.

a subject of a more metaphysical kind, I shall then take up the scientific theories of the constitution of matter.

76. Last of all, I shall give a few lectures to show what are the lessons that a study of scientific procedure teaches with reference to philosophical questions, such as the conception of causation and the like.

---

77. I will assume, then, that scientific doubt never gets completely set to rest in regard to any question until, at last, the very truth about that question becomes established.[11] Taking the phenomenon as a whole, then, without considering how it is brought about, science is foredestined to reach the truth of every problem with as unerring an infallibility as the instincts of animals do their work, this latter result like the former being brought about by some process of which we are as yet unable to give any account. It is, we will say, the working of the human instinct. It is not (always considering it in its entirety,) of a rational nature, since, being infallible, it is not open to criticism, while "rational" means essentially self-criticizing, self-controlling and self-controlled, and therefore open to incessant question. But this instinctive infallibility is brought about by the exercize of reason, which is all along subject to blunder and to go wrong. The manner in which this comes about may be, I will not quite say illustrated, but may be rendered intelligible, by the following skeletal example. I call it skeletal because it involves the one character of research which is here to be considered, while attempting no representation of it in other respects. Let us suppose, then, that you have a die which may, for all you know, be loaded; and that you proceed to experiment upon it by throwing it repeatedly, counting as you go the total number of throws and also the number of them which turn up the ace side. For the sake of simplicity, I will suppose that the die is really perfect, although you do not know that it is so. After you have thrown it six times, it will be more likely to give either no ace or more than one ace than to give just one. Namely, there is one chance in three that there will be no ace in the first six throws, there are two chances

---

[11] (Ed.) Cf. 5.383ff.

in five that there will be just one, one chance in five that there will be just two; and there will remain one chance in fifteen that there will be more than two aces. Suppose you go on throwing the die a great many times, and after each throw you divide the number of aces that have turned up by the whole number of throws so far. The quotient will be [the] result for the probability of throwing an ace with this die. You will get a new and amended, though not always a really improved, result after every throw. Now although the throws are purely fortuitous, so that to most questions about them only probable answers can be given, yet one thing will certainly happen. Namely, sooner or later, probably very soon, but it may be only very late, yet certainly at length, a time will come after which all your values for the probability of throwing an ace with this die will be correct in the first figure after the decimal point. A later time there will be after which all the successive determinations will be correct in the first two figures, and so on. You will never be certain that that time has come, but it certainly some time will have come. Thus to the question, What is the first figure of the probability?; to the question, What are the first two figures, etc.; all the answer you will obtain will after a time be free from error. This will be the necessary result. Now that which is necessarily inerrant may in a somewhat indefinite sense be fairly called *infallible*. Thus, a skillful use of fortuitous events will bring infallibly correct replies to an endless series of questions. This kind of infallibility, which may [be], for aught we know, not to say quite probably is, the infallibility of the instinct of animals, is certainly the only kind of infallibility that can be attributed to the results of science, inasmuch as we can so little know when the very truth is reached that even the second law of motion is at this moment under indictment. Moreover, when we come to subject the processes of science to criticism, we shall find it impossible to deny that a conditional form of this kind of infallibility must be attributed to science.

78.   In the light of what has been said, what are we to say to that logical fatalism whose stock in trade is the argument that I have already indicated? I mean the argument that science is predestined to reach the truth, and that it can therefore make

50

no difference whether she observes carefully or carelessly nor what sort of formulae she treats as reasons. The answer to it is that the only kind of predestination of the attainment of truth by science is an eventual predestination, — a predestination *aliquando denique*. Sooner or later it will attain the truth, nothing more. It means that if you take the most pigheaded and passionate of men who has sworn by all the gods that he never will allow himself to believe the earth is round, and give him time enough, and cram that time with experience in the pertinent sphere, and he will surely come to and rest in the truth about the form of the earth. Such is the infallibility of science. But the secret of the matter is that the man's wilfulness and prejudice will break down before such experience. Such, at least, must be our assumption, if we are to adhere to our faith in the infallibility of science. So far as this assumption goes beyond ordinary everyday experience, it rests on the deeper assumption that that which experience has done for generations of men, who a thousand years ago were substantially in that man's plight, it would do for an individual who were to go through the experiences that those generations have gone through. If one does not believe in this, then the present question does not arise. Our belief in the infallibility of science, which alone prompts the fatalistic suggestion, rests upon our experience of the overwhelming rationalizing power of experience. As long as the man keeps to his determination to exclude from his thoughts whatever might tend to make him assent to the proposition that the earth is round, he certainly will not come to that truth. Granting, therefore, that it is of the nature of experience to develop albuminous matter into rational brain, and to make the mind unceasingly agitate doubt until it finally comes to repose in the true belief, — which is only a more developed way of formulating our belief in the infallibility of science, it is entirely uncertain *when* the truth will be reached. It will be reached; but only after the investigator has come, first, to a conception of the nature of truth, and to a worship of it as the purest emanation of That which is creating the universe, and *then*, to an understanding of the right method to absorb it from the universe of experience. It will infallibly be reached sooner or later, if favorable conditions continue;

51

but man having a short life, and even mankind not a very long one, the question is urgent, How soon? And the answer is, as soon as a sane logic has had time to control conclusions. Everything thus depends upon rational methods of inquiry. They will make that result as speedy as possible, which otherwise would have kicked its heels in the anteroom of chance. Let us remember, then, that the precise practical service of sound theory of logic is to abbreviate the time of waiting to know the truth, to expedite the predestined result. But I here use the words 'abbreviate' and 'expedite' in a peculiar sense. Imagine a derelict wreck to be floating about on the ocean; and suppose that it will be driven hither and thither until it chances to be cast upon a shore. Then, a vessel which should go and take that derelict in tow and deliberately strand it upon the nearest shore, would be "abbreviating" or "expediting" the fulfillment of the destiny of that derelict in the same sense in which I hold that logic "abbreviates" inquiry, and "expedites" its result. It changes a fortuitous event which may take weeks or may take many decennia into an operation governed by intelligence, which will be finished within a month. This is the sense in which logic "abbreviates" and "expedites" the attainment of truth.

§3. SCIENTIFIC METHOD [12]

79. Scientific Method: The general method of successful scientific research. The following are some of its characteristics. Cf. *Science*.[13]

80. (1) The student's first step is to form a perfectly definite and consistent idea of what the problem really is; then he ought to develop the mathematics of the subject in hand as far as possible; and to establish a mathematical method appropriate to the particular problem, if it be one which allows

[12] (Ed.) Paragraphs 79–88 are "Scientific Method," *Dictionary of Philosophy and Psychology* (edited by James Mark Baldwin), Vol. II, 1902, pp. 500–503. Paragraphs 89–91 are "Verification," *ibid.*, pp. 761–762.

[13] (Ed.) Peirce did not define this term for Baldwin's *Dictionary*, but see Section 1 of the present chapter (49ff.).

exact treatment. As examples and models of what is meant, may be mentioned Maxwell's researches on colour sensation in the *Philos. Trans.* for 1860, Flinders Petrie's book *Inductive Metrology*, the last chapters of Pearson's *Grammar of Science*. Of course, as the student's understanding of the matter advances, he will return to this first task, and continually improve upon his first essays.

81. The second step will be to consider the logic and methodeutic of the research in hand, unless it is itself a question of pure mathematics, where the logic is inseparable from the mathematics. He will do well to study the manner in which questions somewhat analogous to his own have been successfully resolved in widely different fields; for the greatest advantage has accrued from the extension of methods from one subject to a widely different one, especially from simple to intricate matters.

82. The third step should be to reform his metaphysics, if the question is a broad one. Perhaps he thinks he has no metaphysics, and does not wish to have any. That will be a sure sign that he is badly handicapped with metaphysics of the crudest quality. The only way to disburden himself of it is to direct his attention to it. But he cannot reduce himself to anything like absolute scepticism in metaphysics without arresting his work.

83. The fourth step will be to study the laws of the phenomena dealt with, so far as they can be made out at this stage. The general order of discovery in the nomological sciences is first to pick up the phenomena by excursions in those fields in which they are to be found, with alertness of observation, with those clear ideas that make the new fact instantly recognizable as new, and with the energy that seizes upon the faint trace and follows it up. Witness the manner in which all the new phenomena of radiation have been brought to light during the last generation: cathode rays, X rays, Becquerel rays, etc. After making some acquaintance with the phenomena, the next discovery is of their laws (nomological). In the light of one's metaphysics and general conception of the department of truth dealt with, one considers what different hypotheses have any claims to investigation. The leading con-

53

siderations here will be those of the 'economics' of research.[14] If, for example, a hypothesis would necessitate an experimental result that can be cheaply refuted if it is not true, or would be greatly at variance with preconceived ideas, that hypothesis has a strong claim to early examination. But one must not give up a hypothesis too readily. Many a discovery has been missed by that fault. Gravitation would have been known a decade earlier if Newton had not hastily thought it refuted, and so set back all the subsequent history of physics by something like that amount of time lost. It is likely that thousands of persons more will die of consumption — as remote as that may seem — than would have died if he had not made that error. The testing of the hypothesis proceeds by deducing from it experimental consequences almost incredible, and finding that they really happen, or that some modification of the theory is required, or else that it must be entirely abandoned. The law of the phenomena once made out, it only remains to measure with precision the values of the coefficients in the equation which expresses it.

84.   The problem under investigation may not be of a nomological kind. Not that the phenomena are not conceivably subject to law, so that the subject may ultimately be received into the nomological sciences, — as chemistry, for example, promises some day to mature into a nomological science; but in the present state of knowledge the question, we will suppose, cannot be so studied. Still, a certain amount of nomological study is a necessary preliminary to engaging with the problem itself. Biology calls for aid from physiology. The student who is studying the growth of languages must avail himself of all the knowledge that there is about the physics of speech sounds. In case, then, the question has not yet reached the nomological stage, the sixth step in the work will be of a classificatory nature. Such order, of a more or less imperfect kind, as can be traced in the phenomena must be made out. Students of the classificatory sciences like to call such regularities laws. The tendency is a symptom of health; because it shows that law is their ideal, and that they are striving to bring their sciences to the nomological stage. But such orderlinesses as

[14] (Ed.) See Chapter 2, "Economy of Research," in the present book.

'Grimm's Law' (see *Gender*) and 'Mendeléef's Law' are not laws in the sense in which the association of ideas and the three laws of motion are laws. They are not satisfactory for a minute. They are nothing that can blend with our metaphysics; they are not of a universal kind; and they are not precise. You may imagine that there might be a chain of more and more universal, precise, and reasonable regularities leading from these to those. But there is, in fact, a great gap, which has to be acknowledged. A hypothesis may be made about the cause of the three laws of motion; but we can have no present hopes of satisfactorily proving the truth of such a thing; while we at once set to work with great hopes of making considerable steps towards explaining Mendeléef's Law and Grimm's Law. But the most important distinction between true laws and such regularities lies in the very different way in which we proceed to the discovery of the one and of the other. The whole attitude of mind is so different that it is difficult to believe that the same man would have great success in the two tasks. We have seen in our day the establishment of a grand example of each kind, the Law of the *Conservation of Energy* (q.v.) and the Periodic Law. The one dealt with a small number of observations. Exactitude was the main thing. The hypothesis itself sprang almost immediately from the natural light of reason. In the other case, it was necessary with a positive effort to put ideas of exactitude aside and to find order in a great tangle of facts.

85.   Perhaps the problem in hand relates to one of those sciences basely called descriptive, that is, sciences which study, not classes of facts, but individual facts, such as history, descriptive astronomy, geography. No science is merely descriptive. These sciences are investigations of causes. The historian's facts of observation are not those contained in his text, but those mentioned in the foot-notes — the documents and monuments.[15] It is the supposed causes of these which make the text. Nor is he contented with a mere chronicle of striking public events; he endeavours to show what the hidden causes of them were. So the astronomer's real business is to

[15] (Ed.) See Chapter 3, "The Logic of Drawing History from Ancient Documents," in the present book.

prove the *Nebular Hypothesis* (q.v.) or whatever ought to re-place it. The geologist does not merely make a geological map, but shows how the existing state of things must have come to pass. To do this the historian has to be a profound psychologist, the geologist a master of physics and dynamics. Just as the classificatory sciences tend to become nomological, so the descriptive, or explanatory, sciences tend to become classificatory. The astronomer finds so many examples of sys-tems in formation, that he can formulate the cycle of events through which they generally pass; as the historian formulates cycles through which communities usually pass, and the geolo-gist formulates cycles through which continents commonly pass. These are analogous to the cyclical laws of the classifica-tory sciences.

86. But perhaps the problem before the student is not one of theoretical physics or of theoretical psychics, but a practical problem. He wishes to invent. In that case he ought to have a great knowledge both of facts about men's minds and of facts about matter; for he has to adapt the one to the other. He ought to know more than any pure scientist can be expected to know. Of course, as the world goes, he does not.

87. (2) The most vital factors in the method of modern science have not been the following of this or that logical prescription — although these have had their value too — but they have been the moral factors. First of these has been the genuine love of truth and conviction that nothing else could long endure. Given that men strive after the truth, and, in the nature of things, they will get it in a measure. The greatest difference between the scientific state of the modern scientific era from Copernicus and the middle ages, is that now the whole concern of students is to find out the truth; while then it was to put into a rational light the faith of which they were already possessed. The chief obstacle to the advance of science among students of science in the modern era has been that they were teachers, and feared the effect of this or that theory. But the salvation from this danger has been the fact that there was no vast institution which anybody for a moment hoped could withstand the mighty tide of fact. The next most vital factor

of the method of modern science is that it has been made social. On the one hand, what a scientific man recognizes as a fact of science must be something open to anybody to observe, provided he fulfils the necessary conditions, external and internal. As long as only one man has been able to see a marking upon the planet Venus, it is not an established fact. Ghost stories and all that cannot become the subject of genuine science until they can in some way be welded to ordinary experience.[16] On the other hand, the method of modern science is social in respect to the solidarity of its efforts. The scientific world is like a colony of insects, in that the individual strives to produce that which he himself cannot hope to enjoy. One generation collects premises in order that a distant generation may discover what they mean. When a problem comes before the scientific world, a hundred men immediately set all their energies to work upon it. One contributes this, another that. Another company, standing upon the shoulders of the first, strike a little higher, until at last the parapet is attained. Still another moral factor of the method of science, perhaps even more vital than the last, is the self-confidence of it. In order to appreciate this, it is to be remembered that the entire fabric of science has to be built up out of surmises at truth. All that experiment can do is to tell us when we have surmised wrong. The right surmise is left for us to produce. The ancient world under these circumstances, with the exception of a few men born out of their time, looked upon physics as something about which only vague surmises could be made, and upon which close study would be thrown away. So, venturing nothing, they naturally could gain nothing. But modern science has never faltered in its confidence that it would ultimately find out the truth concerning any question in which it could apply the check of experiment.

88. These are some of the more vital factors of the method of modern science. For the purely logical elements the reader should consult special topics, e.g. *Reasoning*,[17] *Probable*

[16] (Ed.) Cf. Chapter 5, "Telepathy and Perception," in Book III of the present volume.
[17] (Ed.) 2.773–778.

Inference,[18] *Psychophysical Methods, Errors of Observation, Empirical Logic, Variation,* etc.

———◆———

89. Verification: It is desirable to understand by a verifiable hypothesis one which presents an abundance of necessary consequences open to experimental tests, and which involves no more than is necessary to furnish a source of those consequences. The verification will not consist in searching the facts in order to find features that accord or disagree with the hypothesis. That is to no purpose whatsoever. The verification, on the contrary, must consist in basing upon the hypothesis predictions as to the results of experiments, especially those of such predictions as appear to be otherwise least likely to be true, and in instituting experiments in order to ascertain whether they will be true or not.

90. These experiments need not be experiments in the narrow and technical sense, involving considerable preparation. That preparation may be as simple as it may. The essential thing is that it shall not be known beforehand, otherwise than through conviction of the truth of the hypothesis, how these experiments will turn out. It does not need any long series of experiments, so long as every feature of the hypothesis is covered, to render it worthy of positive scientific credence. What is of much greater importance is that the experiments should be independent, that is, such that from the results of some, the result of no other should be capable of reasonable surmise, except through the hypothesis. But throughout the process of verification the exigencies of the economy of research should be carefully studied from the point of view of its abstract theory.

91. When, in 1839, Auguste Comte laid down the rule that no hypothesis ought to be entertained which was not capable of verification, it was far from receiving general acceptance. But this was chiefly because Comte did not make it clear, nor did he apparently understand, what verification consisted in. He seemed to think, and it was generally understood, that what was meant was that the hypothesis should contain no facts of

———

[18] (Ed.) 2.783–787.

a kind not open to direct observation. That position would leave the memory of the past as something not so much as to be entertained as plausible.

§4. SIMPLICITY [19]

92.   Parsimony (law of): Ockham's razor, i.e. the maxim 'Entia non sunt multiplicanda praeter necessitatem.' The meaning is, that it is bad scientific method to introduce, at once, independent hypotheses to explain the same facts of observation.

93.   Though the maxim was first put forward by nominalists, its validity must be admitted on all hands, with one limitation; namely, it may happen that there are two theories which, so far as can be seen, without further investigation, seem to account for a certain order of facts. One of these theories has the merit of superior simplicity. The other, though less simple, is on the whole more likely. But this second one cannot be thoroughly tested by a deeper penetration into the facts without doing almost all the work that would be required to test the former. In that case, although it is good scientific method to adopt the simpler hypothesis to guide systematic observations, yet it may be better judgment, in advance of more thorough knowledge, to suppose the more complex hypothesis to be true. For example, I know that men's motives are generally mixed. If, then, I see a man pursuing a line of conduct which apparently might be explained as thoroughly selfish, and yet might be explained as partly selfish and partly benevolent, then, since absolutely selfish characters are somewhat rare, it will be safer for me in my dealings with the man to assume the more complex hypothesis to be true; although were I to undertake an elaborate examination of the question, I ought to begin by ascertaining whether the hypothesis of pure selfishness would quite account for all he does.

94.   The whole aim of science is to find out facts, and to work out a satisfactory theory of them. Still, a theory does not necessarily lose its utility by not being altogether true. . . .

[19] (Ed.) Paragraphs 92–93 are "Parsimony (law of)," *Dictionary of Philoso-*

95. No theory in the positive sciences can be supposed to satisfy every feature of the facts. Although we know that the law of gravitation is one of the most perfect of theories, yet still, if bodies were to attract one another inversely as a power of the distance whose exponent were not 2, but 2.000001, the only observable effect would be a very slow rotation of the line of apsides of each planet. Now the lines of apsides all do rotate in consquence of perturbations, which virtually do alter slightly the sun's attraction, and thus such an effect would probably only produce slight discrepancies in the values obtained for the masses of the planets. In very many cases, especially in practical problems, we deliberately go upon theories which we know are not exactly true, but which have the advantage of a simplicity which enables us to deduce their consequences. This is true of almost every theory used by engineers of all kinds. The most extraordinary departure from the known facts occurs when hydrodynamics is applied, where the theory is in striking opposition to facts which obtrude themselves upon every spectator of moving water. Nevertheless, even in this case, the theory is not useless.

96. In all the explanatory sciences theories far more simple than the real facts are of the utmost service in enabling us to analyse the phenomena, and it may truly be said that physics could not possibly deal even with its relatively simple facts without such analytic procedure. Thus, the kinetical theory of gases, when first propounded, was obliged to assume that all the molecules were elastic spheres, which nobody could believe to be true. If this is necessary even in physics, it is far more indispensable in every other science, and most of all in the moral sciences, such as political economy. Here the sane method is to begin by considering persons placed in situations of extreme simplicity, in the utmost contrast to those of all human society, and animated by motives and by reasoning powers equally unlike those of real men. Nevertheless, in this way alone can a base be obtained from which to proceed to the consideration of the effects of different complications. Owing to the necessity of making theories far more

phy and Psychology (edited by James Mark Baldwin), Vol. II, 1902, p. 264.
Paragraphs 94–96 are from "Theory," *ibid.*, pp. 693–694.

simple than the real facts, we are obliged to be cautious in accepting any extreme consequences of them, and to be also upon our guard against apparent refutations of them based upon such extreme consequences.

§5. KINDS OF REASONING [20]

97. *First* of all I must establish, as well as I can, the proposition that all Reasoning is either Deduction, Induction, or Retroduction.[21]

98. Unfortunately, I am unable to make this as *evident* as would be desirable, although I think there is very little room for doubting it, since in the course of a long life of active study of reasonings, during which I have never met with any argument not of a familiar type without carefully analyzing and studying it, I have constantly since 1860, or 50 years, had this question prominently in mind, and if I had ever met with an argument not of one of these three kinds, I must certainly have perceived it. But I never have found any such kind of argument except Analogy, which, as I have shown, is of a nature, — a mixture of the three recognized kinds. Therefore, it may be taken as substantially certain that I have never in 50 years met with a reasoning of any fourth type.

99. Now I have not been the only man whose attention would have been roused by the appearance of any such reasoning; and if anybody in the civilized world had found such an argument, I should have heard of it.

100. Now it is of the nature of a genus of reasoning that it applies to any kind of matter in inexhaustible variety. It is therefore very difficult to believe that there is any kind of reasoning that has not been familiarly employed and known by all the world from time immemorial. On the whole, then, I think my negative experience ought to be pretty convincing, inductively.

[20] (Ed.) "Notes for my Logical Criticism of Articles of the Christian Creed," Widener IB3. Judging by the reference to 1860 in the second paragraph, this is to be dated c.1910.

[21] (Ed.) Peirce also uses "Abduction" and "Hypothesis" for what he here calls "Retroduction."

101. Though I do not profess to render it strictly speaking, *evident* that there are but the three types of reasoning, yet it will be interesting to see how nearly I can approach that desideratum.

102. A sound reasoning justifies us in some kind of belief in the truth of a proposition that in the absence of the reasoning we should not have been so much justified in believing.

103. In reasoning, one is obliged to *think to oneself.* In order to recognize what is needful for doing this it is necessary to recognize, first of all, what "oneself" is. One is not twice in precisely the same mental state. One is *virtually* (i.e. for pertinent purposes, the same as if one were) a somewhat different person, to whom one's present thought has to be communicated. Consequently, one has to express one's thought so that that virtually other person may understand it. One may, with great advantage, however, employ a language, in thinking to oneself, that is free from much explanation that would be needed in explaining oneself to quite a different person. One can establish conventions with oneself, which enable one to express the essence of what [one] has to communicate free from signs that are not essential. For that reason for example a mathematician has, in thinking of mathematical subjects, an immense advantage. Thus if he has to express to himself a force he will think of D_t^2S, which, he will remember, or can readily see if he should not remember it, is the same as $D_s[\frac{1}{2}(D_tS)^2]$.[22] Or he may express the same thing by means of a geometrical diagram, and that in any one of various forms. In like mathematical fashion Existential Graphs [23] enable me here and there greatly to abridge the labor and increase the exactitude of my thought by putting intricate logical relations in the forms that display to me precisely what they involve.

104. In particular, [the system of] Existential Graphs shows clearly that all logical relations are compounds of the relation of *consequence, provided we look upon identity as*

----

[22] (Ed.) That is, in the case of a unit mass, the force is equal to the acceleration, and it is also equal to the derivative of the energy with respect to distance.

[23] (Ed.) See [CP] IV, Book II.

so composed. But Existential Graphs does *not* so regard Identity. That is, it does not assert that to say that the Battle of Waterloo was the final downfall of Napoleon is precisely the same as to say, that if the Battle of Waterloo was the final downfall of Napoleon then for Napoleon to lose that battle as completely as he did, necessarily involved his final overthrow, while if he had not so lost that battle, he would not then and there have been finally overthrown.

105. My reason in constructing the system of Existential Graphs for not allowing such an identity was that no single *actual event* can follow as logically consequent upon any other, since if it [were] otherwise in the smallest particular, it would be a different event. If in the Battle of Waterloo one man's wound were shifted a hundredth of an inch, or if it had occurred a tenth of a second earlier or later, the Battle would not have been that actual event that did take place; and we never can be in a situation to affirm that under specified circumstances that which did take place must have taken place with such absolute precision; and it is the merest moonshine to claim to know that only as any describable circumstances had taken place the Battle of Waterloo or any other actual historical event *must* have taken place *precisely* as it did. It is a pretty theory although there are grave objections to its precise truth, but to claim to know it is a pretension that I do not think any sober minded man who sufficiently considers the subject will allow himself to make. It has all the ear-marks of the *doctrinaire*, the man who is willing to accept theories as absolutely true. All the difficulties into which metaphysicians contrive to snarl themselves up are traceable to just that doctrinaire disposition. Certainly, I will take care that my system of logic is not inoculated with that easily avoidable but fatal infection.

106. Therefore, the System of Graphs is so constructed that nothing can be recognized as an apodictic proof that in any circumstances defined in general terms, an event *must* have happened precisely as it did.

107. But as long as we have to do with general states of things, Existential Graphs analyzes all logical relations into cases of the one relation of *consequence*, that is the relation between one general description of event, A, an antecedent, and

another general description of event, C, a consequent, the relation consisting in the fact that whenever A is realized, C will be realized. All known laws of dynamics as well as all other truths consist of such relations.

108.   I will not, therefore, admit that we know anything whatever with *absolute certainty*.[24] It is possible that twice two is not four. For a computer might commit an error in the multiplication of 2 by 2; and whatever might happen once might happen again. Now 2 has never been multiplied by 2 but a finite number of times; and consequently all such multiplications may have been wrong in the same way. It is true that it would be difficult to imagine a greater folly than to attach any serious importance to such a doubt. Still foolish as that would be, its folly would not be so great as to assert that there is some number of repetitions of a multiplication that renders their result, if all agree, absolutely certain. For if this be the case there is some number which is the *least* that is sufficient to produce certainty. Let this number be denoted by N. Then N–1 repetitions of the multiplication do not yield an absolutely certain result, but one more, if it agree with all the others, will have that result. Consequently a single multiplication will be sufficient to give us *absolute certainty*, that the result is the same, unless some other one of N–1 repetitions should give a different result. Thus, disregarding the particular proposition in question one is driven to maintaining that a single experiment is capable of giving us certain knowledge as to the result of any number of experiments. This is sufficient to show that such an assumption is dangerous in the extreme. It is also absurd from various points of view. The only safety is to say that man is incapable of absolute certainty.

109.   But some one will ask me, "Do you, then, really entertain any doubt that twice two is four?" To this I must answer, "No, as well as I can perceive, there is not the slightest real doubt of it in my mind." [25] "But," he will say, "how can that be? You say it is not certain. Ought you not then, to

---

[24] (Ed.) Peirce's fallibilism, the doctrine that there is no absolute certainty in knowledge, is discussed at 1.8ff., and elsewhere in [CP] I.

[25] (Ed.) Cf. the discussion of unreal doubt as contrasted to genuine doubt at 5.265 and elsewhere in [CP] V.

entertain a doubt of it; and if you feel that it ought to be doubted, do you not, *ipso facto*, actually doubt it?" I reply: "Doubt is a certain kind of feeling. It has not only grades of intensity, but also varieties of quality. Now if I were able to modify my state of mind by a sufficiently slight tincture of the right kind of doubt, I ought to do so. But if I were to attempt really to feel any doubt at all, I should certainly either feel none at all or else millions upon millions of times too much. For I could not in the least recognize a tincture so small nor even one that should be millions of times too great. If I were to devote my whole life to the useless task of trying to make such slight distinctions in my feelings, I could not come near to the requisite delicacy. My feeling of doubt is one of the coarser of my sensations; and there would be no practical use in making it more delicate than it is, for it is already so far more delicate than that of almost all the persons with whom I converse, that I often find an insuperable difficulty in making them comprehend the slighter grades of my feeling, and there is no practical difference in my conduct whether, say, 3/8 or 5/13 be the proper degree of doubt about a matter not measurable. It would be a waste of time to adjust my feeling of doubt more accurately, since it neither would have, nor ought to have, any effect upon my scientific conduct. Instead of wasting effort on my feeling, I devote my energies to learning more about the subjects concerning which I have any considerable doubts, while very small doubts I neglect until I can reduce the amount of my doubt concerning subjects of greater importance."

§6. KINDS OF INDUCTION [26]

110.   Suppose we define Inductive reasoning as that reasoning whose conclusion is justified not by there being any necessity of its being true or approximately true but by its being the result of a method which if steadily persisted in must bring the reasoner to the truth of the matter or must cause his conclusion in its changes to converge to the truth as its limit.

[26] (Ed.) From Vol. I of Lecture 7 of the Lowell Lectures of 1903, Widener IB2–4.

Cf. 2.755–760 and 7.208–217 for related treatments of the same topic.

Adopting this definition, I find that there are three orders of induction of very different degrees of cogency although they are all three indispensable.

111.   The first order of induction, which I will call *Rudimentary Induction*, or the Pooh-pooh argument, proceeds from the premiss that the reasoner has no evidence of the existence of any fact of a given description and concludes that there never was, is not, and never will be any such thing. The justification of this is that it goes by such light as we have, and that truth is bound eventually to come to light; and therefore if this mode of reasoning temporarily leads us away from the truth, yet steadily pursued, it will lead to the truth at last. This is certainly very weak justification; and were it possible to dispense with this method of reasoning, I would certainly not recommend it. But the strong point of it is that it *is* indispensable. It goes upon the roughest kind of information, upon merely negative information; but that is the only information we can have concerning the great majority of subjects.

112.   I find myself introduced to a man without any previous warning. Now if I knew that he had married his grandmother and had subsequently buried her alive, I might decline his acquaintance; but since I have never heard the slightest suspicion of his doing such a thing, and I have no time to investigate idle surmises, I presume he never did anything of the sort. I know a great many men, however, whose whole stock of reasoning seems to consist in this argument, which they continue to use where there *is* positive evidence and where this argument consequently loses all force. If you ask such a man whether he believes in the liquefaction of the blood of St. Januarius, he will say *no*. Why not? Well, nothing of that kind ever came within the range of my experience. But it did come within the range of Sir Humphrey Davy's experience, who was granted every facility for the thorough investigation of it. His careful report simply confirms the usual allegations with more circumstantial details. You are not justified in pooh-poohing such observations; and that the fact is contrary to the apparent ordinary course of nature is no argument whatever. You are bound to believe it, until you can bring some positive reason for disbelieving it.

66

113. In short this rudimentary kind of induction is justified where there is no other way of reasoning; but it is of all
sound arguments the very weakest and must disappear as
soon as any positive evidence is forthcoming.

114. The second order of induction consists in the argument
from the fulfillment of predictions. After a hypothesis has
been suggested to us by the agreement between its consequences
and observed fact, there are two different lines that our further
studies of it may pursue. In the first place, we may look through
the known facts and scrutinize them carefully to see how far
they agree with the hypothesis and how far they call for modifications of it. That is a very proper and needful inquiry. But
it is Abduction, not Induction, and proves nothing but the
ingenuity with which the hypothesis has been adapted to the
facts of the case. To take this for Induction, as a great proportion of students do, is one of the greatest errors of reasoning that can be made. It is the *post hoc ergo propter hoc*
fallacy, if so understood. But if understood to be a process
antecedent to the application of induction, not intended to test
the hypothesis, but intended to aid in perfecting that hypothesis
and making it more definite, this proceeding is an essential
part of a well-conducted inquiry.

115. The other line which our studies of the relation of the
hypothesis to experience may pursue, consists in directing our
attention, not primarily to the facts, but primarily to the hypothesis, and in studying out what effect that hypothesis, if
embraced, must have in modifying our expectations in regard
to future experience. Thereupon we make experiments, or
quasi-experiments,[27] in order to find out how far these new conditional expectations are going to be fulfilled. In so far as they
greatly modify our former expectations of experience and in

[27] (Ed.) "The Deductions which we base upon the hypothesis which has
resulted from Abduction produce conditional predictions concerning our future
experience. That is to say, we infer by Deduction that if the hypothesis be
true, any future phenomena of certain descriptions must present such and
such characters. We now institute a course of quasi-experimentation in
order to bring these predictions to the test, and thus to form our final estimate
of the value of the hypothesis, and this whole proceeding I term Induction.
I speak of quasi-experimentation because the term *experiment* is, according to
the usage of scientific men, restricted to the operation of bringing about
certain conditions. The noting of the results of experiments or of anything

so far as we find them, nevertheless, to be fulfilled, we accord to the hypothesis a due weight in determining all our future conduct and thought. It is true that the observed conformity of the facts to the requirements of the hypothesis may have been fortuitous. But if so, we have only to persist in this same method of research and we shall gradually be brought around to the truth. This gradual process of rectification is in great contrast to what takes place with rudimentary induction where the correction comes with a bang. The strength of any argument of the Second Order depends upon how much the confirmation of the prediction runs counter to what our expectation would have been without the hypothesis. It is entirely a question of how much; and yet there is no measurable quantity. For when such measure is possible the argument assumes quite another complexion, and becomes an induction of the Third Order. Inductions of the second order are of two varieties, that are logically quite distinct.

116.   The weaker of these is where the predictions that are fulfilled are merely of the continuance in future experience of the same phenomena which originally suggested and recommended the hypothesis, expectations directly involved in holding the hypothesis. Even such confirmation may have considerable weight. This, for example, is the way in which the undulatory theory of light stood before Maxwell. The phenomena of interference suggested undulations, which measures of the velocity of light in different media confirmed; and the phenomena of polarization suggested transverse vibrations. All the direct expectations involved in the hypothesis were confirmed, except that there no phenomena due to longitudinal vibrations were found. But all physicists felt that it was a weakness of the theory that no unexpected predictions occurred. The rotation of the plane of polarization was an outstanding fact not accounted for.

117.   The other variety of the argument from the fulfillment

---

else to which our attention is directed in advance of our noting it, is called *Observation*. But by quasi-experimentation I mean the entire operation either of producing or of searching out a state of things to which the conditional predictions deduced from hypothesis shall be applicable and of noting how far the prediction is fulfilled." From an earlier passage of the same lecture (110n26).

of predictions is where truths ascertained subsequently to the provisional adoption of the hypothesis or, at least, not at all seen to have any bearing upon it, lead to new predictions being based upon the hypothesis of an entirely different kind from those originally contemplated and these new predictions are equally found to be verified.

118.   Thus Maxwell, noticing that the velocity of light had the same value as a certain fundamental constant relating to electricity, was led to the hypothesis that light was an electromagnetic oscillation. This explained the magnetic rotation of the plane of polarization, and predicted the Hertzian waves. Not only that, but it further led to the prediction of the mechanical pressure of light, which had not at first been contemplated.

119.   The second order of induction only infers that a theory is very much like the truth, because we are so far from ever being authorized to conclude that a theory is the *very truth* itself, that we can never so much as understand what that means. Light is electro-magnetic vibrations; that is to say, it [is] something very like that. In order to say that it is precisely that, we should have to know precisely what we mean by electro-magnetic vibrations. Now we never can know precisely what we mean by any description whatever.

120.   The third order of induction, which may be called Statistical Induction, differs entirely from the other two in that it assigns a definite value to a quantity. It draws a sample of a class, finds a numerical expression for a predesignate character of that sample and extends this evaluation, under proper qualification, to the entire class, by the aid of the doctrine of chances. The doctrine of chances is, in itself, purely deductive. It draws necessary conclusions only. The third order of induction takes advantage of the information thus deduced to render induction exact.

121.   This family of inductions has three different kinds quite distinct logically. Beginning with the lowest and least certain, we have cases in which a class of individuals recur in endless succession and we do not know in advance whether the occurrences are entirely independent of one another or not. But we have some reason to suppose that they would be inde-

pendent and perhaps that they have some given ratio of frequency. Then what has to be done is to apply all sorts of consequences of independence and see whether the statistics support the assumption. For instance, the value of the ratio of the circumference of a circle to its diameter, a number usually called π has been calculated in the decimal notation, to over seven hundred figures. Now as there is not the slightest reason to suppose that any law expressible in a finite time connects the value of π with the decimal notation or with any whole number, we may presume that the recurrences of any figure say 5 in that succession are independent of one another and that there is simply a probability of 1/10 that any figure will be a 5.

122.   In order to illustrate this mode of induction, I have made a few observations on the calculated number. There ought to be, in 350 successive figures, about 35 fives. The odds are about 2 to 1 that there will be 30-39 [and] 3 to 1 that there will be 29-41. Now I find in the first 350 figures 33 fives, and in the second 350, 28 fives, which is not particularly unlikely under the supposition of a chance distribution. During the process of counting these 5's, it occurred to me that as the expression of a rational fraction in decimals takes the form of a circulating decimal in which the figures recur with perfect regularity, so in the expression of a quantity like π, it was naturally to be expected that the 5's, or any other figure, should recur with some approach to regularity. In order to find out whether anything of this kind was discernible I counted the fives in 70 successive sets of 10 successive figures each. Now were there no regularity at all in the recurrence of the 5's, there ought among these 70 sets of ten numbers each to be 27 that contained just one five each; and the odds against there being more than 32 of the seventy sets that contain just one five each is about 5 to 1. Now it turns out upon examination that there are 33 of the sets of ten figures which contain just one 5. It thus seems as if my surmise were right that the figures will be a little more regularly distributed than they would be if they were entirely independent of one another. But there is not much certainty about it. This will serve to illustrate what this kind of induction is like, in which the question to

be decided is how far a given succession of occurrences are independent of one another and if they are not independent what the nature of the law of their succession is.

123. In the second variety of statistical induction, we are supposed to know whether the occurrences are independent or not, and if not, exactly how they are connected, and the inquiry is limited to ascertaining what the ratio of frequency is, after the effects of the law of succession have been eliminated. As a very simple example, I will take the following. The dice that are sold in the toy shops as apparatus for games . . . are usually excessively irregular. It is no great fault, but rather enhances the Christmas gaiety. Suppose, however, that some old frump with an insatiable appetite for statistics [were to] get hold of a die of that sort, and he will spend his Christmas in throwing it and recording the throws in order to find out the relative frequency with which the different faces turn up. He assumes that the different throws are independent of one another and that the ten thousand or so which he makes will give the same relative frequencies of the different faces as would be found among any similar large number of throws until the die gets worn down. At least he can safely assume that this will be the case as long as the die is thrown out of the same box by the same person in the same fashion.

124. This second variety is the usual and typical case of statistical induction. But it occasionally happens that we can sample a finite collection of objects by such a method that in the long run any one object of the collection would be taken as often as every other and any one succession as often as any other. This may [be] termed a *random* selection. It is obviously possible only in the case of an enumerable collection. When this sort of induction is possible it far surpasses every other in certainty and may closely approach that of demonstration itself.

125. I have now passed in review all the modes of pure induction with which I am acquainted. Induction may, of course, be strengthened or weakened by the addition of other modes of argument leading to the same conclusion or to a contrary conclusion. It may also be strengthened or weakened by arguments which do not directly affect the conclusion of

71

the induction but which increase or diminish the strength of its procedure. There are in particular four kinds of uniformities which may greatly affect an induction.

126. In the first place the members of a class may present a greater or less general resemblance as regards certain kinds of characters. Birds for example are, generally speaking, much more alike than are fishes or mammals; and that will strengthen any induction about birds. Orchids, on the other hand, are extraordinarily various.

127. In the second place a character may have a greater or less tendency to be present or absent throughout the whole of certain kinds of groups. Thus, coloration often differs within one species, while the number of the principal bones of the skeleton, and almost all characters which are developed early in individual life and which persist to maturity are common to all the members of large classes.

128. In the third place, a certain set of characters may be more or less intimately connected, so as probably to be present or absent together in certain kinds of objects. Thus, we generally associate insistency upon minute forms with narrowness of mind, cleanliness with godliness, and so on.

129. In the fourth place, an object may have more or less tendency to possess the whole of certain sets of characters when it possesses any of them. Thus, one meets one man whose views whatever they may be are extreme, while the opinions of another form a strange mosaic.

130. From the knowledge of a uniformity of any one of these four classes or from the knowledge of the lack of such uniformity it may be deductively inferred that a given induction is either stronger or weaker than it otherwise would be.

§7. UNIFORMITY OF NATURE [28]

131. There is still another sense in which we might speak of the uniformity of nature. If we select a good many objects on the principle that they shall belong to a certain class and then find that they all have some common character, pretty

[28] (Ed.) From Lecture IV (c.1866) of the same series from which 7.579–596 are taken, Widener IB2–10; cf. 7.579n34.

much the whole class will generally be found to have that character. Or if we take a good many of the characters of a thing at random, and afterwards find a thing which has all these characters, we shall generally find that the second thing is pretty near the same as the first.

132.   It seems to me that it is this pair of facts rather than any others which are properly expressed by saying that nature is uniform. We shall see that it is they which are the leading principles of scientific inference.

Let us ask, then, whether these facts are statements of a particular constitution of the world so as to be properly speaking matters of fact or whether they are purely formal propositions, laws of logic, having no more application to one state of things than they would have to any other.

133.   In the first place, I would call your attention to the quantitative indeterminateness of both propositions. The first speaks of a *good many* samples being selected, and of *pretty much* all the things in the class from which they are taken being like them, and of this occurring *almost* always. The second speaks of a *good many* characters of a thing being taken, and of any thing found to have them being *pretty near* the same thing, and of this happening *almost always*. We have no means whatsoever of defining the propositions in either of the three respects in which they are thus seen to be so utterly vague.

134.   Now you know how a malicious person [who] wishes to say something ill of another, prefers *insinuation*; that is, he speaks so vaguely that he suggests a great deal while he expressly says nothing at all. In this way he avoids being confronted by fact. It is the same way with these principles of scientific inference. They are so vague that you cannot bring them to any touch-stone of experience. They rather insinuate a uniformity in nature than state it. And as insinuation always expresses the state of feeling of the person who uses it rather than anything concerning its object, so we may suppose these principles express rather the scientific attitude than a scientific result.

135.   But what if we were in a world of chance? How would it be with these principles then, or, to simplify the matter,

with the first principle? In that case, it would be extremely
seldom that, having selected a number of objects as having
certain characters, we should find that they had any other
common character; and thus there would be very little applicability for this principle. But, we have seen that the proportion of cases where this principle applies is indefinitely small
in our present world. Cases might occur, doubtless would in a
world of chance and when they did occur the principle doubtless would hold true.

136. It is a mistake to suppose that there would be no
laws in a world of chance. At least, so I should think. Suppose
we were to throw a die any number of times and set down the
numbers thrown in a column. I could show you that there
would be some very curious laws in reference to those numbers.
They would appear quite surprizing. So that *chance* is not the
abrogation of all laws.

137. But there is a peculiarity about those laws that chance
does not abrogate; suppose that in throwing the die other
numbers had turned up from those which actually turned up,
so that the row of numbers would have been somewhat different;
still the laws would have held; they would hold with one set
of numbers as well as with another. Whereas if we were to
give a whale legs or a woman wings, the laws of the animal
kingdom would be interfered with. So that there are two kinds
of laws, those which in a different state of things would continue to hold good and those which in a different state of things
would not hold good. The former we call *formal* laws, the
latter *material* laws. The formal laws do not depend on any
particular state of things, and hence we say we have not derived them from experience; that is to say, any other experience
would have furnished the premises for them as well as that
which we have experienced; while to discover the material
laws we require to have known just such facts as we did. But
as the laws which we have mentioned, that as is sample so is
the whole and that the sameness of a number of characters
manifests identity, are laws which would hold so long as there
were *any* laws, though only formal ones, it is plain that no
alteration in the constitution of the world would abrogate them,

so that they are themselves formal laws, and therefore not laws of *nature* but of the conditions of knowledge in general.

138.   Two classes of thinkers wish to make the difference between formal and material laws merely relative; namely, those who would reduce all formal laws to material laws, and those who would reduce all material laws to formal laws. But neither can deny that there is a great difference between what we must consider formal and what we must consider material laws. Those who would reduce all material laws to formal laws, have indeed shown that what we call material laws are only those which *we cannot discover* to be formal; and thus that all material laws may be formal; and in so doing they have cut anyone off from saying that there is a peculiar uniformity of nature consisting in its material laws. On the other hand, those who would reduce formal laws to material laws, among whom is Mr. Mill, have shown that laws may be thought to be formal, that is to be such that a violation of them is unimaginable, owing to a want of imaginative power in us arising from a defective experience, and they infer from that that *all* formal laws may be material. But so long as there are any laws whatsoever, *these* laws that the whole is as the sample and that identity goes with similarity in respects [not] chosen to make out the similarity, *these* laws I say must exist. For these are but as much as to say that there *is* law. That we shall see in future lectures. Now all law may, in one sense, be contingent. But that there should be knowledge without the existence of law, that there should be intelligence without anything intelligible, all admit to be impossible. These laws therefore cannot be abrogated without abrogating knowledge; and thus are the formal conditions of all knowledge.

CHAPTER 2

ECONOMY OF RESEARCH

§1. ORIGINAL PAPER [1]

139. When a research is of a quantitative nature, the progress of it is marked by the diminution of the probable error. The results of non-quantitative researches also have an inexactitude or indeterminacy which is analogous to the probable error of quantitative determinations. To this inexactitude, although it be not numerically expressed, the term "probable error" may be conveniently extended.

140. The doctrine of economy, in general, treats of the relations between utility and cost. That branch of it which relates to research considers the relations between the utility and the cost of diminishing the probable error of our knowledge. Its main problem is, how, with a given expenditure of money, time, and energy, to obtain the most valuable addition to our knowledge.

141. Let r denote the probable error of any result, and write $s = \frac{1}{r}$. Let $Ur \cdot dr$ denote the infinitesimal utility of any infinitesimal diminution, dr, of r. Let $Vs \cdot ds$ denote the infinitesimal cost of any infinitesimal increase, ds, of s. The letters U and V are here used as functional symbols. Let subscript letters be attached to r, s, U, and V, to distinguish the different problems into which investigations are made. Then, the total cost of any series of researches will be

$$\Sigma_i \int V_i \, s_i \cdot ds_i;$$

and their total utility will be

$$\Sigma_i \int U_i \, r_i \cdot dr_i.$$

---

[1] (Ed.) "Note on the Theory of the Economy of Research," [CS 1876] 1879, pp. 197–201, with some corrections from a manuscript version in Widener IC2a.

Cf. 5.600ff.; the paper referred to at 5.601n§ is probably this one.

The problem will be to make the second expression a maximum by varying the inferior limits of its integrations, on the condition that the first expression remains of constant value.

142.   The functions U and V will be different for different researches. Let us consider their general and usual properties. And, first, as to the relation between the exactitude of knowledge and its utility. The utility of knowledge consists in its capability of being combined with other knowledge so as to enable us to calculate how we should act. If the knowledge is uncertain, we are obliged to do more than is really necessary, in order to cover this uncertainty. And, thus, the utility of any increase of knowledge is measured by the amount of wasted effort it saves us, multiplied by the specific cost of that species of effort. Now, we know, from the theory of errors, that the uncertainty in the calculated amount of effort necessary to be put forth may be represented by an expression of the form

$$c \sqrt{a + r^2},$$

where a and c are constants. And, therefore, the differential coefficient of this, multiplied by the specific cost of the effort in question, say $\dfrac{h}{c}$, gives

$$\mathrm{U}r = h \, \frac{r}{\sqrt{a + r^2}}.$$

When a is very small compared with r this becomes nearly constant, and in the reverse case it is nearly proportional to r. An analogous proposition must hold for non-quantitative research.

143.   Let us next consider the relation between the exactitude of a result and the cost of attaining it. When we increase our exactitude by multiplying observations, the different observations being independent of one another as to their cost, we know from the theory of errors that $\int \mathrm{V}s \cdot ds$ is proportional to s^2, and that consequently $\mathrm{V}s$ is proportional to s. If the costs of the different observations are not independent (which usually happens), the cost will not increase so fast relatively to the accuracy; but if the errors of the observations are not independent (which also usually happens), the cost will increase faster rela-

tively to the accuracy; and these two perturbing influences may be supposed, in the long run, to balance one another. We may, therefore, take $Vs = ks$, where k represents the specific cost of the investigation.

144.   We thus see that when an investigation is commenced, after the initial expenses are once paid, at little cost we improve our knowledge, and improvement then is especially valuable; but as the investigation goes on, additions to our knowledge cost more and more, and, at the same time, are of less and less worth. Thus, when chemistry sprang into being, Dr. Wollaston, with a few test tubes and phials on a tea-tray, was able to make new discoveries of the greatest moment. In our day, a thousand chemists, with the most elaborate appliances, are not able to reach results which are comparable in interest with those early ones. All the sciences exhibit the same phenomenon, and so does the course of life. At first we learn very easily, and the interest of experience is very great; but it becomes harder and harder, and less and less worth while, until we are glad to sleep in death.

145.   Let us now apply the expressions obtained for Ur and Vs to the economic problem of research. The question is, having certain means at our disposal, to which of two studies they should be applied. The general answer is that we should study that problem for which the economic urgency, or the ratio of the utility to the cost

$$\frac{Ur \cdot dr}{Vs \cdot ds} = r^2 \frac{Ur}{Vs} = \frac{h}{k} \frac{r^4}{\sqrt{a + r^2}}$$

is a maximum. When the investigation has been carried to a certain point this fraction will be reduced to the same value which it has for another research, and the two must then be carried on together, until finally, we shall be carrying on, at once, researches into a great number of questions, with such relative energies as to keep the urgency-fraction of equal values for all of them. When new and promising problems arise they should receive our attention to the exclusion of the old ones, until their urgency becomes no greater than that of others. It will be remarked that our ignorance of a question is a consideration which has between three and four times the economic importance of either the specific value of the solution or the specific cost of the investigation in deciding upon its urgency.

146.   In order to solve an economical problem, we may use as variables

$$x = \int Vs \, . \, ds,$$

or the total cost of an inquiry, and

$$y = \frac{Ur \, . \, dr}{Vs \, . \, ds} \, ,$$

or the economic urgency. Then, C being the total amount we have to spend in certain researches, our equations will be

$$C = x_1 + x_2 + x_3 + \text{etc.}$$
$$y_1 = y_2 = y_3 = \text{etc.}$$

Then, expressing each y in terms of x, we shall have as many equations as unknown quantities.

147.   When we have to choose between two researches only, the solution may be represented graphically, as follows:

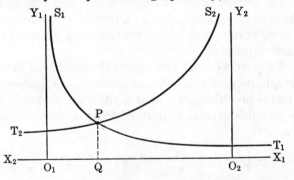

148.   From any point O_1 taken as an origin, draw the axis of abscissas $O_1 X_1$, along which x_1, the total cost of the first investigation, is to be measured. Draw also the axis of ordinates $O_1 Y_1$, along which y_1, the economic urgency of the first investigation, is to be measured. Draw the curve $S_1 T_1$ to represent the relations of x_1 and y_1. Take, on the axis $O_1 X_1$, a point O_2 such that $O_1 O_2$ shall measure the total cost of the two investigations. Let x_2, the total cost of the second investigation, be measured on the same axis as x_1, but in the opposite direc-

tion. From O_2 draw the axis of ordinates O_2 Y_2 parallel to O_1 Y_1, and measure y_2, the economic urgency of the second investigation, along this axis. Draw the curve S_2 T_2 to represent the relations of x_2 and y_2. Then, the two curves S_1 T_1 and S_2 T_2 will generally cut one another at one point, and only one, between the axes O_1 Y_1 and O_2 Y_2. From this point, say P, draw the ordinate PQ, and the abscissas O_1Q and O_2Q will measure the amounts which ought to be expended on the two inquiries.

149.   According to the usual values of U and V, we shall have

$$y = \frac{1}{4} \frac{h\,k}{x \sqrt{a\,x^2 + \frac{1}{2}k\,x}}.$$

150.   In this case, when there are two inquiries, the equation to determine x_1 will be a biquadratic. Two of its roots will be imaginary, one will give a negative value of either x_1 or x_2, and the fourth, which is the significant one, will give positive values of both.

151.   Let us now consider the economic relations of different researches to one another. 1st, as alternative methods of reaching the same result, and 2d, as contributing different premises to the same argument.

152.   Suppose we have two different methods of determining the same quantity. Each of these methods is supposed to have an accidental probable error and a constant probable error, so that the probable errors, as derived from n observations in the two ways, are:

$$r_1 = \sqrt{R_1{}^2 + \frac{\rho_1{}^2}{n}} \text{ and } r_2 = \sqrt{R_2{}^2 + \frac{\rho_2{}^2}{n}}.$$

The probable error of their weighted mean is

$$\frac{1}{\sqrt{\dfrac{1}{r_1{}^2} + \dfrac{1}{r_2{}^2}}},$$

if their constant probable errors are known. The sole utility of any observation of either is to reduce the error of the weighted mean; hence,

$$\mathrm{U}r_1 = \mathrm{D}_{r_1}(r_1^{-2} + r_2^{-2})^{-\frac{1}{2}} = (r_1^{-2} + r_2^{-2})^{-\frac{3}{2}} r_1^{-3}.$$

And as the cost is proportional to the number of observations

$$\mathrm{V}s_1 = k_1 \frac{1}{\mathrm{D}_{n_1} s_1} = \frac{k_1}{\mathrm{D}_{n_1}(\mathrm{R}_1^2 + \rho_1^2 n_1^{-1})^{-\frac{1}{2}}} = \frac{2\,k_1\,r_1^3\,n_1^2}{\rho_1^2}.$$

Hence, the urgency is (omitting a factor common to the values for the two methods)

$$r_1^2 \frac{\mathrm{U}r_1}{\mathrm{V}s_1} = \frac{1}{k_1\rho_1^2 \left(1 + n_1 \dfrac{\mathrm{R}_1^2}{\rho_1^2}\right)^2}.$$

And, as the urgency of the two methods ought to be the same at the conclusion of the work, we should have

$$\sqrt{k_1} \cdot \rho_1 \left(1 + n_1 \frac{\mathrm{R}_1^2}{\rho_1^2}\right) = \sqrt{k_2} \cdot \rho_2 \left(1 + n_2 \frac{\mathrm{R}_2^2}{\rho_2^2}\right),$$

which equation serves to determine the relative values of n_1 and n_2. We again perceive that the cost is the smallest consideration. The method which has the smallest accidental probable error is the one which is to be oftenest used in case only a small number of observations are made; but if a large number are taken the method with the larger accidental probable error is to be oftenest used, unless it has so much greater a probable constant error as to countervail this consideration. If one of the two methods has only $\frac{1}{p}$-th the accidental probable error of the other, but costs p^2 times as much, the rule should be to make the total cost of the two methods inversely proportional to the squares of their constant errors.

153. Let us now consider the case in which two quantities x_1 and x_2 are observed, the knowledge of which serves only to determine a certain function of them, $y.$[2] In this case the probable error $[dy]$ of y is

$$\sqrt{\mathrm{D}_{x_1}y \cdot r_1^2 + \mathrm{D}_{x_2}y \cdot r_2^2}$$

[2] (Ed.) In this paragraph the editor has corrected the second formula according to the manuscript, and rewritten the notation somewhat to make it uniform.

and [since $Ur_1 = D_{r_1}(dy)$] we shall have

$$Ur_1 = \frac{D_{x_1}y \cdot r_1}{\sqrt{D_{x_1}y \cdot r_1{}^2 + D_{x_2}y \cdot r_2{}^2}}.$$

Vs_1 will have the same value as before; but neglecting now the constant error, we may write

$$Vs_1 = 2k_1\rho_1 n_1{}^{\frac{1}{3}}.$$

Then the urgency (with omission of the common factor) is

$$\frac{\rho_1{}^2}{k_1 n_1{}^2} \cdot D_{x_1}y,$$

and, as the two urgencies must be equal, we have

$$\frac{n_1}{n_2} = \frac{\rho_1}{\rho_2} \sqrt{\frac{k_2}{k_1} \cdot \frac{D_{x_1}y}{D_{x_2}y}}.$$

154. The following is an example of the practical application of the theory of economy in research: Given a certain amount of time, which is to be expended in swinging a reversible pendulum, how much should be devoted to experiments with the heavy end up, and how much to those with the heavy end down? [3]

155. Let T_d be the period of oscillation with heavy end down, T_u the same with heavy end up. Let h_d and h_u be the distances of the center of mass from the points of support of the pendulum in the two positions. Then the object of the experiments is to ascertain a quantity proportional to [4]

$$h_d T_d - h_u T_u.$$

Accordingly, if dT_d and dT_u are the probable errors of T_d and T_u, that of the quantity sought will be

$$\sqrt{h_d{}^2 (d\,T_d)^2 + h_u{}^2 (d\,T_u{}^2)}.$$

156. We will suppose that it has been ascertained, by experiment, that the whole duration of the swinging being C, and

---

[3] (Ed.) In the manuscript version (see 139n1) Peirce says that this problem suggested his speculations on the economy of research.
[4] (Ed.) See [Bibliography] G–1879–5d, p. 260.

the excess of the duration of the swinging with heavy end down over that with heavy end up being x, the probable errors of the results are

$$dT_d = \sqrt{a + \left(b + \frac{c}{h_d^2}\right)\frac{1}{C+x}}$$

$$dT_u = \sqrt{a + \left(b + \frac{c}{h_u^2}\right)\frac{1}{C-x}}$$

where a, b, and c are constants. Then, the square of the probable error of the quantity sought will be

$$a(h_d^2 + h_u^2) + (bh_d^2 + c)\frac{1}{C+x} + (bh_u^2 + c)\frac{1}{C-x} .$$

The differential coefficient of this relatively to x is

$$-(bh_d^2 + c)\frac{1}{(C+x)^2} + (bh_u^2 + c)\frac{1}{(C-x)^2} .$$

Putting this equal to zero and solving, we find for the only significant root,

$$\frac{x}{C} = \frac{b(h_d^2 + h_u^2) + 2c}{b(h_d^2 - h_u^2)} - \sqrt{\left(\frac{b(h_d^2 + h_u^2) + 2c}{b(h_d^2 - h_u^2)}\right)^2 - 1}$$

when b vanishes, x reduces to zero, and the pendulum should be swung equally long in the two positions. When c vanishes, as it would if the pendulum experiment were made absolutely free from certain disturbing influences, we have

$$\frac{x}{C} = \frac{h_d - h_u}{h_d + h_u},$$

so that the duration of an experiment ought to be proportional to the distance of the center of mass from the point of support. This would be effected by beginning and ending the experiments in the two positions with the same amplitudes of oscillation.

157. It is to be remarked that the theory here given rests on the supposition that the object of the investigation is the ascertainment of truth. When an investigation is made for the purpose of attaining personal distinction, the economics of the problem are entirely different. But that seems to be well enough understood by those engaged in that sort of investigation.

83

§2. LATER REFLECTIONS [5]

158.   In all economics the laws are ideal formulae from
which there are large deviations, even statistically. In the economics of research the "laws" are mere general tendencies to
which exceptions are frequent. The laws being so indefinite,
at best, there is little advantage in very accurate definitions of
such terms as "amount of knowledge." It is, however, possible
to attach a definite conception to one increment of knowledge
being greater than another. To work this out will be the first
business of the memoir. I also establish a definite meaning
for the amount of an increment in diffusion of knowledge.
I then consider the relation of each of these to the expenditure
of energy and value required to produce them in varying conditions of the advancement or diffusion of knowledge already
attained. Comparing knowledge with a material commodity,
we know that in the latter case a given small increment in the

[5] (Ed.) "[Memoir] No. 28, *On the Economics of Research*," from an application by Peirce for a grant from the Carnegie Institution (stamped by the
Carnegie Institution 30 July 1902) with an added quotation in the present
footnote from an alternative draft, both in Widener VB5. Peirce proposed to
write thirty-six memoirs on logic, most of them of approximately 20,000 words,
a few much shorter, and some of 50,000 words.
   The following are quoted from other parts of the application:
   "Therefore, what I hereby solicit the aid of the Carnegie Institution to
enable me to do is *to draw up some three dozen memoirs, each complete in itself, yet the whole forming a unitary system of logic in all its parts*, which
memoirs shall present in a form quite convincing to a candid mind the results
to which I have found that the scientific method unequivocally leads, adding,
in each case, rational explanations of how opposing opinions have come about;
the whole putting logic, as far as my studies of it have gone, upon the un-
deniable footing of a science," pp. 4–5.
   "It is my belief that science is approaching a critical point in which
the influence of a truly scientific logic will be exceptionally desirable. Science,
as the outlook seems to me, is coming to something not unlike the age of
puberty. Its old and purely materialistic conceptions will no longer suffice;
while yet the great danger involved in the admission of any others, ineluctable
as such admission is, is manifest enough. The influence of the conceptions of
methodeutic will at that moment be decisive," p. 57.
   In an alternative draft of this application he says:
   "What are the researches of which I speak?
   "They are the work of my life, that which I seem to have been put into
the world to do."
   The application was rejected.

supply is very expensive, in most cases, when the supply is very small, that as the supply increases, it sinks to a minimum, from which it increases to a very large but finite value of the supply where no further increment would be possible at any finite cost. Putting instead of supply, the amount of knowledge attained, we find that there is a "law," or general tendency, subject to similar large irregularities as in the case of the supply of a material commodity, but here even greater. The final increase of cost of an increment with the increase of attainment already achieved is marked, on the whole, in almost all cases, while in many cases, at least, there is a point of attainment where the cost of an increment is at a minimum. The same general tendency appears in reference to the diffusion of knowledge; but there is this striking difference, that attainments in advance of sciences are very commonly actually on the upward slope where increments are costing more and more, while there are few branches of knowledge whose diffusion is already so great that a given increment of the diffusion will cost more and more, as the diffusion is increased.

159. I shall next pass to a study of the variation of the *utility* (meaning, generally, the *scientific* utility) of given small increments of scientific knowledge and of the diffusion of knowledge in varying states of attainment. This is to be compared with the variation of the total amount that will be paid for a commodity for a fixed small increment of the *demand*, or amount thrown upon the market to fetch what it will, with varying amounts of that demand. Here, the additional total amount that will be paid for the small increment of amount sold will correspond to the utility of the small fixed increase of scientific knowledge or of the diffusion of knowledge; while, the demand being equal to the supply, this demand, or total amount that is sold, will correspond as before to the amount of attainment in scientific knowledge or in the diffusion of knowledge. For a material commodity we know that if it is given away people will only carry home a finite amount. One would have to pay them to carry away more. On the other hand there is probably some maximum price for most things, above which none at all would be sold. It necessarily follows that beyond a certain amount thrown upon the market, a small

85

increment in that amount would actually diminish the total receipts from the sale of it, while for any smaller amount the increment of receipts for a given small increment of amount sent to market would be less and less. With regard to the scientific utility of a small fixed advance of knowledge, the "law" is certainly very different from that. In the first place, there is no degree of knowledge of which a small increase would be worse than useless, and while the general tendency is that the utility of such fixed increase becomes less and less, yet this curve is rather saw shaped, since like Rayleigh's small addition to our knowledge of the density of nitrogen, now and then a small increment will be of great utility and will then immediately sink to its former level. The scientific advantage of the diffusion of knowledge is difficult to determine. It cannot be believed than any increment of diffusion is positively unfavorable to science. It is favorable in two ways; first, by preparing more men to be eminent researchers; and secondly, by increasing general wealth, and therefore the money bestowed on science. I am inclined to think that the general tendency is that a given increment of diffusion is less and less advantageous to science the greater the attained diffusion. But I am not confident that this is so, at any rate without very important deflexions. The general effect, however, is nearly the same for the advancement as for the diffusion of knowledge. Namely, beginning with dense ignorance, the first increments cost more than they come to. That is, knowledge is increased but scientific energy is spent and not at once recovered. But we very soon reach a state of knowledge which is profitable to science, that is, not only is knowledge increased, but the facility of increasing knowledge gives us a return of more available means for research than we had before the necessary scientific energy was spent. This increases to a maximum, diminishes, and finally, there is no further gain. Yet still, in the case of energy expended upon research, if it is persisted in, a fortunate discovery may result in a new means of research. I shall analyze as far as I can the relative advantages, *for pure science* exclusively, of expending energy (which is of such a kind as to be equally capable of being directed either way) to the direct advancement of knowledge and to the diffusion of knowledge. I find the latter so overwhelmingly more important (although all my personal sympathies are the other way) that it appears to me that, for the present, to give to research, in money, one or two per cent of what is spent upon education is enough. Research must contrive to do business at a profit; by which I mean that it must produce more effective scientific energy than it expends. No doubt, it already does so. But it would do well to become conscious of its economical position and contrive ways of living upon it.

160.   Many years ago I published a little paper on the Economy of Research, in which I considered this problem.[6] Somebody furnishes a fund to be expended upon research without restrictions. What sort of researches should it be expended upon? My answer, to which I still adhere, was this. Researches for which men have been trained, instruments procured, and a plant established, should be continued while those conditions subsist. But the new money should mainly go to opening up new fields; because new fields will probably be more profitable, and, at any rate, will be profitable longer.

161.   I shall remark in the course of the memoir that economical science is particularly profitable to science; and that of all the branches of economy, the economy of research is perhaps the most profitable; that logical methodeutic and logic in general are specially valuable for science, costing little beyond the energies of the researcher, and helping the economy of every other science. It was in the middle of the 13th century that a man distinguished enough to become pope opened his work on logic with the words, "Dialectica est ars artium et scientia scientiarum, ad omnium methodorum principia viam habens." [7] This memorable sentence, whose gothic ornamentation proves upon scrutiny to involve no meaningless expression nor redundant clause, began a work wherein the idea of this sentence was executed satisfactorily enough for the dominant science of the middle ages. Jevons adopted the sentence as the motto of his most scientific contribution to logic; and it would express the purpose of my memoirs, which is, upon the ground well prepared by Jevons and his teacher De

[6] (Ed.) Section 1 of the present chapter.
[7] (Ed.) See the same quotation in 7.59.

Morgan, and by the other great English researchers, especially Boole, Whewell, Berkeley, Glanvill, Ockham, and Duns Scotus, to lay a solid foundation upon which may be erected a new logic fit for the life of twentieth century science.

CHAPTER 3

THE LOGIC OF DRAWING HISTORY FROM ANCIENT DOCUMENTS

§1. ABSTRACT [1]

162.   Mr. C. S. Peirce gave an abstract of a long paper on the logic of the process of drawing history from ancient testimonies. He endeavored to show that the method of balancing the veracity of a witness against the improbability of his narrative, although it may be defended upon the principles of the calculus of probabilities under certain conditions, is nevertheless in the great majority of cases illogical, because there is not the roughest approximation to fulfillment of those conditions. For the testimonies are seldom even approximately independent, and still more seldom independent of the antecedent probability of the narrative; and moreover there is no determinate objective probability that a witness will tell the truth, and often no objective probability that the fact is as stated. Furthermore, we ought not to seek probabilities in such problems, but ought to pursue a method which must ultimately lead to the truth. Nor can such a method pursue the path of mathematical demonstration, which all reasoning that deduces a probability is, at its very best. But the probabilities upon which the critics of history rely are not objective, but are mere expressions of their preconceived notions, than which no guide can be less trustworthy.

163.   Mr. Peirce then undertook to develope the principles

---

[1] (Ed.) From a draft of a report on the meeting of the National Academy of Sciences in November, 1901, Widener IV; see [Bibliography] N–1901–16.

Cf. [Bibliography] G–1901–2b and 2c, both of which touch on the topic of the present chapter and which were written about the same time.

upon which ancient historical research ought to proceed in order to be scientific. He pointed out that the logic of scientific investigation, in which a conclusion is not established for many years, perhaps not for generations, cannot be assumed to be the same as the proper logical procedure for an individual who seeks a practical basis for present action. Although the latter has to be hastily performed, the accurate theory of it is far more difficult than is the logic of scientific procedure, to which the present paper limited itself. Here the question is, what is the process by which the truth will be attained most speedily. It does not content itself with probabilities, although absolute certainty can never be fully attained; nor has it anything to do with belief, which is a practical concern. This scientific procedure consists, according to Mr. Peirce, in carefully framing a hypothesis, in tracing out the experiential consequences of that hypothesis, and in testing those consequences by comparison with facts not taken into account in the formation of the hypothesis. If the facts refute the hypothesis, it must be abandoned and another substituted; but if the predictions based upon it are verified, it will be entitled to be received as a scientific result until we find deductions from it which are contrary to the facts.

§2. THE THEORY OF BALANCING LIKELIHOODS[2]

164. Ancient history is drawn partly from documents and partly from monuments. The last generation has afforded so many examples of the refutation by archeology of the conclusions of the critics of documents as to suggest the question whether the whole logical procedure of the latter class of students has not been radically wrong. The purpose of the

---

[2] (Ed.) The remainder of this chapter is from a typed manuscript, "On the Logic of drawing History from Ancient Documents especially from Testimonies," with two quotations added at 182n7 and 220n18. The material from the manuscript includes additions in Peirce's hand and a few minor editorial corrections taken from a corresponding handwritten manuscript; the quotation in 220n18 is from some alternate pages of the handwritten manuscript. These manuscripts are at Widener IB2–12 and are dated 1c.901 on the basis of Peirce's National Academy of Sciences paper, [Bibliography] G–1901–4.

present paper is to show that this is the case; that the logical
theory upon which the critics proceed is as bad as logic can
be; to set forth and defend the true logical method of treating
ancient historical documents; and to set this new theory in
a clear light by applying it to two or three examples, including
a case where the testimonies are comparatively strong and another where the testimony is at best very feeble.

165.   The theory of the logic of testimony which forms
the basis of the procedure of historical critics today is, I
suppose, old. But it can only have taken a distinct form when
the doctrine of probabilities was developed, in the early years
of the eighteenth century. A popular statement of it was,
I believe, first given by Hume, in his essay on Miracles, in
1748. Hume's statement is, mathematically considered, excessively crude. It seems evident that he had been reading
either De Moivre's *Doctrine of Chances* (first edition, 1716;
second enlarged edition, 1735) or De Montmort's *Essai
d'Analyse sur les Jeux de Hazard* (1708; second edition, 1713).
For Jacob Bernoulli's posthumous *Ars Conjectandi* (1713)
would have been beyond him. Whatever work he read he did
not understand; yet in a confused and untenable form, he put
forth ideas of his own of considerable value. I may restate
Hume's doctrine, correcting such errors as are not inseparable from it, as follows. When a reputable witness makes, or
witnesses make, an assertion which experience renders highly
improbable, or when there are other independent arguments
in its favor, each independent argument *pro* or *con* produces
a certain impression upon the mind of the wise man, dependent for its quantity upon the frequency with which arguments
of those kinds lead to the truth, and the algebraical sum
of these impressions is the resultant impression that measures the wise man's state of opinion on the whole. For example, if there are a number of independent arguments, *pro*,
such that, in general, such arguments lead to the truth, p_1
times, p_2 times, p_3 times, etc., respectively, for every q_1 times,
q_2 times, q_3 times, etc., that they lead to error; and if there
are arguments *con*, which lead to the truth q_5 times, q_6 times,
q_7 times, etc., for every p_5 times, p_6 times, p_7 times, etc., that
they lead to error, then the probability that the arguments *pro*

91

all lead to the truth, and the arguments *con* all lead to error
will be

$$\frac{p_1}{p_1+q_1} \cdot \frac{p_2}{p_2+q_2} \cdot \frac{p_3}{p_3+q_3} \cdot \text{ etc.}$$

$$\times \frac{p_5}{p_5+q_5} \cdot \frac{p_6}{p_6+q_6} \cdot \frac{p_7}{p_7+q_7} \cdot \text{ etc.;}$$

and the probability that all the arguments *pro* lead to error
while all the arguments *con* lead to truth, will be

$$\frac{q_1}{p_1+q_1} \cdot \frac{q_2}{p_2+q_2} \cdot \frac{q_3}{p_3+q_3} \cdot \text{ etc.}$$

$$\times \frac{q_5}{p_5+q_5} \cdot \frac{q_6}{p_6+q_6} \cdot \frac{q_7}{p_7+q_7} \cdot \text{ etc.}$$

But one or [the] other of these two alternatives must be the
case; so that the *odds* or ratio of favorable to unfavorable
probability on the whole is simply

$$\frac{p_1 \cdot p_2 \cdot p_3 \cdot \text{ etc. } p_5 \cdot p_6 \cdot p_7 \text{ etc.}}{q_1 \cdot q_2 \cdot q_3 \cdot \text{ etc. } q_5 \cdot q_6 \cdot q_7 \text{ etc.}} \cdot$$

Now if we suppose that the impression made on the mind of
the wise man is proportional to the logarithm of the *odds* as
its exciting cause, then the total impression will be

$$\log. \left\{ \frac{p_1}{q_1} \cdot \frac{p_2}{q_2} \cdot \frac{p_3}{q_3} \cdot \text{ etc. } \frac{p_5}{q_5} \cdot \frac{p_6}{q_6} \cdot \frac{p_7}{q_7} \cdot \text{ etc.} \right\} =$$

$$\log. \ \frac{p_1}{q_1} + \log. \ \frac{p_2}{q_2} + \log. \ \frac{p_3}{q_3} + \text{ etc.}$$

$$+ \log. \frac{p_5}{q_5} + \log. \frac{p_6}{q_6} + \log. \frac{p_7}{q_7} + \text{ etc.}$$

166. This is *Hume's Theory Improved*, by merely being
disembarrassed of blunders. If we strip the mathematics from
it, we have the simple *theory of balancing likelihoods*, which
is the theory that Hume undertook to elaborate and to render
scientific. It really hardly differs from Hume's Theory Improved except in its vagueness. At any rate, it involves the

notion that the different arguments have likelihoods, that they are quantities upon an algebraical scale, and that they are to be combined as independent.

167.   Now the practice of those modern German critics of ancient history whose works I have read, particularly those who treat of the history of philosophy, and whose methods are generally extolled, is based upon the theory of balancing likelihoods. In so far as their general logical method departs from that of Hume, it is only less refined. The principal difference between Hume and them is that the word 'Proof' is continually in their mouths, a word which Hume scrupulously avoided in speaking of the minor facts of ancient history. He recognized the question as purely one of probabilities. They seem to be discontented with mere probability; and are always in search of an argument that something "must" be. The necessity which enters into the conclusion of such an argument as part of its subject matter is confounded by them with the necessity of a mathematical demonstration, in the conclusion of which the word "must" does not frequently occur. Now since it happens ten times that we can argue that testimony *must* be false to every once that we can argue that it *must* be true, it naturally follows and is a fact, that these critics show far greater favor to views which reject all the historical evidence in our possession than they do to views which are based on some part of the evidence. "That, however, is not *proved*," is their usual comment upon any such hypothesis. Another particular in which they depart from Hume is in applying to history generally the canon of Bentley concerning the criticism of texts, that, in general, the more difficult reading is to be preferred. In like manner, they hold that that narrative which was least likely to be invented, owing to its improbability, is to be preferred. They are thus provided with two defences against historical testimony. If the story told appears to them in any degree unlikely, they reject it without scruple; while if there is no taint of improbability in it, it will fall under the heavier accusation of being too probable; and in this way, they preserve a noble freedom in manufacturing history to suit their subjective impressions.

§3. CRITICISM OF THE THEORY OF BALANCING LIKELIHOODS

168.   I now propose to show some weighty reasons for holding that the theory of balancing likelihoods, however it may be worked out, and though there are, undoubtedly, special cases where it ought to be followed, is nevertheless, as a general method of treating ancient documents, a bad one. In cases where objective and somewhat definite probabilities can be attributed to all the different arguments on both sides, and where they are, as arguments, independent of one another, it seems to be incontestable that Hume's method improved is sound. In the ordinary text books on the Doctrine of Chances, so much of this theory as is given at all is only given in their chapters on the probability of testimony; and I will mention that Professor F. Y. Edgeworth says that in extending it to all independent arguments that have definite general probabilities I am "confusing" testimonies with arguments. But however obliging his attribution to me of this extension may be, it is mistaken; for the same extension has been made by several writers, among them one whom Professor Edgeworth holds in peculiar respect, Augustus De Morgan, who gave the necessary demonstration as far back as 1846 (*Cambridge Phil. Trans.* VIII. 393.). . . . But I will now set down the reasons which compel me to acknowledge the justice of Hume's method when improved as above, and applied to all independent arguments to which definite general probabilities can be attributed. But I will first call attention to a confusion of thought which might easily lead a man to infer that the theory in question was not applicable to arguments in general, unless his mind had been brought to an edge worth assiduous care before one presumes to discuss questions of probability. Taking the time-honored urn from which balls are drawn at random and thrown back after each drawing, I will suppose, that every ball is, in fact, a box, and that out of every 7 of them 3 contain gold and 4 lead. I will also suppose that I have two expert witnesses, one of whom judges by the color, and is right 3 times to every time he fails, while the other judges by the weight, and is right 9

times for every 5 failures. Let us suppose the testimony is independent, the color-expert being just as proportionally often right when the material-expert is right as when he is wrong. In order to fix our ideas, let us suppose the numbers are as follows:

	Auriferous.		*Plumbiferous.*	
	Heavy	Light	Heavy	Light
Yellow,	$_aA_a$ 15	$_pA_a$ 35	$_aP_a$ 14	$_pP_a$ 6
Grey,	$_aA_p$ 21	$_pA_p$ 1	$_aP_p$ 10	$_pP_p$ 66

The total number of auriferous balls is $A = 72$: of plumbiferous is $P = 96$.

The total number of heavy auriferous and light plumbiferous, $_aA + _pP = 108$: that of the light auriferous and heavy plumbiferous is $_pA + _aP = 60$.

The total number of yellow auriferous and grey plumbiferous, $A_a + P_p = 126$: that of the grey auriferous and yellow plumbiferous is $A_p + P_a = 42$.

Now both witnesses report a ball to be auriferous; and according to the rule, I infer that the odds are $9/5 \cdot 3/1 = 27/5$ that it is gold; and that is correct since $(_aA_a + _pP_p)/(_pA_p + _aP_a) = 81/15 = 27/5$. But suppose that the witnesses, instead of testifying to the ball being auriferous, or otherwise, testify, the one that it is heavy, and the other that it is yellow, and leave the inference to me. Then the argument from its being heavy will be true 3 times to every 2 times that it is false, whether the color test succeed or fail; for $_aA_a : _aP_p = 15:10 = 3:2$ and $_aA_p : _aP_a = 21:14 = 3:2$, and in like manner the argument from its being yellow will hold 5 times for every 2 failures; for $_aA_a : _pP_a = 15:6 = 5:2$ and $_pA_a : _aP_a = 35:14 = 5:2$. But if, following the rule, I were to infer that the odds that the ball was auriferous were $3/2 \cdot 5/2 = 15/4$ I should be wrong; for the true odds are $_aA_a : _aP_a = 15:14$. If I should take into account the argument that $3/7$ of all the balls are auriferous, and say the odds were $3/2 \cdot 5/2 \cdot 3/4 = 45/16$, I should still be wrong. From this an unskilled person might suppose that the rule did not hold in case of arguments. But two errors would be involved. In the first place the odds in favor of a sign's signifying a fact are equal to the ratio of the probability of the occurrence of the sign when the fact takes place to the probability of the occurrence of the sign when the fact does not take place; and in the second place the independence of two signs, considered as signifying the same fact, consists in the one occurring with the same proportionate frequency whether the other occurs or not, and when the fact takes place, and further, with the same proportionate frequency whether the other occurs or not, when the fact does not take place. But it is not necessary that the one should occur with the same proportionate frequency whether the other occurs or not, in general, without reference to whether the fact occurs or not. The required independence is not found in the above numbers. It is, however, found in the following:

	Auriferous.		Plumbiferous.	
	Heavy	Light	Heavy	Light
Yellow,	$_aA_a = 21$	$_pA_a = 3$	$_aP_a = 10$	$_pP_a = 2$
Grey,	$_aA_p = 14$	$_pA_p = 2$	$_aP_p = 15$	$_pP_p = 3$

The odds in favor of a ball being auriferous:

Antecedently are	$40 : 30$	$= 4:3$
As yellow are	$24/40 : 12/30 =$	$3:2$
As heavy are	$35/40 : 25/30 =$	$21:20$

Hence, on the whole, the odds in favor of a heavy yellow ball being auriferous are $4/3 . 3/2 . 21/20 = 21/10$, which is, of course, correct. The demonstration that this is always so, is now extremely simple. Write x for $_aA_p/_pA_p$ and y for $_pA_a/_pA_p$. Also ξ for $_aP_p/_pP_p$ and η for $_pP_a/_pP_p$. Then the condition of independence is that

$$_aA_a/_pA_p = xy \text{ and } _aP_a/_pP_p = \xi\eta.$$

Then the odds

Antecedently will be

$$_pA_p (1 + x)(1 + y):_pP_p(1 + \xi)(1+ \eta);$$

As yellow will be $\dfrac{y(1 + \eta)}{(1 + y)\eta}$;

96

As heavy will be $\dfrac{x(1 + \xi)}{(1 + x)\xi}$;

and the product of the three will be $\dfrac{{}_pA_pxy}{{}_pP_p\xi\eta} = \dfrac{{}_aA_a}{{}_aP_a}$,

as it should be.

169.   Thus, when the essential conditions are fulfilled, this method is perfectly correct. Nor is it requisite that they should be fulfilled with any exactitude. A rough approximation is sufficient to give the conclusion some value. But the further from fulfilment the conditions are, the further from any scientific value is the conclusion; and with sufficient time and space I would undertake to show that, in reference to ancient history, they are, in a large majority of those cases in which there is any room for two opinions, so far from fulfilment, that it not only becomes utter nonsense to talk of "proof" and "perfect demonstration," — phrases perpetually in the mouths of the critics, — but, were there no better way of investigation, this method, taken as the general and regular method of treating questions of ancient history, must sink it in all its details to the rank of idle surmise. In this paper, however, I shall only give an outline of what this argument would be, because it is here not my principal object to refute the method now prevalent, but to expound a different logical theory, and to show what method of study results from it.

170.   Let it be clearly understood, then, that what I attack is the method of deciding questions of fact by weighing, that is by algebraically adding, the feelings of approval produced in the mind by the different testimonies and other arguments pertinent to the case. I acknowledge that this method is supported, under abstract conditions, by the doctrine of chances, and that there are cases in which it is useful. But I maintain that these conditions are not often even roughly fulfilled in questions of ancient history; so that in those investigations it commonly has no value worth consideration.

171.   Let us first make sure that we take proper account of everything that can be urged in favor of the method. Now, as far as I am aware, beyond its foundation in the doctrine of chances, the argument which was stated with such consummate

skill by Hume, there are only two things to be said in favor
of this method.

172.   The first is that every science must develop its own
method out of the natural reason of man; and that is the very
way in which this method has been developed. Balancing reasons *pro* and *con* is the natural procedure of every man. No
man can avoid doing so continually; and if he could, he would
only have trained himself to the observance of rules having no
foundation in reason. For reason is nothing but man's natural
way of thinking, carefully and consistently observed.

173.   The remaining argument in favor of this method is
that the only alternatives are that of using this method and
that of swallowing uncriticized all the incredible tales with
which ancient history abounds.

174.   This last argument need not detain us, because I shall
in this paper develop a different method, which, instead of
being less critical than that of balancing likelihoods, is much
more so. But I repeat that I do not maintain that the ordinary
method is never to be employed, but that its use should be
restricted to exceptional cases, instead of being made the regular and standard procedure.

175.   Now as to this method's being natural, I admit that
there is some foundation for that. There is no kind of fallacious
reasoning to which mankind is liable for which as much as that
might not be said. But I appeal to modern psychologists to
support me in the assertion, that it is not at all natural for
men to employ this method as a usual procedure.   On the contrary, the natural thing is to believe anything that one may
hear said, until it is found that that assumption leads to difficulties; and when it is found to lead to difficulties, the most
natural impulse is to make further inquiries, to cross-examine,
etc. The occasions when we naturally balance reasons *pro* and
con mostly relate to what we prefer to do, not to questions of
fact. But, in the next place, I demur to the principle that what
is natural is necessarily reasonable. It is one of the consequences of German preëminence in science and philosophy,
which I hope will not last much longer, that subjective ways
of deciding questions are, at this time, far too highly esteemed.
Logic itself is made a pure question of feeling by Sigwart, whose

treatise is now more in vogue than any other.[3] The Anglo-Saxon mind will never assent to that. I am sorry to say that it has been only too true that, under the German lead, the methods of reasoning in the different branches of science and philosophy have been left to grow up pretty much as they naturally would; and sooner or later, no doubt, natural tendencies do bring them right; but that result would be brought about much more quickly if methods were subjected to a more continual and strict criticism from exact logic; and what I mean by this, I must hope that this very paper may illustrate.

176.   Passing now to the objections to the method of balancing likelihoods in the study of ancient history, the most obvious, perhaps, although not the most important, is, that the different testimonies and other arguments, are not commonly even in a rough sense independent, as the only rational basis for the method requires that they should be. Circumstantial evidences are, no doubt, often sufficiently independent; but direct testimony seldom is so. The same circumstances which lead one witness into error are likely to operate to deceive another. Nor does this want of independence always lead them into agreement. It may, frequently, be the cause of disagreement. Conflict of testimony in the vast majority of cases is *not* principally a mere chance result, as the theory supposes it to be. That concordance of testimony commonly has some other cause than its mere tendency to truth, is too obvious to need saying. The method of balancing likelihoods not only supposes that the testimonies are independent but also that each of them is independent of the antecedent probability of the story; and since it is far more difficult to make allowance for a violation of this requirement than of that of the independence of the testimonies, it becomes a much more serious matter. But how very remote from the real state of things it is to suppose that the narration of an ancient event is independent of the likelihood of the story told! Roughly speaking, it may be said that all detached stories of Greece and Rome, were told chiefly because the writer had something marvellous to recount; so that we may almost say that ancient history is simply the narrative of all the unlikely events that happened

[3] (Ed.) Cf. 2.19ff.

during the centuries it covers. It is evident that this circumstance in itself almost destroys the legitimate weight of any argument from the antecedent improbability, unless that improbability is so great as to render the story absolutely incredible. Examples are useful at this point. It is well-known that three ancient authorities give the story that Pythagoras had a golden thigh; and the custom of modern critics is simply to pass it by, hardly mentioned. Now had any historian asserted that the thigh of Pythagoras was a metallic gold to the centre while his lower leg and foot were solid flesh, that would unquestionably have been a case in which the method under consideration might very properly have been employed to reject the testimony. I may mention, however, that one of the authorities affords an illustration of the opposite kind of influence of antecedent probability upon the matter of testimony. For when Diogenes Laertius softens the story as he does, it is in my opinion, in order to avoid extreme improbability. As another example, let us take a story the extreme improbability of which has caused almost, if not quite, every modern critic to over-rule the testimony of a baker's dozen of the greatest authorities that antiquity can boast. This story is that the mathematician Thales once stumbled and fell into a ditch while he was showing an old woman the constellations. Zeller, one of the few modern writers who so much as condescends to show reasons for almost giving Aristotle, Plato, Cicero, and all the rest the lie, says that it is utterly incredible that Thales should have been such an impracticable theorist. Considering that pretty much all we know about the personality of Thales is that the Greeks considered him as the first of the wise men, and that eccentricity was, according to the Greek conception, essential to the character of a philosopher, that reason of Zeller's shows a wonderful depth of psychological insight. Of all the modern mathematicians whom I have known, there have been perhaps not over one in five, of whom I should not hesitate to believe such a thing. But I should like to know how the story ever came to be so generally stated, both by ancient writers, and by all modern writers until the days of modern criticism, if it is not that the whole thing, both Thales stumbling and old woman's and Zeller's contempt for him for doing so, is too richly true to

100

human nature. If it is not historical, it must surely have been its extreme antecedent likelihood which caused so many authorities to assert that it was true. Many more examples are needed in order to show how very far ancient testimony is from being independent of the antecedent probability of its matter. But I leave this point, in order to hasten to another which is more important.

177.   The theory of probabilities has been called the logic of the modern exact sciences; [4] and it is known to be the basis of the vast business of insurance; and therefore when a literary man learns that the method which he has been pursuing has the sanction of such a great mathematical doctrine, he begins to feel that he is a very scientific person. I notice that this sense of personal scientificality is far more developed in men who write second-hand commentaries on ancient authors than it is in the Faradays, the Helmholtzes, and the Mendeléefs. It is, therefore, well to point out to such persons that the word *probability*, taken in the sense in which the insurance business uses it, means a well-founded statistical generalization. Nor are probabilities assumed in the exact sciences without either a statistical basis or else a thoroughly criticized assurance that no serious error can result. But if by "probability" be meant the degree to which a hypothesis in regard to what happened in ancient Greece recommends itself to a professor in a German university town, then there is no mathematical theory of probabilities which will withstand the artillery of modern mathematical criticism. A probability, in that sense, is nothing but the degree to which a hypothesis accords with one's preconceived notions; and its value depends entirely upon how those notions have been formed, and upon how much objectivity they can lay a solid claim to. If a man bring me a collection of sphygmograph-tracings accompanied with notes of the circumstances under which they were taken, and tells me that he thinks they prove that the pulse of a man is affected by the mental state of another man on the other side of a brick wall, I confess that his hypothesis is so contrary to my preconceived notions that I shall not easily be persuaded to interrupt my

---

[4] (Ed.) Peirce's theory of probability is presented in [CP] II, Part B of Book III.

work to make a study of the case. But those preconceived notions I hold to have a far more solid basis than those which ordinarily influence historical critics to pronounce an ancient narrative improbable. Yet even so, it is only my practical conduct which I allow to be influenced by that improbability. My action has to be decided one way or the other, and without loss of time; and "rough and ready" is unavoidably the character of the majority of practical decisions. But were I once to undertake the study of the sphygmograph-tracings, I would endeavor to get to the bottom of the question, without reference to my preconceived notions. For preconceived notions are only a fit basis for applications of science, not for science itself.

178. Thus everything that is put into one pan of the balance in weighing historical probabilities is utterly uncertain. Yet, if possible, what goes into the other pan is worse still. This consists of the "credibilities" of the testimonies. The inappropriateness of the application of the conception of probability here is striking. In playing a game, say with dice, there is this good reason for the calculation of chances, that any one face turns up as often as any other, quite independently of the result of any other throw, and the cause of the die turning up any particular face at any particular throw is quite beyond our powers of analysis. It is probably due to the combination of many little influences. In like manner, in insurance, though the cause of any one man's death might be ascertained, yet that would have no relation to the purposes of insurance, and why it is that out of a thousand men insured at the age of thirty, just so many will die each year afterward, is a question not to be answered, except that it is due to the cooperation of many causes. It is this which makes the calculation of chances appropriate. So, in making astronomical observations, why it is that out of a thousand observations, just so many will have just such an amount of error, can only be answered by saying that it is due to the summation of many small effects. But now on the other hand, take a question of history. We do not care to know how many times a witness would report a given fact correctly, because he reports that fact but once. If he misstates the matter, there is no cooperation of myriad causes. It is on the contrary, due to some one cause which, if it cannot often be

ascertained with certainty, can at any rate be very plausibly guessed in most cases, if the circumstances are closely inquired into; and it is most pertinent to the business of the historical critic to consider how a mistake, if mistake there be, might credibly have arisen. A mere general ratio of true statements to false, would be utterly insufficient for his purpose, even if it really existed. But it does not exist. In the case of the die, we know that one throw in every six will bring up an ace in the future as it has done in the past; and so it is with insurance, and with the errors of observations. However complex the causes, that simple law *will be* followed, we are sure. But nothing of the kind is true in the case of a witness. His new statements, if he makes any, will necessarily relate to different topics from his old ones which he has exhausted; and his personal relation to them will be different. There is, therefore, no arguing from what his credibility was in one case, to what it will be in another, as there would be if the error were a sum due to the recurrence of myriad small effects. There thus neither is any such quantity as a real, general, and predictive truthfulness of a witness; nor if there were, would it answer the purposes of the historian to deal with it. For he does not want to know merely how many of a witness's statements out of a hundred are wrong; but just which ones of them are wrong.

179. This objection goes vastly deeper and is vastly weightier than that based on the want of independence of the arguments. Yet even this objection is downright insignificant as compared with the principal one, which I now proceed to state, although I have already hinted at it.

180. All mathematical reasoning, even although it relates to probability, is of the nature of necessary reasoning. All necessary reasoning consists of tracing out what is virtually asserted in the assumed premisses. While some of these may be new observations, yet the principal ones relate to states of things not capable of being directly observed. As has often been said, especially since Kant, such reasoning really does not amplify our positive knowledge; although it may render our understanding of our own assumptions more perfect. It is the kind of reasoning proper for any application of science. For example, it is by such reasoning that, assuming the law of

gravitation to have been scientifically established, we go on to predict the time and place of an eclipse of the sun. Or, if our desire is to rectify our theory of the moon, we may do so by comparing such predictions, regarded as conditional, with observations. If, in making the correction, we assume that there can be no error discoverable by these observations except in the values of one or two constants employed, the correction is itself made by a mere application of principles assumed to be already scientifically established; and although it will be called a contribution to science, it leaves the frame-work of the theory untouched, and merely consists in incorporating the new observations into the places provided for them in our existing assumptions, so that there really is, in the logician's sense, no enlargement of our knowledge, but merely an arrangement or preservation of the systematization of knowledge already established. In applying observations to the fundamental correction of a theory, as Kepler applied Tycho's observations to the correction of the crude Copernican system, a kind of reasoning comes in which is not purely mathematical demonstration. If I remember rightly, there were only three points in the orbit of Mars, — I am sure there were only about three or four, — where Kepler ascertained the position of Mars in space by positive triangulation. Even those triangulations involved hypothetical elements, such as the assumption that the orbit was the same at every revolution, which might very well not have been true; and even had they been absolutely positive, they were altogether inadequate to determining the form of the orbit. These, therefore, as well as all the other items of his argument, were merely of this nature, that all simpler theories having been proved inadequate, all the predictions which could be based upon the theory of the elliptical orbit were verified by the observations well within the limits of possible, and even of not apparently unlikely, error. This was not mathematical demonstration; and all the subsequent work upon the solar system has merely multiplied and made more precise the same kind of proof, but has not changed its character. It is not now mathematical demonstration any more than it was then. Empirical science can never be enlarged by mathematical demonstration or any other kind of necessary reasoning; although when nomological science has advanced to a certain point, a mathematical theory can be based upon it which will be useful, not only for nomological science itself, but also for the classificatory and descriptive sciences which depend upon it.

181.   Now ancient history occupies a place among the psychical sciences somewhat analogous to that of astronomy among the physical sciences. The one is a description of what is distant in the world of mind, as the other is a description of what is distant in the world of matter; and curiously enough, or significantly enough, an ancient alliance exists between the two sciences through chronology. Yet the amount of aid which physical astronomy can derive from mathematics is quite moderate, notwithstanding the mathematical perfection of nomological physics.[5] Anybody can convince himself that the reasoning of physical astronomy is not of a demonstrative kind by simply running over any text-book on the subject. But the science of nomological psychics,[6] — psychology, as we call it, — is still far too backward to afford any distinguished aid to history; and consequently, the demonstrative part of rightly reasoned history, exclusive of mere chronology, must, for a long time, remain very small. History, however, is as much more worthy than astronomy of being studied scientifically as mind is more worthy of our attention than matter. The use we should desire to make of ancient history is to *learn* from the study of it, and not to carry our preconceived notions into it, until they can be put upon a much more scientific basis than at present they can. Consequently, the staple of our reasoning in ancient history should not be of the demonstrative kind, as it is, as long as it remains, at best, an application of the mathematical doctrine of chances. If somebody replies that in weighing arguments *pro* and *con* critics make no use of the mathematical calculus of probabilities, the rejoinder will be that their proceeding only differs from that by its greater vagueness, and that a vague and inexact use of probabilities has no logical advantage over a more critical employment of them. If it is said that, as far as possible, the critics avoid likelihoods, and aim at positive certainty, the answer will be that they endeavor to

[5] (Ed.) See 1.188, 1.260, 1.502.
[6] (Ed.) See 1.189.

do this by the employment of apodictic arguments, which only mark a still less exact grade of the same kind of demonstrative reasoning. Fully to appreciate the force of this argument one must have a well-matured comprehension of the logic of science; but when it is fairly apprehended, it cannot but be deemed quite conclusive.

182.　Nevertheless, there still remains a further objection to the method of balancing likelihoods in the study of ancient history which is worthy of attention even after what has been said. We all know that as soon as a hypothesis has been settled upon as preferable to others, the next business in order is to commence deducing from it whatever experiential predictions are extremest and most unlikely among those deducible from it, in order to subject them to the test of experiment, and thus either quite to refute the hypothesis or make such corrections of it as may be called for by the experiments; and the hypothesis must ultimately stand or fall by the result of such experiments. Now what is true of any single hypothesis should equally hold good for any method of constructing many hypotheses. It, too, should have its consequences experimentally tested, and must stand or fall by the ultimate result. Now within the last half of the nineteenth century the merits of the procedure of the historical critics have been many times subjected to the test of archeological exploration; and what has been the result? I have not the necessary knowledge myself to sum it up in a magisterial manner; but from what I have casually heard about the relation of Egyptian exploration to the critics' previous opinion of Manetho and even of Herodotus, about the explorations in the Troiad and in Mycenae, and much else, I gather that, on the whole, it has been shown that the critics were found to be more or less fundamentally wrong in nearly every case, and in particular that their fashion of throwing all the positive evidence overboard in favor of their notions of what was likely, stands condemned by those tests. If this be so, it is no slight modification, but a complete revolution, of their logic which is called for; because, considering their great learning and competence, and the absolute confidence which they attached to their conclusions, as perfectly ineluctable, there is no middle course between pronouncing those men to have been a pack of

106

charlatans and concluding that their method was wrong in principle. If it were not so, their pretensions to scientific determinacy of those conclusions would have been simply disgraceful.[7]

§4. THE LOGIC OF SCIENCE

183.   Having thus outlined the argument for the timeliness of a new logical theory of the proper method of dealing with ancient testimonies, I proceed to show how the question appears from the point of view of the "Minute Logic" [8] of which I am a defender.

184.   I could not present the reason which has the greatest weight to my own mind, so that it should be convincing, unless I were to write a paper more than fifteen times the length of this one. That has to be foregone. Meantime, the secondary considerations that remain will be strong enough to maintain the position successfully.

185.   To begin with, let me say that I propose to confine myself exclusively to the consideration of the proper *scientific* procedure concerning the documents in question. I do not propose to touch upon the question of miracles in so far as it is a practical religious question for an individual man.[9] This is not from timidity or any indisposition to express myself, could I have my whole say; but it is because it would expand this

[7] (Ed.) "On five occasions in my life, and on five occasions *only,* I have had an opportunity of testing my Abductions about historical facts, by the fulfillment of my predictions in subsequent archeological or other discoveries; and on each one of those five occasions my conclusions, which in every case ran counter to that of the highest authorities, turned out to be correct. The last two cases were these. Prof. Petrie published a history of Egypt in which he treated the first three dynasties as mythical. I was just about writing a history of science and in the first chapter I showed why those Dynasties including the name of Menes and other facts ought to be considered historical. Before my book was near completion Petrie himself found the tomb of Menes. Again a few years ago I wrote in the *Nation,* where there was no room for details, that the Babylonians had high scientific genius and that there was reason to conjecture that Alexander sent home a Babylonian celestial globe dating from 2300 years B.C. Now the newest finds show that at that very date they were accomplished astronomers." From the Lowell Lectures of 1903, Lecture VIII, following shortly after 5.604; Widener IB2–4. See [Bibliography] G–1903–2a.

[8] (Ed.) [Bibliography] G–c.1902–2.

[9] (Ed.) Cf. [Bibliography] G–1901–2.

paper beyond all bounds of convenience in all respects. A practical belief is what a man proposes to go upon. A decision is more or less pressing. What ought it to be? That must depend upon what the purpose of his action is. What then, is the purpose of a man? That is the question of pure ethics, a very great question which must be disposed of before the logic of practical belief can be entered upon to any good effect. With science it is entirely different. A problem started today may not reach any scientific solution for generations. The man who begins the inquiry does not expect to learn, in this life, what conclusion it is to which his labors are tending. Strictly speaking, the inquiry never will be completely closed. Even without any logical method at all, the gradual accumulation of knowledge might probably ultimately bring a sufficient solution. Consequently, the object of a logical method is to bring about more speedily and at less expense the result which is destined, in any case, ultimately to be reached, but which, even with the best logic, will not probably come in our day. Really the word belief is out of place in the vocabulary of science. If an engineer or other practical man takes a scientific result, and makes it the basis for action, it is he who converts it into a belief. In pure science, it is merely the formula reached in the existing state of scientific progress. The question of what rules scientific inference ought to follow in order to accelerate the progress of science to the utmost is a comparatively simple one, and may be treated by itself. The question of how a given man, with not much time to give to the subject, had best proceed to form his hasty decision, involves other very serious difficulties, which make it a distinct inquiry. The former question, taken by itself, will be enough for the present communication.

186.   I have said that in order to determine what the logic of the individual man should be, it would be necessary to consider what his purpose was. The same remark applies to the logic of science. It is easier to determine the purpose of science. It does not involve opening the question of ethics. Yet it is not a perfectly simple matter, either. Several definitions of the purpose of science that I have met with made it the business of science to ascertain that certain things were so, to reach foregone conclusions. Nothing could be more contrary to the spirit

108

of science. Science seeks to discover whatever there may be that is true. I am inclined to think that even single perceptual facts are of intrinsic value in its eyes, although their value in themselves is so small that one cannot be quite sure that there is any. But every truth which will prevent a future fact of perception from surprising us, which will give the means of predicting it, or the means of conditionally predicting what would be perceived were anybody to be in a situation to perceive it, this it is, beyond doubt, that which science values. Although some will contradict me, I am bound to say that, as I conceive the matter, science will value these truths for themselves, and not merely as useful. Mathematics appears to me to be a science as much as any science, although it may not contain all the ingredients of the complete idea of a science. But it is a science, as far as it goes; the spirit and purpose of the mathematician are acknowledged by other scientific men to be substantially the same as their own. Yet the greater part of the propositions of mathematics do not correspond to any perceptual facts that are regarded as even being possible. The diagonal of the square is incommensurable with its side; but how could perception ever distinguish between the commensurable and the incommensurable? The mathematical interest of the imaginary inflections of plane curves is quite as great as that of the real inflections. Yet we cannot say that the scientific man's interest is in mere ideas, like a poet's or a musician's. Indeed, we may go so far as to say that he cares for nothing which could not conceivably come to have a bearing on some practical question. Whether a magnitude is commensurable or not has a practical bearing on the mathematician's action. On the other hand, it cannot be said that there is any kind of proportion between the scientific interest of a fact and its probability of becoming practically interesting. So far is that from being the case, that, although we are taught in many ways the lesson [of] the Petersburg problem, — so stupidly obscured by the extraneous consideration of moral expectation, — the lesson that we utterly neglect minute probabilities, yet for all that, facts whose probabilities of ever becoming practical are next to nothing are still regarded with keen scientific interest, not only by scientific men, but even by a large public. Here,

109

then, are the facts to be reconciled in order to determine what
the purpose of science, what scientific interest, consists in.
First, every truth which affords the means of predicting what
would be perceived under any conceivable conditions is scientifically interesting; and nothing which has not conceivable
bearing upon practice is so, unless it be the perceptual facts
themselves. But, second, the scientific interest does not lie in
the application of those truths for the sake of such predictions.
Nor, thirdly, is it true that the scientific interest is a mere poet-
ical interest in the ideas as images; but solid truth, or reality, is
demanded, though not necessarily existential reality. Carefully
comparing these three conditions, we find ourselves forced to
conclude that scientific interest lies in finding what we roughly
call generality or rationality or law to be true, independently
of whether you and I and any generations of men think it to be
so or not. I might enunciate and prove this with more accuracy
and evidence; but since I am not now undertaking to present
the subject with the strictest method, I think what I have said
will answer my purpose. But however this question be argued,
it is one of those concerning which

> A man convinced against his will
> Is of his own opinion still,

(a current corruption worth dozens of such as its original).
The dry light of intelligence is manifestly not sufficient to
determine a great purpose: the whole man goes into it. So the
fact that logic depends upon such a question is sufficient to
account for the endless disputes of which logic is still the
theatre.

187.   Confining ourselves to science, inference, in the broadest sense, is coextensive with the deliberate adoption, in any
measure, of an assertion as true. For deliberation implies that the
adoption is voluntary; and consequently, the observation of
perceptual facts that are forced upon us in experience is excluded. General principles, on the other hand, if deliberately
adopted, must have been subjected to criticism; and any criticism of them that can be called scientific and that results in their
acceptance must involve an argument in favor of their truth.
My statement was that an inference, in the broadest sense, is a

110

deliberate adoption, *in any measure*, of an assertion as true. The phrase "in any measure" is not as clear as might be wished. "Measure," here translates *modus*. The modes of acceptance of an assertion that are traditionally recognized are the necessary, the possible, and the contingent. But we shall learn more accurately, as our inquiry proceeds, how the different measures of acceptance are to be enumerated and defined. Then, as to the word "true," I may be asked what this means. Now the different sciences deal with different kinds of truth; mathematical truth is one thing, ethical truth is another, the actually existing state of the universe is a third; but all those different conceptions have in common something very marked and clear. We all hope that the different scientific inquiries in which we are severally engaged are going ultimately to lead to some definitely established conclusion, which conclusion we endeavor to anticipate in some measure. Agreement with that ultimate proposition that we look forward to, — agreement with that, whatever it may turn out to be, is the scientific truth.

188. Perhaps there will here be no harm in indulging in a little diagrammatic psychology after the manner of the old writers' discussions concerning the *primum cognitum*; for however worthless it may be as psychology, it is not a bad way to get orientated in our logic. No man can recall the time when he had not yet begun a theory of the universe, when any particular course of things was so little expected that nothing could surprise him, even though it startled him. The first surprise would naturally be the first thing that would offer sufficient handle for memory to draw it forth from the general background. It was something new. Of course, nothing can appear as definitely new without being contrasted with a background of the old. At this, the infantile scientific impulse, — what becomes developed later into various kinds of intelligence, but we will call it the scientific impulse because it is science that we are now endeavoring to get a general notion of, — this infantile scientific impulse must strive to reconcile the new to the old. The first new feature of this first surprise is, for example, that it is a surprise; and the only way of accounting for that is that there had been before an expectation. Thus it is that all knowledge begins by the discovery that there has been an

111

erroneous expectation of which we had before hardly been conscious. Each branch of science begins with a new phenomenon which violates a sort of negative subconscious expectation, like the frog's legs of Signore Galvani.

§5. REGULARITY AND EXPLANATION

189.   What, then, is that element of a phenomenon that renders it surprising, in the sense that an explanation for it is demanded? *Par excellence*, it is irregularity, says Dr. Paul Carus, in substance.[10] I cannot but think that there is a faulty analysis here. Nobody is surprised that the trees in a forest do not form a regular pattern, or asks for any explanation of such a fact. So, irregularity does not prompt us to ask for an explanation. Nor can it be said that it is because the explanation is obvious; for there is, on the contrary, no explanation to be given, except that there is no particular reason why there should be a regular pattern, — or rather that there is no sufficient reason, because there must be a tendency for large trees to grow where there is most room, which tendency, if it were strong enough and undisturbed enough, would produce a regular pattern. I mention this to show that, so far is mere irregularity [from being] a motive for demanding an explanation, that, even when there is a slight reason for expecting a regularity and we find irregularity, we do not ask for an explanation; whereas if it were an equally unexpected *regularity* that we had met with, we certainly should have asked for an explanation. I am, for reasons similar to this, as well as for others, confident that mere irregularity, where no definite regularity is expected, creates no surprise nor excites any curiosity. Why should it, when irregularity is the overwhelmingly preponderant rule of experience, and regularity only the strange exception? In what a state of amazement should I pass my life, if I were to wonder why there was no regularity connecting days upon which I receive an even number of letters by mail and nights on which I notice an even number of shooting stars! But who would seek explanations for irregularities like that?

190.   Let me not, however, be understood to make the

[10] (Ed.)   Cf. [Bibliography] G–1891–1.

strength of an emotion of surprise the measure of a logical need for explanation. The emotion is merely the instinctive indication of the logical situation. It is evolution ($\phi\acute{v}\sigma\iota\varsigma$) that has provided us with the emotion. The situation is what we have to study.

191.   Before dismissing irregularity, I may note, as aiding to clear the matter up, that a breach of an existing regularity always stimulates a demand for an explanation; but where, having expected regularity, we only find irregularity without any breach of regularity, we are only induced to revise our reasons for expecting anything. Irregularity, be it noted, cannot be expected, as such. For an expectation is, in every case, founded upon some regularity. For the same reason, merely not finding regularity where no particular regularity was expected, occasions no surprise.

192.   In order to define the circumstances under which a scientific explanation is really needed, the best way is to ask in what way explanation subserves the purpose of science. We shall then see what the evil situation is which it remedies, or what the need is which it may be expected to supply. Now what an explanation of a phenomenon does is to supply a proposition which, if it had been known to be true before the phenomenon presented itself, would have rendered that phenomenon predictable, if not with certainty, at least as something very likely to occur. It thus renders that phenomenon rational, — that is, makes it a logical consequence, necessary or probable. Consequently, if without any particular explanation, a phenomenon is such as must have occurred, there is no room at all for explanation. If the phenomenon is such as need not have occurred on the special occasion, but must occur on occasions differing in no discoverable and exactly assignable pertinent respect from the special occasion on which the phenomenon in question actually occurs, still there is nothing for explanation to do, until it is ascertained in what respects, if any, the individual occasion differs from those other occasions. For example, I throw a die, and it turns up ace. Now I know already that this die will turn up ace once in six times; and I am persuaded that it would be hopeless to attempt, at present, to find any pertinent conditions fulfilled on this occasion which

113

are not fulfilled every time the die is thrown. Hence, no proposed explanation of the die's turning up an ace can be in order, unless we can discover some peculiar and pertinent feature about the present occasion. Why should my lottery-ticket have drawn a blank, and somebody else's a prize? No explanation is called for. The question is silly.

193.   Let us now pass to the case of a phenomenon in which, apart from a particular explanation, there was antecedently no reason for expecting it, and as little for expecting it not to happen. Suppose, for example, that on the day of the Lisbon earthquake the brightest new star had appeared in the heavens. There might possibly have been some explanation for this; but there would have been no motive for searching for one. To have done so would, indeed, have been a foolish proceeding, for reasons we need not now consider.

194.   Thus, the only case in which this method of investigation, namely, by the study of how an explanation can further the purpose of science, leads to the conclusion that an explanation is positively called for, is the case in which a phenomenon presents itself which, without some special explanation, there would be reason to expect would *not* present itself; and the logical demand for an explanation is the greater, the stronger the reason for expecting it not to occur was.

195.   Since it is never prudent to rely upon reasoning that is largely deductive, without a check upon its accuracy, especially where the conclusion is disputed, as this is, I will select a few examples calculated to refute it, if it is to be refuted; and examine its application to them. First, suppose the phenomenon observed consists simply in irregularity; then, if there were no ground for anticipating any particular regularity, there is simply nothing to explain (irregularity being the prevailing character of experience generally). This agrees with our natural judgment. But if we anticipate a regularity, and find simple irregularity, but no *breach* of regularity, — as for example if we were to expect that an attentive observation of a forest would show something like a pattern, then there is nothing to explain except the singular fact that we should have anticipated something that has not been realized. Here, by our theory, there is need of an explanation, not of an objective, but of a

114

subjective phenomenon (pardon the jargon, — slang jargon, at that). This again agrees with our natural judgment; for in such a case we straightway commence reviewing our logic to find how our error is to be explained.

196.   Street cars are famous *ateliers* for speculative modelling. Detained there, with no business to occupy him, one sets to scrutinizing the people opposite, and to working up biographies to fit them. I see a woman of forty. Her countenance is so sinister as scarcely to be matched among a thousand, almost to the border of insanity, yet with a grimace of amiability that few even of her sex are sufficiently trained to command: — along with it, those two ugly lines, right and left of the compressed lips, chronicling years of severe discipline. An expression of servility and hypocrisy there is, too abject for a domestic; while a certain low, yet not quite vulgar, kind of education that is evinced, together with a taste in dress neither gross nor meretricious, but still by no means elevated, bespeak companionship with something superior, beyond any mere contact as of a maid with her mistress. The whole combination, although not striking at first glance, is seen upon close inspection to be a very unusual one. Here our theory declares an explanation is called for; and I should not be long in guessing that the woman was an ex-nun.

197.   In this last case, the emotion of surprise is not felt, because the cognitive part of the mind must be uppermost in order to recognize the rarity of the phenomenon. There are cases in which the most familiar of facts seem to call for explanation. I am myself, for example, fond of urging that no theory of space can be satisfactory which does not explain why it should have three dimensions. Perhaps all will not agree with me on this point. They will say, it must have some number of dimensions; why not three as well as any number? Or I may be asked what number of dimensions I should expect space to have. My reply is, that if I did not know what number of dimensions space really had, and was obliged to investigate the question as we usually investigate scientific questions, by trying successive hypotheses until I found one that experiment would not refute, I should soon see that one dimension would not be sufficient; and I should try two as giving, not only the

simplest, but by far the most comprehensible, of continua. I should guess that it was similar to the field of imaginary quantity. When that was refuted, I should pass to the next most comprehensible continuum, that of the field of real quaternions, quadridimensional space. Although the reasons for those numbers are not at all apodictic, yet I should, I am sure, be much surprised to learn that its dimensionality was three, which is so much more difficult to conceive than four. No doubt, it may be said that rationality has nothing to do with the question; and I have to confess that the fact that space has three dimensions has the air, at least, of proving that rationality has, in fact, nothing to do with it. But if it has not, still it seems to me that three is a number one would decidedly not expect. For triads mostly have some connection with Rationality; while things that are not governed by Rational considerations very seldom have three elements. I say all this, because it seems to me that this is almost a crucial instance for my theory of what it is that demands explanation. For, to the majority of minds, who would not definitely expect one number of dimensions rather than another, the fact that space has three dimensions does not seem to call for any particular explanation. That this is the fact seems to be proved by the circumstance that, of all the philosophers who have elaborated theories of space, hardly one has paid the smallest attention to the number of its dimensions, or regarded it as at all significant. But in me we have an instance of a mind to which it does seem that this feature of space calls for some definite explanation; and this same mind we find differs from the others in that it would decidedly have expected antecedently some other number. Certainly, my theory of what it is that demands explanation appears to be remarkably verified in this instance.

198. It is singular that there are not many logicians who attempt to define the circumstances which render an explanation of a phenomenon desirable or urgent. The majority of them seem tacitly to assume that any one fact calls for explanation as much as any other. Mr. Venn, however, in his *Empirical Logic*,[11] states, without much discussion, that it is the *isola-*

---

[11] (Ed.) *The Principles of Empirical or Inductive Logic*, London, 1889. The quotations given by Peirce in paragraphs 199 and 200 are taken from pages 495 and 498.

tion of a fact that creates the need of an explanation. This approaches pretty close to my opinion, since the work of reason consists in finding connections between facts. Still, the distinctions between the two doctrines are manifold, too. All facts are more or less connected and more or less separated; so that Mr. Venn ought to say, and probably would say, that all facts call for explanation more or less. According to me, however, the demand for explanation is a more definite demand. All conceivable facts are divisible into those which, upon examination, would be found to call for explanation and those which would not. For if any fact would call for explanation, then if that which was ascertained in the consequent investigation was no more nor less than the falsity of that supposed fact, this latter would not call for explanation. Although I have not bestowed upon Mr. Venn's whole volume the minute study which it merits, so that I may be mistaken, I think I can account for this discrepancy. Mr. Venn belongs to a school which considers the logical process as starting at the percepts, if not at impressions of sense. Mr. Venn is himself so candid and so acute that he may perhaps have seen the error of this. But supposing that he has followed his school, the discrepancy between him and me would easily be accounted for, because there can be no doubt that every *percept* does involve elements that call for explanation. But I maintain that logical criticism cannot go behind *perceptual facts*, which are the first judgments which we make concerning percepts. A perceptual fact is therefore an abstract affair. Each such fact covers only certain features of the percept. I look at an object and think that it seems white. That is my judgment of the object perceived, or my judgment concerning the percept, but not the percept itself; and it is idle to attempt to criticize by any logic that part of the performance of the intellect which draws that judgment from the percept, for the excellent reason that it is involuntary and cannot be prevented or corrected. Such a fact which represents the percept in a very meagre way, although it is, in itself, a relatively isolated fact, — as isolated as any fact can be, — nevertheless does not, in itself, call for any explanation. On the contrary, it can only do that when it has been connected with other facts which taken by themselves would justify an

117

expectation of the contrary of this fact. For example, if we should find that this object which seemed white, in the first place *was* white, and then that it was a crow, and finally that all the crows known were black, then the fact of this seeming and really being white would require explanation. It might be an albino, or it might be some new species or variety of crow. But perhaps it will be insisted that this thing's appearing white *does* call for an explanation; — that we want to know the cause of its being white. To this I reply that it has always been agreed that the tendency of the understanding was merely toward synthesis, or unification. Now no fact could possibly be more unified and simple than the fact that this is white, taken in itself. It would seem, therefore, that, if we consider this fact isolated from all others, it completely accomplishes the tendency of reason. To find a cause for the whiteness would only be to complicate our conception of the matter; and I never heard it suggested that intelligence *per se* demands complexity and multiplicity. But I suspect that when Mr. Venn speaks of *isolation*, he is thinking of there being other facts from which the given fact is separated; and that it is not *isolation* that he means, but *separation*. Now separation is itself a kind of connection; so that if that be his meaning, the state of things which calls for explanation is a connection which is not satisfactory to the mind. In that case, it is incumbent on Mr. Venn to explain himself more precisely, and to say in what respect it is unsatisfactory. If he were to say, "unsatisfactory in being contrary to what ought to be expected," he would come to my position, precisely.

199. Further light on the question may be obtained by considering the different types of explanation, of which Mr. Venn admits three after Mill, although he says of the third that it is to be received with reserve. I so far agree with him in this, that I think if the second type is accurately defined, it will be seen to include the third as a special and not important variety. The others I fully accept, though with my own definitions of them. I will take the examples of each which Mr. Venn has himself proposed. In illustration of the first type, he says: "We notice a plant that is flagging on a hot summer day: next morning it stands up again fresh and green. 'Why has it revived in the

morning? ' — 'Oh they always do.' " One may smile at the naïveté of this; and certainly, it is not an explanation in the proper sense of the word. Still, its general function is the same as that of explanation; namely, it renders the fact a conclusion, necessary or probable, from what is already well known. It might be called a *regularization*, explanation and regularization being the two types of *rationalization*. The regularization, stated in full, would be,

> Plants of a certain class usually revive in the morning;
> This plant belongs to that class;
> ∴. This plant might be expected to revive in the morning.

Now it is true that the effect of the regularization is that the fact observed is less isolated than before; but the purpose of the regularization is, I think, much more accurately said to be to show that it might have been expected, had the facts been fully known. That the demand for regularization is due to the contrary being expected is shown by the fact that when that contrary expectation is very strong indeed, a regularization which even leaves the event quite improbable will in great measure satisfy the mind. When my father, Benjamin Peirce, stated (as Leverrier himself also did, at first) that the planet discovered by Galle was not that predicted by Leverrier,[12] people generally, who imagined that, in the absence of any prediction, the entire sphere of the heavens might have had to be swept to find the planet, asked, "How, then, was it that Galle found it in the very telescopic field in which Leverrier located his planet?" This was a challenge for a regularization; to which the response was that Galle's planet was about 50 minutes of longitude distant from Leverrier's place, and that this would occur by pure chance once in two hundred times. It was, therefore, about as extraordinary as that a given man of 75 should live to be a hundred. But the popular notion was that its probability was as one square degree is to the surface of the sphere, or as one to 41254. It is plain that the partial satisfaction which such a regularization affords is due to the great diminution of the unexpectedness.

200. The other type of demand for explanation is exempli-

[12] (Ed.) See R. C. Archibald, *Benjamin Peirce*, p. 14, for an account of this.

fied by Mr. Venn by the question, "Why is it so difficult to walk on ice?" He gives several supposed attempts at explanation; but the one he pronounces satisfactory is, 'Because, owing to the absence of friction, there is no horizontal reaction to the impulse of the feet,' which except for the misuse of the word impulse is correct, but I fear not very perspicuous to anybody who really needed the explanation! If we endeavor to place ourselves into the shoes of such a person, we must imagine ourselves noticing how easy it looks to skate upon ice, and to have remarked some such fact as that if a wagon receives a push from the land to the ice, it moves with the utmost ease on the ice. All these hazy ideas about the ice-surface, jostle one another in the mind in a perplexing way. It is, therefore, not the simple fact that ice is hard to walk on which creates the demand for an explanation: it is, on the contrary, a puzzling complexus of facts. Tell a man who never saw ice that frozen water is very hard to walk on, and he may ask whether the feet stick to it, or put other questions in order to figure to himself what you mean; but as long as the fact is apprehended by him as a simple one, he will no more ask why it should be so than a common man asks why lead should be heavy. The fact is entirely sufficient as long as it is simple and isolated. It is when the difficulty of walking on ice is compared with the extraordinary distance that a ball can be bowled upon it, or with such other facts as would naturally lead one to expect that ice would be particularly easy to walk on, that a scientific explanation is sought. This is shown by the rarity of the inquiry why it is tiresome to walk on sand. Everybody knows that it is hard to make a vehicle go over sand; and so it seems, to minds in the state of ignorance supposed, to be quite natural that walking on sand should be tiresome; and thus no explanation is asked for, although, in other respects, the question is so similar to that about ice. An isolated fact is precisely what a demand for an explanation proper never refers to; it always applies to some fact connected with other facts which seem to render it improbable.

201. I think I have now said enough to show that my theory — that that which makes the need, in science, of an explanation, or in general of any rationalization of any fact, is

120

that without such rationalization the contrary of the fact would
be anticipated, so that reason and experience would be at variance, contrary to the purpose of science — [that this theory]
is correct, or as nearly so as we can make any theory of the
matter at present. I will add, however, one more argument.
Mr. Venn has felt the need of accounting for that desire of getting rid of isolated facts, to which he attributes the demand
for an explanation; and he does so by remarking that isolated
facts are dangerous. Now how, I should be glad to know, are
isolated facts dangerous? The only way in which they would
appear to be so, and it is the only way which Mr. Venn points
out, is that in their presence we do not know what to expect.
But if this is so, getting rid of the isolation of facts is not, after
all, the ultimate motive of seeking an explanation; but on the
contrary, an ulterior purpose has reference to expectation. And
what is this condition described as being full of risk, of not
knowing what to expect? It is not a mere negation of all expectation, — the state of mind in which a man takes his Sunday
afternoon's stroll. It is a state in which a man seems to have
ground for expecting certain things, and yet has evidence that
those expectations may be falsified. Now this precisely describes the conditions under which according to my theory
rationalization is called for. It may, however, be objected that
if we are to go back to the ultimate motive for explanation, I
should have asked what the danger is to which error would
expose us. I reply that were I investigating the practical logic
of the individual man, then, as I have already remarked, the
question of pure ethics would have to be taken up, namely, the
question 'What can a man deliberately accept as his ultimate
purpose?' But restricting myself, as I do, to scientific reasoning, I need not go behind the recognized purpose of science,
which stops at knowledge.

§6. ABDUCTION, INDUCTION,
AND DEDUCTION [13]

202.   Accepting the conclusion that an explanation is needed
when facts contrary to what we should expect emerge, it follows

[13] (Ed.) These subjects are also treated in [CP] II.

that the explanation must be such a proposition as would lead
to the prediction of the observed facts, either as necessary consequences or at least as very probable under the circumstances.
A hypothesis then, has to be adopted, which is likely in itself,
and renders the facts likely. This step of adopting a hypothesis
as being suggested by the facts, is what I call *abduction*. I
reckon it as a form of inference, however problematical the
hypothesis may be held. What are to be the logical rules to
which we are to conform in taking this step? There would be
no logic in imposing rules, and saying that they *ought* to be
followed, until it is made out that the purpose of hypothesis
requires them. Accordingly, it appears that the early scientists,
Thales, Anaximander, and their brethren, seemed to think the
work of science was done when a likely hypothesis was suggested. I applaud their sound logical instinct for that. Even
Plato, in the Timaeus and elsewhere, does not hesitate roundly
to assert the truth of anything, if it seems to render the world
reasonable; and this same procedure, in a more refined modification, is the essence of modern historical criticism. It is all
right as long as it is not found to interfere with the usefulness
of the hypothesis. Aristotle departs a little from that method.
His physical hypotheses are equally unfounded; but he always
adds a 'perhaps.' That, I take it, was because Aristotle had
been a great reader of other philosophers, and it had struck
him that there are various inconsistent ways of explaining the
same facts. Ultimately, the circumstance that a hypothesis, although it may lead us to expect some facts to be as they are,
may in the future lead us to erroneous expectations about other
facts, — this circumstance, which anybody must have admitted
as soon as it was brought home to him, was brought home to
scientific men so forcibly, first in astronomy, and then in other
sciences, that it became axiomatical that a hypothesis adopted
by abduction could only be adopted on probation, and must
be tested.

203.   When this is duly recognized, the first thing that will
be done, as soon as a hypothesis has been adopted, will be
to trace out its necessary and probable experiential consequences. This step is *deduction*. Here I may notice a rule of
abduction much insisted upon by Auguste Comte, to the effect

that metaphysical hypotheses should be excluded; and by a metaphysical hypothesis he means, as he tells us, a hypothesis which has no experiential consequences. I suppose a partially metaphysical hypothesis would be one that had, among its consequences, some not relating to possible experience; and that from those Comte would wish us to tear away the metaphysical part. I have no particular objection to Comte's rule. Indeed, I think it would obviously be fully justified by a consideration of the purposes of hypothesis. Only I beg to remark that its positive utility is limited by the circumstance that such [a] thing as a hypothesis which is either wholly or partially metaphysical cannot be constructed. I may be asked what I should say to the proposition that

> The warranted genuine Snark has a taste
> Which is meagre and hollow, but crisp;
> Like a coat that is rather too tight in the waist,
> With a flavor of Will-o-the-wisp.

I reply that it is not a metaphysical proposition, because it is no proposition at all, but only an imitation proposition. For a proposition is a sign separately indicating what it is a sign of; and analysis shows that this amounts to saying that it represents that an image is similar to something to which actual experience forces the attention. Consequently a proposition cannot predicate a character not capable of sensuous presentation; nor can it refer to anything with which experience does not connect us. A metaphysical proposition in Comte's sense would, therefore, be a grammatical arrangement of words simulating a proposition, but in fact, not a proposition, because destitute of meaning. Comte's use of the word metaphysical, in a sense which makes it synonymous with nonsense, simply marks the nominalistic tendency of Comte's time, from which he was unable to free himself, although the general tendency of his philosophy is rather opposed to it. However, be that as it may, the entire meaning of a hypothesis lies in its conditional experiential predictions: if all its predictions are true, the hypothesis is wholly true.

204. This appears to be in harmony with Kant's view of deduction, namely, that it merely explicates what is implicitly

123

asserted in the premises. This is what is called a half-truth. Deductions are of two kinds, which I call *corollarial* and *theorematic*. The corollarial are those reasonings by which all corollaries and the majority of what are called theorems are deduced; the theorematic are those by which the major theorems are deduced. If you take the thesis of a corollary, — i.e. the proposition to be proved, and carefully analyze its meaning, by substituting for each term its definition, you will find that its truth follows, in a straightforward manner, from previous propositions similarly analyzed. But when it comes to proving a major theorem, you will very often find you have need of a *lemma*, which is a demonstrable proposition about something outside the subject of inquiry; and even if a lemma does not have to be demonstrated, it is necessary to introduce the definition of something which the *thesis* of the theorem does not contemplate. In the most remarkable cases, this is some abstraction; that is to say, a subject whose existence *consists* in some fact about other things. Such, for example, are operations considered as in themselves subject to operation; *lines*, which are nothing but descriptions of the motion of a particle, considered as being themselves movable; collections; numbers; and the like. When the reform of mathematical reasoning now going on is complete, it will be seen that every such supposition ought to be supported by a proper postulate. At any rate Kant himself ought to admit, and would admit if he were alive today, that the conclusion of reasoning of this kind, although it is strictly deductive, does not flow from definitions alone, but that postulates are requisite for it.

205. Deduction, of course, relates exclusively to an ideal state of things. A hypothesis presents such an ideal state of things, and asserts that it is the icon, or analogue of an experience.

206. Having, then, by means of deduction, drawn from a hypothesis predictions as to what the results of experiment will be, we proceed to test the hypothesis by making the experiments and comparing those predictions with the actual results of the experiment. Experiment is very expensive business, in money, in time, and in thought; so that it will be a saving of expense, to begin with that positive prediction from

the hypothesis which seems least likely to be verified. For a single experiment may absolutely refute the most valuable of hypotheses, while a hypothesis must be a trifling one indeed if a single experiment could establish it.[14] When, however, we find that prediction after prediction, notwithstanding a preference for putting the most unlikely ones to the test, is verified by experiment, whether without modification or with a merely quantitative modification, we begin to accord to the hypothesis a standing among scientific results. This sort of inference it is, from experiments testing predictions based on a hypothesis, that is alone properly entitled to be called *induction*.

207.   I may as well say that arguments which I cannot now stop to set forth ought to remove all doubt that, accepting the term induction in this sense, the critical distinction, that is, the distinction in respect to the nature of their validity between deduction and induction consists in this, — namely, deduction professes to show that certain admitted facts could not exist, even in an ideal world constructed for the purpose, either without the existence of the very fact concluded, or without the occurrence of this fact in the long run in that proportion of cases of the fulfilment of certain objective conditions in which it is concluded that it will occur, or in other words, without its having the concluded objective probability. In either case, deductive reasoning is necessary reasoning, although, in the latter case, its subject matter is probability. Induction, on the other hand, is not justified by any relation between the facts stated in the premisses and the fact stated in the conclusion; and it does not infer that the latter fact is either necessary or objectively probable. But the justification of its conclusion is that that conclusion is reached by a method which, steadily persisted in, must lead to true knowledge in the long run of cases of its application, whether to the existing world or to any imaginable world whatsoever. Deduction cannot make any such claim as this; since it does not lead to any positive knowledge at all, but only traces out the ideal consequences of hypotheses.

[14] (Ed.) See Chapter 2, "Economy of Research," in the present book.

§7. THREE KINDS OF INDUCTION [15]

208.   It is desirable to consider a large range of inductions, with a view to distinguishing accurately between induction and abduction, which have generally been much confounded. I will, therefore, mention that, in the present state of my studies, I think I recognize three distinct genera of induction. I somewhat hesitate to publish this division; but it might take more years than I have to live to render it as satisfactory as I could wish. It is not that there seems to be any very serious want of clearness in it, or that the reasons for maintaining it are wanting in conclusiveness, or that I have any particular reason to doubt, either the conclusion or the correctness of the reasoning; but it is simply that the factor of safety is too small. I have not so thoroughly considered the subject as to be quite secure against possible oversights of one kind or another; nor have I collected a sufficient surplus of proofs so that they will hold even although oversights there be. Consequently, I am not yet willing to incorporate this division with the body of results of this investigation. But with this warning, I now state the division.

209.   The first genus of induction is where we judge what approximate proportion of the members of a collection have a predesignate character by a sample drawn under one or other of the following three conditions, forming three species of this genus. First, the sample be a *random* one, an expression to which I attach a peculiar meaning. Namely, I mean by a random sample, a sample drawn from the whole class by a method which if it were applied over and over again would in the long run draw any one possible collection of the members of the whole collection sampled as often as any other collection of the same size, and would produce them in any one order as often as in any other. In this peculiar sense of the term *random sample*, it is only from a finite collection that a random sample can be drawn. And here it will be well to call to mind the exact meaning of a few terms relating to multitudes.[16] . . .

---

[15] (Ed.) Cf. 7.110–130.

[16] (Ed.) There follows a long discussion of collections (sets), of which we have printed here only that part necessary to understand the discussion below.

The multitude of every collection is either *enumerable* or finite, *denumeral* or indefinite, *abnumerable* or transfinite. The scientific definitions of these terms were, I believe, first given by me in 1881;[17] but Dedekind gave, perhaps independently, in 1888, substantially the same definition of a finite multitude. An *enumerable* multitude is the multitude of a collection, — say the A's, — if and only if, no matter what relation ρ may be, either it is not true that every A is in the relation, ρ, to some A to which no other A stands in the relation, ρ, or else to every A some one A, and no other, stands in the relation ρ. This is as much as to say that the A's form a non-enumerable or infinite collection, if and only if there be some relation, ρ, such that every A stands in the relation ρ to an A to which no other A stands in the relation ρ, although there is an A of which it is not true that any A stands in the relation ρ, while no other A does so. Now according to our definition of the relation of being as small as, this is the same as to say, that a collection, say the A's, is non-enumerable or infinite, if and only if, the entire collection of A's is as small as a collection of A's from which some A is excluded; and this again is obviously identical with Dedekind's definition of an infinite collection which is that a collection is infinite if and only if the whole of it is as small as some part of it not the whole. But a more readily intelligible definition, coming to the same thing, is to say that an enumerable multitude is a multitude less than that of all the finite whole numbers. The *denumeral* multitude, for there is but one, is the multitude of a collection, say the A's, if and only if, there is a relation, say σ, and an A, say A_o, such that every A stands in the relation σ to some A to which no other A stands in this relation, and no A stands in the relation σ to A_o, and taking any predicate, P, whatever, either every A has this character, P, or A_o does not possess the character P, or there is an A having the character P which is not in the relation σ to any A that has the character, P. This comes to the same thing as saying that the denumeral multitude is the multitude of the finite whole numbers. Every denumeral collection is numerable; that is to every member of

[17] (Ed.) [Bibliography] G-1881-7 ([AJM]). See also [Bibliography] G–1885–3 ([AJM]).

127

it a separate ordinal number may be assigned; and this may be done in such a way as to exhaust the entire collection of finite whole numbers. Every denumeral collection, therefore, either has an order or may receive an order. . . . To show that the whole is no more numerous than a part, or all the numbers than the even numbers, it suffices to write down

1	2	3	4	5	6	7	8	9, etc.
2	4	6	8	10	12	14	16	18, etc.

Of course, there is no number without a double, and each double is an even number. An *abnumerable* multitude is one of a denumeral succession of multitudes greater than the denumeral multitude; each of these being the multitude of the different possible collections of members of a collection of the next lower abnumerable multitude. I have proved that there is no multitude greater than every abnumerable multitude; and it seems to follow from a theorem of Cantor's about ordinal numbers that there is no multitude intermediate between two abnumerable multitudes. It will, therefore, suffice to define an abnumerable multitude as a multitude greater than that of all the finite whole numbers. If there is room on a line for any multitude of points, however great, a genuine continuity implies, then, that the aggregate of points on a line is too great to form a collection: the points lose their identity; or rather, they never had any numerical identity, for the reason that they are only possibilities, and therefore are essentially general. They only become individual when they are separately marked on the line; and however many be separately marked, there is room to mark more in any multitude.

210.   Returning to the first genus of induction, it now becomes plain that a random sample, in the exact sense defined, can only be drawn from a finite collection. For the definition contains the phrase "the long run." Now what is meant by "the long run?" The phrase is only used in saying that the ratio of frequency of an event has such and such a value in the long run. The meaning is that if the occasion referred to upon which the event might happen were to recur indefinitely, and if tallies were to be kept of the occurrences and the non-occurrences, then [the] ratio of the one number to the other, as

the occasions went on, would indefinitely converge toward a definite limit. The word 'converge' is here used in a different sense from that which is usual in mathematics. The common definition is that a series of values, x_1, x_2, x_3, etc., converges toward a limiting value x, provided, after any discrepancy ϵ has been named it is possible to find one of the members of the series x_ν such that, for every value of n greater than ν, $(x_n - x)^2 < \epsilon^2$. This ought to be called *definite* convergence. No such member x_n can, in the indefinite convergence with which we have to do, be fixed in advance of the experiment. Nevertheless, there will be some such value.

211.   Such being the nature of a long run, we see that the idea of a random sample supposes that in a denumeral series of trials all possible samples of the class sampled are to be capable of being drawn, and that in every possible order *inter se*. But all possible orders in which all possible samples, however small, could be drawn from a denumeral collection, would be abnumerable, and therefore not to be completed in a long run. It follows that it is only a finite or enumerable class from which a random sample in the sense of the definition can be drawn. It is, indeed, evident that one cannot take even a single whole number at random; for a whole number taken at random would be infinitely more likely to be larger than any predesignate number than not.

212.   Let us now consider another species of the first genus of induction. It had better be mentioned, by the way, that no multitude not enumerable is increased by being multiplied by itself; so that a denumeral collection of denumeral collections makes up a denumeral collection of the members of the latter collections. Let us now suppose that we are about to sample a denumeral collection in order to ascertain the proportionate frequency with which its members have a certain character designated in advance of the examination. Usually, there is no sense in speaking of a definite finite proportion of a denumeral collection; but I am going to suppose that this collection has an order which gives it a sense. The sample is to be drawn under the guidance of a precept under which we can enlarge any sample drawn indefinitely and can also draw an indefinite number of samples. Now I shall suppose that in

129

some way, no matter how, we become assured that a relation exists between four correlates, to wit, the predesignate character, the precept of sampling, the collection sampled, and the future course of experience, this relation being such that, in the long run, the distribution of the predesignate character in samples drawn under the precept will be the same as if they had been drawn strictly at random from an indefinitely large finite collection composing all our future experience of members of the same collection. Then, as before, we can infer inductively the proportional frequency of that character in future experiences of members of the same collection; and the induction must approximate indefinitely, though irregularly, to the true proportion. As an example, take a certain die. All the falls of it shall form the denumeral collection. In future experience this die will probably be thrown a very large but finite number of times. Let me sample the throws in order to find out (since it may be loaded or badly made) with what relative frequency it will turn up an ace. My precept shall be to throw it from the dicebox after shaking, replace it, and go on in the same way. I will not stop to inquire how I know that my sample throws will, as far as the distribution of aces is concerned, be determined as if they had been drawn strictly at random among all future throws, because this question has, at this stage, no relevancy, and would only divert our minds from our point. And besides, the elements of the difficulty will find their solution in questions we have presently to take up.

213. Perhaps we may reckon, as a third species under the first genus of induction, those cases in which we find a denumeral series in an objective order of succession, and wish to know what the law of occurrence of a certain character among its members is, without at the outset so much as knowing whether it has any definite frequency in the long run or not. As an example, I will make a very slight examination of the occurrence of the figure 5 in the endless decimal that would express the value of π. Since the enormous labor has been performed of calculating this number to over seven hundred places, it seems a pity that no use whatever should be made of it. An instructor having a class in probabilities might very well give out as an exercise the examination of the calculated

figures with a view to drawing such inferences as might be drawn by the doctrine of chances. I shall confine myself to illustrating this sort of induction by beginning an inquiry whether the figure 5 occurs in a purely chance way. I do not know why I chose this particular figure: I did so before I looked at the value of π. Taking the first 700 places, I separate them into the first 350 and the second 350. If these are quasi-random samples of the whole and all the figures occur equally often, there ought not to be far from 35 fives in each set. The odds that the number will fall in the thirties are about 2 to 1. The odds that it will fall between 28 and 42 *exclusive* is just 3 to 1. We find, in fact, that there are 33 fives in the first 350, and 28 in the second 350. Since the odds against this are only about 2 to 1, we conclude that the *fives*, and presumably the other figures, either occur by chance or very nearly so. It would, however, perhaps not be surprising if they were to occur with a little more approach to regularity than if they were purely fortuitous. Therefore, as a further illustration of this kind of induction, I have counted the number of 5's in each of the seventy sets of ten successive figures. In these seventy sets, the normal number of those having one 5 should be 27⅛. But we suspect there will be more owing to the fives coming a little more regularly than merely by chance. We will ask then what is the probability that there will be no more than 32 tens containing just one 5. It is about 5/6; but the actual number of such tens is 33. There is, therefore, a doubtful indication of such regularity.

214. These are all the species I can mention of the first type of induction, in which we ascertain the value of a ratio and are morally certain to approximate to it indefinitely in the long run for each problem. By "morally certain," I mean that the probability of that event is 1. Of course, there is a difference between probability 1 and absolute certainty. In like manner, "bare possibility" should mean the possibility of that whose probability is zero. It is barely possible that a well made pair of dice should turn up doublets every time they were thrown: it is a conceivable chance, though morally certain not to happen. But that a pair of dice will not turn up *sevens* is absolutely certain; it is not possible.

131

215. The second genus of induction comprises those cases
in which the inductive method if persisted in will certainly
in time correct any error that it may have led us into; but
it will not do so gradually, inasmuch as it is not quantitative;
— not but that it may relate to quantity, but it is not a quantitative induction. It does not discover a ratio of frequency.
The first species under this genus is where the collection to
be sampled is an objective series of which some members have
been experienced, while the rest remain to be experienced,
and we simply conclude that future experience will be like the
past. We may take Quetelet's well-known example of the
ancient Greek who, never having heard of the flux and reflux
of the ocean, should have wandered to the shores of the Bay of
Biscay and should have there seen the tide rise for m successive
half-days. I need hardly say that I utterly reject the doctrine
that there is any consequent definite probability that the event
will happen during the next half-day. That doctrine has been
absolutely disproved. If the Greek's conclusion is that the
tide rises about once every half-day, it is an induction of
the first genus, second species. He may say that the indication
is that the frequency is somewhere between $\dfrac{m-\frac{1}{2}}{m}$ and $\dfrac{m+\frac{1}{2}}{m}$
although this is only a rough approximation. He may, thence,
deduce the conclusion that a tide will not be wanting in the
following m half-days, although he ought not to risk much upon
it. Beyond that it cannot be said that the quantitative induction warrants such a prediction. But if the Greek had seen the
tide rise just often enough to suggest to him that it would rise
every half-day forever, and had proposed then to make observations to test this hypothesis, had done so, and finding the
predictions successful, had provisionally accepted the theory
that the tide would never cease to rise every half-day, there
would be just this justification for this conclusion, that it was
the result of a method which, if it be persisted in, must correct
its result if it were wrong. For if the tide was going to skip a
half-day, he must discover it, if he continued his observations
long enough. This degree of justification and no more he would
have whether he made a dozen trials, or half a dozen, or three,
or two, or one only, or even none at all. The argument would

132

have precisely the same justification in either case. The method would infallibly correct itself, provided he continued this series of experiments; but not if he dropped it and subsequently commenced another series, as would be the case with quantitative induction. For this induction not being quantitative, does not conclude that the probability of the tides rising is 1; but that it raises every half-day without exception. It has nothing to do with probabilities or improbabilities; and if the series of observations skips a single day, that day may be the very day of the exceptional fact. This kind of induction further differs from quantitative induction, inasmuch as there is no probable indication in advance, if its conclusion is to break down; so that, as long as it does not break down, there is nothing to be said but that no reason appears as yet for giving up the hypothesis. It gives, therefore, but a very slight and merely negative support to the hypothesis. It is a proper answer enough to gratuitous hypotheses. It is impossible to avoid making some use of it for that purpose. But it must be set down as the weakest possible of inductive arguments. I have confined myself to cases in which the series of occasions considered is objective. But I am unable to perceive that there is any intrinsic logical distinction between these cases and those in which the series results from our own subdivision of a continuum. It might, for example, be suggested that the action of gravitation may be intermittent, either with a very short period, or without any definite period. In that case, a body moving for a considerable time would show merely the average acceleration; but two molecules might, during the interval of their encounter, either undergo no acceleration, so that it would be as if there were no encounter, or they might undergo acceleration many times that of average gravitation; and this might account for there seeming to be greater attraction at small distances than the law of average gravitation would account for. Moreover, greater masses moving slower than smaller ones, a periodic relation between atomic weights and attractions of atoms might be expected. Now, as a test of that hypothesis, it might be proposed to shorten the period of a pendulum more and more, and try to observe some irregularities of its amplitudes. If we found that, as far as we could go,

133

say with pendulums oscillating 50 times a second, there were
no observable irregularities of amplitude, and were to infer
that there was no intermittency of gravitation, I am unable to
see that the argument would differ from the argument that the
tide will rise on every half-day forever, because it has been seen
to do so on several successive half-days. It is true that this
latter argument is weakened by the consideration that states
of things not universal usually come to an end; while the other
is strengthened by the consideration that, time being continuous,
it is reasonable to suppose that, in sufficiently short intervals,
there will be no further variation of any given phenomenon.
But both of these are extraneous considerations. As far as the
mere argument that what has not been found need not be expected is concerned, there seems to be no logical distinction
between them. Let us consider one more example. By means
of a well-constructed color-box, two adjacent rectangles are
illuminated, each with nearly homogeneous violet light, of the
same apparent luminosity; the one of a wave-length of about
404 micromicrons, the other 402 micromicrons, and the observer
who knows only what he sees, is asked which is the redder.
He says he sees no difference. But the operator insists upon his
deciding for one or the other; and with reluctance he names
one, as it seems to him quite at random. However, the experiment having been repeated several hundred times, it is found
that in each set of a hundred answers, a decided majority makes
the more refrangible the redder. Now then, what do we proceed
to infer from this, — that there is no such thing as a *Differenz-
Schwelle*, but that no matter how small the difference of excitations a sufficient number of answers would betray a difference
of sensation? The only justification for this would be that it
is the result of a method that persisted in must eventually correct any error that it leads us into. I may mention, that the
argument that there is no *Differenz-Schwelle* is, in reality,
stronger than this. But a negative induction of this sort, a refusal to expect what is contrary to experience, will rightly be
resorted to when gratuitous objections are raised to any induction.

216.   I seem to recognize a third genus of inductions where
we draw a sample of an aggregate which can not be considered

as a collection, since it does not consist of units capable of being either counted or measured, however roughly; and where probability therefore cannot enter; but where we can draw the distinction of much and little, so that we can conceive of measurement being established; and where we may expect that any error into which the sampling will lead us, though it may not be corrected by a mere enlargement of the sample, or even by drawing other similar samples, yet must be brought to light, and that gradually, by persistence in the same general method. This kind of reasoning may be described in slightly different terms by saying that it tests a hypothesis by sampling the possible predictions that may be based upon it. Predictions are not units; for they may be more or less detailed. One can say roughly that one is more significant than another; but no approach to actual weighing of their significance can, in most cases, be made. Consequently, we cannot say that a collection of predictions drawn from a hypothesis constitutes a strictly random sample of all that can be drawn. Sometimes we can say that it appears to constitute a very fair, or even a severe, sample of the possible predictions; while in other cases, we cannot even say that, but only that it comprises all the predictions which we can as yet draw and put to the test. Those two classes of cases may be taken as constituting two species under this genus. We cannot ordinarily hope that our hypothesis will pass through the fire of induction, absolutely unmodified. Consequently, we ought not to conclude that it is absolutely correct, but only that it very much resembles the truth. In so far as further induction will modify it, as it must be expected that it will do, if it is not to meet with downright refutation, it can hardly fail that the modification should come about gradually. We shall first find facts, reconcilable yet unexpected. These will be discovered in greater volume, until they show that a modification of the theory is necessary. The familiar history of the kinetical theory of gases well illustrates this. It began with a number of spheres almost infinitesimally small occasionally colliding. It was afterward so far modified that the forces between the spheres, instead of merely separating them, were mainly attractive, that the molecules were not spheres, but systems, and that the part of space within which their motions are free is appreciably less than the entire volume of the gas. There was no new hypothetical element in these modifications. They were partly merely quantitative, and partly such as to make the formal hypothesis represent better what was really supposed to be the case, but which had been simplified for mathematical simplicity. There was, besides, an important modification which was imposed by mathematical necessity. So far as these modifications were introduced in order to bring the hypothesis into better accord with the facts, they were indicated and suspected long before the need of them became quite apparent; so that this genus of induction shares with the first the advantage that where the inductive conclusion errs, it will be but slightly, and the discovery, instead of being shot like a bolt out of the blue, creeps upon us as a dawning day.

217.   The reasonings of science are for the most part complex. Their parts are so put together as to increase their strength. Our attention has been confined to the elements out of which scientific argumentations are built up. We have now passed in review all the logically distinct forms of pure induction. It has been seen that one and all are mere processes for testing hypotheses already in hand. The induction adds nothing. At the very most it corrects the value of a ratio or slightly modifies a hypothesis in a way which had already been contemplated as possible.

§8. ABDUCTION

218.   Abduction, on the other hand, is merely preparatory. It is the first step of scientific reasoning, as induction is the concluding step. Nothing has so much contributed to present chaotic or erroneous ideas of the logic of science as failure to distinguish the essentially different characters of different elements of scientific reasoning; and one of the worst of these confusions, as well as one of the commonest, consists in regarding abduction and induction taken together (often mixed also with deduction) as a simple argument. Abduction and induction have, to be sure, this common feature, that both lead to the acceptance of a hypothesis because observed facts are such as would necessarily or probably result as consequences of that

hypothesis. But for all that, they are the opposite poles of reason, the one the most ineffective, the other the most effective of arguments. The method of either is the very reverse of the other's. Abduction makes its start from the facts, without, at the outset, having any particular theory in view, though it is motived by the feeling that a theory is needed to explain the surprising facts. Induction makes its start from a hypothesis which seems to recommend itself, without at the outset having any particular facts in view, though it feels the need of facts to support the theory. Abduction seeks a theory. Induction seeks for facts. In abduction the consideration of the facts suggests the hypothesis. In induction the study of the hypothesis suggests the experiments which bring to light the very facts to which the hypothesis had pointed. The mode of suggestion by which, in abduction, the facts suggest the hypothesis is by *resemblance*, — the resemblance of the facts to the consequences of the hypothesis. The mode of suggestion by which in induction the hypothesis suggests the facts is by *contiguity*, — familiar knowledge that the conditions of the hypothesis can be realized in certain experimental ways.

219.   I now proceed to consider what principles should guide us in abduction, or the process of choosing a hypothesis. Underlying all such principles there is a fundamental and primary abduction, a hypothesis which we must embrace at the outset, however destitute of evidentiary support it may be. That hypothesis is that the facts in hand admit of rationalization, and of rationalization by us. That we must hope they do, for the same reason that a general who has to capture a position or see his country ruined, must go on the hypothesis that there is some way in which he can and shall capture it. We must be animated by that hope concerning the problem we have in hand, whether we extend it to a general postulate covering all facts, or not. Now, that the matter of no new truth can come from induction or from deduction, we have seen. It can only come from abduction; and abduction is, after all, nothing but guessing. We are therefore bound to hope that, although the possible explanations of our facts may be strictly innumerable, yet our mind will be able, in some finite number of guesses, to guess the sole true explanation of them. *That* we are bound to

assume, independently of any evidence that it is true. Animated by that hope, we are to proceed to the construction of a hypothesis.

220.   Now the only way to discover the principles upon which anything ought to be constructed is to consider what is to be done with the constructed thing after it is constructed. That which is to be done with the hypothesis is to trace out its consequences by deduction, to compare them with results of experiment by induction, and to discard the hypothesis, and try another, as soon as the first has been refuted; as it presumably will be. How long it will be before we light upon the hypothesis which shall resist all tests we cannot tell; but we hope we shall do so, at last. In view of this prospect, it is plain that three considerations should determine our choice of a hypothesis. In the first place, it must be capable of being subjected to experimental testing. It must consist of experiential consequences with only so much logical cement as is needed to render them rational. In the second place, the hypothesis must be such that it will explain the surprising facts we have before us which it is the whole motive of our inquiry to rationalize. This explanation may consist in making the observed facts natural chance results, as the kinetical theory of gases explains facts; or it may render the facts necessary, and in the latter case as implicitly asserting them or as the ground for a mathematical demonstration of their truth. In the third place, quite as necessary a consideration as either of those I have mentioned, in view of the fact that the true hypothesis is only one out of innumerable possible false ones, in view, too, of the enormous expensiveness of experimentation in money, time, energy, and thought, is the consideration of economy.[18] Now economy, in general, depends upon three kinds

---

[18] (Ed.) "[Abduction] alone can propose every proposition. . . . induction is the sole court of last resort in every case.

"This being the case, what does it matter how the work of abduction is performed? It matters much, for the reason that it originates every proposition. It is true that, however carelessly the abduction is performed, the true hypothesis will get suggested at last. But the aid which a correct logic can afford to science consists in enabling that to be done at small expenditure of every kind which, at any rate, is bound to get done somehow. The whole service of logic to science, whatever the nature of its services to individuals may be, is of the nature of an economy. So much truth, — and more than this,

of factors: cost; the value of the thing proposed, in itself; and its effect upon other projects. Under the head of cost, if a hypothesis can be put to the test of experiment with very little expense of any kind, that should be regarded as a recommendation for giving it precedence in the inductive procedure. For even if it be barely admissible for other reasons, still it may clear the ground to have disposed of it. In the beginning of the wonderful reasonings by which the cuneiform inscriptions were made legible, one or two hypotheses which were never considered likely were taken up and soon refuted with great advantage. Under the head of value, we must place those considerations which tend toward an expectation that a given hypothesis may be true. These are of two kinds, the purely instinctive and the reasoned. In regard to instinctive considerations, I have already pointed out that it is a primary hypothesis underlying all abduction that the human mind is akin to the truth in the sense that in a finite number of guesses it will light upon the correct hypothesis. Now inductive experience supports that hypothesis in a remarkable measure. For if there were no tendency of that kind, if when a surprising phenomenon presented itself in our laboratory, we had to make random shots at the determining conditions, trying such hypotheses as that the aspect of the planets had something to do with it, or what the dowager empress had been doing just five hours previously, if such hypotheses had as good a chance of being true as those which seem marked by good sense, then we never could have made any progress in science at all. But that we have made solid gains in knowledge is indisputable; and moreover, the history of science proves that when the phenomena were properly analyzed, upon fundamental points, at least, it has seldom been necessary to try more than two or three hypotheses made by clear genius before the right one was

— I concede to the doctrine of Ernst Mach, although I cannot approve of the extreme length to which he carries the theory of economy. . . .

"The principles upon which abduction ought to be conducted ought to be determined exclusively by considerations of what purpose it subserves and how it may best subserve that purpose. Since, therefore, in scientific investigation abduction can subserve no other purpose than economy, it follows that the rules of scientific abduction ought to be based exclusively upon the economy of research." From a fragmentary alternative draft (see 164n2).

Cf. Chapter 2, "Economy of Research," in the present book (7.139ff.).

found. I have heard it said that Kepler tried nineteen orbits for Mars before he hit upon the right one; but in the first place, I cannot admit that that is a fair description of his elaborate series of inductions, and in the second place the subject of the hypothesis was not of the fundamental class. We cannot go so far as to say that high human intelligence is more often right than wrong in its guesses; but we can say that, after due analysis, and unswerved by prepossessions, it has been, and no doubt will be, not very many times more likely to be wrong than right. As we advance further and further into science, the aid that we can derive from the natural light of reason becomes, no doubt, less and less; but still science will cease to progress if ever we shall reach the point where there is no longer an infinite saving of expense in experimentation to be effected by care that our hypotheses are such as naturally recommend themselves to the mind, and make upon us the impression of simplicity, — which here means facility of comprehension by the human mind, — of aptness, of reasonableness, of good sense. For the existence of a natural instinct for truth is, after all, the sheet-anchor of science. From the instinctive, we pass to reasoned, marks of truth in the hypothesis. Of course, if we know any positive facts which render a given hypothesis objectively probable, they recommend it for inductive testing. When this is not the case, but the hypothesis seems to us likely, or unlikely, this likelihood is an indication that the hypothesis accords or discords with our preconceived ideas; and since those ideas are presumably based upon some experience, it follows that, other things being equal, there will be, in the long run, some economy in giving the hypothesis a place in the order of precedence in accordance with this indication. But experience must be our chart in economical navigation; and experience shows that likelihoods are treacherous guides. Nothing has caused so much waste of time and means, in all sorts of researches, as inquirers' becoming so wedded to certain likelihoods as to forget all the other factors of the economy of research; so that, unless it be very solidly grounded, likelihood is far better disregarded, or nearly so; and even when it seems solidly grounded, it should be proceeded upon with a cautious tread, with an eye to other considerations, and a recollection

of the disasters it has caused. The third category of factors
of economy, those arising from the relation of what is proposed
to other projects, is especially important in abduction, because
very rarely can we positively expect a given hypothesis to
prove entirely satisfactory; and we must always consider what
will happen when the hypothesis proposed breaks down. The
qualities which these considerations induce us to value in a
hypothesis are three, which I may entitle Caution, Breadth,
and Incomplexity. In respect to caution, the game of twenty
questions is instructive. In this game, one party thinks of some
individual object, real or fictitious, which is well-known to all
educated people. The other party is entitled to answers to any
twenty interrogatories they propound which can be answered
by *Yes* or *No*, and are then to guess what was thought of, if
they can. If the questioning is skillful, the object will invariably
be guessed; but if the questioners allow themselves to be led
astray by the will-o-the-wisp of any prepossession, they will
almost as infallibly come to grief. The uniform success of good
questioners is based upon the circumstance that the entire collection of individual objects well-known to all the world does
not amount to a million. If, therefore, each question could exactly bisect the possibilities, so that *yes* and *no* were equally
probable, the right object would be identified among a collection numbering 2^{20}. Now the logarithm of 2 being 0.30103,
that of its twentieth power is 6.0206, which is the logarithm
of about 1,000,000 $(1+.02\times2.3)$ $(1+.0006\times2.3)$ or over one
million and forty-seven thousand, or more than the entire
number of objects from which the selection has been made.
Thus, twenty skillful hypotheses will ascertain what two hundred thousand stupid ones might fail to do. The secret of the
business lies in the caution which breaks a hypothesis up into
its smallest logical components, and only risks one of them at
a time. What a world of futile controversy and of confused
experimentation might have been saved if this principle had
guided investigations into the theory of light! The ancient
and medieval notion was that sight starts from the eye, is shot
to the object from which it is reflected, and returned to the
eye. This idea had, no doubt, been entirely given up before
Römer showed that it took light a quarter of an hour to traverse

the earth's orbit, a discovery which would have refuted it by
the experiment of opening the closed eyes and looking at the
stars. The next point in order was to ascertain of what the ray
of light consisted. But this not being answerable by *yes* or *no*,
the first question should have been 'Is the ray homogeneous
along its length?' Diffraction showed that it was not so. That
being established, the next question should have been 'Is the
ray homogeneous on all sides?' Had that question been put to
experiment, polarization must have been speedily discovered;
and the same sort of procedure would have developed the whole
theory with a gain of half a century.

221.   Correlative to the quality of caution is that of breadth.
For when we break the hypothesis into elementary parts, we
may, and should, inquire how far the same explanation accounts for the same phenomenon when it appears in other subjects. For example, the kinetical theory of gases, although
it was originally proposed with a view merely to explaining the
law of Boyle, never attracted much attention, nor was there
any good reason why it should, until the conservation of energy
was brought to light, and it was found that the kinetical theory
would account, in a remarkably satisfactory way, for non-
conservative phenomena. It accounts for those phenomena,
so far as it does account for them, by representing that they
are results of chance; or, if you please, of the law of high numbers; for it is remarkable that chance operates in one way and
not in the opposite way. Under those circumstances, the economical consideration which we now have in view, would recommend that we at once inquire into non-conservative phenomena,
generally, in order to see whether the same sort of explanation
is equally admissible in all cases, or whether we are thus led
to some broad category of conditions under which non-conservative phenomena appear, or whether there are several distinct
ways in which they are brought about. For great economy
must result in whichever way this question is answered, provided it can be answered at not too great an expense. Thus,
if we find that there are several explanations of non-conservative phenomena, we have only to trace out their several consequences, and we shall have criteria for distinguishing them;
while if we find there is but one cause, we at once reach a

wide generalization which will save repetitious work. It is, therefore, good economy, other things being equal, to make our hypotheses as broad as possible. But, of course, one consideration has to be balanced against another. There still remains one more economic consideration in reference to a hypothesis; namely, that it may give a good "leave," as the billiard-players say. If it does not suit the facts, still the comparison with the facts may be instructive with reference to the next hypothesis. For example, I might be inclined to surmise that an observable quantity y was such a function of a quantity x, determined by the conditions of experiments, as to be expressible in the form $y = a + bx^2$. Still, as I am not sure of this, perhaps it would be wise first to try how well the experiments could be satisfied by $y = cx$; because the residuals will be more readily interpretable in the latter case. As a provisional hypothesis, it will, for this reason, other considerations apart, be better to assume something very simple, even although we imagine that by complicating the hypothesis it could be brought nearer the truth. Let us suppose, for example, that I wished to find some mathematical relation between the Atomic weights and the succession of chemical elements according to Mendeléef's system. In point of fact, I hardly think that the time has yet come when it is worth while to take up that question for its own sake. The discoveries of Gallium, Germanium, and Scandium have proved that there is some truth in one part of Mendeléef's theory; but the non-discovery of hecamagnesium inclines me, I must say, to think that Chromium and Magnesium are exceptional elements; and it seems to me that the groups, unless it be the extreme ones, are founded on pretty superficial characters. And if we are to separate all elements into what Mendeléef calls groups, it seems to me that the rare earths seem to afford symptoms that an additional group must be admitted, say perhaps between the group of Zinc and the group of Gallium. However, if we are to retain Mendeléef's system, let us suppose, as a first rough approximation to the truth, that, in the absence of disturbing conditions of which we know nothing, the atomic weights of the elements would increase from $K = 39$ by $2\frac{1}{2}$ units at each step. Even if it is of little service as chemistry, it will, at least, serve as a tolerable illustration of the point of logic we have under consideration to compare the numbers required by this hypothesis with the numbers found. The latter depend upon the purity of the materials, of which the sole and insufficient guarantee is that atomic weights of material from different sources and subjected to different chemical operations agree. The table [next page] shows the comparison.

222. There are 16 consecutive elements undiscovered, according to Mendeléef's theory. Those that we know of the same groups, that is those in the table just above and just below the vacant spaces, may very well be contaminated with the unknown elements. The 24 first, not open to this suspicion, mostly differ from our calculation by not more than 1. Those just above the missing elements have on the average atomic weights 2 units too great, those just below are on the average about ½ a unit too small. Thus, this very incomplex and even rough hypothesis has done for us what a more elaborate one would almost surely have failed to do, namely, it has brought to light an indication that all the elements from Ruthenium up are probably largely contaminated with undiscovered elements, which contaminations have mostly atomic weights between 146 and 182, but are partly of large atomic weights, say from 211 up. Since this perturbation is largest in tellurium and barium, we should naturally look in these elements, especially, for admixtures of substances of higher atomic weight. In tellurium they have been sought, in vain; yet one cannot say that the negative has been rendered altogether improbable. In barium, on the other hand, there are indications of something of the sort, though whether it is sufficient to account for the large atomic weight, it is impossible to decide at present. I will not say that the hypothesis merits much attention, for the reason that it rests upon the acceptance of Mendeléef's arrangement, and that arrangement is itself in considerable doubt.

§9. THE LOGIC OF HISTORY

223. Having now passed in review all the elements of merit of an hypothesis, I ought, in regular procedure, to consider the general principles of synthesis of these elements. But I think that that would delay us to no advantage; for once it is granted that the elements I have enumerated are the points

	K	Ca	Sc	Ti	V	Cr	Mn	Fe	Co	Ni	Cu	Zn	Ga	Ge	As	Se	Br	Kr
Element	K	Ca	Sc	Ti	V	Cr	Mn	Fe	Co	Ni	Cu	Zn	Ga	Ge	As	Se	Br	Kr
Calc	39	41½	44	46½	49	51½	54	56½	59	61½	64	66½	69	71½	74	76½	79	81½
Obs	39.1	40.0	44	48.2	51.4	52.1	55.0	55.9	59.0	58.7	63.6	65.4	70.0	72.5	75.0	79.2	80.0	81.6
O-C	+0	−1½	0	+1½	+2½	+½	+1	−½	0	−3	−½	−1	+1	+1	+1	+2½	+1	+0

	Rb	Sr	Y	Zr	Cb	Mo		Ru	Rh	Pd	Ag	Cd	In	Sn	Sb	Te	I	X
Element	Rb	Sr	Y	Zr	Cb	Mo		Ru	Rh	Pd	Ag	Cd	In	Sn	Sb	Te	I	X
Calc	84	86½	89	91½	94	96½	99	101½	104	106½	109	111½	114	116½	119	121½	124	126½
Obs	85.4	87.7	89.0	90.6	94	96.0	∶	101.7	103.0	106.5	107.9	112.3	114	119.0	120.0	127.5	126.8	128.0
O-C	+1½	+1	0	−1	0	−½	∶	+0	−1	−1	−1	+1	0	+2½	+1	+6	+3	+1½

	Cs	Ba	La	Ce	Pr	Nd												
Element	Cs	Ba	La	Ce	Pr	Nd												
Calc	129	131½	134	136½	139	141½	144	146½	149	151½	154	156½	159	161½	164	166½	169	171½
Obs	132.9	137.4	138.5	140	140.5	143.6	∶	∶	∶	∶	∶	∶	∶	∶	∶	∶	∶	∶
O-C	+4	+6	+4½	+3½	+1½	+2	∶	∶	∶	∶	∶	∶	∶	∶	∶	∶	∶	∶

					Ta	W		Os	Ir	Pt	Au	Hg	Tl	Pb	Bi			
Element					Ta	W		Os	Ir	Pt	Au	Hg	Tl	Pb	Bi			
Calc	174	176½	179	181½	184	186½	189	191½	194	196½	199	201½	204	206½	209	211½	214	216½
Obs	∶	∶	∶	∶	183	184	∶	190.8	193	195.2	197.3	200.0	204.2	206.9	208	∶	∶	∶
O-C	∶	∶	∶	∶	−1	−2½	∶	−½	−1	−1½	−1½	−1½	0	+½	−1	∶	∶	∶

to consider, the mode in which they are to be combined in the case of ancient history is too obvious for dispute. The elements are as follows:

Experiential character of the hypothesis.

$$\text{Its explaining all the facts} \begin{cases} \text{as natural concomitants.} \\ \text{as deductions} \begin{cases} \text{Corollarial.} \\ \text{Theorematic.} \end{cases} \end{cases}$$

$$\text{Economical considerations} \begin{cases} \text{Cheapness.} \\ \text{Intrinsic Value} \begin{cases} \text{Naturalness.} \\ \text{Likelihood.} \end{cases} \\ \\ \text{Relation of Hypotheses} \begin{cases} \text{Caution.} \\ \text{Breadth.} \\ \text{Incomplexity.} \end{cases} \end{cases}$$

224.   In the case of ancient history, the facts to be explained are, in part, of the nature of monuments, among which are to be reckoned the manuscripts; but the facts in greater part are documentary; that is, they are assertions and virtual assertions which we read either in the manuscripts or upon inscriptions. This latter class of facts is so much in excess, that ancient history may be said to consist in the interpretation of testimonies, occasionally supported or refuted by the indirect evidence of the monuments.

225.   Now the first rule which we should set up is that our hypothesis ought to explain *all* the related facts. It is not sufficient to say that testimony is not true, it is our business to explain how it came to be such as it is.

226.   The second rule is that our first hypothesis should be that the principal testimonies are true; and this hypothesis should not be abandoned until it is conclusively refuted. No practice is more wasteful than that of abandoning a hypothesis once taken up, until it becomes evident that it is quite untenable. An excellent method in the great majority of those cases in which it is applicable and in which it leads to any unequivocal results is to give precedence to that hypothesis which reposes upon a deep and primary instinct, such as is the instinct

to believe testimony, without which human society could not exist. There is no surer mark of inexperience in dealing with witnesses than a tendency to believe that they are falsifying, without any definite, objective, and strong reason for the suspicion. But especially in ancient history, where the only facts we have are, in most cases, testimonies, the extremely bad economy of supposing those testimonies false, before we have first thoroughly tried the hypothesis that they are true, and have found it quite inadmissible, is so obvious, that it is difficult to repress a certain contempt for the reasoning powers of those critics who are given to this procedure.

227. The third rule will be that probabilities that are strictly objective and at the same time very great, although they can never be absolutely conclusive, ought nevertheless to influence our preference for one hypothesis over another; but slight probabilities, even if objective, are not worth consideration; and merely subjective likelihoods should be disregarded altogether. For they are merely expressions of our preconceived notions. Now one of the main purposes of studying history ought to be to free us from the tyranny of our preconceived notions.

228. The fourth rule will be that we should split up a hypothesis into its items as much as possible, so as to test each one singly.

229. The fifth rule will be that when we are in doubt which of two hypotheses ought to have precedence, we should try whether, by enlarging the field of facts which they are to explain, a good reason will not appear for giving one of them a decided preference over the other.

230. The sixth rule will be that if the work of testing a particular hypothesis will have substantially or largely to be done in any case, in the process of testing another hypothesis, that circumstance should, other things being equal, give this hypothesis which thus involves little or no extra expense, a preference over another which would require special work of no value except for testing it.

231. A hypothesis having been adopted on probation, the process of testing it will consist, not in examining the facts, in order to see how well they accord with the hypothesis, but

147

on the contrary in examining such of the probable consequences of the hypothesis as would be capable of direct verification, especially those consequences which would be very unlikely or surprising in case the hypothesis were not true. It is not easy to enumerate the different kinds of consequences; but among them may be, that the hypothesis would render the present existence of a monument probable, or would result in giving a known monument a certain character; that if it were true, certain ancient documents ought to contain some allusion to it; that if it is misstated by some authority not considered in the selection of the hypothesis, that misstatement would be likely to be of a certain kind; that if the hypothesis is true, and an assertion or allusion found in an ancient work is to be explained by the author's knowing it to be true, he must have had certain other knowledge, etc. When the hypothesis has sustained a testing as severe as the present state of our knowledge of the particular branch of history to which it belongs renders imperative, it will be admitted provisionally into the list of our present historical results, subject of course to reconsideration along with all those other results, when we are in a condition to insist upon a higher grade of security. In order to make the difference between this method and that usually pursued quite clear, I propose to give three illustrative examples. I shall draw them from the history of philosophy, with which I am better acquainted than I am with political history. I shall endeavor to make the examples illustrative of different kinds of questions, and in departments of history where various grades of probability can be insisted upon. I shall, in each case, first show how the question would be treated in accordance with the method of this paper; and then I shall show how some one or more of the best critics actually have treated it. I shall not notice the theories of those who carry higher criticism to its last extravagances, but shall confine myself to those who are most esteemed for their sobriety and thoroughness. It will be necessary to confine our illustrations to some minor points, because these are the only ones which can be discussed within moderate limits.

232. If the necessity of this rule is not at once apparent, it will soon become so; for I am going to begin by breaking it

in taking up the question of the authenticity of the writings
of Aristotle, — a question which has formed the subject of
several laborious books, and which I can here consider only
in the most insufficient manner.

§10. APPLICATION OF THE METHOD

233. The facts to be explained may be outlined as follows.
The works in our edition of Aristotle are forty-six in number,
containing a million words, equal, if translated, to perhaps ten
volumes of Herbert Spencer. In addition, a hundred ancient
authors give some six hundred fragments from some sixty other
works. Diogenes Laertius gives a catalogue of the writings of
Aristotle, probably made in Alexandria, (but the date of it is
a matter for conjecture,) which contains 146 titles, which
Diogenes says had 445,270 lines, which would be more than
three times the size of our edition. Yet this catalogue does not
seem to refer to any large part of the substance of the works
that we possess. Moreover, down to the time of Cicero, Aristotle, whose reputation was more Roman than Greek, was
chiefly known by works which we do not possess. The style
of those works, as it is described, and as we see it in the fragments, was highly artistic; while that of the general mass of
the works we possess is harsh and excessively condensed. They
seem like notes for books rather than finished books. We find,
however, in them a few long passages in the same polished style
as the fragments, as if Jeremy Bentham had allowed Ruskin
to write a few pages for him. The works we possess are also
extremely repetitious. More than once, a whole book, or even
a whole work, is substantially written again. And of the lost
works, some, we are told by those who had seen them, agreed
in substance with some of those in our possession. Shorter
passages, and especially definitions, are often repeated almost
verbatim. Our Aristotle abounds in references to his own
works, sometimes to lost works, but mostly apparently to the
works we know under other titles, but the nomenclature of the
titles in the references presents no fixity; the same work will
receive from Aristotle himself various names, — unless he
means to refer to some works that we do not know. Two differ-

149

ent works will refer reciprocally to one another, and a work
will contain a reference to a part further on in the same work.
In one case, at least, it seems pretty clear that the reference
involves a misunderstanding of the passage referred to; but I
do not know why a voluminous author may not fall into a misunderstanding of a passage of his own writing. The surprising
circumstances will in part be explained if we trust to a narrative given by Strabo in the XIIIth book of his Geography, of
which we know that the IVth book, or a passage of it, was
composed A.D. 19, — and Strabo is supposed, on tolerably
good grounds, to have been born 66 B.C. This narrative is confirmed by Strabo's younger contemporary Plutarch in his life
of Sulla, and in great part by Athenaeus in the IIIrd century
of our era, and in part by Porphyry, also of the IIIrd century.
The story is as follows.

234.   Alexander died in June 323 B.C., Aristotle's school
having been running in Athens for twelve years, and in the later
years Aristotle was supposed to be almost the secret boss of
Athens, was enormously rich, and was decidedly unpopular.
Athens and Macedonia were instantly at war, and Aristotle re-
tired to Chalcis in Euboea where there was a Macedonian garrison, leaving Theophrastus in charge of his school. Athens
was subdued in September 322 B.C.; but just about that time
Aristotle died. His will does not mention his precious library
nor his personal papers; but it seems they passed into the possession of Theophrastus. Theophrastus lived until 287 B.C.,
and at his death bequeathed his books to a friend, Neleus, who
lived at Scepsis in Aeolis, Asia Minor. Strabo is of opinion
that this loss of Aristotle's writings was a severe blow to the
peripatetic school; for many of the writings, it would seem,
had not been published. At any rate, it seems to be a fact that
the school became rather colorless. Meantime, about 250 B.C.,
the kings of Pergamus, to whom Scepsis belonged, began to
collect a vast library, by the simple method of seizing books
wherever they could lay hands upon them. The consequence
was that the heirs of Neleus hid the books in a cellar. The cellar
was damp; but there the books remained until, in 133 B.C., the
last of that dynasty of kings bequeathed his kingdom to the
Roman people. Soon after this, it would seem that the peri-

patetic school had been somewhat drawn into politics, although this is an obscure point. However, it is certain that a peripatetic, Aristion, or Athenion, became tyrant of Athens; and a peripatetic friend of his, Apellicon, who was so fond of books that he would steal them from the archives of Greek cities, and who had become rich by plunder, as an agent of Aristion, — this Apellicon, purchased the library of Neleus and brought it back to Athens. The papers of Aristotle had suffered grievously, during their century and a half of incarceration, from damp and insects, and were in places illegible; but Apellicon, in the intervals of his raids, occupied himself with copying and editing them. But in 87 B.C., Apellicon having died shortly before, Sulla took Athens, executed Aristion, and carried away the library to Rome. Without this accident, Aristotle would probably be to us today a name like Democritus; for the Greeks never regarded him as a supremely great philosopher. In mind and in breeding he was not exactly a Greek, but, like Democritus, was a Thracian. At any rate, Sulla took the library to Rome, and handed it over to the learned peripatetic Tyrannion, whose library finally amounted, according to Suidas, to 30,000 volumes. Tyrannion found that the editing of Apellicon was excessively bad. Ultimately, the peripatetic scholiarch Andronicus of Rhodes undertook the arrangement of the papers, the correction of the text, and the publication of a new edition.

235. The hypothesis that this story is true is so natural, and it ought to be so easily refuted if it is not true, that I am strongly inclined, in spite of the jeers of all the great German critics, to admit it on probation.[19] When I ask what, then, would be the source of information of Strabo, I find that he was the personal scholar of Tyrannion, and that the labors of Andronicus, which would have made considerable noise in the world of letters, were probably performed in his life-time. Still, before admitting the hypothesis to probation, we must ask whether it would explain all the principal facts. It explains the two styles. The one was for the outer public, the other for use in the school, whether as notes for lectures only, or for general reference, we have not sufficient positive evidence

[19] (Ed.) The essentials of this story are credited in John Edwin Sandys, *A History of Classical Scholarship*, Vol. 1, 3rd edition, University Press, Cambridge, 1921, pp. 85–86.

concerning the methods of instruction there to say, or not. The
question has been put, as an unanswerable one, how it could
be, according to this hypothesis, that some of the works of our
collection were known previously to Andronicus. But this seems
to mark a great eagerness to raise difficulties. Even if Strabo
had said that none of these works had been published before,
and on the contrary, he implies that some of them had been
published, we should still be inclined to think that this could
not be true in every sense. For how could the notes of students
upon Aristotle's lectures have been prevented from circulating?
We shall undoubtedly naturally conclude that the publication
of Andronicus would be of *Opera Inedita*, including all works of
which a decidedly new recension was found; but naturally of
Aristotle's polished and finished productions no such text would
be found. Strabo, it is true, surmises that the decadence of
the peripatetic school was due to their want of Aristotle's writings; but that, from the nature of things, could only be Strabo's
surmise. We are at liberty, on our side, if we think it best to do
so, to suppose that it was because Aristotelianism was a little
outside the general current of Greek thought. Nevertheless,
if in place of imperfect notes by students, the school had had
the works of Aristotle which we have, we too may surmise, if
we find reason for it, that the school would have been somewhat better able to stem the current of thought, and not have
been so swept into it as it seems to have been.

236.   We are also asked how, upon this hypothesis can the
cross-references have been inserted? But to make a difficulty
of this does seem a little childish. The manuscripts had been
upon the average six years in the school at Aristotle's death,
and remained there for 35 years longer. Was not this time
enough to insert any cross-references which had not been inserted in the first writing?

237.   A more difficult question is how, upon the hypothesis,
we are to explain the insertion of some spurious works; and
how we are to explain the fact that Andronicus is said to have
himself believed that the book of the categories was spurious.
It seems, certainly, to be probable that there had originally
been autographs of all the writings, except perhaps some of the
most polished ones, which do not concern us, and perhaps

some of the memoranda of facts. But those which touched upon subjects often gone through by classes would naturally be revised and copied; especially since papyrus, judging by what was made in Sicily in 1870, is not nearly so durable as modern paper. Thus, a considerable part of the works, and those of evident authenticity, would not be autographs. Consequently, if a book were marked as being by Aristotle, which might accidentally have happened by error, it could not be excluded. Other manuscripts were perhaps neither autographs nor distinctly attributed to Aristotle; and in such case, Andronicus would have been guided by such information as he could obtain. [It is certain that chirography could not have been, at that time, so characteristic of the individual as now.] [20]

238. Another apparent difficulty is that Athenaeus, in one passage, says that Ptolemy Philadelphus purchased the books of Aristotle from Theophrastus; while, in another passage, he says the same king purchased the same books from Neleus. But Athenaeus must not be supposed to be acquainted with all the details of a transaction that happened five centuries before his time, especially since he seems not even to know that Theophrastus died before Ptolemy Philadelphus acceded to the throne. It is also to be noted that it was for the interest of the heirs of Neleus to say that Ptolemy Philadelphus had bought all the books, since it was about the end of his reign that they secreted the books lest Eumenes, King of Pergamus, should grab them. It is further to be noted that the reputation of Aristotle as a philosopher was not, at that time, very high; and such reputation as he had was chiefly that of a rhetorician. If there was a purchase it would probably be of copies. At any rate, copies would be returned to the seller, according to practice in other cases. What the agents of the libraries would want of the writings of the rhetorician Aristotle would be finished works. They would not care for lecture notes nor for memoranda.

239. Having thus reviewed all the supposed difficulties of this hypothesis and having found that they are not serious, we may admit it upon probation, and proceed to trace out its consequences. In the first place, then, supposing it to be true,

[20] (Ed.) Peirce's brackets.

the works of Aristotle which we possess should be expected to belong to the following classes: first, unfinished works intended for publication; second, lecture notes, or memoirs of investigations; third, brief outlines of theories to be studied further; fourth, memoranda of facts concerning subjects upon which Aristotle had not completed any theory nor written any book; fifth, jottings of ideas. In the third of these classes, that of briefs, almost every writer has a tendency to write nearly to the end of his last sheet, often crowding a little at the end; or, if his sheets are large, he may cut the last into halves and use but one half. In order to ascertain whether or not Aristotle had this habit, I have counted the number of lines in the Berlin edition in nineteen of the shortest books. I have added ten to each number to allow for the heading; and comparing the numbers so increased I find that in the majority of cases, namely in 11 out of the 19, they differ from the nearest multiples of 68 by less than $\frac{1}{8}$ of 68, which, of course, ought by chance to happen only once in 4 times. The probability of its occurring 11 times out of 19, is less than 1/500. But in addition to that these eleven cases embrace all but one of the books whose length is short enough to afford decided indications, say less than 6 times 68 lines. Moreover, of the remaining 8 cases all but two are equally near to being multiples of half 68. Finally, the only two real exceptions are both spurious works. The following table gives the numbers. I think we may conclude with reasonable certainty that Aristotle generally wrote about 70 Berlin lines on a sheet. I put it at 70, because I think the method would naturally tend to give too small a number. The amount would be determined by the average size of a sheet of papyrus and the average size of Aristotle's writing, both of which would vary considerably.

	Lines + 10	
De Ventorum situs et appell. . . .	$60 + 8 =$	1×68
De Divinatione per somnum	$134 + 2 =$	2×68
De longi. et brevitate vitae	$198 + 6 =$	3×68
De juventute et senectute	$206 - 2 =$	3×68
De memoria et reminisentia	$266 + 6 =$	4×68
De insomniis	$277 - 5 =$	4×68
De somno et vigiliis	$341 - 1 =$	5×68

De insecalibus lineis	324 + 16 =	5 × 68
De audibilibus	408	= 6 × 68
De Xenoph. Lenone et Gorgia . . .	489 − 13 =	7 × 68
De respiratione	676 + 4 =	10 × 68
De animalium incessu	686 − 6 =	10 × 68
Physiognomica	679 + 1 =	10 × 68
De spiritu	444 − 2 =	6½ × 68
De animalium motione	434 + 8 =	6½ × 68
De coloribus	576 + 2 =	8½ × 68
De plantio I	577 + 1 =	8½ × 68
De plantio II	656 − 8 =	9½ × 68
De Mundo	643 + 3 =	9½ × 68

240. I may add that a cursory examination leads me to think that Aristotle liked to fill a sheet with the whole of a chapter; for a large part of the chapters are of about that length.

241. Now let us consider what would be done with the sheets. When the work was finished, they would be pasted together, rolled up, and sent to the copyist. They would not be pasted together before the work was quite written, since that might prove inconvenient; for insertions might be desirable, or even rearrangement. Now our collection probably does not contain any finished works. For although it does contain a few which were published during Aristotle's life-time, yet the quoted fragments of them indicate that what we now possess come from MSS. in more or less unfinished states. At any rate the great bulk of what we have are either short essays, lecture notes or notes of researches, memoranda of facts, or memoranda of ideas. It is unlikely that the sheets were pasted together. They must have been rolled up; because the method of keeping papers flat is so superior, that had it once come into use, rolls would have been almost given up, as they are today. Before being rolled up, they would have been arranged in order, with the end at the back; and they would be rolled up face inwards, and most likely put into leather cases. The manuscripts were in very bad condition, and it would be the outside of the roll which would be most exposed to injuries, which would often penetrate several sheets, so that bad places would occur at intervals of about seventy Berlin lines. Cocoons would also

155

be deposited on the insides of the rolls, unless they were wound tight about their sticks; so that, in some cases, the beginnings of books would be injured.

242.   For the sake of brevity, I pass over my reasons for thinking that the heirs of Neleus disposed of all the works that appeared to be finished, and that neither Neleus nor anybody else meddled much with the MSS. of those that have come down to us, until they passed into the hands of that Apellicon who corrected them so stupidly. We need to take account of the character of Apellicon. He was a peripatetic and a great book-collector. He stole a number of books from the archives of different cities; and having been detected, was obliged to abscond. He joined himself to another peripatetic scoundrel, Aristion, or Athenion, by whom he was sent to loot the sacred treasury of Delos. This he succeeded in doing, and both conspirators were made enormously rich, although by the extreme recklessness and carelessness of Apellicon his army was destroyed. Apellicon then bought the library of Neleus, while Aristion at once made himself tyrant of Athens, where he distinguished himself by his frightful cruelty, in which Apellicon was his right hand man. It was during the brief tyranny of Aristion at Athens that Apellicon's work upon the MSS. of Aristotle was done. It must have been marked by extreme carelessness and utter want of conscience, though we are told that its stupidity was its most striking characteristic.

243.   Owing to the subsequent editing by Andronicus, the traces of Apellicon's work would naturally be obliterated in great measure. But we cannot doubt that such a character as we see him to have been would not hesitate to write over the bad places, so as to make what he judged to be sense; and in some cases, Andronicus must have been forced to accept what Apellicon had written, although, by close attention, we may be led to very strong suspicion that the text is not what Aristotle wrote. If Apellicon had any pet doctrine of philosophy, nothing but want of ingenuity would stand in the way of his altering the text of Aristotle, so as to get that philosopher's apparent support for his own views.

244.   At any rate, some of the phenomena to which our hypothesis points as probable are as follows:

156

1st, strange stupidities, or commonplaces, where what went before led us to think that a remarkable idea was to be developed.

2nd, stupidities, commonplaces, and puzzling places occurring toward the ends of books at intervals of about 70 Berlin lines or multiples thereof; at least when Aristotle's autographs and not copies were there.

3rd, the appearance of transpositions of passages of about 70 Berlin lines, under the same limiting condition.

4th, omissions of matter which it was in the line of Aristotle's highly systematic thought to insert, and which he would probably have treated in about 70 Berlin lines or a multiple.

245.   Now I have noted the first of these four phenomena, as I suppose every reader has done. But I have not had time to make any search for the others. It is, perhaps, just as well that I have not; because their predictive character is thus made manifest. Only since drawing up this list of predictions, I have had the curiosity to make a hasty examination of one book in order to see whether any of the phenomena would present themselves. I have chosen the second book of the Prior Analytics, in which my attention had already been directed to a circumstance which has influenced me to give the name of abduction to the process of selecting a hypothesis to be tested.

246.   In the beginning of this book, I find nothing suspicious unless it be the word method ($\mu\acute{\epsilon}\theta o\delta o\nu$) in the fifth line, for a syllogistic figure. As the test stands, Aristotle is made to say that he has already done precisely what it is his intention in the present book to do. The first four chapters are devoted to considering how true conclusions may happen to be drawn from false premises. Then follow three chapters, of about twice 70, or exactly 146 lines, concerning demonstration in a circle. These appear to me to be out of place, for the reason that Aristotle has not yet concluded his purely formal investigation which these interrupt; and for the further reason that as soon as these inquiries are brought to a close, with the 15th chapter, Aristotle has a chapter on the *Petitio Principii*, which is almost exactly the same thing as circular demonstration; and I do not think that so systematic a thinker would have separated them. The next three chapters, VIII, IX, X, relate to the apagogical

contraposition of syllogisms, which come in here very well, but a subsequent chapter, the XXIInd, of 63 lines, on almost exactly the same subject should have followed them immediately. Next follow four chapters on the *Reductio ad absurdum*; and after these is placed a chapter, which, being of purely formal interest, ought to have preceded them. This chapter relates to syllogisms from two premisses which contradict one another, like this:

> No A is B
> Some A is B
> ∴ Some A is not A.

I am all but certain that Aristotle, with his mind directed, as it was, to contrapositions of syllogisms, which is the main subject of this book, would not have treated syllogisms which conclude [to] logical absurdities, without also considering syllogisms which take truisms as premisses, such as:

> No A is B   All A is A
> All B is B   Some A is B
> ∴ No B is A   ∴ Some B is A.

I therefore suspect that this matter was originally there. If we suppose that Aristotle would have treated these in 50 lines, which I estimate to be correct from a minute study, the chapter would have been brought up from its present length of 87 lines to 137, or two sheets of papyrus, which I am inclined to suspect originally preceded those on the *Reductio ad absurdum*. After a chapter on reasonings that conclude that such and such circumstance explains the non-occurrence of an expected event, there are a series of chapters on false reasonings and disputations. Then comes the XXIInd chapter which, as just observed, seems to be misplaced; and the rest of the book is devoted to Induction in a broad sense, except one chapter on Objections, which is perhaps not out of place. This chapter on Objections ends with the remark "We have to consider objections adduced from what is contrary, what is like, and what is according to opinion; and further whether a particular objection can be urged in the first or second figure." Evidently the intention was to take up these subjects, at once. But nothing further is said about objection, although some things in the following chapter, which is the last of the book, may be understood as virtually fulfilling the promise. But we cannot believe that Aristotle intended this XXVIth chapter to end as it does. We thus find abundant reason for suspecting omissions, and also transpositions of sheets.

247. Let us now look for corrupt passages. The last chapter but one being apparently incomplete, we must suppose that the last chapter began a sheet. It is 72 lines long, and therefore would just fill the sheet. The unfinished penultimate chapter XXVI was probably written on a sheet, being only 43 lines long. Chapters XXIII, XXIV, XXV, which are intimately connected, fill just 70 Berlin lines, and, no doubt, just filled a sheet, which would be the third from the end. There is some doubt what it was which originally preceded them.

248. In chapters XXIII, XXIV, XXV, I strongly suspect two blunders. As an example of an induction, Aristotle supposes that by a simple induction we prove that all animals without gall are long-lived. Using the letters A, B, Γ, he says that he is to prove that the predicate A belongs [to] B, by an induction from Γ. Then the text now reads: "Let A be long-lived, B without gall, Γ the single long-lived animals, as man, horse, mule. Then to the whole of Γ belongs A, because everything without gall is long-lived." It is perfectly evident to anybody but another Apellicon, that Γ is the single animals without gall. That is, he has put $\mu\alpha\kappa\rho\delta\beta\iota o\nu$ where he ought to read $\check{\alpha}\chi o\lambda o\nu$, unless Aristotle or a copyist made the blunder.

249. The other blunder requires much more careful study to assure oneself of it. It is to be observed that Aristotle's theory of induction, in the narrow sense, is that it is the inference of the major premiss of a syllogism in Barbara or Celarent, from the minor premiss and conclusion, as data, or premisses. I may add that this is, as far as it goes, the correct theory. Only it is not from any syllogism in Barbara or Celarent, but from a statistical deduction in which the distinctions between Barbara, Celarent, Darii, and Ferio, disappear. Having treated of induction proper, Aristotle goes on to $\Pi\alpha\rho\acute{\alpha}\delta\epsilon\iota\gamma\mu\alpha$, or Analogy, which he regards as a modification of induction proper. Now, Aristotle is throughout the Prior Analytics, especially,

so unfailingly thorough in examining every case which is formally analogous to other cases treated by him, that we cannot
doubt for an instant that, having remarked that induction,
Ἐπαγωγή, is the inference of the major premiss of a syllogism
in Barbara or Celarent from its other two propositions as data,
[he] would have asked himself whether the minor premiss of
such a syllogism is not sometimes inferred from its other two
propositions as data. Certainly, he would not be Aristotle, to
have overlooked that question; and it would no sooner be asked
than he would perceive that such inferences are very common.
Accordingly, when he opens the next chapter with the word
Ἀπαγωγή a word evidently chosen to form a pendant to
Ἐπαγωγή, we feel sure that this is what he is coming to. In
the excessively abridged and obscure style of the Analytics, he
begins as follows: "Abduction, ἀπαγωγή, is when it is well-
known that the major term is true of the middle, and that the
middle is true of the last is not known, but yet is antecedently
more credible than is the conclusion." He should have added,
"which conclusion we find to be a fact," but he overlooks that,
in his wish to add the clause, "and if moreover the middles between the middle and the minor term be few; for thus it will
be decidedly nearer to a thorough comprehension of the matter,
ἐπιστήμη."

250. To translate this into our ordinary conceptions, as
nearly as possible, it means that it will be better if the minor
premiss which is not known to be true but is so easy to believe,
is such that it seems as if little were needed to render it evident;
and the object of the proceeding is to approach the thorough
comprehension of things. In order to make sure of his meaning,
we need examples; and it is to be observed that Aristotle's
examples are almost always arguments well-known at his time
to have been actually employed. He immediately proceeds to
give the needed examples. The first is this: "Let A be capable of being taught, διδακτόν; B, science or comprehension,
ἐπιστήμη; Γ, righteousness, δικαιοσύνη. Now that comprehension is capable of being taught is plain; but that virtue is comprehension is not known. If, however, this is as antecedently
likely or more so, than that virtue should be capable of being
taught [which, it seems needless to say, everybody knows to

160

be the fact],[21] then there is ground for the abduction; since we are brought by the hypothesis, 'τὸ προειληφέναι,' nearer to a comprehension of virtue being capable of being taught, than we were before." This seems very clear. He is giving as his illustration the incessant argument of Socrates that virtue must be comprehension, since how otherwise could one explain the patent fact that it can be taught. I have translated ἐπιστήμη comprehension, because this is what Aristotle meant by it; and the ordinary translation *science* conveys an utterly wrong idea to the modern mind. It must be admitted, however, that before Aristotle wrote this men had paradoxically doubted righteousness being taught. Consequently, this example is neutral, favoring neither the old interpretation nor mine more than the other. He now gives another example to illustrate the case in which the hypothesis brings us nearer to comprehension because, to use his phrase, "the middles are few"; that is, it seems near to first principles. It is here that the text seems to me corrupt. It reads as follows:

"Let Δ be capable of being squared; E, rectilinear; Z, the circle. If there is only one middle to EZ, that the circle is equal to a rectilinear figure, then the circles being equal by lunes to a rectilinear figure, is near to being known."

251.   Let us endeavor to make sense out of that. The reference plainly is to the discovery of Hippocrates of Chios that certain lunes, or figures bounded by two arcs of circles, were equal to rectilinear figures and capable of being squared; and Aristotle plainly meant that this fact justified the hope, which we know was entertained on this ground, that the circle could be squared. There was "only one middle," or remove from knowledge, concerning the circle's being equal to a constructible rectilinear figure, since it is evidently equal to *some* square. Mathematics was not Aristotle's strong point, and possibly he did not clearly understand that it was only two or three special lunes that Hippocrates had squared. It is likely, however, that he understood the argument to be the inference of the minor premiss of the following syllogism from its other two propositions:

[21] (Ed.) Peirce's brackets.

Whatever is equal to a constructible rectilinear figure
is equal to a sum of lunes;
The circle is equal to a constructible rectilinear figure;
∴ The circle is equal to a sum of lunes.

To make this out, we have to change just one word of the text.
In place of saying that the major term is τετραγωνίζεσθαι we
have to put ἴσον μηνίσκοις. This change of a single word of the
text, not only renders the whole chapter intelligible; but gives
it the very meaning which it ought to have in the development
of Aristotle's doctrine. Such a singular corruption of the text
as I suppose could hardly have taken place without an Apellicon; but with him, it was easy enough.[22] If we do not suppose
this corruption to have taken place, we are reduced to accepting the text as it stands; and if we accept the text as it stands
we must accept the usual interpretation of it. This interpretation is that abduction is nothing but an ordinary syllogism of
the first figure, when we are not sure of the minor premiss,
but still are more inclined to admit it than we should be to
admit the conclusion if the latter were not a necessary consequence of the former. The abstract description at the beginning of the chapter will bear this construction perfectly
well; only it makes the chapter an impertinent obtruder at this
point, and not in the style of Aristotle's thought. But when we
come to the examples, the ordinary interpretation reduces the
latter, at least, to nonsense. The first becomes,

Comprehension can be taught,
Virtue is comprehension;
∴ Virtue can be taught.

In the first place, this is a *petitio principii*, or very near to one
since there is no way of proving that virtue is comprehension,
except by its being taught. In the next place, few in Aristotle's
time had used this absurd argument; it had scarcely been seriously doubted, what all experience shows, that virtue can be
taught. A very few ethical writers of modern times have denied
it; but it had hardly been denied then, except as a temporary
shift in debate. A philosopher who, like Socrates, maintained

[22] (Ed.) Peirce advanced the same theory at 2.776, but at 8.209 (c.1905)
he confesses that it is doubtful.

that it was better to do wrong, knowing it was wrong, than not knowing this, could not doubt that righteousness could be taught.

252.   The other example is still worse. It becomes,

> Whatever is equal to a rectilinear figure can be squared,
> Every circle is equal to a rectilinear figure;
> ∴ Every circle can be squared.

We here naturally understand by "equal to a rectilinear figure," equal to a rectilinear figure, constructible or inconstructible. But in that case, the minor premiss, instead of being not known, is the most evident thing in the world; while the major premiss which ought to be manifest, is far from being so; for if a figure cannot be constructed it cannot be squared. Supposing however that by a rectilinear figure is meant one that can be constructed, which must have been the meaning, since Aristotle says that it is almost known through lunes, who ever used such a ridiculous argument? And how can Aristotle say, as he does, that lunes in any way help the matter, or are at all relevant? Whatever bearing lunes were supposed to have upon the quadrature of the circle disappears entirely from this representation. Nothing can be more utterly unlike Aristotle's usual examples, which bring up in vivid aptness actual reasonings well known to his scholars.

253.   I think, then, that my interpretation of the passage, considering its being what the current of thought demands, considering how the word Ἀπαγωγή balances Ἐπαγωγή and considering that it renders both the examples their real historic forms, comes within a tolerably close approach to certainty. If we accept it, it affords a remarkable confirmation of the Scepsis story; because of the bold insertion it supposes to have been made in the text.

254.   I have looked forward seventy lines from each of the two corruptions I have mentioned; but the measure falls in each case upon a passage so plain, that had it been totally obliterated, not even an Apellicon could fail to restore it correctly. I have said enough to show how I think this hypothesis should be treated.

255.   All the best critics of Germany, on the other hand,

163

utterly reject the Scepsis story. Their reasons I have already indicated. They are so weak that I think I am justified in surmising that the real motive of their rejection is a reluctance to accepting any ancient testimony without dressing it up and putting a new face upon it. At any rate, their general principle is that they think the story told by Strabo is less likely than that Strabo should tell a false story; and that principle seems to me to amount to believing whatever they are inclined to believe.[23]

[23] (Ed.) Peirce then proceeds to give two more illustrative examples. The first is a problem of the chronology of Plato's dialogues, and the second concerns the life of Pythagoras. This part of the manuscript is more than half as long as the part reprinted here.

CHAPTER 4

NOTES ON SCIENCE

§1. THE STUDY OF GREAT MEN [1]

256. Having been asked to write something about the productiveness of the nineteenth century in great men, I ought to begin by frankly confessing just what the facts are that, being known, will lead the reader to attach a certain value, and no more, to my opinions on this subject. In the year 1883, having charge of the instruction in logic in the Johns Hopkins University, I cast about for a subject that might afford valuable training in such inductive investigation [as] the members of my class might need in future life and which they would not be likely to acquire in their other studies. I wished it to be a subject susceptible of mathematical treatment, since an inductive investigation so treated may throw abundant light on the proper logical procedure where mathematics is not available, while the converse can hardly be true. Yet there were several reasons for selecting a subject concerning which no exact observations could be made. Much more logical caution is requisite in such a field; and it was desirable to explode the ordinary notions that mathematical treatment is of no advantage when observations are devoid of precision and that no scientific use can be made of very inexact observations. Besides, very little training is required in the purely observational part

[1] (Ed.) Paragraphs 256–261 are from one draft of a manuscript on the productiveness of the nineteenth century in great men; paragraphs 262–266 are from an alternative draft. Both drafts are in Widener IC1b, and are dated c.1900 on the basis of their resemblance to [Bibliography] G–1901–5a and internal references to dates.

For additional information on Peirce's study of great men see [Fisch-Cope] 290–291 and Joseph Jastrow, "Charles S. Peirce as a Teacher," *The Journal of Philosophy, Psychology, and Scientific Method* 13 (21 Dec 1916) 724–725.

of the business of making observations that can be rendered extremely precise; while great training is requisite for the making of the very observations themselves when the observations are of the kind which can never be made precise. In order to make my meaning clear, I will take an example of each kind. The matching of two colors is an observation that can be rendered precise. In order to learn to perform this observation what is chiefly requisite is to appreciate the fact that the two surfaces to be compared have to be put in precisely the same light, and that, unless various precautions are taken, they will not usually receive light of the same intensity and color though they be held quite close together. The mere observation itself of whether they match or not will very soon be made so accurately that all the effort has to be expended, not upon that pure observational part of the work, but on the experimentation. On the other hand, an example of an observation that can never be rendered precise is that of saying which of two different colors, say a red and a blue, is the more luminous. Here, no extraordinary experimental precautions are called for. The thing is to look at the colors and disregarding entirely their extreme difference of hue, as well as the circumstance that red is a very high color while blue is comparatively greyish, to just note the relative impressions of luminousness that they make upon us. A great deal of training is required before a person can do this well enough to give any uniformity to his judgments. It is not an education of the eye or of part of the brain particularly connected with the eye, so much as it is of the mind. A certain person upon hearing a note struck upon the piano was utterly unable to pick out any harmonic by ear. He then went through a course of training with a color-box, involving observations of the general kind I have mentioned, until he acquired a good deal of skill. Upon now returning casually to the observation upon the piano-tone he found to his surprise that he could pick out three or four harmonics without difficulty. Now this pure observational power is of great value in life. It is true that the only thing that is disclosed by such pure observation is one's own feelings. But then different persons' feelings are so closely similar, that that is of the utmost use in a world of men and women. It is this

166

that the word *tact* ought to denote independent of adroitness in
playing upon people. A Sherlock Holmes's habit of making deductions from minor circumstances is all very well, in itself;
but if attention to these circumstances is to draw it away from
the Lavaterian, artist-like, direct, and pure observation of the
suspected person, it will do more harm than good. I should be
afraid to tell what I have known this power to accomplish, because it is unpleasant to have one's veracity doubted. Lavater's
'Essays on Physiognomy' is a book very much discredited; and
I cannot say that I am a strong believer in such notions, as
that a large and prominent nose is associated with push and
energy. But matter of that sort makes but a small part of the
work, the diligent study of which, in a good edition, will, I can
testify, stimulate a young person to train the faculty of which
I am speaking. At any rate, ever since I read it, I have been
convinced that psychology would assume its legitimate dignity
among the sciences from the day on which it should be recognized as based mainly upon the pure observation of which I
speak, and not before. The sciences of objective nature do
not train this power, because they can make no use of the sort
of data it affords. The exact sciences, physics and chemistry,
do not teach any observation of any kind, to speak of; but only
manipulation and experimentation. The purely observational
business is confined to such trifles as bisecting stars, putting
crosswires upon spectral lines, reading verniers and the like.
Natural history undoubtedly trains a certain kind of observational power, the taking note of circumstances that would
escape an untrained attention. But that is not the power I had
in view.[2] These are among the reasons that led to my pitching
upon the study of great men as affording useful training for
my class. I have dwelt upon these reasons at some length,
simply because they throw some light upon the matter with
which I seek to acquaint the reader, the degree of my qualifications to give an opinion upon a subject upon which any

[2] The fact that some of the finest observations of the naturalist were made
by a blind man sufficiently shows that that science does not call for any extraordinary amount of the power I have in view.

(Ed.) Peirce is probably referring here to François Huber, 1750–1831, a
Swiss naturalist who became blind at age fifteen. He was noted for his investigations of bees.

opinion must be largely subjective and rough, even though it should attain a certain degree of validity. . . .

257.   The first thing we did was to make what I called an impressionist list of great men, — *impressionist*, because the admission to it of any name was to depend upon our pure observation of the impression of greatness which we received from the contemplation of his life and labors, while carefully abstaining from any analysis of greatness or of the reason for the impression we felt, since one of the very purposes of the list was to serve as a test of any theory of the nature of greatness and the cause of the impression it makes upon us. A preliminary list of nearly a thousand names was first formed; and these were considered and reconsidered, three or four times with increasing care, until we finally settled upon 288 great men. I was desirous of having this include substantially all the great men of history. Yet I was less concerned that it should omit none whom it ought to contain than that those that it did contain should form a fair sample of what great men were like. Since we were all students, no doubt we had a bias in favor of men of intellect; but against this we were on our guard. There was naturally some moral leaning, and the social atmosphere of Baltimore must have affected our judgments. Moreover, it is humanly impossible in such a selection to do justice to contemporaries, compatriots, and acquaintances, whose greatness we are too close by to discern. I could now improve the list in details, besides doing something toward bringing it down to date. But it was formed with so much care that I would not venture to touch it short of a good six months solid preparatory study.

258.   The list having been formed was found to be too large for so small a class to study to advantage, and we therefore restricted ourselves to the consideration of every sixth name. I do not intend to weary the reader with any account of the elaborate inductive inquiries, about seventy in number, which we undertook in regard to those men, and which I have followed out with some diligence all through the seventeen years which have since elapsed. But there is one point which it is important for my present purpose that I should explain. Everybody knows, I suppose, that the ancient astronomers divided the

168

stars visible to the naked eye into six orders of brightness, called "magnitudes," the first magnitude containing the brightest stars, and the sixth those that are barely visible in an ordinary atmosphere on a clear and moonless night. Ptolemy already subdivided each magnitude into thirds, and in our century they were first divided into tenths, and after the introduction of photometrics into hundredths. Now when photometry came into use, it was found that there was a nearly constant ratio of light between the light of average stars of successive magnitudes. Thus, in my book entitled 'Photometric Researches' p. 47,[3] I show that the differences between the light of the faintest stars normally referred by Ptolemy to the first four magnitudes, expressed upon a scale of magnitudes which makes the ratio of light strictly equable, are 0.94, 1.07, 0.99, which are practically equal. This remarkable fact is connected with Fechner's psychophysical law (at which the utter ignorance of German philosophical professors of the mathematical theory of metrics, their fondness for expressing opinions about matters of which they are ignorant, and the awe with which they are copied by Americans, has made it the fashion to sneer) according to which equal ratios of excitation produce equal differences of sensation. The old astronomers assigned successive numbers to stars which gave equal differences of sensation, and these, when the stars are not so faint that another influence, the nature of which is made clear in my book, interferes, correspond to a geometrical progression of intensities of light measured physically, so as to make the intensity of light proportional to the square of the amplitude of vibration. The scale of star-magnitudes, having been found to lend itself perfectly to mathematical treatment, was imitated by us in expressing our impressions of the greatness of the different men. That is to say, we marked the greatest man on our list 1 and the least 6. Some member of the class to whom the duty had been assigned would read an account drawn up by him of one of the men, and each member would then secretly jot down in units and tenths, his evaluation of the impression produced upon him. The ballots giving these numbers would then be handed up to me and the mean would be

[3] (Ed.) [Bibliography] G–1878–6.

adopted as the "magnitude" of that man. As this method was no novelty to me, I having often applied it to all sorts of feelings, so that I knew about how well the numbers would agree, I never took the trouble to preserve the individual estimates; so that I can now only put before the reader the results of the ballotings in three cases which occurred at an informal meeting when the whole class was not present, and when I calculated the means upon the margin of a paper which has been preserved for another purpose. These three ballotings thus casually preserved are as follows:

	Bolivar	Julian	Swedenborg
	4.2	3.6	4.0
	4.2	3.8	4.5
	4.0	3.8	4.3
	3.8	4.8[4]	3.8
	3.9		
Means	4.0	4.0	4.1

259. I do not think that there was any man for whom the extreme estimates exceeded two magnitudes. Such a discrepancy could only occur in the case of some vaguely known and semi-mythical hero, such as King David. It is obvious, therefore, that if what we mean by a judgment being "objectively valid" is that all the world will agree in it, and after all Kant's discussion that is about what it comes to, then there was a satisfactory degree of "objectivity" in the mean magnitudes we assigned, although they referred, not to the man as he really was, but to the man as he was presented in the account read to the class, and although the marking could not escape a large "subjective" percentage due to our common, but not thoroughly catholic, culture and environment.

260. At the meeting I have just spoken of, we tried estimating, in the same way, the "magnitude" of the average man. This was a matter of difficulty and uncertainty, for two reasons. The value was so far removed from the part of the scale to which we were habituated that slight differences in the value of the unit of "magnitude," as employed by different members of the class would necessarily be exaggerated. This, however,

⁴ This vote was probably influenced by religious bias.

was probably of little account compared with the uncertainty as to what kind of a person the truly "average man," with whom we were none of us accustomed to associate, really was. It is not surprising, therefore, that the ballots, which here follow were pretty wild.

Average Man

10.5
13
13
11
—

Mean   11.9

261.   At the same meeting we balloted, with very little preparatory discussion, for the "magnitude" of the leader of the Baltimore bar, with the following results:

Leader of the bar

8
8.8
9
8.5
—

Mean   8.4

262.   Just as a young gentleman nine years of age looks upon a lad of eight as a person of little knowledge of the world or experience of life, and as altogether inferior in intellectual grasp, so the nineteenth century has had the habit of looking down upon the eighteenth; and no doubt the judgment is a sound one in both cases. But when we ask whether the nine-teenth century had shown any vastly superior productiveness of great personalities, we have a difficult question before us. A pretty careful sampling enables one to say that if we were to enumerate the men whose achievements in art, in practical life, or in science, can never be forgotten by history, we should find upwards of a thousand in the nineteenth century against not more than five hundred in the eighteenth. But there is a vast difference between a man who accomplishes something great, — say, the introduction of the first anaesthetic, ether, —

171

and the man who, upon the whole, impresses us as a great man; and if we confine ourselves to great men, we shall find only about seventy in the nineteenth century against some sixty in the eighteenth, — a very marked falling off, when the increase in the number who can read and write, and in the opportunities for distinction, generally, is considered.

263. It is an observation as true as it is trite that the nineteenth century has been an era of machinery, — not of machinery of steel merely, but of machinery in politics and in business, such as trusts and trade-unions, machinery in all the methods of research, physical, philological, historical, philosophical, mathematical, even of machinery in art and in poetry. Consider Mathematics, as a field where, if anywhere, it might be supposed that machinery would be of little avail. In the early eighteenth century the greatest geometers in Europe were still "stumping" one another with problems, and the discovery of a theorem might raise a man to greatness, — witness Taylor's theorem, published in 1717. Subsequently, it must be a *method*, no longer a mere *theorem*, to impress the world so powerfully. Nowadays, methods of the greatest profundity and power are turned out at such an astonishing rate that nobody but professional mathematicians ever hear of them singly, at all. Hermann Schubert's Calculus of Geometry, which enables us, for example, by a brief computation, to determine that the number of cubic curves each of which shall touch any twelve given spheroids, is just 5 billion 819,539 million, 783,680, hardly makes a ripple in the ocean of modern mathematics. In Addison's time, the man who could write graceful English was a prodigy. Now, everybody writes decently well: the leader-writer of the yellowest journal has a better command of his pen than the accomplished Shaftesbury or the learned Toland. An age which in every department has offered a thousand new appliances to enable a puny man to do a giant's work has been an age of machinery, indeed.

264. Whether machinery, organization, and a great development of methods and of the *methodus methodorum*,[5] with their fruits of incessant new discoveries, inventions, improvements of all kinds, ought *a priori* to be unfavorable to

[5] (Ed.) Cf. Peirce's "Introductory Lecture on the Study of Logic," 7.59–76.

the production of great personalities is a problem for a more
sagacious man than I can pretend to be, to compute with any
confidence. One might incline to think not; for, on the one
hand, just as we know that plants transferred to new soil are
the more apt to sport, so it might be expected that under novel
social conditions the proportion of births of extraordinary
minds would be increased, while on the other hand, once born,
one would suppose they would find in novel situations just the
opportunities that were needed to bring their superiority into
exercise. History, too, seems to confirm this, in always showing us a wealth of great men at every great social transformation. The list of heroes of our own country shows this. Rigidly
exclude every man not unquestionably great, and how few will
be left outside the groups that cluster about our two cataclysmic upheavals, the revolution and the rebellion!

265.   Yet somehow, the nineteenth century has certainly
lacked its due quota of great personalities. When about a fifth
of the century was still in the future, I drew up, with the cooperation of a class at the Johns Hopkins University, and with
much outside assistance, what I called an Impressionist List
of about 300 Great Men. It was one of those matchless classes,
— the very salt of the earth, — which it was my privilege to
enjoy in Baltimore. Almost every member of it has since
signally distinguished himself, and those who have less obtru-
sively done so are among those whose observations I now, after
twenty years, most frequently recall as forcible and just. I
called it an impressionist list, not that it was at all hastily
drawn up, but because, in the process of sifting out the names
from a much larger list, we were to set aside all preconceived
ideas of what greatness consists in, and were simply to estimate
the impression made upon us by a fair review of each man's
life and labors. Being all of us students, no doubt, we had some
bias in favor of the philosophers; but against this we endeavored, as much as possible, to be upon our guard. The social
atmosphere of Baltimore, too, probably affected us somewhat;
and I think we had a human prejudice against monsters of
iniquity and against men of greed. Everybody would, I know,
find fault with our list. Not a few of its omissions were violently
counter to my own personal impressions. Still, it would be very

difficult, if not impossible, to draw up a much better list. I may mention that this list formed the basis for much subsequent study; and one of my main purposes was to train the men to the nice observation of their own sensations, to show them that feelings are capable of direct evaluation with sufficient precision to serve a scientific purpose, and to admit of mathematical treatment, and to demonstrate that they do not, for the most part, differ extravagantly among different persons in the same environment. For instance, after an account of a man had been read to the class, we would each estimate the impression of greatness produced upon him, somewhat as astronomers estimate the magnitude of a star, calling Pythagoras, as he is represented in the life of Iamblichus, a first magnitude man, and Cola Rienzi a tenth magnitude man. Each of us would, after hearing the account, secretly mark upon paper his estimate of the man's magnitude. The papers would then be collected and the values copied in a column upon the blackboard. The extreme variation would not ordinarily exceed two magnitudes, so that we all came to feel pretty confident that the averages of our estimates would for the most part be pretty close to those that would be produced in the average man of the same general breeding and culture, by the same biographies. I have, since the list was first made, never allowed it entirely to drop out of mind, but have spent a good deal of time, all told, in the further study of the 288 great men it includes, and recently, with all the aid I could get, in adding such names as seemed to [be] required by the history of [the] last twenty years.

266. This long explanation was necessary in order to show what degree of objectivity might fairly be attributed to my impressions of the productiveness of the century in historic personalities. This objectivity is, like Mercutio's wound, not as wide as a church door, yet 'twill serve. It will not be valid for every normal mind as my matching of a color might be valid for every normal eye; but it tolerably represents how an average student of science sixty years old, not unobservant of human life, and not very narrow in his interests, would be likely to be impressed.[6]

[6] (Ed.) Peirce then proceeds to discuss the great men of the nineteenth century. He discusses the century's great men in science in [Bibliography] G–1901–5a.

§2. THE HISTORY OF SCIENCE [7]

267. I have now expounded to you as much of the history of science as I found myself able to do in 12 hours. Of course, a great deal remains to be considered; but even the few facts we have collected will do something to answer the questions with which I set out.[8]

268. We have found as I suggested at the outset that there are three ways by which Human Thought grows, by the forma-

[7] (Ed.) Paragraphs 267–275 are the concluding remarks to a series of lectures on the history of science, Widener IC1b, with quotations added at 267n8. The first paragraph of 267n8 is from Lecture V of this series, Widener IC1b. These are most probably the lectures delivered on "The History of Science" to the Lowell Institute, 1892–1893. On the basis of this probability and internal references, Lecture V is dated c.1892, and the concluding remarks 1893.

Paragraphs 276–278 are Section 13, "Varieties of Medisense," of an incomplete manuscript, undated, Widener IB2–10. This manuscript has some resemblance to 7.539–552, [Bibliography] G–undated–9, and may have been written about the same time.

Paragraph 279 is from Section 1, "Classification of the Sciences," of *Minute Logic*, Chapter 2, "Prelogical Notions," Widener IB2–2. The marginal sidehead is "Three Stages of Physical Research." One of the manuscript pages is stamped "Mar 12 1902." This selection lies between 7.374n10 and 7.362; cf. 7.362n1.

[8] (Ed.) In Lecture V of the series (see 267n7), Peirce says: "For my part, I am quite sure that, however it may be with the rank and file of the great army of general readers, those who come here will be interested in the history of science not as a mere Wonder Book, but as an instance, a specimen, of how the laws of growth apply to the human mind. As this Century is drawing to a close, it is interesting to pause and look about us and to ask ourselves in what great questions science is now most interested. The answer must be that *the* question that everybody is now asking, in metaphysics, in the theory of reasoning, in psychology, in general history, in philology, in sociology, in astronomy, perhaps even in molecular physics, is the question *How things grow*; and by far the most interesting aspect of the history of science, is that it shows how an important department of human thought has been developed from generation to generation, with a view of comparing this growth with the historical development of art, of religion, of politics, and of institutions generally, and not only with historical development but also with the growth of the individual mind, and not only of mind, but of organisms both in their geological succession and in their individual development, and with the formation of worlds, and even with the gradual coming into being and crystallization of the fundamental laws of matter and of mind, — from all of which facts taken together we are to expect in the future a grand cosmogony or philosophy of creation."

In the "Introduction" to a planned history of science, Widener IC1b (undated), Peirce says: "For that which the author had at heart throughout his studies of the history of science was to gain an understanding of the whole logic of every pathway to the truth."

tion of habits, by the violent breaking up of habits, and by the action of innumerable fortuitous variations of ideas combined with differences in the fecundity of different variations.

269.   As for the last mode of Development which I have called Darwinian, however important it may be in reference to some of the growths of mind, — and I will say that in my opinion we should find it a considerable factor in individual thinking, — yet in the history of science it has made as far as we have been able to see, no figure at all, except in retrograde movements. In all these cases it betrays itself infallibly by its two symptoms of proceeding by insensible steps and of proceeding in a direction different from that of any strivings. Whether or not it may not be more or less influential in other cases, in which its action is masked, the means of investigation which I have so far been able to bring to bear fail to disclose.

270.   The manner in which the great and startling advances in scientific thought have been made appears very clearly. It is by the violent breaking up of certain habits, combined with the action of other habits not broken up. Thus, the highest level of Egyptian thought seems to have been reached at a very early age. So it appears to us, and so it always appeared to the Egyptians, for they always reverence the ideas of antiquity, as superior to those of their own time. Now the great factor in the development of the Egyptian mind was undoubtedly the physical geography of the country which probably produced its effects in a reasonably small number of generations after it was first felt. So with the Greeks. Their thought remained in its primeval condition until the extension of commerce brought them within the sphere of influence of other peoples, the Phoenicians, the Egyptians, and the Babylonians, and then within a few generations they made great strides in thought, to be succeeded by a slower movement of another kind. At first, we have a rather servile copying of the ideas of those countries, a syncretism such as we see in Pythagoras. But soon the foreign ideas begin to react with the ideas and faculties peculiar to the Greeks, and a great original life commences. So it was again, when in the 13th century, the ideas of the Dark Ages were rudely shaken up by contact with the more civilized Saracens; although as far as science was concerned that move-

ment was quickly stifled by the rapid development of theological ideas.

271.   The renaissance in Italy was of slower growth, because foreign ideas had been slowly filtering in since the thirteenth century uninterrupted. However, after the fall of Constantinople in 1454, there was a much more rapid movement. That movement was first strongest in the direction of art, which I take to be a mark of rapidly growing minds, of minds receiving nutrition too rapidly to be packed down into the forms of science. But the scientific development came later. Galileo was born the very day of Michelangelo's death.

272.   In this early development of science there were two great factors. In the first place, the direct strivings of the astronomers, the European successors of the Arabians, who brought to astronomy more masculine intellects than the Arabians had, had brought out at length a world-shaking idea, the Copernican conception. In the existing state of the church, this was more easily accomplished in Northern Europe, and there it was brought to its perfection by Kepler, and I have traced out the birth of this conception with some minuteness because it is remarkable as being a birth from within, not an influence from without. Although the authors of this, Copernicus, Tycho, and Kepler were all Teutons, the value of their work was better understood and more accurately appreciated in Italy than north of the Alps.

273.   The other great factor, which chiefly influenced the development of dynamics, was the study of the works of Archimedes; and a strongly Hellenic color is apparent everywhere in that branch of science down to the time of Newton. It is shown in the great fondness for demonstrations from axioms, in the desire to put all special experimentation out of sight, and to rely on the Light of Nature. It is also shown in the geometrical methods which are preferentially employed.

274.   As to the third mode of intellectual development, we should see more of it if we were to trace out the history of science into its later era. Though it is not so startlingly manifest, it is certainly the method of the ordinary successful prosecution of scientific inquiry. We see its action clearly in the history of astronomy at all periods, and especially in Kep-

ler's gigantic work. It is growth by exercise, or by direct efforts in the direction of the growth. If we have seen little of it, it is because I felt it necessary to the understanding of the subject to begin at the beginning and I could not in twelve hours carry you on to the point in which science, except in astronomy and to some extent in the last developments of dynamics, was really settled down to its work. I will mention, however, that in the January number of the *Monist*,[9] I have endeavored to give an analysis of this kind of evolution, and especially have connected it with the Christian theory of the way in which the world is to be made better and wiser.

275. I have to thank the company very gratefully for the patience and kind indulgence with which my lectures have been listened to. I have done what lay in my power to present as much of the History of Science as I have been able to treat in a lucid manner, and to show that it is governed by Law like other departments of nature. But these laws are not of the nature of mechanical forces, such that the individual and the spirit of man is swallowed up in cosmical movements, but on the contrary it is a law by virtue of which lofty results require for their attainment lofty thinkers of original power and individual value. You cannot silence or stifle or starve a single one of them without a loss of civilization from which it never can wholly recover. It is not more certain that the inches of a man's stature will be affected all his life by an attack of fever as a baby, than that we are now less happy because of the many great geniuses whom untoward circumstances have put down. The country that can first find the means not to provide the million with miscellaneous reading matter, and elementary education, but to utilize its superior intellects for the general good, will experience a wonderful acceleration of civilization from which the benefit of the million, in much more valuable ways, will come about of itself.

———————————

276. Although by far the greater part of almost every treatise on psychology is devoted to the department of Cognition, yet it is curious that less is known about thought than

[9] (Ed.) [Bibliography] G–1891–1e (1893).

about either of the other two modes of consciousness. What I have to say about it is even more inadequate than what I have said of Primisense and Altersense.[10] In order to make out what the main processes of Thought, or varieties of Medisense, are, I naturally turn to Logic, which has been my chief study for the last forty years. In the process of inference, or the self-controlled formation of new belief on the basis of Knowledge already possessed, I remark three chief steps. They are, first, the putting together of facts which it had not occurred to us to consider in their bearings upon one another, second, experimentation, observation, and experimental analysis, which is substantially the same process whether it be performed with physical apparatus such as the chemist uses or with an apparatus of diagrams of our own creation, such as the mathematician employs, and third, the generalization of experimental results, that is, the recognition of the general conditions governing the experiment, and the formation of a habit of thought under the influence of it. If we turn to the history of the physical sciences, as the most perfect example of the successful application of thought to the external world, we find that they have all gone through five stages. First, an interesting phenomenon has attracted attention. Here, inquiry has often come to a stop for a long time. It does not proceed until, Secondly, somebody invents an instrument or a method by means of which the elements of the phenomenon can be subjected to experiment. Third, a process of experimental analysis has been carried out, resulting in the ascertainment of a law, or exact relation between the different elements of the phenomenon. Thus, the lodestone must have been known for a long time, before somebody invented the idea of experimenting upon it with iron rings. This rude instrument led to the discovery that a second ring would be supported by the first, that a third could be hung to that, and so on. Nothing more was discovered until Petrus Peregrinus invented a new method of experimentation.[11] Namely, he shaped the lodestone into a terella or ball, and then applied to it short pieces of iron needles. With this apparatus he at once discovered the poles of the

[10] (Ed.) Cf. 7.539–552.
[11] (Ed.) Cf. [Bibliography] G–c.1893–4.

magnet and their properties. Then, discovery stuck fast again; because nothing more could be made out with those instruments; until Gilbert invented a new instrument consisting of an iron needle balanced on a point, and free to turn round.[12] Such has been the history of every science. After a while a Fourth class of studies has commenced, consisting in the exact measurement of the constants concerned. In optics there was, for example, the velocity of light. Finally, Fifthly, has come the construction of mechanical theories by which the causes of the phenomena were probably assigned.

277. Comparing the teachings of the history of science, on the one hand, with those of logic, on the other, we notice a certain agreement between the two. The interesting phenomenon which gives the first impulse to scientific thought corresponds with that interesting colligation of facts, which is the first step of the inferential procedure. Experimental analysis plays a great part in both. Finally, the generalization of the experimental result which completes the inference is represented in physical inquiry by speculation into the mechanical causes of the phenomenon. For as the mechanical explanation of the physicist consists in a reference of the experimental result to the higher principle of dynamics, so the generalization of the reasoner is the reference of the experimental result to the higher principle of mathematical necessity or probability.

278. Perhaps, just as the study of a physical phenomenon must depend upon applying such instruments as we can find, so in our attempt to enumerate the processes of thought, we cannot do better than to begin by laying hold of the suggestions that are offered by these analogies between the process of inference and the history of physical science.

---

279. Some thirty years ago I made a remark upon the course of physical studies which has been repeated by very competent men, to the effect that there were three stages; first, the observation and miscellaneous research into the phenomena; secondly, the analysis of the phenomena and formulation of their laws, including hypothetical explanations of them; thirdly,

[12] (Ed.)   Cf. [Bibliography] N–1894–4.

the determination of the constants. Nothing intellectual, — no casts of mind, — more diverse than those needed for these three steps can well be imagined within the sphere of physics. These three steps occur in every branch. True, ordinary observation supplies many of the phenomena in optics and acoustics; but not all, by any means. Not circular polarization; not the zones of silence about a fog-horn. In electricity, in galvanism, in X-rays, and other radiations, in fluorescence, the first breaking of ground required a peculiar genius, not to be undervalued, yet not for an instant to be likened to that which analyzes the phenomena, — the work of a Galileo, a Kepler, a Faraday, a Maxwell. Then the painful and technical business of accurately determining the constants is not one of genius or insight but of perfect thoroughness and flawless technique. It is the work of the Regnaults, the Michelsons, the Rowlands, — the accomplished experts.

§3. MEASUREMENT [13]

280. *Definition.* A *character* is a possible fact regarded as concerning a particular thing or things.

Illustration. The moon may come between the sun and the earth so as to cast a shadow upon the latter. That is a possible fact. Now, if we think of this fact as something that concerns, or modifies what we can say of, the sun, we call it an eclipse of the sun; and so considered, it is what we mean by a *character* of the sun at such an instant.

281. *Explanation.* I say a *possible* fact, because if a character is not actually true of a given thing, that is not sufficient to prevent its being a character. Thus, when the sun is not eclipsed, it does not possess that character, but we do not say that there is no such character. If it could be shown that the supposition of the moon coming between the sun and the earth so as to cast a shadow on the latter, could only be carried out in ways which, being examined, would prove all of them to involve contradictions, then we should say this is no real character, but only a phrase, which cannot be realized in any imagin-

---

[13] (Ed.) From "Of the Nature of Measurement," an undated, incomplete manuscript in Widener IA-4. Cf. 4.142–152 which are on the same topic.

able manner. In short, the character in itself does not pretend to belong to the world of experience; to be a character it only needs to have a place in the realm of ideas. When the character is attributed to any particular thing, that thing is something having its place in experience. It is not needful, for the purposes of mathematics, to inquire particularly what experience is. It may be said, however, that it is something which is forced upon us; so that one element of it is its insistence, whether we like it or not. And it is also something which forces itself not merely momentarily upon me; but upon me and you alike, at various times, so that it has a certain consistency and extension in its forcefulness. Finally, it is something of which our knowledge can never be complete; so that there is always a difference between the experienced thing and our idea of it. But since the character, to be a character, need not really belong to the particular thing, but it is sufficient if we can really ask whether or not it belongs to that thing, it will be seen that we do not need to go very far into a study of its nature.

282. *Analysis.* Characters may be more or less precisely defined. A general character may be conceived as a multitude of precise characters. Mathematical thought consists in the study of precise relationships between ideal objects. But a possible fact may vary in an indefinite multitude of different ways. The moon coming between the earth and the sun, may not only have a multitude of different positions, but it may have a multitude of different shapes and colors and chemical compositions; and so may the sun and earth. For the purposes of mathematics, it is necessary, in the first place, to abstract from most of those differences, and consider them as insignificant and, for our purposes, nil. Then, those varieties which still, for our purposes, are different, have to be arranged, as far as possible, dimensionally. To do this, we imagine any one precise variety of the character, — precise, I mean, after the proper abstractions have been made, — and conceive that as undergoing a multitude of variations in time, from the infinitely distant past to the infinitely distant future, such that in the course of all time it will be continually changing; and we prefer to take this series so that the character will ultimately return to its initial state, and just barely return to that state. If this series of changes

does not include all the variations, we think of the whole multitude of states through which the character passes in all time, as belonging at one instant to an equal multitude of objects; and then we conceive the characters of those objects to undergo in the whole course of time a continuous series of changes of a different kind, so as to be entirely distinct. We call this a second dimension, or series of variations. We can make any number of these dimensions; and as far as possible we thus seek to give some precise arrangement to all the variations of characters. When this method fails us, we can resort to other systems of arrangement, of some of which we shall have examples in geometry.

283. Any one of those dimensions is such that the characters can pass through the whole series of states in the course of time. It is easy to imagine multitudes of variations so related to one another that one precise character could not even in all time pass through them all by insensible gradations. For example, colors differ from one another, not merely in hue, but also in luminosity, and in chroma, or intensity of departure from grey. Now, starting with a color of some precise hue, precise luminosity, and precise chroma, if it is to change its hue gradually, for each precise hue that it takes, it will have just one sole luminosity and one sole chroma; so that, when it has gone through the whole cycle of hues, it will have had for each of them but one single luminosity and but one single chroma. Though it should pass through the cycle of hues times without end, it would still not have begun to exhaust the possible luminosities and chromas for each hue. The student may admit that it might be possible (and, in fact, it might be shown to be possible) that if the color were so to jump from hue to hue, from luminosity to luminosity, and from chroma to chroma, that taking any two instants, no matter how near to one another, if during the interval between them the variations should embrace the whole cycle of hues, the whole range of luminosity, and the whole range of chroma, then the color might in the course of time precisely assume for an instant every special variety of color. But if the variation is to take place *gradually*, then it is not possible that the color should in the course of time assume every possible variation.

183

284. The meaning of this seems to be clear. That is, it possesses the first grade of clearness of ideas, that of containing no element which perfect familiarity does not enable us to use with entire confidence.[14] But that grade of clearness is not sufficient for precision of statement, and logical security. For that purpose, we must say what we mean by "gradually." In attempting to state this, it first occurs to us to say that we mean by a gradual change of hue, such a change that in passing from one exact hue to another we pass through all intermediate hues. There are two reflections to be made upon this statement. First, it supposes that the different hues are so related in our minds that we are able to say what ones are, and what ones are not, intermediate between any given pair of hues. That is to say, we must have a precise idea of what it means to say that the hues are mentally arranged in a line. But if that be so, we need not introduce the conception of a change in time; for that was only a device to enable us to describe what we mean by a line of variations of character. In truth, though the introduction of the idea of time gives sensuous clearness to our idea, it contributes not in the least to logical clearness. The second reflection which has to be made upon our attempt to define gradual change of hue is that the hues form a circle, the so-called color-circle; so that it is possible to pass from any one to any other by going either way round the circle; and thus there is no particular hue that we need pass through. To define a linear arrangement, the line being permitted to return into itself, it is necessary to speak of four points on the line.

285. *Definition*. A *state* is an exact character, that is, one which, certain understood abstractions being made, admits of no varieties.

286. *Definition*. A *line of variations of states* is a continuous multitude of states such that, taking any four of them all different, there are in the nature of the characters two that are adjacent to any one, or else it would be so were two that are extremes made adjacent to one another; and any fifth character of the same line occupies in its nature a definite position between two adjacent characters of the first four.

[14] (Ed.) Cf. 5.389.

287. *Definition*. A *circuit of states* is a line of variation of states which returns into itself and has no extreme states.

Illustrations. Suppose a light to be increasing in intensity from that of a fire-fly toward that of the planet Venus at such a rate that it would at a certain instant, say Midnight, attain that brightness. Suppose next that it increases at a more and more rapid rate, so that after a while its rate of brightening is such that at that rate it would attain the brightness of Venus at 11 o'clock. Suppose it continues to increase more rapidly, so that after a while, its rate of brightening is such that it would attain the brightness of Venus at 10 o'clock. Finally, suppose that its increase becomes so rapid that at that rate it would become as bright as Venus at 9 o'clock. Thus, there is this order among these characters: such a change of brightness as would make it equal Venus at 12, at 11, at 10, at 9. But when it was increasing at a rate to make it equal Venus at 12, its increase might become slower and slower so that the time at which it would equal Venus would become later and later. If it ceased to increase, the time would be thrown into the indefinite future. If it began slowly to decrease, its change would be as if it had been as bright as Venus a long time before. If it decreased faster, this time might become nearer and nearer, until at some time after 9, it was decreasing as if it had been as bright as Venus at 9 o'clock. At a little after 10, it might be at ten o'clock, at a little after 11, at 11 o'clock, and at a little after 12, at 12 o'clock. Thus the order would be reversed. But there is no imaginable way in which the time could gradually change from 12 o'clock to 10 o'clock without passing through either 11 o'clock or 9 o'clock. This shows that the instants of time form a circuit.

288. *Definition*. A *Quality* is that character of a character which consists in its belonging to a particular line of variation of states.

Illustrations. Thus, temperature, probability, wealth, the happening earlier or later than something else are qualities.

289. *Scholium*. The order of states in a line of variation may be shown by attaching to sensibly different states different numbers. For if the line of variation forms a circuit, its states are related to one another like the real numbers, rational and

irrational, positive and negative, including ∞, except that the states may perhaps be so multitudinous that it is impossible to assign distinct numbers to them all. Whether any example can be given of a quality in which there are sensible variations too multitudinous for numbers to discriminate or not, there can be no doubt that such a quality might exist.[15]

290. In mathematics, we have to deal with an ideal condition of things. We imagine ourselves to be in possession of a general method of working by which definite states can be assigned, in the first place, to all rational numbers, in their order. That is, the states in their own nature shall have the same order of succession as the values of the rational numbers. We then suppose states for the irrational numbers to be interposed in their orders. States which the particular method of assignment of numbers may leave unnumbered, between the numbered states, are for this method not sensibly different from the irrational numbers that are near them. A new distribution of numbers by a different method might possibly distinguish some of these, and in doing so it might, or might not, leave others undistinguished.

291. The numbers may occur in every assignable part of the circuit, or may be contained between two limits, or a part of the series of numbers may cover the whole circuit. In the last case, we suppose the remaining numbers to be assigned to the circuit taken over and over again in regular arithmetical progression. In the second case, we are at liberty to fill up the vacant part of the circuit with a second series of numbers which will be distinguished by having a quantity not a number added to it. But in doing this, we shall assume that the numbers are so assigned that taking any three states A, B, C, a state, D, can be found whose number diminished by that of C equals the number of B diminished by that of A.

292. *Definition.* A *method of measurement* upon a circuit of variation is a general rule according to which, it is possible to assign each rational number to an exact state and to but one; and conversely, given the numbers assigned to any three states, it is possible to ascertain whether any fourth rational number is exactly assignable to a given state or not, and if not

---

[15] (Ed.) Cf. 3.567ff., 4.639ff., 6.174ff.

in what one of the four intervals between the four numbers, the number that ought to be assigned to the given state falls. [*Corollary*. This affords the means of vaguely assigning states to the irrational numbers.] [16] Numbers so assigned to states may be called *state-numbers*. States to which definitely different places in the scale of numbers cannot be assigned are said not to be *measurably* distinct, according to the particular system of measurement employed. If the whole circuit of numbers does not precisely correspond to the whole circuit of states, it is assumed that either, on the one hand, the same state receives different numbers or, on the other hand, that different states receive the same numbers distinguished by the addition of a non-numerical quantity. But in all such cases the numbers are to be so distributed that if any three states have a, b, c for state-numbers not infinite (in the same system of measurement) then there shall be one state and but one which has for a state-number, $a+b-c$.

293. *Scholium*. Were we to say, at once, that there is a state for every syzygy of two state-numbers, we should no longer have a line of variation, in case a non-numerical increment is required for part of the circuit.

294. *Scholium*. Suppose we have two objects both capable of taking states of the same quality and of changing those states, but only in the inherent order of the circuit of variation. Suppose further that the whole pair has but a single degree of freedom of changes, so that for each state of the one there is one and but one state of the other. Finally, suppose that one member of the pair can always be changed to the state which before the change was that of the other. If, then, we affix numbers to the states in such a way that every change in the state-number of one of the pair shall be equal to that of the other, these numbers will fulfil the necessary conditions. But if there is a region over which the pair cannot be moved, then it will be necessary to have as many such changeable pairs as there are regions. Each pair may conveniently consist of one object in one region and one in another.

295. Another method of measurement would be obtained if we had a multitude of objects so that there was just one for

[16] (Ed.) Brackets in the original.

each state of the quality in the whole circuit, and if the whole multitude had but a single degree of freedom of change and two positions of the whole multitude were given.

296.   Of course, it would be still more convenient if we had given all states of such a multitude of objects. But in that case, they must conform [to] the condition that, let A, B, C, D, be what different states they may, if a change of one member of the multitude from A to B is synchronous with the change of another member from C to D, then every change of any member from A to B is simultaneous with the change of the member in state C to D.

297.   *Definition.* A *standard of measurement* upon a circuit of variation is a pair of objects subject to the quality of the circuit, such that either can be changed to the state of the other in respect to that quality, but all its changes must follow the inherent order of the states, and the whole pair has but one degree of freedom of position, so that if one of the pair is in any given state there is but one state in which the other can be; and the method of measurement is such that station-numbers of the states of the two objects change by equal differences simultaneously.

298.   *Definition.* A *metron* is an object composed of parts in one to one correspondence with all the states of a circuit of variation, such that any two form a standard of measurement, and the whole has *steady displacements*, that is, if the change of one part from state A to state B is synchronous with the change of the part at first in state C to state D, then the change of any other part from state A to state B is synchronous with the change of the part at first in state C to state D.

299.   *Definition.* The *quantity*, or *modular quantity*, of an interval between two states in a line of variation is that which there is in the inherent difference between two states which justifies their receiving state-numbers whose difference has this or that amount. Otherwise, it is that whose *measure* is the difference of their state-numbers multiplied by a unit expressive of the unit of difference.

300.   *Division.* Measurement is either

A. *Parabolic*, when the circuit of real numbers corresponds to the circuit of variation of states, or

B. *Non-parabolic*, when the two circuits are not coincident. *Non-parabolic* measurement is of two kinds, viz.: —

  a. *Elliptic*, when the entire circuit of states coincides with a finite part of the circuit of numbers.
  b. *Hyperbolic*, when the entire line of finite numbers occupies but a portion of the circuit of variation, and leaves a portion vacant.

301. *Definition.* An *absolute*, or *firmamental*, state is a state to which or from which no member of the metron can change.

302. *Theorem. In parabolic measurement upon one circuit there is just one firmamental state.*

Demonstration. In every measurable change of the metron, the station-numbers of all members are changed by the same finite increment. Now, a finite number added to any number gives a different number with one sole exception. Namely, if the number increased is infinite, the sum has the same value. But only one state has a given state-number. Therefore, the state of that member of the metron which has ∞ for its state-number is never changed. Hence, since every change can be reversed, no member is by any measurable change carried to the state whose state-number is infinite.

303. *Theorem. In elliptical motion there is no firmamental state, and the modular quantity of the whole circuit is finite, and the measurement proceeds in one annular order.*

Demonstration. If the entire circuit of variation is covered by a finite part of the scale of numbers, let the metron receive any measurable change. Then, the state-numbers of all its members will receive the same finite increment. Consequently, those members whose state-numbers were sufficiently great will be made greater than the finite difference of numbers of the whole circuit, and will be made greater than any of the numbers were at first. Since no state-number is infinite no member will have its state unchanged. And every member will have an arithmetical progression of state-numbers, the difference of all these progressions being the same. That difference will be the modular quantity of the circuit.

304. *Theorem. In hyperbolic motion there are just two firmamental states, and in both the regions into which they sever the circuit the state-numbers increase toward one of these*

*and away from the other; and the quantity of the whole circuit
is not infinite. . . .*[17]

305. *Analysis.* Our measures of space are of various descriptions. Some of them, as square measure, cubic measure,
etc. are composite. Thus, square measure depends upon long
measures of length and breadth. Other kinds of measure are
derivative. Thus, the distance of a point from a surface is the
distance of the point from the nearest point of the surface.
The measures which are neither composite nor derivative are
two: long measure between pairs of points and angular measure between pairs of planes.

306.   There are many different sorts of standards which
might be assumed for long measure. From the point of view
of theoretical physics the average distance that a molecule of
hydrogen at a standard temperature would move in a day would
have something to recommend it. But the primitive and most
usual sort of standard, as well as the most convenient for the
purposes of geometry, is a rigid body which is carried about
from place to place, such as a yard-stick.

307.   Let us ask what we mean by a rigid body. If we say
that it is a body whose measures remain fixed, somebody may
reply that if it is taken as the standard of measure it means
nothing to say that its measure relatively to itself remains the
measure of itself. Some care is, therefore, required in saying
what we mean by a rigid body. If a rigid body were a single
body there would be less meaning in the word rigid than there
is when it is a kind of body which the working of Nature makes
to be a usual kind, or a kind toward the ideal properties of
which many objects closely approximate. Our general experience leads us to think that solid bodies come very near to being
bodies which at fixed temperature and free from external influences have certain properties which we proceed to consider.
First, every particle of such a body, or part of it occupying an
indivisible place, always occupies a single indivisible place.
It never goes out of existence or out of space; nor does it separate so as to occupy a number of points, nor does it enlarge
so as to occupy a line or a surface or a solid space. Second,

---

[17] (Ed.) The proof, which is quite long, and a scholium are omitted.
The title, "Of Space Measurement," precedes the following paragraphs.

every flat film of such a body, or part of it occupying a plane, always continues (there being no stress upon the body) to occupy a plane. It neither breaks nor bends. Third, in any straight fibre of such a body, or part of it occupying a ray, (and which must always continue to occupy a ray, since every flat film in which it lies continues to lie in a plane) the order and continuity of the particles remain always the same, and round such straight fibre the order and continuity of the flat films through it remain always the same. These three properties, taken together, may be termed the optical property of the rigid body.

308.   In the next place, our general experience leads us to believe that a perfectly rigid body, which ordinary solid bodies sensibly resemble, is such that if a given particle of it be brought to a point [M] and the straight filament through that particle and a second particle be brought into a given ray through [M], then there are just two points to which that second particle can be brought. In like manner, if of three particles two are brought to two points [M] and [N], there are, in each plane through {MN} just two points to which the third particle might be brought. But there is a difference between the two cases. Namely, as long as the straight filament remains in the ray, if at one time one particle is at the point [M] and another at the point [N], then, no matter how the filament is moved in the ray, every time the first particle is brought back to [M] the second particle can be brought to no other point than [N]. But in the plane, though the flat film remain in all its movements in that plane, yet if the first particle is at first at [M] the second at [N] and the third at [P], if the first two particles are carried along {MN} until they have performed an entire circuit, while the third always remains in the plane, it will not return to the same point [P] (supposing it has ever left that point) but will return to a fourth point [Q] and it will not be until a second circuit has been performed that it returns to [P]. We shall demonstrate that this must be so. It is mentioned now for a special purpose. We shall find the difference is owing to the ray having an odd number, and the plane an even number of dimensions. Hence, in three dimensions if of four particles of a rigid body three are restored to their initial

191

positions, there is only one point to which the fourth can be brought, although there is another point which it could perfectly well occupy (as shown by its looking glass image) if there were only any fourth dimension through which it could be carried to that point. On this account, it is convenient in geometry to imagine ourselves to be in possession of a rigid body to be used as a standard of measurement which shall have the purely imaginary property that, while any three of its particles remain fixed, it shall be capable of being *perverted*, that is, of being suddenly converted into its looking glass image. On account of this property, we will denominate the thing, not a rigid body, but a rigid image.

309.   Finally, we are led to believe that if any number of parts of a rigid body occupy at one time certain positions and at another time certain other positions, then any other parts which may at any time occupy the first set of positions may be carried into the second set of positions.

310.   There is another property of rigid bodies which makes all long measure to be parabolical and all angular measure to be elliptical; but it is best, at first, to consider the consequences of the other properties, and to reserve the consideration of this until later.

311.   *Definition.* A *metrical image* is a continuous multitude of particles, straight filaments, and flat films having the following properties:

1st, it has the optical property that whatever part occupies at one instant a point or a plane occupies the same kind of place (whichever it may be) at every instant, and with the same connective relations to straight filaments.

2nd, the fixation of a particle of such image at a point or of a flat film in a plane diminishes by unity the freedom of motion of all other such parts of the same metrical image.

3rd, when the particles and flat films of [a] metrical image are subject to such conditions as just suffice to reduce the freedom of motion to zero, there are just two positions, said to be *perverse* of one another, in which it can fulfill those conditions.

4th, if one metrical image or part of such image can occupy one place at one instant and another at another instant, then every such image or part of an image which can occupy the former place at one instant can occupy the latter place at another instant.

312. *Definition.* Two places (whether the same or different) are said to be equal which can be occupied by the same metrical image or by the same part of one metrical image. And the order of the occupied parts makes no difference.[18]

[18] (Ed.) The manuscript continues for several pages and then breaks off in the middle of a sentence.

CHAPTER 5

THE LOGIC OF 1873 [1]

§1. INVESTIGATION [2]

313. The very first of distinctions which logic supposes is between doubt and belief, a question and a proposition. Doubt and belief are two states of mind which feel different, so that

[1] (Ed.) This chapter is from a set of associated manuscripts in Widener IB2–8, with the addition of a quotation in the present footnote. These manuscripts seem to be a number of partial drafts of a book to be titled "Logic." One set of chapters includes several bearing dates in March, 1873, and one chapter of another set is dated "1873 July 1." Others may have been written in 1872; in a letter to his brother Henry dated November 24, 1872, William James says, "Charles Peirce . . . read us an admirable introductory chapter to his book on logic the other day" ([Perry] I, 332). Some of the manuscripts have no heading, but probably belong to this undertaking. The portions bearing no date are dated here c.1873.

The contents of the present chapter should be compared with "The Fixation of Belief" (1877), 5.358–387, and "How to Make Our Ideas Clear" (1878), 5.388–410. Several pages in the set of manuscripts from which the present chapter is taken contain passages to be found in the first of these two articles. In 1909 and 1910 Peirce worked on a revision of these two articles, to be published under a single title. A draft for this work is titled, "Essays Toward the Interpretation of Our Thoughts (Provisional Title of volume); My Pragmatism (Provisional Title of the Essay), set forth in Two Chapters," Widener IB2–11. On page 1 of the draft, in a preface for the work, Peirce says: "The main part of this Essay, — the characterizations of Belief and of Doubt, the argument as to the effective aim of inquiry, the description of four methods directed toward that aim, with the criticisms of them, the discussion of the proper function of thinking, and the consequent maxim for attaining clear concepts, — reproduces almost verbatim a paper I read, — it must have been in 1872, — to a group of young men who used, at that time, to meet once a fortnight in Cambridge, Mass., under the name of 'The Metaphysical Club,' — a name chosen to alienate such as it would alienate." This page is headed "1909 Apr 6 2AM, MEANING, Pragmatism." Cf. 5.13 and [Bibliography] G–1909–1.

[2] (Ed.) Paragraphs 313–314 are "Chapter 1 (Enlarged abstract)," with added quotations at 313n3 and 314n4. Paragraphs 315–316 are from an abstract

we can distinguish them by immediate sensation. We almost always know without any experiment when we are in doubt and when we are convinced. This is such a difference as there is between red and blue, or pleasure and pain. Were this the whole distinction, it would be almost without significance. But in point of fact the mere sensible distinguishability is attended with an important practical difference.[3] When we believe, there is a proposition which according to some rule determines our actions, so that our belief being known, the way in which we shall behave may be surely deduced, but in the case of doubt we have such a proposition more or less distinctly in our minds but do not act from it. There is something further removed from belief than doubt, that is to say not to conceive the proposition at all. Nor is doubt wholly without effect upon our conduct. It makes us waver. Conviction determines us to act in a particular way while pure unconscious ignorance alone which is the true contrary of belief has no effect at all.

314. Belief and doubt may be conceived to be distinguished only in degree.[4]

315. Living doubt is the life of investigation. When doubt is set at rest inquiry must stop. . . .[5]

---

of the first few chapters. Paragraphs 317–325 are the contents of an untitled manuscript. See 313n1.

[3] (Ed.) ". . . the characters of belief are three. First, there is a certain feeling with regard to a proposition. Second, there is a disposition to be satisfied with the proposition. And third, there is a clear impulse to act in certain ways, in consequence." From "Of Reality" (see 313n1).

[4] (Ed.) "Doubt has degrees and may approximate indefinitely to belief, but when I doubt, the effect of the mental judgment will not be seen in my conduct as invariably or to the full extent that it will when I believe. Thus, if I am perfectly confident that an insurance company will fulfill their engagements I will pay them a certain sum for a policy, but if I think there is a risk of their breaking, I shall not pay them so much." From a fragment (see 313n1).

[5] (Ed.) In the omitted portion of the manuscript Peirce briefly outlines three of his four "methods of effecting a settlement of opinion." The first is "obstinate adhering to whatever happens to be one's existing opinions." The second is by persecution. The third is "by the natural development of opinion," which fails when "one community comes in contact with another. Then it is seen that the result is quite accidental and dependent on surrounding circumstances and initial conditions and belief gets all unsettled.

"In this way once more the conviction is forced on man that another's opinion, if derived by the same process as his own, is as good as his own, and that other's opinion is taken by him for his own. Then he says we in the sense of the learned world."

Peirce's fourth method is discussed in our following paragraph.

316.   From this conception springs the desire to get a settlement of opinion [that] is some conclusion which shall be independent of all individual limitations, independent of caprice, of tyranny, of accidents of situation . . . , — a conclusion to which every man would come who should pursue the same method and push it far enough. The effort to produce such a settlement of opinion is called *investigation*. Logic is the science which teaches whether such efforts are rightly directed or not.

317.   There is an important difference between the settlement of opinion which results from investigation and every other such settlement. It is that investigation will not fix one answer to a question as well as another, but on the contrary it tends to unsettle opinions at first, to change them and to confirm a certain opinion which depends only on the nature of investigation itself. The method of producing fixity of belief by adhering obstinately to one's belief, tends only to fix such opinions as each man already holds. The method of persecution tends only to spread the opinions which happen to be approved by rulers; and except so far as rulers are likely to adopt views of a certain cast does not determine at all what opinions shall become settled. The method of public opinion tends to develop a particular body of doctrine in every community. Some more widely spread and deeply rooted conviction will gradually drive out the opposing opinions, becoming itself in the strife somewhat modified by these. But different communities, removed from mutual influence, will develop very different bodies of doctrine, and in the same community there will be a constant tendency to sporting which may at any time carry the whole public. What we know of growth, in general, shows that this will take place; and history confirms us. The early history of sciences before they begin to be really investigated, especially of psychology, metaphysics, etc., illustrates as well as anything the pure effect of this method of fixing opinions. The numerous well-defined species of doctrines which have existed on such subjects and their progressive historical succession give the science of the history of philosophy considerable resemblance to that of paleontology.

318.   Thus no one of these methods can as a matter of fact

attain its end of settling opinions. Men's opinions will act upon one another and the method of obstinacy will infallibly be succeeded by the method of persecution and this will yield in time to the method of public opinion and this produces no stable result.

319. Investigation differs entirely from these methods in that the nature of the final conclusion to which it leads is in every case destined from the beginning, without reference to the initial state of belief. Let any two minds investigate any question independently and if they carry the process far enough they will come to an agreement which no further investigation will disturb.

320. But this will not be true for any process which anybody may choose to call investigation, but only for investigation which is made in accordance with appropriate rules. Here, therefore, we find there is a distinction between good and bad investigation. This distinction is the subject of study in logic. Some persons will doubt whether any sort of investigation will settle all questions. I refrain, however, from arguing the matter, because I should thus be led to anticipate what comes later, and because after any demonstration I might give I should still rest on *some* assumption and it is as easy to see that investigation assumes its own success as that it assumes anything else.

321. Logic is the doctrine of truth, its nature and the manner in which it is to be discovered.

322. The first condition of learning is to know that we are ignorant. A man begins to inquire and to reason with himself as soon as he really questions anything and when he is convinced he reasons no more. Elementary geometry produces formal proofs of propositions which nobody doubts, but that cannot properly be called reasoning which does not carry us from the known to the unknown, and the only value in the first demonstrations of geometry is that they exhibit the dependence of certain theorems on certain axioms, a thing which is not clear without the demonstrations. When two men discuss a question, each first endeavors to raise a doubt in the mind of the other, and that is often half the battle. When the doubt ceases there is no use in further discussion. Thus real inquiry begins when genuine doubt begins and ends when this doubt

197

ends. And the premises of the reasoning are facts not doubted.
It is therefore idle to tell a man to begin by doubting familiar
beliefs, unless you say something which shall cause him really
to doubt them. Again, it is false to say that reasoning must
rest either on first principles or on ultimate facts. For we cannot go behind what we are unable to doubt, but it would be
unphilosophical to suppose that any particular fact will never
be brought into doubt.

324. It is easy to see what truth would be for a mind which
could not doubt. That mind could not regard anything as
possible except what it believed in. By all existing things it
would mean only what it thought existed, and everything else
would be what it would mean by *nonexistent*. It would, therefore, be omniscient in its universe. To say that an omniscient
being is necessarily destitute of the faculty of reason, sounds
paradoxical; yet if the act of reasoning must be directed to an
end, when that end is attained the act naturally becomes impossible.

324. The only justification for reasoning is that it settles
doubts, and when doubt finally ceases, no matter how, the
end of reasoning is attained. Let a man resolve never to
change his existing opinions, let him obstinately shut his eyes
to all evidence against them, and if his will is strong enough
so that he actually does not waver in his faith, he has no motive
for reasoning at all, and it would be absurd for him to do it.
That is method number one for attaining the end of reasoning,
and it is a method which has been much practised and highly
approved, especially by people whose experience has been that
reasoning only leads from doubt to doubt. There is no valid
objection to this procedure if it only succeeds. It is true, it is
utterly irrational; that is to say it is foolish from the point of
view of those who do reason. But to assume that point of view
is to beg the question. In fact, however, it does not succeed;
and the first cause of failure is that different people have
different opinions and the man who sees this begins to feel
uncertain. It is therefore desirable to produce unanimity of
opinion and this gives rise to method number two, which is
to force people by fire and sword to adopt one belief, to massacre
all who dissent from it and burn their books. This way of bring-

ing about a catholic consent has proved highly successful for centuries in some cases, but it is not practicable in our days. A modification of this is method number three, to cultivate a public opinion by oratory and preaching and by fostering certain sentiments and passions in the minds of the young. This method is the most generally successful in our day. The fourth and last method is that of reasoning. It will never be adopted when any of the others will succeed and it has itself been successful only in certain spheres of thought. Nevertheless those who reason think that it must be successful in the end, and so it would if all men could reason. There is this to be said in favor of it. He who reasons will regard the opinions of the majority of mankind with contemptuous indifference; they will not in the least disturb his opinions. He will also neglect the beliefs of those who are not informed, and among the small residue he may fairly expect some unanimity on many questions.

325. I hope it will now be plain to the reader, that the only rational ground for preferring the method of reasoning to the other methods is that it fixes belief more surely. A man who proposes to adopt the first method may consistently do so simply because he chooses to do so. But if we are to decide in favor of reasoning, we ought to do so on rational grounds. Now if belief is fixed, no matter how, doubt has as a matter of fact ceased, and there is no motive, rational or other, for reasoning any more. Any settlement of opinion, therefore, if it is full and perfect, is entirely satisfactory and nothing could be better. It is the peculiarity of the method of reasoning, that if a man thinks that it will not burn him to put his hand in the fire, reasoning will not confirm that belief but will change it. This is a vast advantage to the mind of a rationalist. But the advocate of any one of the first three methods, will be able to say (if either of these methods will yield a fixed belief) either that he *knows* by his method that fire will burn, so that reasoning is inferior to his method in that it may permit a man for a moment to doubt this, or else that he *knows* that fire will not burn, so that reasoning leads all astray. In either case therefore he will conceive that which to the rationalist seems the great advantage of reasoning, to be a great fault. Thus the

only ground of a fair decision between the methods must be that one actually succeeds while the others break up and dissolve. Pope expresses the philosophy of the matter perfectly:

> Truth struck to earth shall rise again
> The eternal years of God are hers
> While error . . . writhes in pain
> And dies amidst her worshippers.

§2. LOGIC [6]

326. It is the business of the logician to study the nature of the fourth method of inquiry and to discover the rules for conducting it with success. The whole subject will in the exposition of it here offered to the reader be divided into three parts. The first shall treat of the essence of investigation in general, by whatever mind it is conducted and to whatever subject it is applied. The second shall treat of those maxims of investigation which become necessary owing to the peculiar constitution of man in his senses, and his mental nature. The third shall give some slight outline of the special methods of research which are applicable in the different branches of science, and which arise from the peculiarities of the matter investigated. In this first part then we have, broadly speaking, nothing to do with the nature of the human mind. Only as there are some faculties which must belong to any mind which can investigate at all, these must come under our consideration. All inquiry, for example, presupposes a passage from a state of doubt to a state of belief; and therefore there must be a succession of time in the thoughts of any mind which is able to inquire. In the fourth method of inquiry a certain predetermined though not pre-known belief is sure to result from the process; no matter what may have been the opinion of the inquirer at the outset. It follows that during the investigation elements of thought must have sprung up in the mind which were not caused by any thought which was present at the time the investigation was commenced. Such new ideas springing up in the mind and not produced by anything in the mind, are called sensations. Every mind capable of investigation must

[6] (Ed.) From "LOGIC, Chap. 4 (—— draft)" (see 313n1).

therefore have a capacity for sensations. But were all thoughts of this kind investigation would be almost an involuntary process. We might will to investigate but we could not change the course which investigation should take. There would therefore be no distinction between a right and a wrong method of investigation. Now we have seen in the last chapter, that such a distinction is essential to the fourth method of inquiry and is, in fact, the only thing which distinguishes it from the third. There must be thoughts therefore which are determined by previous thoughts. And such a faculty of producing thoughts from others must belong to every mind which can investigate. Without a succession of ideas in time it is clear that no reasoning is possible. I shall proceed to show that without it and without the determination of one idea by another no *thought* in any proper sense of the word is possible.

§3. OBSERVATION AND REASONING [7]

327. Because the only purpose of inquiry is the settlement of opinion, we have seen that everyone who investigates, that is, pursues an inquiry by the fourth method assumes that that process will, if carried far enough, lead him to a certain conclusion, he knows not what beforehand, but which no further investigation will change. No matter what his opinion at the outset may be, it is assumed that he will end in one predestinated belief. Hence it appears that in the process of investigation wholly new ideas and elements of belief must spring up in the mind which were not there before.

328. Some thoughts are produced by previous thoughts according to regular laws of association,[8] so that if the previous thoughts be known, and the rule of association be given, the thought which is so produced may be predicted. This is the elaborative operation of thought, or thinking *par excellence*. But when an idea comes up in the mind which has no such relation to former ideas, but is something new to us, we say that it is caused by something out of the mind, and we call

[7] (Ed.) From "LOGIC, Chap. 4. — Of Reality (1st draft)," with an added quotation in 331n9. See 313n1.

[8] (Ed.) See Book III, Chapter 2, "Association," in the present volume.

the process by which such thoughts spring up, sensation. And those parts of investigation which consist chiefly in supplying such materials for thought to work over, combine and analyze, are termed observations. The first thing to be noted then is that since investigation leads us from whatever state of opinion we may happen to have to an opinion which is predetermined, it must be that investigation involves observation as one part of it, and, in fact, the conclusion to which we finally come ultimately depends entirely upon the observations.

329. We may pause here to make a practical application of this principle. No argument can possibly be a correct one which pretends to disclose to us a fact wholly new without being based on evidence which is new. The metaphysicians are given to this kind of reasoning; even those of them who are the most energetic in maintaining that all our knowledge comes from sense. Writers upon the nature of the human mind, especially, have built up a great body of doctrine without the aid of any observations or facts, except such as are familiar to all the world. Such things justly excite our suspicion. When Hobbes, for example, would persuade us that no man can act otherwise than for the sake of pleasure, it is clear that this belief would deeply modify our conceptions of men, and our plans of life; but when on asking what supports this momentous conclusion we learn that it is but the simple fact — if it can be dignified by that name — that every man desires to do what he does do, we are led at once to suspect that there is some sophistry in the process by which so novel a conclusion can be drawn from so familiar a premise. So, when modern necessitarians maintain that every act of the will proceeds from the strongest motive, they lay down a principle which should be expected to give rise to a psychological science as exact as mechanics, and capable of reducing human actions to precise calculation. But when we find that the advocates of this principle have made no experiments to test their law, we are strongly inclined to think that there has been some juggle of reasoning which has enabled them thus to create something out of nothing.

330. An observation, as we have defined it, is merely an idea arising in the mind, and not produced by previous ideas.

This is not the complete description of observation as understood by scientific men, and we must be careful that the word does not lead us to conclusions which we are not yet warranted in drawing. For example a dream, a presentiment or some fancied inspiration from on high, might, as far as we have yet seen, involve entirely new elements of thought, and, therefore, be an observation in the sense of our definition, so that we are not yet warranted in saying that such things cannot be the ground of legitimate reasoning. This is a question which we shall have again to examine when we come to consider those maxims of inference which depend upon the peculiar constitution of man.

331. But Observation alone cannot constitute investigation; for if it did the only active part which we should have to play in this method of inquiry would be simply the willing to observe, and there would be no distinction of a wrong method and a right method of investigation. But we have seen that such a distinction is essential to the idea of investigation, and that it is, in fact the only thing which separates this from the third method of inquiry. Accordingly, besides observation it must be that there is also an elaborative process of thought by which the ideas given by observation produce others in the mind.[9] Besides, the observations are most varied and are never exactly repeated or reproduced so that they cannot constitute that settled opinion to which investigation leads. Two men, for example, agree in an opinion, and if you ask upon what their opinions rest they will perhaps allege the same fact. But trace the matter back further; ask them upon what grounds they believe that fact again and you will eventually come to premises that are different. Two minds, for example, may have formed the same judgment of a certain person's character and yet may have based their opinions on observing his behavior on different occasions. The rotation of the earth was at first inferred from the movement of the heavenly bodies; but afterwards the manner in which a long pendulum when allowed to swing would gradually turn around and change its direction

---

[9] (Ed.) Investigation involves, besides sensation, "the production of new beliefs out of old ones according to logical laws. This process is the *logical process*, but by an extension of the meaning of a familiar word I call it also *inference*." From "*Of Reality*," the same manuscript quoted at 313n3.

of oscillation, afforded an entirely new proof; and there are
certain very small movements of the stars, which, if they were
capable of sufficiently exact observation, would show another
ground for the same conclusion. Indeed, the fact which one
man observes, is in no case precisely the same as the fact which
another man observes. One astronomer observes that the moon
passes over a star so as to hide it at a certain instant at his
observatory, another astronomer observes that the same star
is occulted at a certain instant at his observatory. These two
facts are not the same, because they relate to different stations
of observation. What is so plain in regard to astronomical observation, because we are accustomed to precision of thought
about this, is equally true in regard to the most familiar facts.
You and I both see an ink-stand on the table; but what you observe, is that there is a certain appearance from where you
sit, and what I observe, is that there is a certain appearance
from where I sit. The fact in which we agree, that there is an
ink-stand there, is what we conclude from the different appearances which we each severally observe. We may change
places and still we shall fail to get each other's observations;
for the difference of time then comes in. I may observe that
there is such an appearance now as you describe as having
existed a few moments before; but I cannot observe that there
was such an appearance before I took your place. It is needless to multiply these examples, because the slightest reflection
will supply them in any number; but what have been adduced
are sufficient to show that observations are for every man
wholly private and peculiar. And not only can no man make
another man's observations, or reproduce them; but he cannot
even make at one time those observations which he himself
made at another time. They belong to the particular situation
of the observer, and the particular instant of time.

332. Indeed, if we carefully distinguish that which is first
given by sensation, from the conclusion which we immediately
draw from it, it is not difficult to see that different observations
are not in themselves even so much as alike; for what does
the resemblance between the two observations consist in?
What does it mean to say that two thoughts are alike? It
can only mean that any mind that should compare them to-

gether, would pronounce them to be alike. But that comparison would be an act of thought not included in the two observations severally; for the two observations existing at different times, perhaps in different minds, cannot be brought together to be compared directly in themselves, but only by the aid of the memory, or some other process which makes a thought out of previous thoughts, and which is, therefore, not observation. Since, therefore, the likeness of these thoughts consists entirely in the result of comparison, and comparison is not observation, it follows that observations are not alike except so far as there is a possibility of some mental process besides observation.

333.   Without however insisting upon this point which may be found too subtile, the fact remains that the observations are not the same in the sense in which the conclusions to which they give rise are the same. All astronomers, for example, will agree that the earth is ninety-two or ninety-three millions of miles from the sun. And yet, one would base his conclusion on observations of the passage of Venus across the sun's disk; another upon observations of the planet Mars; another upon experiments upon light combined with observations of the satellites of Jupiter. And the same thing is equally true in regard to most of the ordinary affairs of life.

334.   Now how is it that the springing up into the mind of thoughts so dissimilar should lead us inevitably though sometimes not until after a long time to one fixed conclusion? Disputes undoubtedly occur among those who pursue a proper method of investigation. But these disputes come to an end. At least that is the assumption upon which we go in entering into the discussion at all, for unless investigation is to lead to settled opinion it is of no service to us whatever. We do believe then in regard to every question which we try to investigate that the observations though they may be as varied and as unlike in themselves as possible, yet have some power of bringing about in our minds a predetermined state of belief. This reminds us of the species of necessity which is known as fate. The fairy stories are full of such examples as this: A king shuts his daughter up in a tower because he has been warned that she is destined to suffer some misfortune from falling in love before a certain age and it turns out that the very

205

means which he has employed to prevent it is just what brings the prophecy to fulfillment. Had he pursued a different course, the idea seems to be that that would equally have brought about the destined result. Fate then is that necessity by which a certain result will surely be brought to pass according to the natural course of events however we may vary the particular circumstances which precede the event. In the same manner we seem fated to come to the final conclusion. For whatever be the circumstances under which the observations are made and by which they are modified they will inevitably carry us at last to this belief.

335.   The strangeness of this fact disappears entirely when we adopt the conception of external realities. We say that the observations are the result of the action upon the mind of outward things, and that their diversity is due to the diversity of our relations to these things; while the identity of the conclusion to which the mind is led by them is owing to the identity of the things observed, the reasoning process serving to separate from the many different observations that we make of the same thing the constant element which depends upon the thing itself from the differing and variable elements which depend on our varying relations to the thing. This hypothesis I say removes the strangeness of the fact that observations however different yield one identical result. It removes the strangeness of this fact by putting it in a form and under an aspect in which it resembles other facts with which we are familiar. We are accustomed very rightly to think that causes always precede their effects and to disbelieve in fate, which is a fancied necessity by which some future event as it were forces the conditions which precede to be such as would bring it about. That there is no such intrinsic and unconditional necessity to bring about events Western nations are fully and rightly convinced. This is why it seems strange to assert that the final conclusion of the investigation is predestined and why it is satisfactory to the mind to find a hypothesis which shall assign a cause preceding the final belief which would account for the production of it, and of the truth of this conception of external realities there can be no doubt. Even the idealists, if their doctrines are rightly understood have not usually denied the existence

of real external things. But though the conception involves no error and is convenient for certain purposes, it does not follow that it affords the point of view from which it is proper to look at the matter in order to understand its true philosophy. It removes the strangeness of a certain fact by assimilating it to other familiar facts; but is not that fact that investigation leads to a definite conclusion really of so different a character from the ordinary events in the world to which we apply the conception of causation that such an assimilation and classification of it really puts it in a light which, though not absolutely false, fails nevertheless to bring into due prominence the real peculiarity of its nature? That observation and reasoning produce a settled belief which we call the truth seems a principle to be placed at the head of all special truths which are only the particular beliefs to which observation and reasoning in such cases lead. And it is hardly desirable to merge it among the rest by an analogy which serves no other purpose.

§4. REALITY [10]

336. The question is, "Whether corresponding to our thoughts and sensations, and represented in some sense by them, there are realities, which are not only independent of the thought of you, and me, and any number of men, but which are absolutely independent of thought altogether." The objective final opinion is independent of the thoughts of any particular men, but is not independent of thought *in general*.[11]

[10] (Ed.) An untitled manuscript originally in one paragraph, with an added quotation in 336n11. See 313n1.

[11] (Ed.) "The final settled opinion is not any particular cognition, in such and such a mind, at such and such a time, although an individual opinion may chance to coincide with it. If an opinion coincides with the final settled opinion, it is because the general current of investigation will not affect it. The object of that individual opinion is whatever is thought at that time. But if anything else than that one thing is thought, the object of that opinion changes and it thereby ceases to coincide with the object of the final opinion which does not change. The perversity or ignorance of mankind may make this thing or that to be held for true, for any number of generations, but it can not affect what would be the result of sufficient experience and reasoning. And this it is which is meant by the final settled opinion. This therefore is no particular opinion but is entirely independent of what you, I, or any number of men may think about it; and therefore it directly satisfies the definition of reality." From *"Logic,* Chap. 6th," March 10, 1873 (see 313n1).

That is to say, if there were no thought, there would be no opinion, and therefore, no final opinion.

337.   All that we directly experience is our thought — what passes through our minds; and that only, at the moment at which it is passing through. We here see thoughts determining and causing other thoughts, and a chain of reasoning or of association is produced. But the beginning and the end of this chain, are not distinctly perceived. A current is another image under which thought is often spoken of, and perhaps more suitably. We have particularly drawn attention to the point to which thought flows, and that it finally reaches: a certain level, as it were — a certain basin, where reality becomes unchanging. It has reached its destination, and that permanency, that fixed reality, which every thought strives to represent and image, we have placed in this objective point, towards which the current of thought flows.

338.   But the matter has often been regarded from an opposite point of view; attention being particularly drawn to the spring, and origin of thought. It is said that all other thoughts are ultimately derived from sensations; that all conclusions of reasoning are valid only so far as they are true to the sensations; that the real cause of sensation therefore, is the reality which thought presents. Now such a reality, which causes all thought, would seem to be wholly external to the mind — at least to the thinking part of the mind, as distinguished from the feeling part; for it might be conceived to be, in some way, dependent upon sensation.

339.   Here then are two opposite modes of conceiving reality. The one which has before been developed at some length, and which naturally results from the principles which have been set forth in the previous chapters of this book is an idea which was obscurely in the minds of the medieval realists; while the other was the motive principle of nominalism. I do not think that the two views are absolutely irreconcilable, although they are taken from very widely separated stand-points. The realistic view emphasizes particularly the permanence and fixity of reality; the nominalistic view emphasizes its externality. But the realists need not, and should not, deny that the reality exists externally to the mind; nor have

they historically done so, as a general thing. That is external to the mind, which is what it is, whatever our thoughts may be on any subject; just as that is real which is what it is, whatever our thoughts may be concerning that particular thing. Thus an emotion of the mind is real, in the sense that it exists in the mind whether we are distinctly conscious of it or not. But it is not external because although it does not depend upon what we think about it, it does depend upon the state of our thoughts about something. Now the object of the final opinion which we have seen to be independent of what any particular person thinks, may very well be external to the mind. And there is no objection to saying that this external reality causes the sensation, and through the sensation has caused all that line of thought which has finally led to the belief.

340. At first sight it seems no doubt a paradoxical statement that, "The object of final belief which exists only in consequence of the belief, should itself produce the belief"; but there have been a great many instances in which we have adopted a conception of existence similar to this. The object of the belief exists it is true, only because the belief exists; but this is not the same as to say that it begins to exist first when the belief begins to exist. We say that a diamond is hard. And in what does the hardness consist? It consists merely in the fact that nothing will scratch it; therefore its hardness is entirely constituted by the fact of something rubbing against it with force without scratching it. And were it impossible that anything should rub against it in this way, it would be quite without meaning, to say that it was hard, just as it is entirely without meaning to say that virtue or any other abstraction is hard.[12] But though the hardness is entirely constituted by the fact of another stone rubbing against the diamond yet we do not conceive of it as beginning to be hard when the other stone is rubbed against it; on the contrary, we say that it is really hard the whole time, and has been hard since it began to be a diamond. And yet there was no fact, no event, nothing whatever, which made it different from any other thing which is not so hard, until the other stone was rubbed against it.

341. So we say that the inkstand upon the table is heavy.

[12] (Ed.) Cf. 5.403.

And what do we mean by that? We only mean, that if its support be removed it will fall to the ground. This may perhaps never happen to it at all — and yet we say that it is really heavy all the time; though there is no respect whatever, in which it is different from what it would be if it were not heavy, until that support is taken away from it. The same is true in regard to the existence of any other force. It exists only by virtue of a condition, that something will happen under certain circumstances; but we do not conceive it as first beginning to exist when these circumstances arise; on the contrary, it will exist though the circumstances should never happen to arise. And now, what is matter itself? The physicist is perfectly accustomed to conceive of it as merely the centre of the forces. It exists, therefore, only so far as these forces exist. Since, therefore, these forces exist only by virtue of the fact, that something will happen under certain circumstances, it follows that matter itself only exists in this way.

342. Nor is this conception one which is peculiar to the physicists and to our views of the external world. A man is said to know a foreign language. And what does that mean? Only that if the occasion arises, the words of that language will come into his mind; it does not mean that they are actually in his mind all the time. And yet we do not say that he only knows the language at the moment that the particular words occur to him that he is to say; for in that way he never could be certain of knowing the whole language if he only knew the particular word necessary at the time. So that his knowledge of the thing which exists all the time, exists only by virtue of the fact that when a certain occasion arises a certain idea will come into his mind.

343. A man is said to possess certain mental powers and susceptibilities, and we conceive of him as constantly endowed with these faculties; but they only consist in the fact that he will have certain ideas in his mind under certain circumstances; and not in the fact of his having certain ideas in his mind all the time. It is perfectly conceivable that the man should have faculties which are never called forth: in which case the existence of the faculties depends upon a condition which never occurs. But what is the mind itself but the focus of all the

210

faculties? and what does the existence of the mind consist in but in these faculties? Does the mind cease to exist when it sleeps? and is it a new man who wakes every morning?

344. It appears then that the existence of mind equally with that of matter according to these arguments which have led to this view which is held by all psychologists, as well as physicists, depends only upon certain hypothetical conditions which may first occur in the future, or which may not occur at all. There is nothing extraordinary therefore in saying that the existence of external realities depends upon the fact, that opinion will finally settle in the belief in them. And yet that these realities existed before the belief took rise, and were even the cause of that belief, just as the force of gravity is the cause of the falling of the inkstand — although the force of gravity consists merely in the fact that the inkstand and other objects will fall.

345. But if it be asked us, whether some realities do not exist, which are entirely independent of thought; I would in turn ask, what is meant by such an expression and what can be meant by it. What idea can be attached to that of which there is no idea? For if there be an idea of such a reality, it is the object of that idea of which we are speaking, and which is not independent of thought. It is clear that it is quite beyond the power of the mind to have an idea of something entirely independent of thought — it would have to extract itself from itself for that purpose; and since there is no such idea there is no meaning in the expression.[13] The experience of ignorance, or of error, which we have, and which we gain by means of correcting our errors, or enlarging our knowledge, does enable us to experience and conceive something which is independent of our own limited views; but as there can be no correction of the sum total of opinions, and no enlargement of the sum total of knowledge, we have no such means, and can have no such means of acquiring a conception of something independent of all opinion and thought.

[13] (Ed.) Cf. 5.255.

§5. TIME AND THOUGHT [14]

346. Any mind which has the power of investigation, and which therefore passes from doubt to belief, must have its ideas follow after one another in time. And if there is to be any distinction of a right and a wrong method of investigation, it must have some control over the process. So that there must be such a thing as the production of one idea from another which was previously in the mind. This is what takes place in reasoning, where the conclusion is brought into the mind by the premises.

347. We may imagine a mind which should reason and never know that it reasoned; never being aware that its conclusion was a conclusion, or was derived from anything which went before. For such a mind there might be a right and a wrong method of thinking; but it could not be aware that there was such a distinction, nor criticise in any degree its own operations. To be capable of logical criticism, the mind must be aware that one idea is determined by another

348. Now when this happens, after the first idea comes the second. There is a process which can only take place in a space of time; but an idea is not present to the mind during a space of time — at least not during a space of time in which this idea is replaced by another; for when the moment of its being present is passed, it is no longer in the mind at all. Therefore, the fact that one idea succeeds another is not a thing which in itself can be present to the mind, any more than the experiences of a whole day or of a year can be said to be present to the mind. It is something which can be lived through; but not be present in any one instant; and therefore, which can not be present to the mind at all; for nothing is present but the passing moment, and what it contains. The only way therefore in which we can be aware of a process of inference, or of any other process, is by its producing some idea in us. Not only therefore is it necessary that one idea should produce another;

[14] (Ed.) An untitled manuscript originally in one paragraph. The date is hardly legible, but is probably March 6, 1873. A manuscript dated March 8, 1873, seems to be an alternative draft, but in the opinion of the editor the manuscript printed here is superior to the later draft. See 313n1.

but it is also requisite that a mental process should produce an idea. These three things must be found in every logical mind: First, ideas; second, determinations of ideas by previous ideas; third, determinations of ideas by previous processes. And nothing will be found which does not come under one of these three heads.

349. The determination of one thing by another, implies that the former not only follows after the latter, but follows after it according to a general rule, in consequence of which, every such idea would be followed by such a second one. There can therefore be no determination of one idea by another except so far as ideas can be distributed into classes, or have some resemblances. But how can one idea resemble another? An idea can contain nothing but what is present to the mind in that idea. Two ideas exist at different times; consequently what is present to the mind in one is present only at that time, and is absent at the time when the other idea is present. Literally, therefore, one idea contains nothing of another idea; and in themselves they can have no resemblance. They certainly do not resemble one another except so far as the mind can detect a resemblance; for they exist only in the mind, and are nothing but what they are thought to be. Now when each is present to the mind the other is not in the mind at all. No reference to it is in the mind, and no idea of it is in the mind. Neither idea therefore when it is in the mind, is thought to resemble the other which is not present in the mind. And an idea can not be thought, except when it is present in the mind. And, therefore, one idea can not be thought to resemble another, strictly speaking.

350. In order to escape from this paradox, let us see how we have been led into it. Causation supposes a general rule, and therefore similarity. Now so long as we suppose that what is present to the mind at one time is absolutely distinct from what is present to the mind at another time, our ideas are absolutely individual, and without any similarity. It is necessary, therefore, that we should conceive a process as present to the mind. And this process consists of parts existing at different times and absolutely distinct. And during the time that one part is in the mind, the other is not in the mind. To unite

213

them, we have to suppose that there is a consciousness running
through the time. So that of the succession of ideas which
occur in a second of time, there is but one consciousness, and
of the succession of ideas which occurs in a minute of time
there is another consciousness, and so on, perhaps indefinitely.
So that there may be a consciousness of the events that happened in a whole day or a whole life time.

351. According to this, two parts of a process separated
in time — though they are absolutely separate, in so far as
there is a consciousness of the one, from which the other is
entirely excluded — are yet so far not separate, that there is
a more general consciousness of the two together. This conception of consciousness is something which takes up time. It
seems forced upon us to escape the contradictions which we
have just encountered. And if consciousness has a duration,
then there is no such thing as an instantaneous consciousness;
but all consciousness relates to a process. And no thought,
however simple, is at any instant present to the mind in its
entirety, but it is something which we live through or experience
as we do the events of a day. And as the experiences of a day
are made up of the experiences of shorter spaces of time so
any thought whatever is made up of more special thoughts
which in their turn are themselves made up by others and so
on indefinitely.

352. It may indeed very likely be that there is some minimum space of time within which in some sense only an indivisible thought can exist and as we know nothing of such a fact
at present we may content ourselves with the simpler conception of an indefinite continuity in consciousness. It will easily
be seen that when this conception is once grasped the process
of the determination of one idea by another becomes explicable.
What is present to the mind during the whole of an interval
of time is something generally consisting of what there was in
common in what was present to the mind during the parts of
that interval. And this may be the same with what is present to
the mind during any interval of time; or if not the same, at
least similar — that is, the two may be such that they have
much in common. These two thoughts which are similar may
be followed by others that are similar and according to a gener-

al law by which every thought similar to either of these is followed by another similar to those by which they are followed. If a succession of thoughts have anything in common this may belong to every part of these thoughts however minute, and therefore it may be said to be present at every instant. This element of consciousness which belongs to a whole only so far as it belongs to its parts is termed the matter of thought.

353.   There is besides this a causation running through our consciousness by which the thought of any one moment determines the thought of the next moment no matter how minute these moments may be. And this causation is necessarily of the nature of a reproduction; because if a thought of a certain kind continues for a certain length of time as it must do to come into consciousness the immediate effect produced by this causality must also be present during the whole time, so that it is a part of that thought. Therefore when this thought ceases, that which continues after it by virtue of this action is a part of the thought itself. In addition to this there must be an effect produced by the following of one idea after a different idea; otherwise there would be no process of inference except that of the reproduction of the premises.

§6. BELIEF [15]

354.   We have seen that an inference is the process by which one belief determines another. But a belief is itself a habit of the mind by virtue of which one idea gives rise to another. When I say that I know the French language, I do not mean that as long as I know it I have all the words which compose it in my mind, or a single one of them. But only that when I think of an object, the French word for it will occur to me, and that when a French word is brought to my attention I shall think of the object it signifies. What is true of knowledge is equally true of belief, since the truth or falsehood of the cognition does not alter its character in this respect. I believe that prussic acid is poison, and always have believed it. This does not mean that I have always had the idea of prussic acid

[15] (Ed.) "*Logic*, Chap. 5th," March 10, 1873, originally in one paragraph. See 313n1.

in my mind, but only that on the proper occasion, on thinking of drinking it, for example, the idea of poison and all the other ideas that that idea would bring up, would arise in my mind.

355.   Thus there are three elements of cognition: thoughts, the habitual connection between thoughts, and processes establishing a habitual connection between thoughts. We have seen already that an idea cannot be instantaneously present, that consciousness occupies time, and that we have no consciousness in an instant. So that at no time have we a thought. But now it further appears that in reference to a belief not only can we not have it in an instant, but it can not be present to the mind in any period of time. It does not consist in anything which is present to the mind, but in an habitual connection among the things which are successively present. That is to say, it consists in ideas succeeding one another according to a general rule; but not in the mere thinking of this general rule, nor in the mere succession of ideas one upon another, nor in both together. A thought must therefore be a sign of a belief; but is never the belief itself. The same thing is obviously true in regard to an inference; and even a simple idea is of intellectual value to us not for what it is in itself but as standing for some object to which it relates. Now a thing which stands for another thing is a representation or sign. So that it appears that every species of actual cognition is of the nature of a sign. It will be found highly advantageous to consider the subject from this point of view, because many general properties of signs can be discovered by a set of words and the like which are free from the intricacies which perplex us in the direct study of thought.

356.   Let us examine some of the characters of signs in general. A sign must in the first place have some qualities in itself which serve to distinguish it, a word must have a peculiar sound different from the sound of another word; but it makes no difference what the sound is, so long as it is something distinguishable. In the next place, a sign must have a real physical connection with the thing it signifies so as to be affected by that thing. A weather-cock, which is a sign of the direction of the wind, must really turn with the wind. This word in this connection is an indirect one; but unless there be some way

or other which shall connect words with the things they signify, and shall ensure their correspondence with them, they have no value as signs of those things. Whatever has these two characters is fit to become a sign. It is at least a symptom, but it is not actually a sign unless it is used as such; that is unless it is interpreted to thought and addresses itself to some mind. As thought is itself a sign we may express this by saying that the sign must be interpreted as another sign.[16] Let us see however, whether this is true of thought itself that it must address itself to some other thought. There are some cases in which it is not difficult to see that this must be the case. I have no belief that prussic acid is poisonous unless when the particular occasion comes up I am led to the further belief that that particular acid is poisonous; and unless I am further led to the belief that it is a thing to avoid drinking. For all these things are necessary to my acting on my belief. A belief which will not be acted on ceases to be a belief.

357.   It may be that I shall finally come to a belief which is a motive for action directly without the intervention of a more special belief. In this case how does the belief address itself to a sign? When a person is said to act upon a certain belief the meaning is that his actions have a certain consistency; that is to say, that they possess a certain intellectual unity. But this implies that they are interpreted in the light of thought. So that even if a belief is a direct motive to action it still is a belief only because that action is interpretable again. And thus the intellectual character of beliefs at least are dependent upon the capability of the endless translation of sign into sign. An inference translates itself directly into a belief. A thought which is not capable of affecting belief in any way, obviously has no signification or intellectual value at all. If it does affect belief it is then translated from one sign to another as the belief itself is interpreted. And therefore this character of signs that they must be capable of interpretation in every sense belongs to every kind of cognition. And consequently no cognition is such or has an intellectual significance for what it is in itself, but only for what it is in its effects upon other thoughts. And the existence of a cognition is not something actual, but

[16] Cf. 5.253.

consists in the fact that under certain circumstances some other cognition will arise.

§7. PRAGMATISM [17]

358. In every logical mind there must be 1st, ideas; 2nd, general rules according to which one idea determines another, or habits of mind which connect ideas; and, 3rd, processes whereby such habitual connections are established.

359. A belief is an habitual connection of ideas. For example, to say that I believe prussic acid is a poison is to say that when the idea of drinking it occurs to me, the idea of it as a poison with all the other ideas which follow in the train of this will arise in my mind. Among these ideas, or objects present to me, is the sense of refusing to drink it. This, if I am in a normal condition, will be followed by an action of the nerves when needed which will remove the cup from my lips. It seems probable that every habitual connection of ideas may produce such an effect upon the will. If this is actually so, a belief and an habitual connection of ideas are one and the same.

360. In a mind which is capable of logical criticism of its beliefs, there must be a sensation of believing, which shall serve to show what ideas are connected. The recognition that two objects present belong together as one is a judgment. All ideas arise in judgments. This is clearly the case if they are caused by previous ideas. If they are sensations then they at once cause other ideas and are connected with these in judgments. The intellectual value of ideas lies evidently in their relations to one another in judgments and not to their qualities in themselves.[18] All that seems blue to me might seem red and *vice versa* and yet all that I now find true of those objects I should equally find true then, if nothing else were changed. I should still perceive the same distinctions of things that I do now. The intellectual significance of beliefs lies wholly in the conclusions which may be drawn from them, and ultimately

---

[17] (Ed.) Chapter V, "*That the significance of thought lies in its reference to the future.*" A draft of Chapter IV, "*The Conception of Time essential in Logic,*" dated "1873 July 1," seems to belong with this Chapter V as parts of one series. See 313n1.

[18] (Ed.) Cf. 5.287ff.

in their effects upon our conduct. For there does not seem to be any important distinction between two propositions which never can yield different practical results.[19] Only the difference in the facility with which a conclusion can be reached from two propositions must be regarded as a difference in their effects upon our actions.

361. It appears then that the intellectual significance of all thought ultimately lies in its effect upon our actions. Now in what does the intellectual character of conduct consist? Clearly in its harmony to the eye of reason; that is in the fact that the mind in contemplating it shall find a harmony of purposes in it. In other words it must be capable of rational interpretation to a future thought. Thus thought is rational only so far as it recommends itself to a possible future thought. Or in other words the rationality of thought lies in its reference to a possible future.[20]

[19] (Ed.) Cf. 8.33 (1871) and 5.400 (1878).
[20] (Ed.) The manuscript ends without a period.

BOOK III

PHILOSOPHY OF MIND

CHAPTER 1

PSYCHOGNOSY [1]

§1. INTRODUCTION

362. The next business before us is to run through the Subclass of Psychognosy once more, and note its Families, etc. [2] The first order is Nomological Psychognosy, which coincides with what is called Psychology, except that under this latter head, sundry classificatory studies, such as of Criminals, Insects, Great Men, Devil-fishes, Insanity, Sexual, Professional, and Racial characters, are usually included. Such studies cannot be pursued to advantage without a good knowledge of psychology; and here and there, they do contribute a few useful facts to the psychologist. Still, they are not generally pursued by the regular psychologists; nor is the elucidation of the laws of mind their aim, — unless it be a distant and dubious one; so that to a fair and discriminating mind they hardly appear to belong naturally to psychology. It is merely the influence of the abstract definition which has caused them to be called psychological; and we must be on our guard against the deceptions of abstract definitions.

[1] (Ed.) Peirce uses the terms "psychognosy" and "physiognosy" for the psychical and physical sciences, respectively (cf. 1.242).

This chapter is from Section 1, "Classification of the Sciences," of *Minute Logic*, Chapter 2, "Prelogical Notions," including some alternative pages, Widener IB2–2, with a quotation added in 381n19. The manuscript has dates of early 1902 stamped in the margin of several sheets. All but one of Peirce's marginal sideheads are omitted, and some of his marginal notes have been treated as footnotes rather than as insertions in the text.

1.203–283 are from the first part of this manuscript. Paragraph 374n10 follows shortly after 1.283. The rest of the present chapter follows considerably after 374n10; in the manuscript between 374n10 and 362, Peirce deals with the subdivisions of Physiognosy. Cf. 7.267n7.

[2] (Ed.) Cf. 1.269–272.

363.   We have already recognized two Suborders of Psychology,— General Psychology and Special Psychology.[3] But here we meet with the serious difficulty that we find ourselves in disaccord with the psychologist's conception of his own science. Not that the psychologist will have any objection to a division into General and Special Psychology. But he will draw the line in quite another place from that in which we have drawn it. We have conceived of General Psychology as the study of the law of final causation. The psychologists will disapprove of that. They will say that purpose is characteristic only of a special department of mind, and that what they are studying is the phenomenon of consciousness generally. Now it is my intention in another chapter to examine seriously the question which of us is right.[4] I do not think that such a discussion would be quite relevant here. But when an author (it is my case), having for many years pushed a line of investigation over a path, very old indeed, — *uralt*, as the Germans say, — yet for centuries unused and grown over with brush, finds that in order to set forth his results, he has to persuade the reader to look at matters from points of view from which everything must seem to him unfamiliar and paradoxical; it will be an advantage, when the two come to the serious argumentation, if the author has already made the reader somewhat acquainted with the propositions he desires to defend. He will do well (so it has seemed to me) to expose what he has to offer to the sunlight, that its garish colors may fade a little, before the time comes for deciding whether it is to be accepted or rejected. To be sure, this will involve considerable repetition; but the repetition will not be without a purpose, and I hope not without its convenience for both parties. Let it be understood, then, that what I say here on the subject of my difference with the modern psychologists, for the scientific character of whose work I have a high degree of respect, is not my argument. That will be presented later; it is not needed here. All I wish to bring before the reader here is the fact that there is a very different opinion from that now current among the psy-

---

[3] (Ed.) 1.269–270.
[4] (Ed.) No such chapter is among the manuscripts. A list of all the chapters for which there are manuscripts is given at [Bibliography] G–c.1902–2.

chologists, and an opinion which a man who has anxiously examined into the question, fully alive to the perils of pet-theories and knowing well that no other force than that of the truth that comes from observation can possibly cause an opinion to endure, can entertain with modest confidence as the more conformed to the facts.[5]

§2. CONSCIOUSNESS AND PURPOSE

364. To begin with the psychologists have not yet made it clear what Mind is. I do not mean its substratum; but they have not even made it clear what a psychical phenomenon is. Far less has any notion of mind been established and generally acknowledged which can compare for an instant in distinctness to the dynamical conception of matter. Almost all the psychologists still tell us that mind is consciousness. But to my apprehension Hartmann has proved conclusively that unconscious mind exists. What is meant by consciousness is really in itself nothing but feeling. Gay and Hartley were quite right about that; and though there may be, and probably is, something of the general nature of feeling almost everywhere, yet feeling in any ascertainable degree is a mere property of protoplasm, perhaps only of nerve matter. Now it so happens that biological organisms, and especially a nervous system are favorably conditioned for exhibiting the phenomena of mind also; and therefore it is not surprising that mind and feeling should be confounded. But I do not believe that psychology can be set to rights until the importance of Hartmann's argument is acknowledged, and it is seen that feeling is nothing but the inward aspect of things, while mind on the contrary is essentially an external phenomenon. The error is very much like that which was so long prevalent that an electrical current moved through the metallic wire; while it is now known that that is just the only place from which it is cut off, being wholly external to the wire. Again, the psychologists undertake to locate various mental powers in the brain; and above all consider it as quite certain that the faculty of language resides in a certain

[5] (Ed.) The text continues at paragraph 366. Paragraph 364 is from some alternative sheets, and 365 is from some other alternative sheets (see 362n1).

lobe; but I believe it comes decidedly nearer the truth (though not really true) that language resides in the tongue. In my opinion it is much more true that the thoughts of a living writer are in any printed copy of his book than that they are in his brain.

365. What the psychologists study is mind, not consciousness exclusively. Their mistake upon this point has had a singularly disastrous result, because consciousness is a very simple thing. Only take care not to make the blunder of supposing that Self-consciousness is meant, and it will be seen that consciousness is nothing but Feeling, in general, — not feeling in the German sense, but more generally, the immediate element of experience generalized to its utmost. Mind, on the contrary, when you once grasp the truth that it is not consciousness nor proportionate in any way to consciousness, is a very difficult thing to analyze. I am not speaking of Soul, the metaphysical substratum of Mind (if it has any), but of Mind phenomenally understood. To get such a conception of Mind, or mental phenomena, as the science of Dynamics affords of Matter, or material events, is a business which can only be accomplished by resolute scientific investigation. But the psychologists have been prevented from making that investigation by their delusion that Mind is just Consciousness, a simple affair, as far as the mere phenomenon goes, about which there is no room for error or doubt.

366. The psychologists say that consciousness is the essential attribute of mind; and that purpose is only a special modification. I hold that purpose, or rather, final causation, of which purpose is the conscious modification, is the essential subject of psychologists' own studies; and that consciousness is a special, and not a universal, accompaniment of mind. Von Hartmann, as long ago as 1869, proved conclusively that unconscious mind exists.[6] True, we may suppose that, in the cases instanced by him, there is a rudiment of consciousness; but such an objection would not meet his argument, which goes to show that the mental phenomena may be strong where the

[6] Not being a German university professor, his arguments were not fairly considered by German university professors, and were treated with contempt by those who pin their faith upon the philosophical fashions that happen for the moment to prevail in those universities. [Peirce's marginal insert.]

consciousness, if there be any, is almost nil, and where there is reason to believe that more consciousness would be rather unfavorable than otherwise to the action of mind. A psychologist cuts out a lobe of my brain (*nihil animale me alienum puto*) and then, when I find I cannot express myself, he says, "You see your faculty of language was localized in that lobe." No doubt it was; and so, if he had filched my inkstand, I should not have been able to continue my discussion until I had got another. Yea, the very thoughts would not come to me. So my faculty of discussion is equally localized in my inkstand. It is localization in a sense in which a thing may be in two places at once. On the theory that the distinction between psychical and physical phenomena is the distinction between final and efficient causation, it is plain enough that the inkstand and the brain-lobe have the same general relation to the functions of the mind. I suppose that if I were to ask a modern psychologist whether he holds that the mind "resides" in the brain, he would pronounce that to be a crude expression; and yet he holds that the protoplasmal content of a brain-cell feels, I suppose: there is every evidence that it does so. This feeling, however, is consciousness. Consciousness, *per se*, is nothing else: and consciousness, he maintains, is Mind. So that he really does hold that Mind resides in, or is a property of, the brain-matter. The early students of electricity, who assumed that an electrical current resides in the metallic circuit, had infinitely more reason for their mistaken opinion. Yes, without exaggeration, infinitely more; for the ratio of something to nothing is infinite.

367. No doubt, it seems an extraordinary piece of presumption for a man to tell a large body of scientific men for whom he professes high respect that they do not know what are the problems which they are endeavoring to solve; that while they think they are trying to make clear the phenomena of consciousness, it is really something quite different that they are trying to do.[7] I admit that the notion that phenomena of conscious-

---

[7] Professor Baldwin in the preface of his Dictionary distinctly places himself upon the platform that philosophical and scientific questions ought to be settled by majorities. 'We are many: you are one,' he says. But in the history of science majorities short of unanimity have more often been wrong than right. Majorities do not form their opinions rationally. [Peirce's marginal insert.]

ness are the objects of psychology has caused a disproportion-
ate development of certain departments, and has caused other
departments to be much neglected. Nevertheless, I hold my
ground. For if psychology were restricted to phenomena of
consciousness, the establishment of mental associations, the
taking of habits, which is the very market-place of psychology,
would be outside its boulevards. To say of such departments
of psychology, — from every point of view, the most essential
parts of it, — that they are studies of phenomena of consciousness, is as if an ichthyologist were to define his science as a
study of water.

§3. MIND AND BODY

368. There can be no better touch-stone of a psychology
than the question of the relation between soul and body. Here
the current psychology, instead of producing a scientific theory,
finds itself driven into metaphysics. If you want to know how
the doctrine of psychophysical parallelism will appear when
it comes to be viewed [from] a distance of a couple of centuries,
there is a closely similar theory from which the lesson may be
learned, — the theory of Pre-established Harmony. What does
good sense say to this today? The doctrine of Parallelism,
which is that that which when viewed from the outside appears
as material, when viewed from the inside appears as mental,
encounters apparently insuperable difficulties when it is examined in its application to details. It has been adopted as the
only means of reconciling the contradiction that the law of
dynamics is never violated and that the law of mind is never
violated. Neither of the members of this contradiction are
rigidly proved to be true. Here, then, are two pretty serious
defects in this theory of parallelism. Still, it is conceivable that
satisfactory answers should be found to both objections. There
is, however, a third objection which seems to knock the ground
from under it, once for all; and this is that the two propositions which are supposed to be in contradiction with one another, unless metaphysics is brought in to reconcile them in a
superphenomenal manner, can, in fact, be seen to be not in
the least in conflict with one another, if we scrutinize them with

a logical microscope. The facts which are supposed to conflict with one another are these. First, ideas produce material effects. A whisper in the ear may cause motions on the earth's surface sufficient to attract the attention of the inhabitants of the planet Venus. And reciprocally motions of matter affect ideas. That is one side of the truth; and no sane man can question it. But, secondly, according to the law of dynamics, no change of motion can take place except through accelerations which are dependent exclusively upon the mutual positions of particles or parts of matter; and according to the law of mind, no idea can arise except by virtue of an association. These propositions cannot properly be said to be proved; but they are postulated; and for the sake of argument we may admit that they are strictly true. Indeed, we should not be justified in believing that they are so very false as it would be necessary to suppose them to be, if this were the only way of preventing their clashing with the obvious fact of the reaction between mind and matter. But in point of fact, there is no contradiction in the propositions stated.

369.   Let us imagine a case where matter, the external world, acts upon mind and where mind responsively acts upon matter. Let it be an extremely simple case, yet not so rudimentary as not to display the principal features of such cases. Suppose that while I am sitting writing in my study, which has an outside door, my dog comes and touches me with his nose; which I know is his sign that he wishes to go out. I do not mind the slight interruption of getting up and opening the door for him; but there is a newly made garden-patch out there, where I do not wish him to go; and I object to standing at the door to watch him. However, I know that the first thing he will do, if he is allowed to go out, will be to run to another door to see if my wife is there, so that he can greet her; and I remember that on this day of the week, at this hour, it being a fine day, she will be seated on a certain balcony where she will hear the dog; and I further know that, under those circumstances, she will look out and call him away from the garden-patch, if he starts to go there. Consequently, I get up, and go to the door, let the dog out, shut the door, and return to my table and to my writing. Now I ask the reader whether he will believe that

those motions of my body were purely automatic, my mental reflexions being mere surplusage, provided I can show him that there is no necessary violation of the laws of dynamics in supposing that the mental operations were an essential factor of the phenomenon? Do not ask me in return whether I hold it to be inconceivable that an automaton should be made that would act like that; because that is not the question, for two reasons. The first is, that if such an automaton were to be constructed, a vast expenditure of thought would be necessary to design it. While here, the question being whether or not mind is an essential factor in the motions of matter, the theory of parallelism requires us to suppose, not that such an automaton gets constructed, but that it comes into being without any design at all, or automatically and independently of any design. The second reason why the supposed question would not be relevant is that the true question is not what is conceivable but what is credible. Here am I counting upon what the dog will do, and upon what my wife will do. That is, future events determine my present action. True, it is possible that something may interfere to falsify my expectation; but still experience assures us that such expectations are reasonably sure. Such being the fact, those modes of inference upon which we always rely in science lead us, lead the man whose good sense is not sophisticated by a metaphysical theory, to believe that it was my reflections which caused me first to hesitate and then to go and open the door. Nobody would doubt that that was the true account of the matter, were it not that it is contrary to the law of dynamics that mind should act on matter and contrary to the law of purpose that matter should act on mind. Grant that it is so: but the man who regards that as an objection to the common sense theory is simply allowing himself to be taken in by the Achilles sophism.

370. Which do you prefer; one of those ghost-like hypotheses about things-in-themselves which anybody can set up but nobody can refute; or a flesh-and-blood hypothesis that nothing prevents you from wrestling with and flinging it to the ground by any one of a hundred experimental tricks, except that, when you come to try them, they one and all unexpectedly turn out just the other way? I will bring you a hypothesis that

is ready to try a bout with you, if you like. This hypothesis may prove false in all its details; I rather guess it will. But in one respect, it certainly is not false; namely, insofar as it shows that matter's acting immediately solely on matter and mind's acting immediately solely on mind in no wise conflicts with matter's truly and literally acting on mind and mind's acting on matter. I will suppose, then, — and this is only one of innumerable hypotheses of the same general type, and leading to the same conclusion, — that when the dog touches his nose to my person, he sets up sound waves in the matter of my body, which, of course, will be propagated with the velocity of sound. I will suppose, however, that, owing to the viscosity of the matter in which these waves reside, a part of the motion is quickly converted into heat, which is a motion of the molecules, atoms, and corpuscles of this matter. But these atoms are really vortices in an ether, and along with the heat there will be vibrations of this ether, which will constitute light and be propagated with the velocity of light. I will further suppose that this ether is not devoid of viscosity, so that part of this vibratory and vortical motion will be converted into what we may call a heating of the ether, a motion of *its* atoms. But these atoms, I will suppose, are really vortices in an ether's ether; and along with this heat of the ether, vibrations of this ether's ether will be excited, and be propagated at a velocity as much greater than that of light as the velocity of light is greater than that of sound. I will further suppose that this ether's ether is not devoid of viscosity; so that a part of those vibrations will be converted just as before. I will suppose that there is an endless series of these ethers below ethers, and that in consequence of the increase of velocity as the motion passes from each to the next, the entire infinite series of transformations of motion will be accomplished in a fraction of a second of time. All this motion will be purely dynamical; the mind will have nothing to do with it.

371. The third of our diagrams of spirals will be useful here, in helping the reader to grasp my meaning.[8] Let the radius vector measure the time, beginning at the outermost point, as the instant when the dog's nose touches me and proceeding in-

---

[8] (Ed.) Cf. 1.276, 8.122n19, and 8.274.

wards. Let each coil of the spiral represent the transformation of the motion from one ether to the next. At the end of the period of time represented by one inch of the radius, all that infinite series of transformations will be complete. Now let us suppose that the inner series of coils of the spiral, which, instead of being endless, is beginningless in terms of the coils, though not in time, represents operations governed exclusively by final causation, and therefore purely mental. Let us suppose that, although mental, they are not noticeably conscious until the innermost end of the coil is approached. Here begin those reflections of which I am able to give any account, although from ever so early in the second series of coils the mind was acting rationally, in the sense in which unconscious, and therefore uncritical, action can be called rational. Finally, at the innermost end of the spiral will occur my volition to let the dog out. Another similar diagram would be required to show what happens next. If the dog is to be let out, the door must be opened; if the door is to be opened, I must open it. But if I am to open it, I must go to it; if I am to go to it, I must walk; if I am to walk, I must stand; if I am to stand, I must rise; if I am to rise, I had better put down my pen; and there consciousness becomes dim. But there must be an infinite series of such ratiocinations if the mind only acts rationally. Take any instant after the work of the mind has been done, and at that instant, an infinite series of dynamical transformations will have taken place which are to terminate in the door being opened.

372.   I repeat that I will not here argue the question. All I have said is not intended as argument. But neither is it vain talk. It is the necessary preparation for an inquiry. How the inquiry itself is to be conducted shall be shown in another chapter.[9] All I wish now to convince the reader of is that, notwithstanding the admirable, conscientious, and most useful studies for which we have to be grateful to Wilhelm Wundt and his hundreds of disciples, — for all modern psychologists are his loyal disciples, — the science is still too unsettled even to understand its own motives; so that a classification which should not look at all beyond the present state of the study could

[9] (Ed.) No such chapter is among the manuscripts. Cf. 363n4.

hardly be expected to be really helpful. In this place, therefore, by exception, I shall allow myself to anticipate, as far as such a thing is possible, a state of the science in the near future.

§4. NOMOLOGICAL PSYCHOGNOSY

373.   I shall, then, recognize that Nomological Psychognosy must separate into two Suborders; the first of General Psychonomy, the second of Special Psychonomy, or Nomological Psychology. The former will study the law of final causation and seek to formulate it with exactitude, while the latter will study subordinate laws of mind, of which that of Association is the first.

374.   General Psychonomy will have four Families.[10] Family 1 will define the essence of Mind and the law of final Causation, together with its application to non-biological phenomena. We may term it phenomenalistic Pneumatology. Family 2 will

[10] (Ed.) "As the different Orders are distinguished by the different conceptions which govern them, so it has seemed to me that the different Families are distinguished by the differences of their methods of investigation, when these different methods are applied to different problems. For if there are two different methods, both of them sound and scientific, which are applicable to the same problem, they ought to be employed jointly; or if not, they at any rate are too closely associated to make different families of science. Nothing, for example, can be in stronger contrast than the method of investigating ancient history from monuments and from documents. But the only proper course is to use both methods conjointly. It is true that one man may not be strong enough to work in both ways to advantage; but still he will thoroughly know that his own work is only a result of the division of labour and that it has to be joined to another man's work by a third workman, before anything can be settled. On the other hand, a mere difference of problems, where the methods of investigation are identical does not constitute a division that can rank as a division between Families of science.

"Different Genera of the same Family of science are studies which have precisely the same general character, but of which each is strongly distinguished by some marked feature. This is a sufficiently vague statement, not to have the effect of imposing an artificial classification, while it is clear enough to be of material service in enabling us to determine whether a given subdivision is a division into Families or into Genera.

"Finally, the different Species of one Genus of science, are studies which, though morphologically identical in all their features, even similar in their proportions, and undistinguished by any leading peculiarities, lie nevertheless not so exactly in one path that the man who is everywhere prepared for the pursuit of the one will be quite *ipso facto* expert in the other, without having anything to learn of new kinds of precaution; in sharpening his attention to unfamiliar observations, in manipulating an instrument that has been strange

233

show how final causation works in the development of biological stocks. Family 3 will study the law in its application
to biological individuals and to consciousness. Family 4 may
be called Demonomy, although it should study the application of the law, not merely to Societies, but also to mere Associations, such as that of a profession. This Family has a truly
remarkable analogy to that Family of Dynamics which treats
of stationary motion. One Subfamily (or possibly only a
Genus) of it will work out the general laws of concert and strife.
A second will apply these principles to special phenomena.
One Genus will apply them to Law and the Constitution of
Society, in Subgenera; another to Wealth.

375. Nomological Psychology will treat of laws of mind
subordinate to the general principles of final causation. I recognize in it but two Families, of which the one is devoted to the
study of the great law of Association (including, of course,
Fusion) or that of the mutual attraction of all ideas, the analogue of Gravitation in the Physical world, while the other
analyzes the laws of the connection of body and mind. The
former Family seems to involve three Subfamilies of which
one treats of Association *per se*, a second association as modified by dissociation, etc., and a third, the laws of the growth
of mind in individual and in society or stock. The second of
these Subfamilies will have Genera relating, the first to Habit,
the second to Imagination and Vividness, the third to Generalization and Reason, the fourth to Recognition and Belief. The
Subfamily of the laws of Growth of Mind must have four
Genera relating, the first to General Laws; the second to growth,
the morphogeny, etc.; the third to growth in the conscious mind,
with three Subgenera relating to natural immaturity (with In-
fant Psychology and Child Psychology as species), to growth
under education, and to growth by experience; and the fourth
Genus to the laws of growth of the Social Consciousness. Family 2 will have two Subfamilies treating respectively of elementary laws and of the laws of peculiar states of mind. The
first Subfamily will have three Genera. Genus 1 will study the
general law of the reaction between Body and Mind. Genus 2,

---

to him, or in putting a familiar one to unfamiliar uses." From the manuscript,
following shortly after 1.283 (see 362n1).

Psychophysics, will treat of Sensation and whatever may be analogous to it. Genus 3 will treat of Volition, with three species relating to Impulse, Control, and Controlled Volition, each of these having one Subspecies for direct, or outward volition, another for attention. Perhaps the first of these species must have a third Subspecies for Emotion. The Subfamily relating to laws of special states of mind would have three Genera. Genus 1 will treat of the laws of dissolution and double consciousness, with five Subgenera studying the general law *per se*, studying fatigue, studying sleepiness and sleep, normal and abnormal, studying dreams and hallucinations, normal and abnormal, and studying double consciousness, normal and abnormal. For it is commonly recognized that there is a multiple personality that is perfectly normal. Genus 2 will treat of the laws of "credenciveness," including what is carelessly called "suggestion," a term which was already preoccupied for one of the general phenomena of association. Genus 3 will treat of the laws of the Passions.

§5. PSYCHOLOGY

376. All this is but a preliminary sketch of what I should imagine might be the division of a psychology of the future, subject to modifications to adapt it to existing psychology. The usual division now is into Introspective, Experimental, and Physiological Psychology. These divisions exist; but they are unimportant, and can only be regarded as constituting species under several of the genera. Let us consider them a moment, beginning with Physiological Psychology. This term may be taken in a strict sense; but it is almost invariably understood in a loose sense. In a strict sense, Physiological Psychology means making experiments on the brain, and from the results of these experiments drawing inferences concerning the Mind. The one fair inference to be drawn from those experiments is that the connection between the mind and the brain is an accidental one. When a lobe of the brain is extirpated, we find that the connection between certain organs of the body is deranged or broken. Of course, for the time being, that prevents mental action, just as if you abstracted my inkstand you would find

me transformed for a time from a student working sixteen hours
a day into an ardent devotee of amusement. The injury may
be such that there is no recovery. But usually recovery does
take place. Other parts of the brain are made to do the work,
after a fashion, with perhaps other parts of the body. The remarkable thing is, that those very actions, now performed with
other organs, show the same mental idiosyncrasies, down to
minute details that they did before. The man who has had to
learn to write with his other hand directed by another part of
the brain, may write pretty badly, but his very handwriting will
show the same inimitable characteristics it had before. A few
such general truths as that may be established by Physiological
Psychology proper. They may be summed up in the proposition: The brain has no radically peculiar relation to mind. But
this is only a negative proposition, and, as such, of no positive
importance. But what is ordinarily meant by physiological psychology is not these supremely difficult and uncertain experiments, but work done very commodiously with a diagrammatic
figure of the brain and its connections. What psychology thus
derives from anatomy rather than from physiology is suggestions of theories. When it is conscious mind that is to be
studied, no doubt those suggestions are often of great value.
In other departments of psychology, they are largely fallacious.
But in any case, it is not a method of investigation, but only
a help in forming those hypotheses from which investigation
takes its start. It cannot, then, constitute one of the higher
groups of psychology. As for Experimental Psychology, it is
commonly said that this can only be practised in conjunction
with introspection. I cannot admit the truth of this. In many
experiments there is nothing that any form of statement can
torture into introspection.[11] In others, there is no introspection
unless nice observation, — such as saying for example which
of two colors is the brighter, — is introspection. But this is in
reality nothing but the attentive observation of an outward object. It is nonsense to call attention to an outward object by
the name of introspection. Introspection is direct observation
of the operations of the mind as mental operations; because, as

[11] Take, as an example, Cattell's observations of the motions of a reader's
eyeball. [Peirce's marginal insert.]

for feelings, they are always referred to some object, and there is no observation of feelings except as characters of objects. I will say a word more about this presently. The type of true psychological experiment consists of putting a man in peculiar and carefully defined conditions, requesting him to do something, typically, of a natural and ordinary kind, and then carefully measuring a certain feature of his action. That will be a scientific observation which may serve to explode a psychological hypothesis. It is the only scientific basis of psychology. There is no introspection in it. Introspective Psychology is the old false psychology which ought not to be countenanced. It is true that a good deal is known about the mind from ordinary observation. There is a considerable store of wisdom concerning man before scientific psychology begins its work. But so far as this is anything more than instinctive knowledge, it really rests on experiments. Only, they are such experiments as any man can perform, by simply resolving to watch all cases in his experience where certain conditions are fulfilled, and noting how far certain results accompany them. As for the mind's watching its own operations, no such thing is possible. It is pure delusion. Take, for example, a train of ideas. A man may recall some of the ideas of the train. But what are they? They are objects, imaginary objects, — *products* of the mind's operation, but not the movement of mind itself. Whether even these objects can afterward be described or known as they actually presented themselves during the process, — whether they are not really subsequent creations, — is usually very doubtful. It is certain that unless the train of thought was arrested at any one of them long enough to make such an object as can be described, in which case it is not at all the operation of the mind but only an elaborate product that is known, then we cannot afterward know them as they were in the fleeting thought. And even our falsified knowledge of them is not knowledge of thought's movement, but only of a product which it stops in order to throw off. Moreover, even of these, it is experimentally certain that only a small part can be recovered. Thus, the real operation of thought is something purely inferential, at best; and I shall give reason for thinking that it is commonly mistaken. But the Introspective Psychologists, while

237

they acknowledge that there is some force in these objections, though not so much as I think, insist that we have an introspective knowledge of the characters of feelings. They say, for example, that we can perceive that red and green are simple sensations, that yellow is a third simple sensation, not a mixture of the sensations of red and green, but that orange is not a simple sensation, but is a mixture of red and yellow. In weighing the truth of this assertion, the first thing to be clearly understood is that red, orange, yellow, and green, are not pure feelings, but are generalizations of feelings. Red and green lights falling together upon the *fovea* do produce the sensation of yellow. It is commonly supposed that this is only very roughly true. But this is because proper precautions are not taken in performing the experiment. If it is accurately done, although there is a slight whitishness in the yellow produced, it is only slight. It is very likely, however, that this varies with different eyes, because it probably depends upon the number of rods in that part of the retina. If there were no rods, it might likely be exactly true. For some reason we put the yellow into a different class from red or green. The introspectionists, however, admit that yellow is more like red and more like green than red and green are like one another. If that be so, then we class red and yellow together, and see in them some common element, and we also class yellow and green together, and see in them some common element. Therefore, in yellow we do see a mixture of an element of red and an element of green. They therefore fall into self-contradiction when they say that we perceive that yellow is a simple sensation. It is true that we do not see red in yellow, nor do we see green in it, but only an element of red-likeness and an element of green-likeness; and furthermore we see something peculiar in yellow which predominates over its red-likeness and its green-likeness. But then this is more or less the case whenever from any motive we are led to regard a certain class of phenomena as a class by itself. Any collection of objects in the world, no matter how artificial, has some character common and peculiar to its members. It must be so, or we could not have thought of them as forming a collection. Now in cases where it seems important to regard the objects as a class, this character in which they are utterly dissimilar from all other objects, assumes a mental predominance. But yellow is an important kind of sensation for the reason that any color when highly illuminated looks more yellow. Now since the illumination of surfaces is constantly changing, this yellowishness has to be allowed for specially in classing the color of the surface; and thus it is very natural that the peculiar character yellow should acquire a special importance. But this does not constitute any simplicity of it as a feeling which does not belong to any class of sensations in proportion as it acquires importance. It must be so, in accordance with the general laws of mental phenomena. Orange, on the contrary, is not particularly significant, and therefore its reddishness and its yellowishness seem to us sufficiently to describe it. But if we look at it accurately, we shall see that it is not red and not yellow, but only red-like and yellow-like, and with a peculiar character of its own. The truth is that the phrase *simple sensation* is devoid of all meaning, unless by simple be meant important. For if the phrase simple sensation means anything, it must mean that no other two sensations are like this in different respects; that is, all others can only differ from it in one way. For if sensations vary along a continuous line, tell me if you can, what it can mean to take a single point of that line and say it is more simple than any of the other points. If you mean that some circumstance gives it a special importance, that I can understand. But that circumstance is probably some fact of astronomy or geognosy, not essentially related to consciousness. If, then, the psychologists wish me to admit merely that yellow seems to be a peculiar color, I grant it is a fact about our minds that they are educated to regard it so. But in that same sense, the sensation of nakedness is a simple sensation; and the sensation of a letter of the alphabet is a simple sensation. These considerations ought to convince anybody who has carefully gone through the introspectional psychology of the present day that it never can again be an important department of the science. It is merely a preliminary study in several Genera.

377.   In the rough sketch given above of my impression of what psychology ought to be, I have omitted, by negligence partly, several topics upon which books enough have been writ-

ten to bend our shelves. The remarkable thing is how valuable they are on the average. It shows what virgin soil psychology is that with so little exertion of strength good fruit can be obtained in this field. Reviewing my preliminary scheme and comparing it with current ideas, the first thing that strikes me is the absence of the terms relating to association which the Germans and their lackeys have introduced; such as Fusion, Assimilation, Synthesis, Complication, Apperception. These are connected with valuable contributions to psychology, no doubt. But I think that the conceptions of the English Associationalists, which are now met with a smile, are of vastly greater importance; such as the distinction between the radically different processes, now generally overlooked, between association and associative suggestion, and the capital distinction between Association by Resemblance and Association by Contiguity, which goes down to the root of the matter as none of the distinctions based on speculations about the brain begin to do.[12] Another modern term that I miss is synesthesia, a trifling variety of imagination. But there is Memory, concerning which there is a whole library of books of exceptional average foolishness. No doubt, under the Genus of Imagination and Vividness, a Species must be devoted to Memory. Attention is a faculty which many excellent psychologists regard as of fundamental importance, not at all to be relegated to subspecies of Volition, as I have relegated it. Of course, I may be wrong; but I adhere to my opinion on this point. I have not said a word about Telepathy; and in general I have not admitted that abnormal phenomena differ deeply from normal phenomena. I cannot admit that there is any special nomology of the abnormal. It is the condition of a science of laws that it is restricted to what it can find to be regular.[13]

§6. CLASSIFICATORY PSYCHOGNOSY [14]

378. Of Classificatory Psychology, which for brevity I term Psychotaxy, two Suborders have already been designated, studying respectively Kinds of Performances and Kinds of In-

[12] (Ed.) See the following chapter, "Association."
[13] (Ed.) See Chapter 5, "Telepathy and Perception," in the present book.
[14] (Ed.) Cf. 1.271.

dividuals. The word performance must here be taken in a broad sense to include actions that are simple and involuntary. I have been tempted to substitute the word "faculties" and have not done so because this word would certainly be positively misunderstood, while "performance" has no greater fault than unintelligibility at first sight. The Classification of Performances seems, on the whole, to consist of two Families, the one of Elements of Performance, the other of Systems of Performance. But this is one of those cases in which my conclusion is reached by that process of balancing one consideration with another which the history of science, and, as we shall find, the theory of logic, alike stamp as extremely apt to lead to error.[15] The first Family consists (such is my hesitating conclusion) of two Genera relating respectively to Kinds of Sensation and their relations, and to Kinds of Emotion and their relations. It [is] questionable, I admit, whether I ought thus cut the studies of Sensation and of Emotion into two parts belonging to different Orders. If I am wrong about this, I would, at any rate, retain the two Genera of the Classificatory Order. Whether, however, they are separate Genera, rather than Subgenera of one Genus, is another question which I may have answered wrongly. One naturally baulks, too, at admitting that this Family has no Genera studying any other mental faculties than those of Feeling; yet this is a point upon which I permit myself a certain degree of confidence. The second Family, that of Systems of Performance, has quite clearly two Subfamilies. Both the one and the other are, substantially, and in the gross, confined to animal and human performances, including organized associations. One Subfamily studies those systems of performance which are mainly confined to the brutes, to the lower animals generally, being in the instinctive stage of development; so that there is an inborn faculty by virtue of which the performance is determined in almost all its details. The Instincts are said to be all adaptive, although it would seem to be in very small measure that play is so. However, the instincts seem to be of two distinct kinds, those which are adapted

---

[15] (Ed.) Cf. Chapter 3, "The Logic of Drawing History from Ancient Documents," Book II, present volume.

to the preservation of the stock, if at all,[16] through preserving
the individual in whom the instinct acts, and those which are
social, and therefore, so far as they are adaptive, are adaptive
primarily to the advantage of some other individual or individuals than the agent. Association may happen to be of advantage to the associating individuals; but each individual's instinct brings no more advantage to him than the sum of all the
advantages that it brings to so many others. It is double-entry
book-keeping; and the sides of the ledger must balance. But
then, over and above this, association is generally connected
with reproduction, and is therefore advantageous to the stock
quite independently of its advantage to the individual. In many
cases, the social instincts are expensive to the individual, even
dangerous, sometimes fatal. It appears to me that this Subfamily has but one Genus and that this Genus has two Subgenera relating to the two kinds of instincts. There is a certain
difficulty in the fact that instincts for war are on the one hand
social, since war is a sort of social reaction, and is moreover
often dangerous, sometimes certainly fatal, yet on the other
hand, it seems improper to distinguish war from preying, and
preying is generally an affair of bread-winning, adapted to the
preservation of the agent. It seems to me, however, that in war
the enemy is not looked upon as fellow-creatures, but is treated
as a thing, and I believe that though the instinct brings danger,
it is nevertheless a selfish one, and ought to be classed with
those which go to preserve the agent. This is inconvenient, it
is true, as regards duels motived by jealousy, which is the chief
kind of fighting among herbivora. The leading instincts studied
in the first Subgenus are those of Feeding and Food Getting.
The study of these will make the first Species. The study of
instincts of War will be the second, with two Subspecies, the
study of instincts of active war making one, the study of self-
preservation including the instincts of self-concealment being
the other. Other species will study the minor instincts, such
as those of personal Cleanliness, of Medicine (dogs eating grass,
etc.), of hibernation, and the singular instinct for collecting
and hoarding all sorts of useless things, as seen in rats, in mag-

[16] Of course, if they are not so, they are not what the Darwinian means by
"adaptive." For example, Weismann says that death is an adaptive character.

pies, and some other animals, a genuine collecting mania, apparently quite useless. Then I am inclined to think that we must admit a Species for the study of instincts of working materials, such as the tree-felling instinct of beavers, the instinct of the wood-pecker. With this I would reckon all instinctive mechanical skill.

379. The Subgenus of Social Instinct has as its nucleus, so to speak, the Reproductive Instincts proper, to which the first Species will be devoted. Next in importance will be the Instincts of Communication; for some kind of language there is among nearly all animals. Not only do animals of the same species convey their assertions, but different classes of animals do so, as when a snake hypnotizes a bird. Two particularly important varieties of this Species of study will relate to Cries and Songs (among mammals and birds chiefly) and to facial expression among mammals.[17] As belonging to this Species I would include all studies of Instincts for understanding mind. But the subdivision of this Species requires much further study. A third Species will relate to the Architectural Instincts which I place here, although they are sometimes a bachelor establishment or even only a machine, like a cobweb. Passing by as unimportant the Instincts for Clothing, a fourth species will study Instincts of Locomotion and Migration. A fifth Species will relate to Instincts for Games; a sixth, to [the] Instinct for Adornment and Decoration, an Instinct which though associated with the Reproductive Instinct is quite distinct from it. The horse is delighted with a handsome harness. The poodle just trimmed goes to display himself to all his human friends without any teaching.

380. Passing to the second Subfamily of the Psychotaxy of Systems of Performance which relates to such systems in minds that are too highly developed for much wealth of Instinct, let me say, at once, that I doubt very much whether the Instinctive mind could ever develop into a Rational mind. I should expect the reverse process sooner. The Rational mind is the Progressive mind, and as such, by its very capacity for growth, seems more infantile than the Instinctive mind. Still, it would seem

---

[17] I can tell by the expression of face the state of mind of my horse just as unmistakably as I can that of my dog or my wife.

that Progressive minds must have, in some mysterious way, probably by arrested development, grown from Instinctive minds; and they are certainly enormously higher. The Deity of the Théodicée of Leibniz is as high an Instinctive mind as can well be imagined; but it impresses a scientific reader as distinctly inferior to the human mind. It reminds one of the view of the Greeks that Infinitude is a defect; for although Leibniz imagines that he is making the Divine Mind infinite, by making its knowledge Perfect and Complete, he fails to see that in thus refusing it the powers of thought and the possibility of improvement he is in fact taking away something far higher than knowledge. It is the human mind that is infinite. One of the most remarkable distinctions between the Instinctive mind of animals and the Rational mind of man is that animals rarely make mistakes, while the human mind almost invariably blunders at first, and repeatedly, where it is really exercised in the manner that is distinctive of it. If you look upon this as a defect, you ought to find an Instinctive mind higher than a Rational one, and probably, if you cross-examine yourself, you will find you do. The greatness of the human mind lies in its ability to discover truth notwithstanding its not having Instincts strong enough to exempt it from error.[18] This comes out strongly in almost any concrete instance. Frederic the Great is a notable example. Kant's power of making use of confused conceptions and working out so much truth as he did in spite of them illustrates this virtue. Hardly any really great inventor thoroughly comprehends his own invention until long after it is achieved.

381. The conception of the Rational Mind as an Unmatured Instinctive Mind which takes another development precisely because of its childlike character is confirmed, not only by the prolonged childhood of men, but also by the fact that all systems of rational performances have had instinct for their first germ. Not only has instinct been the first germ, but every step in the development of those systems of performance comes from instinct.[19] It is precisely because this Instinct is a weak,

---

[18] This is the marvel and admirable in it; and this essentially supposes a generous portion of capacity for blundering. [Peirce's marginal insert.]

[19] (Ed.) "Descriptive Definition of a Human Instinct, as the term will here be used. An animal instinct is a natural disposition, or inborn determination of

uncertain Instinct that it becomes infinitely plastic, and never reaches an ultimate state beyond which it cannot progress. Uncertain tendencies, unstable states of equilibrium are conditions *sine qua non* for the manifestation of Mind.

382.   It does not appear that all the animal instincts have produced great systems of human performance.[20] In a general way we can see that, in much the same sense in which it would be true that, according to the theory of Natural Selection, every step of the development from the moner to man has been due to fortuitous variations in reproduction, we can equally say that every step of the progress of physiognosy has been due to a guess prompted by one of those instincts studied in the First Subgenus of the science of Instinct, or as we may call them, the mechanical instincts, and that every step in the progress of psychical science has been due to a guess prompted by one of the social instincts. But science is, after all, but a small part of the rational developments that have had instinct for what we may call their efficient cause; that is, their cause so long as we consider them only as aggregates of their smallest parts, neglecting all that we do neglect when we say that Natural Selection makes man the result of fortuitous variations at birth; in one word, neglecting the rational, the integral, element altogether.

383.   But the importance of the different Intellectual Systems of Performance which have developed from the different instincts have had not the slightest relation to the strength or

---

the individual's Nature (his 'nature' being that within him which causes his behaviour to be such as it is), manifested by a certain unity of quasi-purpose in his behaviour. In man, at least, this behaviour is always conscious, and not purely spasmodic. More than that, unless he is under some extraordinary stress, the behaviour is always partially controlled by the deliberate exercise of imagination and reflexion; so much so that to the man himself his action appears to be entirely rational, so far is it from being merely sensori-motor. General analogy and many special phenomena warrant the presumption that the same thing is true of the lower animals, though they are undoubtedly far less reflective than men. Yet the adaptation of the behaviour to its quasi-purpose in some definite part overlaps all control. . . . So then the three essential characters of instinctive conduct are that it is conscious, is determined to a quasi-purpose, and that in definite respects it escapes all control." From "Of the Classification of the Sciences. Second Paper. Of the Practical Sciences," Widener II, c.1902 (see 7.49n1).

[20] (Ed.) The marginal sidehead "Science is but a Development of Instinct" appears opposite this paragraph.

to the adaptiveness of those instincts. In a general way, the useful arts have mostly developed from the Selfish Instincts. But of all these instincts perhaps those of Food getting and Feeding are the strongest. What has developed from these? Agriculture is by far the most respectable of their offspring. The Instincts of War have given rise to the Arts of War. Mechanical Instincts connected with the human hand, and therefore peculiar to man, have probably affected tool-making. But it is a general mechanical instinct, common to almost all animals, which has produced physics and the physical arts generally. Self-preservation has been a motive, or final cause, of the Art of Medicine; but it does not seem to have contributed anything to Medicine as an efficient effect of this instinct.

384.   The Social Instincts were more sympathetic to Reason; and it is they that have been the efficient cause of most human performances, and of the higher ones. For although it happens that perspective at this time makes Physiognosy seem very great, it is not in the nature of things that it should be so. True, [it] is pure; it is unblotted by all the ignoble passions which disfigure other elements of civilization. That is its most admirable feature; and it is not a merely negative one. But at the end of the twenty-first century that will no longer be the achievement upon which man can most plume himself. Of the Social Instincts, by far the most violent are of course the Reproductive Instincts; and in man they strongly color all but one of the Social Instincts, to such a degree as almost to weld them all together. The earliest Art of man, after that of trapping animals, was doubtless the Art of making a home. A cluster of arts there are there; as architecture, heating, lighting, etc. Families became communities; and there gradually arose a notion of what customs and behaviour were tolerable. It must have been early in this state of things when men were leading an easy and joyous life, — perhaps in the flush of some great victory which brought them slaves, — or perhaps having recently domesticated cows, — that language began to take a grammatical form, so that sentences could be constructed, and to acquire a relatively copious vocabulary. I have never seen a satisfactory account of how it came about; but the time is ripe for such an account. Next month's *Popular Science Monthly*

may tell us that some Italian has accomplished the feat. Language gave man distinct conceptions, and awakened in him the idea of understanding things. The first fruit of the scientific spirit must have been a Theology, and some confused Cosmogony; [21] for it is man's way to attack the most difficult questions first, and attempt detailed answers to them. What the first religion was like one would give something to know. To tell us would be a suitable task for a Shakespeare and a Browning, in collaboration with a Darwin, a Spencer, and a Hegel. Records we have none of any faith that has not undergone corruption and reform; senility and rejuvenation by fards, hair-dyes, and false teeth; revolution and restoration; death and galvanization, over and over again.

385. Let us see how far we can utilize such reflexions in classifying the Classificatory Sciences of Intellectual Systems of Performance. In the light of what has been said, there seem to be about seven Genera. The first embraces studies of the kinds of purely Material Arts; the second, studies of Ways of Individual Life; the third, studies of Customs and Laws and of Constitutions of Society; the fourth, of Religions; the fifth, of Classifications of Sciences, the very subject upon which we are now engaged, so that we are in the somewhat embarrassing position of having to criticize the very thing we are doing before it can get done; the sixth, of Fine Arts; the seventh, of Language. . . .[22]

[21] As I write, the *Monist* XII.321 brings me the account of such a thing dating from the XVIth century before Christ, or earlier. Several sciences are known to have been earlier than that; but they were probably looked upon as Useful Arts. This seems purely speculative.

(Ed.) The reference is to James H. Breasted, "The First Philosopher," *The Monist* 12(April, 1902)321–336.

[22] (Ed.) We omit a long section on linguistics and anthropology. The following is from an alternate page of this part of the manuscript (see 362n1): "The Indo-European languages are singular in having the common noun distinctly and fully developed as a separate part of speech, and by more or less development even of abstract nouns. I do not mean to say that the common noun is not fully developed in any other language; but only that such a phenomenon is exceptional in every other great family of speech. This requires and evidences considerable power of thought on the part of those who use these languages. With the exercise of a little ingenuity it is possible to express anything in these languages, provided no higher relations than dyadic ones enter. Only very simple propositions can be expressed involving higher relations; and those whose mental education is limited by the powers of these languages are unable to grasp the meaning of a complex triple relation; . . ."

386. The second Suborder of Classificatory Psychognosy deals with kinds of minds. This, very evidently, if we exclude the minds of plants, and of communities, divides into two Families treating respectively of Animal Instinct and of Types of Men. A fair beginning has been made of the study of animal minds. We really seem to be penetrating the psychical nature of the Hymenoptera, — souls so utterly unlike our own. It is most desirable that we should add to this an understanding of some third kind of mind different from both the others, — say, for example, that of the octopus, whose passions are betrayed by the waves of color that pass over his person. For one can hardly make a beginning of generalization until three instances are at hand. The worms, echinoderms, coelenterates and sponges do not seem to be very interesting psychically. But the squids have a sort of horrible fascination. . . .

387. Of types of men, serious investigations have been made of genius, of criminals, of men of science, and of great men, generally.[23] Theophrastus began the study of types of character; and different authors have, in various ages and countries, displayed the most splendid power for this sort of research. But unfortunately, they have all been seduced by the glamour of literary glory, — even St. Simon, (the ancestor, I mean), whose memoirs were not published until three quarters of a century after his death; so that a field of science of whose cultivation there is the most urgent need, both theoretically and practically has been for millennia lying fallow ground awaiting a conscientious ploughman.[24]

[23] (Ed.) Cf. 7.256–266.

[24] (Ed.) The manuscript continues, "In Descriptive Psychognosy we have recognized two Suborders, the one relating to Situations, the other to Events." Cf. 1.272. Peirce then discusses bibliography, books of travels, numismatics, metrology, history, etc.

CHAPTER 2

ASSOCIATION [1]

§1. GENERAL CHARACTERISTICS OF MENTAL ACTION

388. In the absence of external impressions of interest, thoughts begin to dance through the mind, each leading in another by the hand, like a train of Bacchants on a Grecian vase, as Hegel says. After a while the clear train of thought breaks, and for a time ideas are scattered, soon, however, to take places again in another train.

There is a *law* in this succession of ideas. We may roughly say it is the law of habit. It is the great "Law of the Association of Ideas," — the one law of all psychical action.

389. Many psychologists hold that this law as strictly necessitates what idea shall rise on a given occasion as the law of mechanics necessitates how a body in a given relative position to other bodies endowed with given forces shall have its motion altered. This is a theory hard to disprove; but it is a mere forejudgment, or prejudice: no observed facts afford the slightest warrant for it. I do not mean to condemn the trial of it, in psychology, as a working hypothesis: on the contrary, logic fully approves of it in that sense. But many things are worth trial, which do not seem at any time probably true. What is,

[1] (Ed.) Sections 1–7 are "Introduction, Association of Ideas," c.1893, from *Grand Logic*, Widener IB2–1, with the omission of Art. 3, a long section devoted to the history of the doctrine of association, of which only a few sentences are printed (417n21), and with an added quotation in 392n7. Sections 1 and 2 are Peirce's Art. 1 and 2, respectively, and sections 3 through 7 are Peirce's Art. 4 through Art. 8, respectively. The titles of all these sections, except that of Section 5, are taken from a partial table of contents in Widener IB2–1, with some changes in capitalization.

far more than unyielding uniformity, characteristic of the phenomenon of *suggestion*, as the calling up of an idea through
association is called,[2] is its *gentleness*. There is another natural
operation that, from every point of view, seems much nearer
allied to the psychological sequence than is mechanical causation; I mean heredity. Now heredity, powerful as it is, leaves
room for sporting, or variations. Remark that the development
of species, whether by Natural Selection or by Artificial Breeding, would be impossible were variations not to occur in the
teeth of heredity; and in like manner without the element of
spontaneous originality, or something acting like it, the development of thought would be instantly arrested.[3] Hume, whose
cogitations led up to the recognition of Association as the one
law of mind, most judiciously remarks, "This uniting principle
among ideas is not to be considered as an inseparable connex-
ion; for that has been already excluded from the imagination:
Nor yet are we to conclude, that without it the mind cannot
join two ideas; for nothing is more free than that faculty: but
we are only to regard it as a gentle force, which commonly prevails." [4] That phrase "a *gentle* force which *commonly* prevails"
describes the phenomenon to perfection.

390.   But it is hopeless to expect men to agree about the
question of spontaneity. The observed facts all tend to support it; but some men *will* deny it, because they are disinclined
to that view; thus exercising that very freedom that they refuse
to recognize.

§2. CONTIGUITY AND RESEMBLANCE

391.   Psychologists differ in regard to what they call the primary principles of association; but the usual doctrine is that
suggestion takes place either by *Contiguity* or by *Resemblance*.
These are Hume's terms, which psychologists have agreed to
retain as convenient names, although as descriptions they are

[2] It is now more often called *reproduction*, which is the German term. I
prefer to write English; and certainly no reader will suppose that I am speaking of suggestion in its hypnotic connection.

[3] (Ed.) Cf. 6.60.

[4] (Ed.) *A Treatise of Human Nature*. In the Everyman's Library edition,
No. 548, 1939, edited by Ernest Rhys, this passage appears in Vol. I, page 19.

acknowledged to be faulty enough. Suggestion by contiguity means that when an idea is familiar to us as part of a system of ideas, that idea may call the system to our minds, and from the system, one of the other ideas may, for some reason, detach itself and come to be thought of by itself. Thus, mention "the judicial branch of government," and you suggest the idea of a government composed of an executive, a legislature, and a judiciary; and shortly after, the person to whom you are speaking, if you are boring him, will have his ideas running, it may be, upon executive power, it may be upon the conduct of a legislative assembly. So, mention a *wife*, and your hearer will think of husband and wife, and thereupon, most likely, of a married man. Mention a knife-blade and the whole knife will be thought of, and thence a knife-handle. Thus, suggestion by contiguity may be defined as the suggestion by an idea of another, which has been associated with it, not by the nature of thought, but by *experience*, or the course of life.[5]

392. Suggestion by *resemblance* is easily enough understood, as soon as the conception is once grasped that the similarity of two ideas *consists* in the fact that the mind naturally joins them in thought in a certain way. For instance, yesterday I saw a blue color; and here *is* a blue color. I recall that sensation of yesterday, and I observe that of today. I find myself disposed to say the two are closely allied; *in that disposition their similarity consists*. For they are two different ideas. One was in my mind yesterday, and consequently that identical idea is not present now. However, I accept the impression it has left on my memory as probably about right. I look again at the color before me. The idea of yesterday and that of today are two ideas; they have nothing in common, unless it be that the mind naturally throws them together. Some beginner may object that they have both a *blueness* in them; but I reply that blueness is nothing but the idea of these sensations and of others I have had, thrown together and indistinctly thought at once. Blueness is the idea of the *class*. It is absurd to say that different things which cannot be compared are alike, except in the sense that they act alike. Now, two ideas are compared only in the idea of the class, lot, or set to which they belong;

[5] (Ed.) Cf. 1.383.

and they act alike only in so far as they have one and the same relation to that connecting idea. Resemblance, then, is a mode of association by the inward nature of ideas and of mind.[6] There are other modes of such association. Thus, contrary ideas are thrown into pairs by [the] inward nature of ideas and of mind. Numbers run into a succession, or sequence, by the same force. What does this figure show? The answer will be a broken star. That answer shows how the mind naturally looks at those lines from the point of view of a *set*, or regular figure, to which they do not even conform. As experience clusters certain ideas into *sets*, so does the mind too, by its occult nature,[7] cluster certain ideas into *sets*. These sets have various forms of connection.[8] The simplest are sets of things all on one footing and agreeing in each belonging to the set. Such a set is a *class*. The clustering of ideas into *classes* is the simplest form which the association of ideas by the occult nature of ideas, or of the mind, can take. Now, just as in association by contiguity an idea calls up the idea of the *set* in which experience has placed it, and thence one of the other ideas of that set, so in association by resemblance an idea calls up the idea of the *set* in which the mind's occult virtue places it, and that conception perhaps gives, owing to some other circumstance, another of the particular ideas of the same set. Everybody has heard in conversation a person remark, "What you say puts me in mind of a similar occurrence." That is suggestion by resemblance. Association by contrast is a case of association by resemblance, which is so called after its most prominent variety. Suggestion by resemblance means, let it be repeated, the indirect suggestion by one idea of another which has, by virtue of the occult nature of ideas or of the mind, been associated with it into one set. All the suggestions of pure mathematics, of which there is a vast body, are associations by resemblance. Some psychologists

[6] (Ed.) Cf. 4.157.

[7] (Ed.) "An 'occult property' is a property which is only brought to light by experiment. 'Occult Science' means, therefore, precisely experimental science. The reason these properties were called occult was that they could not be deduced after the manner of Aristotle from the prime qualities hot and cold, moist and dry." A footnote, p. 16, from Peirce's Prospectus of *The Treatise of Petrus Peregrinus on the Lodestone*, [Bibliography] G–c.1893–4.

[8] See Mr. A. B. Kempe's Memoir upon Mathematical Form.

252

refuse to acknowledge association by resemblance. The reason is that they conceive that two different principles of association break the law of association into two; now the idea that there must be *one* law for a given group of phenomena is an idea so natural to the mind, that for the sake of it, those psychologists allow themselves to wrench all the facts, thus illustrating by their own action the strength of the kind of association which they refuse to acknowledge. . . .[9]

§3. DEFENCE OF AUTHOR'S OPINIONS STATED IN ART. 2 [SEC. 2]

393.   The reader, having thus been railroaded through the history of the doctrine of association, will perceive that the present writer differs from an important minority of the authorities in holding to two principles of association, and that he differs from all the English psychologists while agreeing with the Herbartians, in splitting the suggestion of B by A into two operations, one leading from A to AB and the other from AB to B.

394.   As a sufficient defence of association by resemblance, as a fundamental mode of association, he offers the remark that resemblance *consists* in an association due to the occult substratum of thought.

395.   The defence of the division of suggestion into two steps cannot be quite so summary. In the first place, there are many cases in association in which parts of the train of thought do not appear in memory. Different psychologists have different ways of treating this difficulty. Some maintain that they are performed with lightning rapidity and also with a low degree of consciousness. This is very improbable. Others, as Leibniz, Hamilton, Hartmann,[10] Samuel Butler,[11] and others maintain that they are totally unconscious, or practically so. The present writer will not countenance the rejection of a theory because of metaphysical difficulties. The great object of the metaphysics of Duns Scotus is so to state the results of ordinary

[9] (Ed.) Art. 3, on the history of the doctrine of association, is deleted here (see 388n1).

[10] Hartmann's account of association is well worth reading.

[11] *Unconscious Memory*.

experience, that it shall not close any positive experimental inquiry, or pronounce anything possibly observable to be *a priori*
impossible. In Scotus, this naturally led to loyalty to Authority,
then the recognized fountain of truth; in our day it will produce unfaltering faith in Observation. Still others are of opinion that parts of a train of association may be altogether sup-
pressed. We cannot deny the possibility of such a thing.

396.   The present writer has made a good many quantitative
experiments to ascertain what he could of the nature of consciousness and of attention. It would not be convenient to set
these forth in this place.[12] But the conclusions to which they
lead will be mentioned. An excitement of the nerves will spread,
and affect more and more nerve matter. The total excitement
may considerably increase, in this. No equation is preserved.
It may also wear itself out. Considerable excitements expend
themselves *out of* the spinal nerves, either in contractions of
voluntary muscles, attended mostly with a sober activity of
mind, or in glandular secretions, actions on involuntary muscles, probably through the sympathetic nerves, and these cases
are apt to be accompanied by emotional excitement of the soul.
Ideas tending to either of these modes of suggestion present the
phenomenon of interest. The intensity of ideas is of two kinds,
an *objective* and a *subjective intensity*. A high color, a loud
sound, a burn have, *per se*, high objective intensity. I have not
been to Niagara for three or four years. But I well recall the
tremendous roar; objectively the intensity of the idea is great,
as great as it was when it was present (possibly more so), but
subjectively my memory of it is getting now a little dim. I
remember some time about 37 years ago sitting in the dark
room of my class-mate, Albert Stickney, he having just carried
away the lamp, I believe. I suddenly saw everything lit up and
quickly looking out the window I caught sight of a great meteor.
Objectively, my memory of it is of an intense light; subjectively, it is very dim.[13] Ideas of great objective intensity have

---

[12] They are written out, but as for seeing the light, even if they were printed,
that does in no wise depend on their merit. Men do not want to know the truth
and they ought to have their way.

(Ed.)   But cf. 7.546, 7.215.

[13] The distinction is virtually made by James Mill. J. S. Mill, and I think
Bain too, mistakenly calls subjective intensity *emotional* intensity.

their subjective intensity, other things being equal, greatly reinforced; but the distinction is unmistakable. The word *interest*
probably *means* suggestiveness of action or emotion; but it is
accompanied with considerable subjective intensity of direct
consciousness. The phenomenon of the heightening of the subjective intensity of an idea as it draws into the vortex of an
interesting suggestion, is called *attention*. Ribot and others
wish to make attention a fundamental element of consciousness.
I grant the fundamental element that they are groping for really
exists, and that to some extent it affects attention; but attention
itself does not consist in that, nor does that element show out
with remarkable clearness in attention. When we try to say
what is immediately in consciousness, we have a difficult task.
We have to tear down a whole structure which the mind has
built round it; and throw that away, while leaving the original
elements. Nothing requires greater energy, and energetic determination to be passive; nothing is more fatiguing; and no
mental process is so slow. Suppose, you are asked of two colors
which is the more agreeable. If you have no training in introspective observation, you may answer quickly; so you may, if
there is a marked difference in agreeability. But otherwise, it
may take a minute or more of fatiguing strain to reply. Of two
pressures brought upon the skin, which seems the stronger, is
a direct question of introspective observation. But it is difficult.
Sensations differing so slightly, that an exhausting effort of
attention, under the most favorable surroundings, leaves us a
feeling of utter inability to make out any difference, can, nevertheless, be proved to affect the mind. For instance, it is found
that in such cases, if the observer forces himself to say which
is the stronger sensation, though his answer seems to him to be
given at random, yet taking a dozen sets of a hundred answers,
in each set there will be a decided preponderance of true answers.[14] Pass now to sensations differing quite markedly, —
or which according to the difference of excitations ought to do
so, — and try thousands of times asking which is the stronger.
It will be found that erroneous answers are given, oftener than
anybody would believe possible in advance of the experiment.

[14] (Ed.) See Chapter 2, "Small Differences of Sensation," of Book I of the
present volume.

That this is not due entirely to the sensations not being what the excitations ought to produce is shown by other mental effects they produce. Take a series of efforts of given degree; for instance, in frames of mind which are marked by the observer on a scale as seeming to have about the same vigor, let a given time say 30 seconds be given to an introspective effort; let this effort be applied to the attempt to discriminate two sensations, and let the resulting feeling of confidence that they are correctly distinguished be marked on a scale. Now out of a thousand observations, where the difference of excitations was the same, the mean difference of sensations will be less than in another thousand observations where the difference of excitations was twice as great. We can then count the proportion of cases in which the degree of confidence in the reply reached a certain point on the scale. Thence, we can, by the usual mathematical methods, find a formula connecting the proportion of cases in which the given degree of confidence is reached with the difference of excitation. Then, we uniformly find that if that degree of confidence is not so high as to invalidate the formula, owing to the small number of cases in which it is observed, [then] it makes no difference what its degree may be in respect to this: that the proportion of cases in which it occurs only sinks to zero when the difference of excitations sinks to zero. It follows, I think, that there is no sensation which can affect the mind at all, which cannot be detected in consciousness by a sufficient exertion of attention.

397. The result of the study of the above formulae and of many others (which I have never published, because no psychologist has paid the slightest attention to those I have published) is that the contents of immediate consciousness range all the way from feelings which an indefinitely great effort is required to reduce to [a] given grade of subjective intensity to feelings which an indefinitely great effort is required to magnify to any given grade of subjective intensity. If we assume, as a convenient scale of measurement, that the measure of subjective intensity of an idea before such effort is applied to it is, other things being equal, proportional to a base raised to a power expressing the degree of effort required to lower its subjective intensity to an assumed standard, then I find that

no feelings affecting the mind have the measures of their subjective intensities 0 or ∞; but that they approach indefinitely to those limits. Without any effort of attention at all, certain feelings have sufficient subjective intensity to affect us in certain ways, for instance, to cause us, in an off-hand answer, to reply that we are affected by them. The subjective intensity of many a feeling is sufficient for *that* without being sufficient to rouse us to decided exertion. On the other hand, the subjective intensity of many a feeling, though insufficient for that, is sufficient to affect our actions and color our emotions strongly.

398. Ideas become subjectively intense, if they are objectively intense. They become for a moment subjectively intense and directly after dim, if their suggestions are interesting. They become subjectively intense in small sets, especially sets of two; and become subjectively faint in large sets. They rapidly lose subjective intensity with time, while at the same time they spread into sets.

399. It follows from the above that the compound idea AB may be operative as an intermediate stage between A and B, notwithstanding our seldom being able to detect it in contiguous suggestion.

Very often this intermediate stage *can* be directly detected. In others, [it] is demonstrably there, as in ideas of motion where the preservation of the identity in idea of the mobile [is such] that one stage must have been imagined before the imagination of the previous stage was relinquished.

In other cases, whether the compound is present as intermediacy or not can only be a matter of hypothesis. That theory must be adopted which (1) best and (2) most simply explains the observed facts, is (3) in the closest analogy with the rest of our knowledge, and (4) is attributable to causes known to operate or most likely to be operative.

400. The theory here advocated is called, for convenience, the "new" theory. It is not really new; but it has been furbished up so as to be as good as new; and the designation is handy.[15]

401. (1) It is true that the new theory does not so well

[15] (Ed.) In the following paragraphs, Peirce shows the inter-relationship between the points he is making by numbering them in a special way. We have placed these numbers in parentheses to separate them from the paragraph num-

explain the observed facts in the majority of suggestions by contiguity, because it supposes an idea to pass unnoticed. See (11), below.

But it has the advantage in those cases of contiguity where it is observed that A suggests AB. For this kind of suggestion does not come under the old formula. And it is difficult to explain how AB should be somtimes suggested by A and not always suggested.

In the case of association by resemblance, on the other hand, all the testimony of consciousness is that A almost always suggests AB, and perhaps never directly B. See (12), below.

402. (2) In regard to the simplicity of the theory a trifold distinction has to be made. In the sense of presenting many more features requiring study, and suggesting many more questions, the new theory is infinitely more complicated than the old one. See (21), below.

In the sense of being a more natural conception, it is doubtful which theory is superior. But this point is not an important one. See (22), below.

In the sense [of] giving a more unitary account of all the facts, the new theory is superior. See (23), below.

403. (3) In the general analogy with attraction the superiority is with the new theory. See (31), below.

In the general analogy with other changes of state, the superiority is with the new theory. See (32), below.

The new theory is more in conformity with current views of philologists about changes in the signification of words. See (33), below.

The new theory is favored by those modern psychologists who have made the most thorough study of association. See (34), below.

404. (4) There is a psychological cause which would probably produce the process supposed in the new theory. See (41), below.

405. Let us now consider the ten points just mentioned a little more closely.[16]

---

bers. Note that (22) is the second point under (2), (32) is the second point subordinate to (3), (321) the first sub-item under (32), etc.

[16] (Ed.) In the manuscript paragraph 404 was inserted between the lines after paragraph 405. We have adopted the present order so that there will be

406. (11) The new theory supposes a fact of consciousness usually to pass unnoticed in suggestions by contiguity, namely that when A suggests B, the compound idea AB intervenes.

But, then, it is to be observed that this is a sort of fact of consciousness very likely to pass unnoticed. It is well-known that ideas containing peculiar elements often do pass through the mind unnoticed. But in this case, there is no peculiar element. What is supposed is that instead of A jumping out of consciousness at the very instant B opens the door, quicker than a mouse could run into its hole, it stays until it finds itself *de trop*. Since it is necessary to suppose that the star of A is on the wane, very little interest would be had in it; and its remaining would not be noticed at the time, and still less be remembered. When you are entertaining a bore, if a visitor of consequence enters the room; and the bore behaves modestly, nobody can say afterwards whether he took his departure at that moment or not. It is, therefore, certain that the number of cases in which we remember positively that A did suggest AB and only later B, which cases are after all numerous, *cannot*, according to known principles of attention, be but a small percentage of all the cases in which this happened. But dividing the observed frequency of the intermediate suggestion by this small percentage we certainly get a large percentage, and it may be unity. Not knowing the percentages numerically, we cannot positively say that the quotient *is* unity; but it is not at all unlikely that it is so.

407. (12) We have seen [17] that Bain, as high an authority as any desultory observer can be, and there are as yet too few scientific observations of association to be of much importance, holds that generalization is the direct effect of "an effort of similarity." Why not say, at once, it is the first half of a suggestion by similarity? I am trying to recall the precise hue of a certain emerald that my mother used to wear. A sequence of shades runs through my mind. Perhaps they run into a continuum; but that makes no difference. They are a multitude of colors suggested by that one color. Conceived under what

---

references to ten numbered points, (11), (12), (21), (22), (23), (31), (32), (33), (34), and (41), preceding paragraph 405.

[17] (Ed.) In the deleted Art. 3; see 392n9.

Kant imperfectly describes as a rule or schema, they constitute
a *general* conception of a green something like that emerald.
The old-fashioned nominalists would say nothing was in my
mind but a *word*, or other *symbol*. For my part, I am not quite
prepared to say what precisely is in my consciousness; but of
this I am sure, that every memory of a sensation is more or
less vague, that is, general. Every *memory*! Why, the sensation itself, when present for a few moments, is so; as every
person who has made careful photometric measures is aware.
In working with a photometer, I have confined myself to observations of a square centimetre some 10 inches from the eye;
and have found the most elaborate arrangements hardly adequate to make the illumination of that small surface sensibly
uniform. What, then, must be the vagueness of our observation
when we look at a whole sheet of paper and pronounce it to be
of one shade throughout? How is it possible to reconcile our
notions of the origin of errors of observation with the doctrine
that the sensation is absolutely free from all vagueness, all
generality? But if it be granted that every memory of a sensation is more or less general, the distinction of intuitive and
symbolical knowledge breaks down, as an absolute distinction.
The vague memory of a sensation is just an aggregate, whether
continuous or not makes no difference, of ideas which are called
up together by a suggesting idea. The apparent direct suggestion of a single, or anything that can be taken for a single,
idea by resemblance, is so rare, if not altogether dubious, a
phenomenon, that William James declares that "there is no
tendency on the part of simple ideas or qualities to remind us
of their like." [18]

408.   (21) If A remains in consciousness after it has called
in B, we have to inquire in what form A and B coexist in consciousness at such times and what their relation is, a question

---

[18] Professor James seems to think it to the purpose to remark that "the similarity of two things does not exist till both are there." That may be; it is so,
in a sense. But how he infers that "it is meaningless to talk of it as an agent
of production" I cannot see. Nobody means that the *appearance* of resemblance
is an agent but that what there is in the depths of the soul that makes the appearance also makes the association.

(Ed.) The quotation from James in the text is from *The Principles of Psychology*, Vol. 1, Henry Holt and Company, New York, 1890, p. 579; the quotation in this footnote is from the same volume, p. 591.

which we escape, of course, if A vanishes in the act of bringing in B. Nor is this question so innocent and easy as it may appear at first blush; on the contrary, it leads to considerable discussion and creates an extensive theory. Moreover, when A and B are both present, a new problem presents itself. Namely, how A drops out; and that phenomenon, examined closely, turns out to be far from the simple thing one might fancy it would be. Besides, the cases are few in which the *set* of associated ideas [19] consists of a pair. Most often it is what the country-people in my neighborhood call "quite a few," that is, almost a good many. At other times, though more rarely, it is three or more. Now if A calls up ABCD etc., it is a serious question how all these coexist in consciousness, and another why and how ACD etc. all disappear. Do they all depart in company, or do they sneak out one by one? And in the latter case, do those that remain have to rearrange themselves at each departure? And *why* should this desertion take place? And what determines who is to be left as IT, to use the terminology of children's games? All these questions are avoided on the old theory.

409. (22) In a question like this, it really makes little difference whether the hypothesis adopted is a natural one or not. We ought to give high authority to natural, instinctive conceptions of the mind, so far as they are of any practical utility. For natural selection, or whatever the principle of evolution may be, is there to adapt them to the welfare of the species. But in questions like that now on the *tapis*, natural psychology is quite beyond its depth. We will not stop, therefore, to argue this question.

410. (23) The purpose of a theory may be said to be to embrace the manifold of observed facts in one statement, and other things being equal that theory best fulfils its function which brings the most facts under a single formula. Besides, it will be shown in the chapter [20] devoted to the reckoning of

---

[19] James wants us to say *things*. I reply that *ideas* were always meant as *objects*, direct objects, not matters of psychology, by those who talked of them. When he says *things* he cannot mean the real external things; for they are beyond the power of thought. He can only mean the perceived *objects*, which are precisely what is meant by "ideas." What is *perceived* is an *idea*, in contradistinction to a raw sensation.

[20] (Ed.) Chapters XVIII (2.645–660) and XIX of the *Grand Logic* were to

the probabilities about such reasoning that the credibility of
the more unitary hypothesis is far superior.

Now the new theory makes the whole action of the soul, so
far as it is subject to law, consist of nothing but taking up and
letting drop in ceaseless alternation. The old theory is obliged
to recognize the same processes, and besides supposes, quite
unnecessarily, an additional elementary process of passing over
from A to B by a saltus. *Entia non sunt multiplicanda praeter
necessitatem* is a maxim of science, which, we shall find, applies
to forbid all unnecessary elements of hypothesis.

411. (31) Several philosophers of high rank consider the
analogy between association and attraction to be a true and
intrinsic one. Whether it really is so or not is doubtful; besides
attraction is a little out of fashion among the physicists of
our day. Studies of elasticity, in particular, have undermined
its philosophical ascendancy. Still, taking the analogy for what
it is worth, it is certainly much closer with the new theory. For
according to the old theory, while A attracts B, B not only
repels A, but repels it with such violence that A goes as soon as
B begins to appear. The law of action and reaction would forbid
such a phenomenon in physics. We there see one thing strike
against another and knock it out; but we do not see it do this
by virtue of the attraction of that second thing. On the new
theory on the other hand, a wave of condensation brings B up
to A, when the completion of the undulation carries A away.

412. (32) Of a good deal more significance are analogies
with physical changes in general; and these are two. Under
(321), we consider the saltus involved in the old theory; under
(322) the rhythm involved in the new theory.

413. (321) Nowhere in nature is there the slightest reason
to believe that any *saltus* takes place during changes. The more
we learn of physics, the more we are led to exclude such hypotheses. Nor is there the slightest appearance of the phenomena of the mind being more sudden than those of matter. On
the contrary the general evidence of experimental psychology
is that mental actions are particularly gradual and gentle.

The old theory, understood as opposed to the new, supposes

be on probability and induction, respectively; no manuscript of Chapter XIX
has been found.

that at every instant up to a certain instant A is present and B absent, and at every instant after the same instant A is absent and B present.

According to the doctrine of limits, used in the calculus, that is, according to the geometer's conception of time and space, it would follow that *at* the limiting instant A and B were both present and absent. Now, it may be that time is not really continuous in the way in which the mathematician takes it to be; but logic will not justify the hypothesis that it is not continuous.

Everywhere in nature things that appear and disappear do so little by little. For instance, we can suppose the idea A fades out of attention and out of consciousness, while B quickly grows prominent. But, there, both must be present at once, or else A must be entirely extinct before B begins to appear. It is far more rational to suppose both are present, at once; first, because it is more natural and analogical to suppose A acts as a cause while it is in existence, second, because quantitative experiment shows that A would not naturally fade out quickly until B is already present to accelerate the fading.

414.   (322) Everywhere in the world of life there is an alternating motion, an inspiration and expiration. Now according to the new theory, the whole activity of the mind consists of a drawing in and dropping out. One thing's moving in just as another moves out might be supposed in the case of an incompressible fluid not subject to diffusion; but there is no reason to think it really takes place in any case.

415.   (33) The changes in the significations of words obey, of course, the law of association; and having been studied until of comparatively recent years as facts of observation, in themselves, without prejudice from psychological theory, they are independent evidence. Now, philologists, from their observations of such changes, have reduced them to successive broadenings and narrowings. The broadenings consist in the taking in of new ideas, the narrowings in the dropping out of little-used ideas.

416.   (34) The Herbartians have made the most elaborate and minute studies of association of any psychologists, except the somewhat desultory but very extended studies of the

263

English associationalists. Now, the Herbartian theory of apperception is precisely the theory that A suggests AB. It perfectly agrees with the present theory, only that the Herbartians do not admit that A is ever dropped, again. AB becomes what may be figured as ᴀB, the A becoming faint; but even this is, according to them, unusual. They hold that the ordinary phenomenon is rather Aᴮ.

417.   (41) Finally, there is a good reason why A should not disappear, until B has been present for some time. For ideas persist in consciousness for a long time after they are gone from the field of easy attention. See Hartley's Proposition 3, a doctrine elaborately studied by the modern school.[21]

§4. PSYCHOLOGICAL TRUTHS NEEDED IN LOGIC

418.   Reasoning is performed by the mind. Hence, the logician must not be entirely neglectful of the science of mind. This science, more than any other, is embarrassed by metaphysical puzzles. The attempt to avoid these only leads to careless and noxious solutions of them. What are the observed facts of psychology? They are the behaviour of men, especially what they *say*, together with our observation of what takes place within us, termed *introspection*.

419.   What is the nature of introspection? The pre-scientific psychologists, such as Hamilton, believed that introspection was infallible. "To know, and to know that we know, are one and the same thing," said that philosopher.[22] They also had the naïve opinion that the things which are immediately present to consciousness are the things which introspection reveals. If those psychologists had been at all acquainted with

[21] (Ed.) In the discussion of Hartley in the omitted Art. 3, Peirce says: "Proposition 3: sensations remain in the soul for a brief interval of time after the object is removed. This seems like a genuine psychological observation; and the acuteness of the physician is certainly shown in giving it this foremost place. But the proof offered is perfectly futile."

[22] (Ed.) In *Discussions on Philosophy and Literature, Education and University Reform,* Harper and Brothers, New York, 1861, p. 53, Sir William Hamilton says: "*We know*; and *We know that we know*: — these propositions, *logically* distinct, are *really* identical; each implies the other. . . . The attempt to analyze the cognition *I know*, and the cognition *I know that I know*, into the separate energies of distinct faculties, **is** therefore vain."

the experimental sciences, they would have seen (what they would, doubtless, readily have acknowledged) that in these respects psychology, as they conceived it, was radically unlike any other observational science. The things we observe in a physical science, say in astronomy, are not the elementary facts, at all. Kepler, for example, was not, as even J. S. Mill seems to fancy, provided, in the observations of Tycho, with the real places of the planet Mars, by the study of which he made out two of his three laws. No astronomer can directly *observe* the situation of a planet relatively to the sun. He only observes, the secondary and derivative fact, that the planet as viewed from the earth, and subject to aberration and the equation of time, is in such and such a *direction* at such a time. According to the method of observation, this direction will be more or less affected by refraction, etc. Moreover, the astronomer is forced to recognize that every single observation he makes is more or less affected by *error*. Those errors have to be corrected by reasoning whose only premises are the erroneous observations themselves.

420.   Now the truth is that the data of introspection are in these respects altogether analogous to those of external observation. Introspection does not directly reveal what is immediately present to consciousness, at all; but only what seems to have been present from the standpoint of subsequent reflection. It does not even tell what the normal appearance from this subsequent standpoint is, without its testimony being falsified at all times with serious accidental errors.[23]

We cannot directly observe even so much as that there is such a thing as present consciousness.

421.   We set out with a mass of opinions about the mind, which are not testified to by introspection. They are simply man's natural psychology. It is instinctive, no doubt, in part; for we can see that the lower animals have virtually such a psychology. In part also, it grows up nearly the same in all men as the natural result of similar experiences acting upon similar understandings. There is not the smallest reason for supposing that that natural psychology is at all accurately true; on the contrary, it probably involves great errors. At the same time,

[23] (Ed.) Cf. 5.213ff.

its authority must be allowed to be very high indeed in regard to all features which are of importance in the conduct of life; for, on the whole, man has prospered under such beliefs.

422.   A part of this instinctive science, as we may call it, is that events succeed one another in time, that the past, when not too remote, is remembered, that the future, when not too remote, can be with some probability conjectured or antici- pated, and that a single moment between the past and the future, (that is, *some* facts belonging to that *moment*), is directly before the mind.

423.   This is the first item of our instinctive psychology. It makes a distribution of knowledge which has the closest bear- ing upon practical life; and to doubt its practical truth would be idle. At the same time, we have no reason at all for pre- suming it to be minutely true. Indeed, criticism shows that minutely examined it will not hold water; it is at issue with itself. The justification for this statement will be adduced in a subsequent chapter.

424.   Meantime, we shall have to assume that, practically speaking, there is a flow of ideas through the mind, that is, of *objects*, of which we have the barest glimpse while they are with us, but which are reported by memory after they have been associated together and considerably transformed; and this report, though not very accurate, is substantially accept- able as correct.

425.   Still, we must never forget that when we say, this idea is *the same* [that] I had yesterday, this idea *resembles* that, this idea *involves* or *contains* that, these are not things that are true of the ideas in their presentation. They suppose a mind, — *our* mind, — in which it seems that the workings of ideas involve those judgments. Perhaps, some of them would be true for all minds, and in that sense of the ideas themselves; but that cannot be averred at the outset. The point to remember is, that whatever we say of ideas as they are in consciousness is said of something unknowable in its immediacy. The only thought that is really present to us is a thought we can neither think about nor talk about. "Of thine eye I am eyebeam," says the Sphinx. We have no reason to deny the dicta of introspec- tion; but we have to remember that they are all results of associ-

ation, are all theoretical, bits of instinctive psychology. We accept them, but not as literally true; only as expressive of the impression which has naturally been made upon our understandings.

426. By the time we can examine our ideas at all, we find the process of combining them into sets has begun. But we seem to be able to discriminate roughly between a *matter* of cognition, as Kant calls it, forced upon us by the mysterious power without and within, and a skeleton of a *set*, in providing which we feel as if we have had a *comparative* freedom, which skeleton is nearly what Kant means by the *form* of cognition. For example, I hear at this moment a bird calling. I think he is on a lilac-tree close by the verandah. Every time he calls, I seem to see the bird. It is not much like *seeing*, but still it is a visual idea. Now that visual idea I think of as the bird *itself*, and the *call* I think of as something appertaining to that idea. Though the association is quite involuntary, I could banish the visual idea if I chose. Yet *that*, I recognize as forced upon my belief by experience. I cannot help believing there *is* a bird there, that would look something as I imagine it to look. But I have besides the visual idea of the bird and the sound of the call, a skeleton idea of *connection between two things*. It is a dim idea in itself; but if I want to think about it, I have a visual idea ⟋ of two dots connected by a line, or of a knot in a string. However, when I just think of the bird calling, I do not think the idea of connection so distinctly. Nevertheless, I *do* think it, and think of the call and the visual bird as belonging to it. Under ordinary circumstances, I might not remark the idea of connection; but *potentially* it would be there, that is, it would be all ready to be called into existence, as soon as there should be need of it. Before me on the table is a nearly cubical box, containing a photometer. As I look at it, I see three faces. I not only see them, at once, which associates them in contiguity; but I regard them as coming up to form a square corner, and thus associate them by means of a skeleton idea △ of a triplet.

427. In all association, even by contiguity, the potential idea of the *form* of the set is *operative*. It is the instrument without which the association would take no hold upon the mind. It is not necessary that the formal idea should be clearly

apprehended. As to the metaphysics of the causation, I do not care a straw for that. If any nominalist fancies it is more philosophical to say that the force of mind which can produce the idea of the set, has to operate to produce the association, I am not concerned at present to enter into that discussion. Only this must be insisted upon, that the skeleton of the set is something of which a mathematical diagram can be made. It is something in itself intelligible; though it is not necessary that it should emerge into the field of easy attention. For example, if a mind is under the influence of the skeleton idea of connection shown in the accompanying figure of the ten dots,

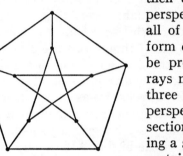

then upon seeing two triangles in perspective,[24] without thinking at all of this figure, or much of any form of connection, that mind will be pretty sure to regard the six rays making the two triangles, the three rays to the eye, or centre of perspective, and the ray of intersection of the two planes as forming a set of ten rays, an idea which certainly would not occur to a mind which was not so dominated by the form of connection.

By subsequent examination of the set of associated ideas, namely, the ten lines, the form of their connection might be perceived.

428. Looking out of the window, I see the cow whose milk we generally drink. There are certain difficulties which have occasioned a good deal of thought, so that I imagine I see a boy sitting by the cow milking her. The boy, and the stool, and the pail are added to my idea. Thence, I imagine that boy carrying the pail to the house. The cow and stool have dropped out. The straining of the milk presents itself to my imagination. A bowl is there and the pail. The boy is standing by; but I lose sight of him. I am following along the train dramatically, that is, following the interesting history.

429. As I followed that series of events in my mind (as I

[24] (Ed.) The editor suggests that the two triangles in perspective constitute a figure distinct from the figure of the ten dots; and that the association is between ten dots in the original figure, and ten rays in the second figure.

did; for I do not take make-believe observations), there was always something identical carried along. The boy going up to the house with the pail, was thought as that same boy, the pail that same pail, and the occasion that same occasion that I had just before been thinking of. The new ideas must, therefore, have always been taken in before the old ones were allowed to drop. By the time the milk was straining in imagination I had already begun to think that it would be good for my wife, who is threatened with nervous prostration.

430. To one skeleton-set another is added to form a compound set. Then, the first, perhaps, is dropped and the ideas which remain are viewed in a new light.

431. I saw a lady yesterday. I had not seen her since one evening when she and her husband drove up as my wife and I were standing at the well. A handsome man! He and she are both very fond of his nephew who seems to us too a charming fellow; and only yesterday my wife showed me a newspaper-paragraph that he had been arrested for debt. So his centi-millionaire cousin paid his tailor's bill of $5000. The last time I saw him he was hardly presentable. So my thoughts ran on in spite of me. First, the lady. Then, she in a set with her husband, my wife, myself, the buggy, and the well. Then mingles with this set another, the lady, her husband, my wife, myself, the nephew, and his agreeability; now that nephew brings in something concentrating him, my wife, myself, the newspaper. I forget the others. Then, him, and that Newport house, and the Croesus cousin. The skeleton-sets themselves I do not think particularly about; but they are operative. The marriage relation, the familiar intercourse of people in the country, the relation of handsome nephew to a message; newspaper-publications about people; the relation of a man of stupendous fortune to his cousins. All of these skeleton-sets, though not attended to, influenced my thought; and they followed one another by the same alternating process of taking up and dropping.

432. When these skeleton-sets were joined intermediately to the passage from one to another, these connections of them had *their* skeleton-sets. But these latter were all of that simple form expressible by the sign +, and had no specific character.

There are, however, cases in which the connections of the skeleton-sets have skeleton-sets of more interest.

§5. THEORETICAL INTEREST

433. Interest has been spoken of as either connected with voluntary action or as emotional. We must not, however, lose sight of the fact that there is such a thing as *theoretical* interest, which has reference not to outward action but to the voluntary agency we put forth in directing our own ideas. Whether or not this is muscular is, as far as I can see, of no great importance for our purpose. It would be a pretty large hypothesis to suppose that we could contract and expand the arteries of our brains by a direct exertion. Let us rather content ourselves with acknowledging that this sort of voluntary action is of a nature not understood. It exists; there is a corresponding kind of interest referring to it; and there is a kind of attention, or heightening of consciousness in the initial stage of suggestions interesting in that way.

434. An immense number of associations are formed, and remain as long as they endure, in the background of consciousness, that is, in subjective obscurity. But as soon as a cerebro-motor suggestion is made, — that is a suggestion of the idea of voluntarily exercising thought, — the whole set brightens up. At the same time the action of forming and annulling sets, — say the metabolism of thought, — becomes more active. So that our instinctive psychological explanation is that the heightened consciousness is an *agent* that performs the action. If there is nothing in this but a word, we need not quarrel about it; but it would seem that as a matter of dynamics heightened consciousness, or attention, is nothing but a concomitant of the idea of voluntary action, and that it is the approach to a discharge of the excitement out of the cerebro-spinal nerves (although *upon* the same nerves again,) which accelerates the movement of thought, somewhat as the current of a stream is accelerated in approaching a cataract.

435. But when we undertake to give an account of any train of thought, as I have done in a few examples, when we say such and such ideas *occurred* to us, it is not at all true that

they then came into consciousness. All that is true is, that at those moments they became connected with the idea of a voluntary act of thought, and consequently, became subjectively vivid enough to find a place in our narrative. In my train of thought about the cow, I have no doubt the idea of *doing something* to help my wife was what made me notice the creature at all, and caused my thought to be active in that direction. The set *wife-milk* was in the deeper shaded part of consciousness. The set *cow-milk* joined itself to this and gave *wife-milk-cow*, and thence *wife-cow*. This did not emerge into the glare of attention but was working all the time.

436. The subjective vividness which an idea gets from exciting interest is very transient. If it connects itself permanently with an enduring interest, it is very soon found that it has *less* vividness than it would naturally have had if it had not been connected with that interest. For instance, we have the most erroneous notions of how words sound in our own mouths and those of others. If we did not know the language the mere total impression of the peculiarity of sound, I do not say the analysis of the articulations, but the general character of the noise, would be much more vividly apprehended. This may be explained by remembering that the impression we speak of means our *recollection* of the impression; now this is the sum of the effect it makes while it is present. But if the idea is interesting, it suggests another so quickly, that it is present itself but a very short time; and its total effect does not amount to much. It is like a thermometer dipped for a moment into very hot water and immediately withdrawn. It is hardly affected at all. Still, however the fact be explained, it remains true that old ideas, while they have generally gained in interest and suggestiveness, have lost subjective vividness. On the other hand, an idea that is new and fresh seems quickly to gain vividness from that circumstance. Hence we say that as the excitation spreads it loses intensity.

§6. EXPERIENCE AND INFERENCE

437. The examples which have hitherto been dwelt upon are instances of the free play of imagination. But in order to become aware of the whole range of association, or of that side

271

of it which is of most interest to the logician, we have to consider *experience*.

Experience may be defined as the sum of ideas which have been irresistibly borne in upon us, overwhelming all free-play of thought, by the tenor of our lives. The authority of experience consists in the fact that its power cannot be resisted; it is a flood against which nothing can stand. The maxim that we ought to be "guided" by experience amounts to this, that what we have got to yield to at last we shall economically do well to be submissive to from the first. "Guided" is too egotistical a word.

438.   We naturally make all our distinctions too absolute. We are accustomed to speak of an external universe and an inner world of thought. But they are merely vicinities with no real boundary line between them. It comes to this: there are some ideas, — *objects*, be it remembered, — which will have their own way, and we cannot swerve them much, and the little effect we can produce upon them we only produce indirectly. They make up or indicate the outward world. There are other ideas which seem very docile, they are just as we think they ought to be. They form the inner world. Yet it will be found that the inner world has its surprises for us, sometimes. It isn't so exactly as we would have it as we fancy. It is rather our wishes which conform to it, Mahomet that repairs to the mountain. Neither is the moderate amount of control which we exercise upon the world of ideas nearly so direct as we fancy it to be. We go about instinctively, and without being aware how circuitously we proceed to change the current of thought. There is an intermediate world, our own neighborhood, household, and persons, which belongs to us, which we sometimes feel inclined to class with the outer world and sometimes with the inner world.

439.   Experience being something forced upon us, belongs to the external type. Yet in so far as it is I or you who experiences the constraint, the experience is *mine* or *yours*, and thus belongs to the inner world.

440.   Experience is double, as much as reality is. That is, there is an *outward* and an *inward experience*. Under the latter head ought particularly to be reckoned a mathematical ex-

perience, not usually so called, which has compelled the development of pure thought to take a determinate course.

441.   There is also an emotional experience, which has all the authority of any experience, provided it is equally irresistible. But experience and its irresistibility has a *public* character, which we shall study in another chapter.

442.   Under the influence of association, the lash of experience needs only to be shown to us to cause us to submit. Now, there are indications by which we recognize the experiential character of certain ideas. One of these is the glowing blaze of their subjective vividness; but there are others, besides.

443.   When an idea bearing the stamp of experience suggests another, that other in many cases itself carries that same stamp, which is carried forward in suggestion and thus a derivative authority from experience is conferred upon an idea which may have neither the vividness nor the other marks of directer experience. This sort of suggestion is *inference*. The law of association will divide inference into inferences by contiguity and inferences by resemblance, meaning by these latter inference from the occult inward nature of ideas or of the soul.

§7. UNCONTROLLED INFERENCE

444.   All inferences are really performed under the influence of the law of association. But all psychical actions divide into two great classes, those which are performed under the *uncontrolled* governance of association and those in which by the "agency" of consciousness, — whatever that may mean, — the actions come under self-criticism and self-control. The latter class of actions may be pronounced *good* or *bad;* the former could not be otherwise than they were.

445.   Uncontrolled inference from contiguity, or experiential connection, is the most rudimentary of all reasoning. The lower animals so reason. A dog, when he hears his master's voice, runs expecting to see him; and if he does not find him, will manifest surprise, or, at any rate, perplexity.

446.   Inference from resemblance perhaps implies a higher degree of self-consciousness than any of the brutes possess.

It involves somewhat steady attention to qualities, as such; and this must rest on a capacity, at least, for language, if not on language, itself. Primitive man is very industrious in this sort of reasoning. Mythology, says Major Powell, is the philosophy of the Savage. It is certainly composed of inferences from resemblance. Our ancestors saw something man-like in the Sun, and could even tell what sort of a character the Sun-God's was.

447. Our daily life is full of involuntary determinations of belief. It is the egotism of the ego, or field of attention, which imposes upon [us] with its High German modest conviction that whatever is known is known through it. It is not so. I converse with a man and learn how he is thinking: I fancy he has *told me*, that is, has "stated" the fact in accurate forms of speech. But he has not, and how I have found out his thought is too subtle a process for this psychologist writing to find out. You hear a new slang word: you never ask for a definition of it; and you never get one. You do not get even any simple example of its use; you only hear it in ironical, twisted, humorous sentences whose meaning is turned inside out and tied in a hard knot; yet you know what that word means much better than any abstract definition could have informed you. In riding a horse; rider and ridden understand one another in [a] way of which the former can no more give an account than the latter.

448. Such inferences are beyond the jurisdiction of criticism. It is the part of psychology to explain their processes as it can; but, as long as they are out of the focal plane of consciousness, they are out of our control; and to call them good or bad were idle. The ordinary business of life is, however, best conducted without too much self-criticism. Respiration, circulation, and digestion are, depend upon it, better carried on as they are, without any meddling by Reason; and the countless little inferences we are continually making, — be they ever so defective, — are, at any rate, less ill performed unconsciously than they would be under the regimen of a captious and hypochondriac logic.

449. Quite otherwise is it with the actions which carry out our grander purposes. Here all must be voluntary, thoroughly conscious, based on critical reflection. Logic is wanted here, to

pull inferences to pieces, to show whether they be sound or not, to advise how they may be strengthened, to consider by what methods they ought to proceed.

450. Intermediate between the lesser and the greater inferences lies a class which are best governed by habits, yet by habits formed or corrected under conscious criticism. Within a man's own special profession, his habits of thinking will in the natural course of things have been subjected to a good deal of criticism, — perhaps not remarkably intelligent, yet at all events based on experience. Outside of that narrow beaten path, if he has not studied logic, his habits of thinking will have been carelessly formed. If he has been educated under the traditional logic, they will have been formed under an influence positively baleful.

§8. ASSOCIATION AND INFERENCE [25]

451. In the absence of external impressions, thoughts chase one another through the mind in a sort of Bacchic train. Each suggests another. After a while, the clear train of thought is broken, the ideas remain scattered for a time, and then reconcentrate in another train. Psychologists recognize that the suggestion of one idea by another may take place according to either one of two different principles; for an idea may suggest another like it, or it may suggest another which has been connected with it in experience. Thus, the thought of Niagara may suggest a hero or anything else that is grand, and so similar to the cataract, or it may suggest a crowd of importunate hack-drivers, which is connected with the place in every visitor's experience.

452. Association of the latter kind, association by *contiguity* as it is called, is the more typical. In it the characteristics

[25] (Ed.) From *Qualitative Logic*, a partially completed book intended for young people, Widener IB2–9, undated. Paragraphs 451–457 are a draft of Chapter I, "The Association of Ideas." Paragraphs 458–462 are a draft of Chapter II, "The Simple Consequence."

The reader's attention is called to the similarity between 7.454–457 of this section and 7.445–450 which come from *Grand Logic*. Paragraphs 7.457 and 7.448–450 are nearly identical. This similarity provides some information as to when *Qualitative Logic* was written.

of mental association are more strongly marked. Association by similarity is related to association by contiguity somewhat as our inward consciousness is related to outward experience; the one association is due to a connection in outward experience, the other to a connection in our feelings. Many psychologists have proposed to reduce association by similarity to a special kind of association by contiguity; few have been inclined to reduce the latter principle to the former.

453.   Suggestions of these two kinds characterize not merely dreams and dreamy meditations, but also thoughts referred to the real world, or in technical language *categorical judgments*. Association is the only force which exists within the intellect, and whatever power of controlling the thoughts there may be can be exercised only by utilizing these forces; indeed, the power, and even the wish, to control ourselves can come about only by the action of the same principles. Still, the force of association in its native strength and wildness is seen best in persons whose understandings are so little developed that they can hardly be said to reason at all. Believing one thing puts it into their heads to believe in another thing; but they know not how they come by their beliefs, and can exercise no control over the inferential process. These unconscious and uncontrolled reasonings hardly merit that name; although they are very often truer than if they were regulated by an imperfect logic, showing in this the usual superiority of instinct over reason, and of practice over theory.[26] They take place like other mental suggestions according to the two principles of similarity and connection in experience.

454.   Inference from connection in experience is most rudimentary of all reasoning. The lower animals plainly reason in this way. The dog, when he hears the voice of his master runs expecting to see him, and if he does not find him will manifest surprize, or at any rate perplexity. This is as good an example of inference from connection in experience as could easily be given.

455.   Inference from resemblance probably implies a higher degree of self-consciousness than any of the brutes possess. It involves a somewhat steady attention to qualities as such;

[26] (Ed.) Cf. 1.626ff.

and this must rest on the capacity for language, if not on language itself. Primitive man, however, reasons in this way; for mythology is built of such inferences. Our ancestors saw something manlike in the sun, and could even tell what kind of a man the sun-god was.

456. But we need not go to the lower animals nor to savages for examples of associational determinations of belief. Our daily life is full of such phenomena. We have the naive idea that our beliefs are principally determined by the exercise of our conscious intellect; but it is not so. I converse with a man and learn how he is thinking: I fancy that he has told me, but he has not. I hear a new slang word, but I need not ask for a definition of it; I understand its meaning much better without a definition, I know not how, than I should with one. In riding a horse, I understand him and he understands me; but how we understand one another I know hardly better than he.

457. All such inferences are, of course, beyond the jurisdiction of criticism. It is the part of psychology to explain their processes as it can; but as long as they are out of consciousness, they are out of our control and it is idle to call them good or bad. We may, however, say that the ordinary business of life is best conducted without too much self-criticism. Just as our respiration, circulation, and digestion are far better carried on by involuntary than they could possibly be by voluntary actions, so the countless little reasonings which we are continually making, — although they may often be defective, — are nevertheless much better performed unconsciously than they would be if we were to try to interfere with them by a captious and hypochondriac logic. It is very different with the actions which we undertake in order to carry out our grander purposes. Here, all must be voluntary, thoroughly conscious, and based upon the most critical reflection. Here logic is wanted, to pull to pieces our inferences, to show whether they are good or bad, how they can be strengthened, and by what methods they ought to proceed. Intermediate between the lesser and the greater inferences, lies an intermediate class which are best governed by habits, yet by habits formed or corrected under conscious criticism. Within a man's own special pro-

fession, his habits of thinking will have been subjected to a good deal of criticism (not necessarily the most intelligent, but based on experience); outside of that, if he has not studied logic, his habits of thinking will have been carelessly formed, or if he has studied the traditional logic, they will have been formed under an influence truly baleful.

————◀————

458.   Reasoning unconsciously can hardly be called reasoning at all. As long as I simply find myself seized with a belief, without being able to give any account of how I came by it, logic has nothing to say except to warn me of the extreme danger that I shall err.

459.   Reasoning proper begins when I am conscious that the judgment I reach is the effect in my mind of a certain judgment which I had formed before. The judgment which is the cause is called the *premise*, that which is the effect is called the *conclusion*. When I am aware that a certain conclusion which I draw is determined by a certain premise, there are three things which I have more or less clearly in my mind. First, I have a peculiar sense of constraint to believe the conclusion, connected with a sense that that constraint comes from the premise; second, I have a conception that there is a whole class of possible analogous inferences (though I may not be able to define the class) in which a similar constraint would be felt by me; and third I have a present belief that all of these inferences, or at least the great body of them would be true.

460.   The lowest kind of conscious reasoning is where I know what the premise is from which my belief in the conclusion follows, and I feel that it follows upon some principle, — technically called the *leading principle* of the inference, — but I do not distinctly know what that principle is. Such an inference is called a *simple consequence*.

461.   Such inferences are common enough. Uneducated people seldom reason in a higher way; and educated people reason so very often. Since the object of reasoning is merely to arrive at the truth, if the leading principle of our inference be really true, it is not necessary for us to know it, for in that

case the mode of inference based upon it can in no case carry us away from a true premise to a false conclusion. Such a mode of inference is *valid*, that is, its leading principle is true; but it is only *materially valid*, that is, valid because as a matter of fact the leading principle happens to be true; it is not *logically valid*, that is, the leading principle might be false. Although the simple consequence may be valid, logic condemns it. A conclusion may be true, though the inference by which it was reached was invalid; that is, it may chance to be true. But the inference is condemned because other conclusions similarly drawn may be false. In the same way, a simple consequence may happen to be valid; but since the leading principle is not recognized, there is no security for its validity, and the next simple consequence drawn, though indistinguishable from the first (the leading principle being unrecognized), may very likely fail.

462. Simple consequences have occasionally been introduced into philosophy. The most remarkable instance is the *Cogito, ergo sum* of Descartes, who wished every philosopher to begin by doubting everything without exception. But even in doubting everything he must, says Descartes, be aware that he doubts, that he thinks. Now from this belief that he thinks he is led by a blind but irresistible constraint to believe in his own existence. This inference, "I think, therefore I am," is a simple consequence, for as long as the philosopher doubts everything he can have no fuller reason to give. He cannot, for example, say that thought supposes a thinker, for he is bound as a Cartesian to doubt that among other things at the outset. Such is the doctrine of Descartes. Of course, were there nothing to check the absolutely resistless force of a belief, logic must be silent, *Leges silent inter arma*. But in point of fact, no belief is found thus absolutely irresistible. There is always room for the reflection that an error may have been committed.[27] [28]

---

[27] Absolute doubt is also impossible.

[28] (Ed.) The manuscript then continues with Chapter III, "The Modus Ponens"; Chapter IV, "The Traditional Syllogistic"; etc.

§9. ASSOCIATION AND THE LAW OF MIND [29]

463. In reflecting upon the work which has hitherto been done upon association, we are led to remark how many writers have been led astray by futile attempts to seek guidance for their psychological studies in physiological hypotheses. Their idea has, no doubt, been that physical facts are more tangible, certain, and easily intelligible than psychical facts; and that knowledge of the less easily ascertained truths ought to be based upon an acquaintance with more easily ascertained truths. How far is this just? The present writer holds that in advance of positive knowledge, the presumption ought to be that there is such a unity in the universe that the difference between mental and natural phenomena is only a difference of degree. Presumably, the same elements are in both; and if so, *so far* there is no essential difference in their intelligibility. But upon the opposite supposition, namely that the phenomena of mind are essentially more complicated than those of matter, the study of mind through physiology must necessarily be misleading. It may be said that, at all events, we do understand physical phenomena the best. This, however, is open to doubt. Those physical phenomena which we really understand, the motions of the planets and the like, are quite exceptionally simple; and the assumption that all physical phenomena are regulated by the laws of mechanics, which since Helmholtz has been the ruling idea of science, appears in the light of the logical rules to be developed in this treatise, as a good "working hypothesis," but as a dogmatic proposition, — in which way it is used, when a method of psychological investigation is founded upon it, — as exceedingly improbable. Nothing is less understood than the action of the nerves, in the sense in which they would require to be understood for such a purpose. The psychological phenomena, on the other hand, are revealed to us in the complicated process of "introspection," in language, in behaviour, and in our instinctive, and (we may presume) approximately correct, notions of the way of the mind, with an eminent degree of

[29] (Ed.) From Chapter VI of *Grand Logic*, Widener IB2-1, coming after 4.52. This is dated 1893 on the basis of 4.21n*.

clearness. This method is far more accurate and scientific than the other, at least, in the present stage of the inquiry.

464. Our object is to formulate the law of mind. We have to consider all mental action whatsoever and, generalizing it, to say not what all the elements of it are, but what that element of it is which is *legislative*. "Generalization," is the old answer. Pretty well that for a first essay; but open to the following objections. First, it is logical, it contemplates only the product, while what we aim at is the psychological law, relating to the action itself; second, it confines itself to the logic of non-relative terms, and is therein very imperfect, indeed; third, it is a meagre word, while we want the whole process with all its characteristics at large. Still, we remark that all attempts to say what mind does, that it reduces the manifold of sense to unity, that it assimilates, that it shapes action to purposes, have one thing in common.

465. A feeling is an element of consciousness just as it immediately is in the moment when it is there for itself and not as delegate of some other feeling not present. Such a feeling is not a psychological datum. The data are highly complex. That there is a cream colored surface with black characters on it is as near as I can readily describe the datum of my consciousness at this minute, — but in truth the moment I pick it to pieces, as I must do to describe it, it ceases to be a datum. As for the pure feeling, *that* is a hypothetical entity, and is as completely veiled from me by its own immediacy as a material particle, as it exists in itself, is veiled by the somewhat absurd requirement that it shall be considered in itself. The truth is there are no data. We have a lot of inferences from data, liable to error, and these we have to correct as best we can by putting them together. The state of the case is quite similar to that of a physical science, say astronomy. All we have to go upon in astronomy is observations, and all those observations are erroneous. But we collect them and take their means and find a general description of the path of the observed object; and from this we can calculate an ephemeris, and finally, if there is any interest in doing so, ascertain what those observations ought to have been. We can no more start with immediate feelings in psychology than we can start with accurate places of the

planets, as affected by parallax, aberration, refraction, etc. in astronomy. We start with mediate data, subject to error, and requiring correction.

466.   The mind pronounces that what I see now resembles something I saw yesterday. The whole aspect of things as flowing in time is, it is plain, virtually a *theory* of the mind's creation. But, for the present, we take that theory as *true*, that is, as a stable one. Taking it as true, it seems to provide no possible means by which the mind could compare what is present to it now with what is past and gone and done with. This compels us to say that the time idea, — at least, in its first crude shape, — needs correction, like an erroneous observation in astronomy. Examining it more carefully, we observe that the idea is that the series of instants of time is *continuous*. Analyzing this idea of continuity, as we shall do in a future chapter with the most minute accuracy which an improved art of logic puts at our disposition,[30] we find that it implies that there are instants *infinitesimally* close together; that is that there are durations of time so short, that every one such starting with a given date has a character exactly like the one before it in some respect, without any limitation to this rule, while yet a time a little later does *not* possess that character. This enables us to suppose that the consciousness is not limited to a single instant but that it *immediately* and objectively extends over a lapse of time, without thereby extending over any sensible lapse of time. We are thus able to suppose that consciousness is carried along from one time to another, and is able to compare what is present to it at different times. Such we may suppose to be the process of memory; and this is the account of it which best squares with those natural beliefs which are all the data the psychologist can possibly have upon which to found his science, corresponding, as they do, to the observations of the astronomer.

467.   But granting that memory is thus justified, — while errors may, of course, creep in during the process, — it still remains that when the mind declares that what it sees now, or remembers to have seen yesterday, is *like* what it remembers to have seen last week, the *likeness*, which though accompanied

[30] (Ed.) Cf. 4.121ff.

like all mental processes with a peculiar and characteristic sensation, is mainly a *fact*, a mental fact, and the sensation of it is of no consequence except as an advertisement of that fact. That fact is that by virtue of the occult working of the depths within us, those two feelings coalesce into one notion. For the sake of calling this by a familiar name, I call this association by similarity. But the ideas united by virtue of an occult inward power, are not always regarded as *similar*. Contraries are also so joined. Ideas and feelings are so joined which are neither merely declared by the mind to be similar nor to be contrary. Such, for instance, are length, breadth, and thickness. The mind delights in triads. In general, what the mind pronounces is that the feeling or idea of yesterday and that of today belong to one system, of which it forms a conception. A concept is not a mere jumble of particulars, — that is only its crudest species. A concept is the living influence upon us of a *diagram*, or *icon*, with whose several parts are connected in thought an equal number of feelings or ideas. The law of mind is that feelings and ideas attach themselves in thought so as to form systems. But the icon is not always clearly apprehended. We may not know at all what it is; or we may have learned it by the observation of nature.

CHAPTER 3

HABIT [1]

§1. LAWS OF PHYSICS

468. The books on physics are replete with examples of what they call "empirical laws," that is to say, formulas which are satisfied as nearly as men have succeeded in observing the facts and under certain limited circumstances, but which nobody supposes go down to the roots of existence, or to exhibit the general forms of all phenomena. They are, on the contrary, supposed to be merely special modifications which the universal formulæ assume under special conditions. Of such a pseudo-law centrifugal force affords a good example. When a railway-train moves round a curve, there is always a pressure away from the centre of curvature. It must be so; for since a body not subjected to any force naturally moves in a right line, while this railway-train does not so move, it follows that the guiding rail exerts a force upon it in a direction toward the centre of curvature; and consequently by virtue of the law of action and reaction, the train must exert an equal and opposite force upon the rail. This is a perfectly real force. Namely, it is the elastic force of the iron rail which is strained by the tendency of the train to preserve a rectilinear motion. If you examine the rail you will detect manifestations of the reality of the centrifugal pressure; or if you whirl a sling, you will actually feel the centrifugal force. But now certain natural philosophers extend the formula of centrifugal force, which is a genuine force where

[1] (Ed.) Sections 1–8 are "Habit," Widener IB3, c.1898, with a quotation added in 494n9. The manuscript, "Habit," is probably a version of Lecture 7 of the Cambridge series, [Bibliography] G–1898–1. The manuscript from which 494n9 is taken is probably a version of Lecture 2 of this series. Section 9 is from Lecture 4 of the Cambridge series; cf. 518n16.

the motion is constrained by a rigid guide to cases where there is no such constraint. They say that a planet is held to its circular orbit by the balance between centrifugal and centripetal forces. In this case, centrifugal force is a mere formula, — a formula which is undoubtedly quite correct as far as the effect goes, while yet the centrifugal force is a merely formal affair with nothing at all corresponding to it in nature. It is very much as if between two men, A and B, there has been a single transaction consisting in A lending B \$5. Now if B were to keep his books in such a manner that the state of the account as entered on those books made A owe him \$100 with \$105 on the opposite side of the account, the entries would in effect be correct; but yet that hundred dollars would be a fiction of bookkeeping. In like manner the centrifugal force of a planet is a fiction due to using polar coördinates in place of rectangular coördinates. It is true that were the gravitation of the sun suddenly to be annihilated there would be at the first instant an acceleration of the planet away from the circular orbit equal to the centrifugal force; and it is certainly true that what we call *force* in Dynamics is nothing more than the product of an acceleration multiplied by a mass. Only, this acceleration away from the circular motion of the natural motion of the planet were it suddenly emancipated from gravitation is nothing in the world but the entry we have to make on one side of our accounts to balance that fictitious entry which we have virtually made on the other side when we took the circular motion as the standard or origin from which to reckon accelerations.

469. Now the question is, whether or not there is any ratiocinative method by which we can assure ourselves that any law which we may discover by the observation of nature is not like centrifugal force a mere fiction of bookkeeping but represents a real and a living action in nature. Many nominalistic logicians will deny at once that any such distinction can be made; but in doing so, they will be merely adhering to preconceived metaphysical opinions. They have no real evidence to offer upon the subject. Of absolute knowledge there can be no question. But if we see that as soon as circumstances are somewhat varied, the form of the law is lost, the inference would seem

to be that it is not a universal or living mode of action. If on the other hand, we find that as soon as the form is prevented from manifestation in one shape it immediately reappears in another shape, and especially if it shows a power of spreading and of reproducing itself, these phenomena may be considered as evidence of genuine vitality and fundamental reality in the form of the law.

But I confess I think it will, and ought to be, harder to convince you of the truth of this general principle than it will be to assure you of the consequence which leads me to formulate it. Namely, what I wish to show is that causation, as distinct from the action of conservative force, is a real, fundamental, and vital element both in the outer and in the inner world.

470. As to those explanations which the physicists propose for irreversible phenomena by means of the doctrine of chances as applied to trillions of molecules, I accept them fully as one of the finest achievements of science. Judge Stallo[2] performed an acceptable service in his earnest assault upon them, which was conducted with as much ability as so poor a cause could possibly be expected to command. Other writers have recently attempted to reinforce the attack, one of them with some understanding of the subject. But the judgment of a really scientific logic must be altogether in favor of the accepted theory. Its explanation of the facts is altogether admirable and is fortified by a variety of new phenomena which were not known at the time the theory was first proposed, but which fit into their places like the pieces of a boy's dissected map, after he has once begun to put a few of them rightly together. This explanation demonstrates that the agency of energy is disseminated through every department of physical phenomena. But in one thing it fails; namely, it fails to show the absence of a very different kind of agency; and it not only fails to show its absence, but even supplies the means of proving its presence.

§2. NON-CONSERVATIVE ACTIONS

471. Those non-conservative actions which seem to violate the law of energy, and which physics explains away as due to chance-action among trillions of molecules, are one and all

[2] (Ed.) Cf. 6.240.

marked by two characters. The first is that they act in one
determinate direction and tend asymptotically toward bringing about an ultimate state of things. If teleological is too
strong a word to apply to them, we might invent the word
finious, to express their tendency toward a final state. The
other character of non-conservative actions is that they are
irreversible.[3] If a falling stone, which moves under the conservative force of gravity, were suddenly to strike a perfectly
elastic horizontal fixed surface, its motion would be reversed
and it would move upwards to the point from which it fell with
precisely the velocities it had in falling, only in reverse order.
So it would be if every planet in the solar system suddenly had
its motions reversed. Whatever motion conservative forces can
effect, the very reverse of that motion they are equally capable
of effecting.

472.   There is some objection to taking either of the two
characters of finiosity and irreversibility as *criteria* of the conservative or non-conservative character of an action. That
which strictly constitutes an action as conservative is that the
forces depend solely on the relative positions of the particles,
and do not depend on the velocities. But *theoretically* that
which makes an action irreversible is that the forces do not depend upon odd powers of the velocities. *Practically*, however,
the irreversibility is an infallible criterion. For example, the
friction of sliding motion is altogether independent of the velocity; so that according to the definition it is a conservative action.
The velocity of a sliding motion is retarded by friction according
to precisely the same formula as the velocity of a body shot ver-
tically upwards. The only difference is that when the instantaneous state of rest is reached, a new kind of friction, rest-fric-
tion, suddenly begins to act and breaks the continuity of the
motion. Sliding friction is a unique example of a non-conservative action that simulates conservative action. The reason that
it does so undoubtedly is that conservative action enters into it
in a singularly uniform manner. When one solid body is set
down upon another, there will be many points at which they
come into contact, and where this occurs the paths of the atoms,
— for I do not half believe in the molecules of solids, will be-

[3] (Ed.)   See also 6.23, 6.72, and [Bibliography] N–1890–3.

gin to be interlaced. The result is that when one begins to slide over the other, many ruptures have to be made, and before the ruptured parts have attained their positions of equilibrium they will on the average come into new contacts with the other body and thus there is a perpetual average state of elastic strain. The elastic stress of this strain is the friction, and it really is a conservative force. The parts of the action which are non-conservative are two, first and most important the ruptures, by which the elastic potential is at once converted into heat, and second and less important the contacts. You will observe that by friction the energy of molar motion is not immediately converted into heat but into elastic potential and it is only after the action is over that this becomes converted into heat, and that fact explains why friction acts like a conservative force.

473.   The resistance of a fluid according to the analysis of Newton and his contemporaries is proportional to an even power of the velocity, namely the square. It ought therefore to be reversible; and probably it would be so in part for a moment. But the truth is [that] the whole analysis is an example of the unskillful application of mathematics, the hypotheses being too unlike the real facts to be useful. Of course, no resistance proper can be reversible.

474.   The other character of non-conservative action, namely, its finiosity, is, as a criterion, open on the theoretical side to still more serious objection. Namely, it is not true that only non-conservative forces can bring about enduring states of things.

475.   In the first place, let me remark that it is not generally true that a particle moving about an attracting centre describes any fixed orbit. In order that that should be the case, it is requisite that the law of the force should be subject to peculiar numerical conditions. We know that if the attraction is inversely as the square of the distance, and the velocity is not too great, the moving particle will describe an ellipse having the attracting centre at the focus. If, however, at the smaller distances the attraction is a little greater than the law of the inverse square of the distance requires, the result will mainly be that the ellipse itself will revolve slowly about the centre in

the same direction in which the moving particle revolves. If there is any commensurable ratio between the periods of the two revolutions, the motion will finally return into itself; otherwise not.

476. If the attraction is inversely as the cube of the distance, the revolving orbit will make infinitely many revolutions while the moving body is making one-half revolution in that orbit; so that it will describe a spiral line having in general an outer and an inner boundary. The outer boundary may however be at an infinite distance or even further away. Here then we have a case in which conservative action asymptotically moves toward a final and ultimate state of things. Suppose the inner limit be distant from the centre by an insensibly minute interval. Then, it will appear to remain fixed in one spot, although it will really be in tremendously rapid motion. The fact that tremendously rapid or even infinitely rapid motion may simulate rest is what makes the conservative action simulate the finiosity of non-conservative action.

477. The attraction may vary according to such a law that the moving body winds in indefinitely near to the centre without ever passing out or passing through the centre. It certainly seems as if the atoms of the chemical elements may have been formed by some such aggregation. For in that way Prout's law could be accounted for.

478. It is important to remark that even if the attraction varies inversely as the cube of the distance, and still more easily if it varies more rapidly, the moving particle may pass through or, at any rate, *to* the centre. And this it will generally do by performing infinitely many revolutions in an infinitesimal moment of time. What the motion will be when it does arrive at the centre it is hard to say. My father [4] in his *Analytic Mechanics* says that after that the body will proceed in a straight line. This, of course, would violate the principle of areas. He does not mention the circumstance that the direction of that straight line would in many cases be indeterminate. It appears to me that a general law being essentially continuous, to suppose an infinite velocity, or any other discontinuity in the action is to suppose that general law to be violated. If therefore a general law is

---

[4] (Ed.) Benjamin Peirce.

such that it essentially involves such a phenomenon, the law is, in so far, self-contradictory. Still, the contradiction only amounts to this, that there is a point of discontinuity in the continuum. It is only a slight departure from generality in one particular instance. It is not that the state of facts supposed is self-contradictory; but only that it is self-contradictory to suppose such a phenomenon to be a result of a perfectly general law.

479. If such an event can happen then it follows as a necessary consequence that there is such a thing as an absolutely chance event. For even an infinitesimal variation in the conditions will make a finite difference in the result.

480. But as to whether or not there is any such law, inquiry in that direction is absolutely barricaded and brought to an eternal standstill, unless there has been some logical process in nature whereby the laws of nature have been brought about. Since, therefore, it is a corollary from the First Rule of Reasoning [5] that we must not make hypotheses that will absolutely stop inquiry, it follows that we are bound to hope that such a logical process of the evolution of law in nature may be discovered and that it is our duty as scientific men to search for it.

481. But let us return to those spiral motions which reach the centre only at the end of an infinite time. It must be confessed that here the simulation of non-conservative action by a conservative action is not a false or extrinsic simulation, but is true and intrinsic. It is just one of those extreme cases which throw the most light on philosophical problems and to which a powerfully solvent method of reasoning must pay particular attention. We note in the first place that the simulation depends in part on the bringing together into one infinitesimal moment motions which undo one another, and in declining to analyze this moment because it is absolutely infinitesimal. Thus the velocities in that moment, though instantaneously infinite are in their resultant zero; and with the attractive forces the same thing is true. From this point of view, it becomes absurd to say that an attraction varies inversely as the cube or any higher power of the distance down to the very centre of attrac-

[5] (Ed.) Cf. 1.135.

tion. Indeed, a somewhat similar difficulty arises whenever there is any attraction at all at the centre.

482.   This leads me to remark that the finiosity of non-conservative action is also manifested in hyperbolic orbits under the attraction inversely as the square of the distance. That is 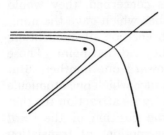 to say a moving body which starts from an infinite distance in one direction reaches at the end of infinite time an infinite distance in another direction. This finiosity might be regarded as due to the circumstance that time has an absolute limit. For could the motion continue beyond the infinitely distant instant of time it would continue through the infinitely distant line in the plane and complete the closed hyperbolic orbit. But I do not think that this simple way of solving the difficulty ought to be regarded as satisfactory. At any rate, if a similar solution be sought for the spiral, one is led to imaginaries, which seems to show that the mathematical hypothesis does not correspond to the facts.

483.   It will be remarked that both these cases, that of the spiral orbit and that of the hyperbolic orbit, are connected with angular displacements. Any kind of rectilinear motion is continued by virtue of momentum, and from this circumstance arises the result that conservative forces affect not directly the velocities, but only the accelerations; and in the fact that such forces depend upon the relative positions of the particles lies their conservative character. But it is different with rotations. There is *no* momentum continuing an angular displacement as such, but only so far as that angular displacement involves rectilinear displacements. The mere rotation of an absolute particle, strictly occupying a single point, has no momentum at all. So if a rectilinear displacement is effected as in the hyperbolic orbit by means of motions which in their limits become radial, the momentum has no tendency to continue the angular motion. Thus angular motion *per se* is not a conservative action. If, for example, atomicules are Boscovichian points, the attractions of those atomicules may be different on different

sides of them. Many facts in elaterics, crystallography, and chemistry render it almost certain, for reasons which it would be too long here to discuss, that, as far as *atoms* are concerned, this is actually true. Suppose for the moment that it be also true of atomicules. What would be the result? As far as the mutual action of two atomicules was concerned, they would instantly turn those sides to one another which gave the minimum potential energy; and in the absence of all momentum, there would be no tendency to swing beyond that point. Those two sides would always be turned toward one another. But when there were *three* such points, the face which one atomicule turned toward another, and consequently its attraction for that other, would depend in part upon the position of the third atomicule. In this case, although the motions of translation would be conservative, the rotations of the atomicules would be regulated by the old formula of causation.

§3. RELATIVE AND ABSOLUTE MOTION

484.   Now from our modern point of view of the non-Euclidean geometry, it appears that, strictly speaking, there is no kind of motion having the properties which we associate with *translation*. That is to say there is no motion which is merely relative. It would not be convenient to attempt to explain this here, before we have examined further into the nature of Continuity.

485.   But let me here say a word about the attempt of Ernst Mach to show that all motion, even rotation, is merely relative. Mach belongs to that school of *soi disant* experiential philosophers whose aim it is to emancipate themselves from all metaphysics and go straight to the facts. This attempt would be highly laudable, — were it possible to carry it out. But experience shows that the experientialists are just as metaphysical as any other philosophers, with this difference, however, that their pre-conceived ideas not being recognized by them as such, are much more insidious and much more apt to fly in the face of all the facts of observation.

486.   Newton in his *Principia* maintains that Time and Space are substances, or in the jargon of French philosophers that

they are *Entities*. The doctrine was a new one, well-recognized as such by Newton. Mach seems to think it was a blunder which Newton fell into inadvertently. It was nothing of the sort. We have historical testimony to show that Newton himself and his contemporaries regarded it as a peculiar, definite, and deliberate theory. Newton does not overtly argue the question in the Principia for the reason that he was a stickler for the traditions of mathematical exposition; and that tradition compelled him to confine himself to demonstrations and comments upon demonstrations. But he contrives to make his reason plain enough. That reason is that the laws of motion make velocity of rotation to be something absolute and not merely relative. Now velocity is the ratio of the amount of a space-displacement to the amount of time in which this displacement takes place. If therefore, argued Newton, velocity is not merely *relative*, neither is a displacement in space nor a lapse of time relative; and therefore Space and Time are not mere relations but are absolute subjects or substances. Now this reasoning is founded on positive facts of observation; and it appears to me to be sound reasoning. I will not say that it draws a *necessary* conclusion; but I do say it is an excellent hypothesis to account for the facts.

487. Mach on the other hand lays it down as an Axiom that Space and Time are merely relative. No facts lend any support whatever to such an assertion. The most that could be said, — more than is really true, — is that facts concerning the composition of motions of Translation go to show that space-position has an element that is merely relative. Mach's struggles to define angular motion as motion relative to the mean position of all the bodies in the universe are not only struggling against all observation, and not only involve the absurdity that the centrifugal force of sling would be influenced by the angular motion of stars very far away, and more influenced by the more remote than by the nearer stars, contrary to his own conception of space as an image of dynamical relations; but, what is still worse, this gratuitous theory is in mathematical contradiction to the point he most insists upon, namely that rectilinear motion is purely relative.

488. It is true that Space, in so far as it is a continuum, is a

293

mere law, — a mere Thirdness.[6] But that does not stand in the way of its being a *thing* too. If besides its continuity it presents arbitrary *thisness*,[7] we must admit that it is something more than a mere law. The question of the relativity of motion is a question of the measurement of space, not of the nature of space itself; and therefore, although motion be not relative, it would not necessarily follow that space *itself* is non-relative, however good the inference may be, considered as a retroduction. But there are characters belonging to space *per se* which seem to involve *thisness*, such as its having three dimensions, — which is an arbitrary limitation. Its *cyclosis* and *periphraxis*,[8] whether these be supposed equal to 0 or to 1 are apparently arbitrary Facts. You cannot reduce them to mere formalities without supposing that space has some kind of topical singularity, — which is still more manifestly an arbitrary fact of existence. As to the Fourth Listing number, all must admit that its value is 1. That is to say, a body filling all space could not by gradual degrees shrink to a point without being ruptured, while the slightest explosion which should separate the body entirely from a single place however small, — the smallest vacuous cist in it, — would suffice to enable the collapse to take place. This I believe nobody who has carefully considered the matter has doubted or is likely to doubt, — at least unless it be supposed that space has modes of connection of which observation affords not the slightest trace. Here again, then, is an arbitrary existential fact about Space, which is simply the way it insists upon being, without any logical necessity. Now insistence upon being in some quite arbitrary way is Secondness, which is the characteristic of the actually existing thing. It is its self-willedness.

489. Now if you examine the matter more closely than I have time to do in this lecture, you will find that it is precisely in those respects in which Space shows such indications of Secondness that motions act as though governed by the law of causality, while in those respects in which Space preserves all its Thirdness the motions preserve their dynamical character.

[6] (Ed.) Cf. 6.82ff. Peirce's categories of First, Second, and Third are discussed especially in [CP] I.

[7] (Ed.) See the discussion of indices in [CP] II and elsewhere.

[8] (Ed.) Cf. 6.6, 6.211–212.

490.   Let us next consider actions of which the space-element is not an intrinsic part. For example, I slip a nickel into the hand of a mendicant. One might say that this was a space motion. But the non-conservative friction is so great that neither the beggar nor the giver remarks any effects of *momentum*. The coin is not thrown but pushed along, and the dynamical part of the action is altogether insignificant. The fact that there is any space motion at all is accidental as far as the determination of the events goes. The money is caused to become the beggar's and remains his. Take the purest kind of temporal action. The very flow of time itself. The event passes out of the problematical state of futury into the state of a *fait accompli*. All psychical action has this character. A question is answered, and answered it remains. A mere duality, a passage from a first state into a second state, here takes the place of that determination of a relation between three states which characterizes physical dynamics.

491.   My father, Benjamin Peirce, drew my attention to the psychological peculiarity of an experiment which I am going to show you. I do not now remember how he formulated the matter. It is that a mathematical analysis of the conditions of motions often gives an expression of what happens conceived under one aspect; while anybody looking at the experiment would instinctively express what he saw under quite another aspect. The dictum of the eye is that one of the pendulums is ahead of the other in its oscillations by half an oscillation, i.e. by a quarter of a vibration, and that the oscillations [of] this pendulum are continually losing their amplitude and transferring it to the other. This is quite true, too. But analytic mechanics looks upon the fact from quite a different point of view. According to it each pendulum oscillates in two different ways at once. One of the components of its oscillation has the period of the two pendulums when they are swinging together and both pendulums partake equally of this component, while the other has the period of the two pendulums swinging opposite ways and the two pendulums are opposite one another in the phases of this component. I remember distinctly that my father remarked that while the view of analytic mechanics corresponds to the formula

$$\theta_1 = \Theta \cos [(a-b)t] + \Theta \cos [(a+b)t]$$
$$\theta_2 = \Theta \cos [(a-b)t] - \Theta \cos [(a+b)t]$$

the instinctive, or intuitional, view corresponds to the formula

$$\theta_1 = 2 \, \Theta \cos at \, . \, \sin (bt+90°)$$
$$\theta_2 = 2 \, \Theta \sin at \, . \, \sin bt.$$

And I further remember his remarking that the decided choice of this last view showed a peculiarity of our mental constitution. But I cannot remember that he attempted to formulate this peculiarity. It is, however, clear to me that it is nothing but our natural tendency to prefer the formula of causation. We regard the pendulum which is ahead as the agent and the one which lags behind as the patient.

492.   To the reason of the mathematician the intuitional mode of conception is singularly crooked and unphilosophical. It happens to be pretty simple because the two pendulums are of equal weight and equal length. Were they not so, the phenomenon would appear very complicated from that point of view, though almost as simple as before from the point of view of analytical mechanics.

§4. PSYCHICAL ACTION

493.   It is now time to inquire whether psychical action be of the conservative or the causational type. You know I make no pretension to competing with the profound psychologists under whom you sit here in Harvard; and I do not promise to bring the question to a satisfactory conclusion. But I shall hope in the few minutes that I can devote to it to make you all understand what the question is, and I hope the provisional reply I make to it may recommend itself as provisional good sense.

494.   I read out to you the rules of philosophical terminology that seem to me to recommend themselves at once to the logic of science and to the ethics of science.[9] Those reasons

[9] (Ed.) This is probably a reference to the following rules (cf. 2.226):

"Rule I. Assign to every scientific conception a scientific name of its own, preferably a new word rather than one already appropriated to an unscientific and dubious conception.

"That was the practice adopted by the scholastic doctors, how advantageously every student will testify. The *renaissance*, on the other hand, condemned the scholastic terms as not being Ciceronian, with the result of making

for adopting them were so weighty, that I would not range any
other consideration alongside of them. But now that I am no
longer arguing the question, let me add that I for one entertain
a deep feeling of reverence for the traditions of the English
language. It has not the amazing psychical and especially emotional wealth of German. It has not half as many words for
tools and manipulations as French; nor has it the delightful
social *finesse* of French. But in all that concerns logic and reasoning, it has a spirit of accuracy which is due to the fact that
the language spoken in State Street and other market places
preserves to an extraordinary degree the sharp distinctions of
the scholastic lore of the middle ages; and where those distinctions are not available, our vernacular language still preserves
the spirit of them. I regret very much that those who of late
years have written in English upon philosophy and psychology
seem most of them to have a contempt for all English thought
and English speech so great that it produces an utter insensi-
bility to the distinctions of the language. The French language
has long been cut off from medieval traditions; and moreover
it is the genius of the French to rely upon skillful phraseology to
express their precise thoughts rather than upon accurate terminology. But notwithstanding this, large numbers of French
words which happen to be spelled like English words but which
bear quite different meanings have by recent writers been used
in their French meanings threatening an utter break-down of
the spirit of English speech and of English thought. For exam-

---

renaissance philosophy as soft and savorless as a sage pudding. There is a rule
of good writing higher than Ciceronian purity, that of expressing your thought,
both accurately and *concisely*. More than a rule of good writing, this is a fundamental condition of scientific thinking; for man cannot think *at all* without
formulas, nor think *powerfully* without concise formulas. . . .

"Rule II. The author of a scientific conception has the first right to name it;
and his name ought to be accepted, unless there are grave substantial objections
to it. But if *he* fails to give it a scientific name, somebody else must do so; and
in that case the earliest good scientific name shall be employed. . . .

"Rule III. After a scientific conception has once received a suitable name,
let it not be called by any other scientific name, old or new. . . .

"Rule IV. As far as practicable, let the terms of philosophy be modelled
after those of scholasticism. . . ." From "Detached Ideas; Induction, Deduction, and Hypothesis," Widener IB2–10, c.1898, probably a draft of one of the
lectures (possibly the second) on "Detached Ideas on Vitally Important Topics"
of the Cambridge series (see 468n1).

ple, the word *Entartung*, having been translated into French by *dégeneration*, becomes "degeneration" in English, although what is meant is degeneracy, which is an entirely different thing. So *spontanée* becomes in this new lingo *spontaneous*, which is almost the reverse of the correct *English* meaning of *spontaneous*. *Suggestion* becomes "suggestion," regardless of the fact that suggestion was already an exact term of philosophy in English in a different sense. The German *Association* is rendered by "association," although if ever there was a school of writers who by the clearness of their definitions and the accuracy of their thought deserved to have their usage of terms respected, it was the English Associationalists. I might expend the rest of the hour on this theme. When these neologists have succeeded in thus dishonoring their mother-tongue, till no vestige of her pristine virtue remains, they will by the same act have hopelessly corrupted all the old virility and health of English thought.

495. However, putting aside all such regrets, which are probably futile, — and saying no more about vernacular speech, I am still obliged in the interest of the logic of science to employ a scientific terminology; and this must follow the only rules by which confusion can possibly be avoided. According to those rules I am bound to use scientific terms in the senses in which they first became terms of science. Accordingly, the English associationalists having first made *association* a term of science, and they having been careful never to extend it to the operation or event whereby one idea calls up another into the mind, but to restrict it primarily to a *habit* or *disposition* of mind in consequence of which an idea of one description is likely to bring into comparative vividness of consciousness an idea of another description, or, when they applied the term association to any operation or event, to designate by it only that process of habituation by which such a habit or disposition of mind acquires strength, they having been punctilious in this matter, my code of rules obliges me logically and morally, to follow them. As for that mental event which corresponds, as we suppose, to the nervous discharge of one part of the cortex upon another, — or the action of one idea to render another idea which is associated with it vivid, — for that they employed the term *suggestion*.

This word is now applied mostly to motor phenomena or to such manifestations of mind as can be observed from without; and therefore, although the two meanings doubtless are in real facts connected together, the meanings themselves are different. But here a compromise is possible; for I shall violate no rule of terminology by speaking of the "suggestion" of the associationalists as *associational suggestion* and that of the hypnotists as *nervous suggestion*. The adjectives may be dropped, — especially the former, — in cases where there is no possibility of the meaning being mistaken.

496. I next remark that different sense-qualities have different degrees of intensity. The sound of thunder is more intense than the sound of a dozen people clapping their hands; and the light of an electric arc is more intense than that of a star. It is also true that the sound of thunder is more intense than the light of a star, and that the electric arc light is more intense than the sound of a dozen people clapping their hands. It is not at random that I say this. Besides this intensity of the sense-qualities, ideas have another mode of intensity, — their *vividness*. The contrary of *vividness* we call *dimness*. Although my personal imagination and memory of colors is very dim compared with that of most persons, yet it is decidedly above the average in accuracy; and in matching a color by memory I am no more likely to select a paler or darker color than I am to select a higher or more luminous color. This *vividness*, which is so much more intense in my memory of the red pencil which I saw this afternoon than it is in my memory of a certain red fan which I possessed when I was nine years old, appears, as far as I have been able to experiment, to be entirely distinct from the intensity of the qualities remembered; although, no doubt, other things being equal my memory of an intense sensation is likely to be more vivid than my memory of a faint sensation. It does not belong to the *Firstness* of the quality, but to the *Secondness* or insistency of the particular apparition of that quality.

497. At any one time I have a great multitude of ideas in my consciousness of different degrees of vividness. How vivid the most vivid of them are depends upon how wide awake I am. In any given state of mental wakefulness or alertness,

there is a certain maximum limit of vividness which none of my ideas surpass, but which a few of them always attain. There is only room in my consciousness for a few at this highest level of vividness. If others force themselves up, some of those that were at the surface must subside. Below these there are others less vivid, and still deeper others that are so dim that only by intense effort, perhaps by no effort that I can possibly exert, can I assure myself of their presence. And yet it may be proved indirectly that they are really there. For example, I have occupied myself for weeks in answering questions about the relative intensity of excitations of sense when with the most vigorous effort I could not seem to detect the slightest difference between them, so that my answers seemed quite random guesses; and yet the decided majority of the answers would be right every day, thus proving that sensations were capable of affecting my answers although I could not seem to be aware of them at all.[10] Moreover, ideas of which we do not seem to be aware will sometimes suggest or call up others by association, these others being vivid enough. I have endeavored to ascertain whether there is in any ordinary state of consciousness a definite minimum degree of vividness, as there certainly is a maximum degree. But all my experiments upon careful mathematical discussion point to the presence of ideas so very *dim*, or wanting in *vividness*, that I am strongly inclined to say, as a first approximation at any rate, that the vividness ranges all the way down to *zero*, and that every cell that ever can be sentient is in some degree sentient as long as it is alive at all.

§5. ASSOCIATION

498. Association is of two kinds.[11] For, on the one hand, it may be a natural disposition, which was from birth destined to develop itself whatever the child's outward experiences might be, so long as he was not maimed nor virtually maimed, say by being imprisoned. This sort of association by virtue of which certain kinds of ideas become naturally allied, as *crimson* and *scarlet*, is called *association by resemblance*. The name is not

---

[10] (Ed.) See Chapter 2, "On Small Differences of Sensation," in Book I of the present volume.

[11] (Ed.) See also the preceding chapter, "Association."

a good one, since it implies that the resemblance causes the association, while in point of fact it is the association which constitutes the resemblance. In themselves considered any two sense-qualities are what they are to themselves alone and have no relation to one another. But could they be compared by a mind that brought no tinge of its own nature into the comparison, any two ideas would appear somewhat alike and somewhat different. But the human mind attaches a peculiar value and emphasis to some resemblances, and that consists in this, that when one quality is brought vividly to consciousness, others will at once have their vividness increased, some more, some less. Thus, an idea which may be roughly compared to a composite photograph surges up into vividness, and this composite idea may be called a *general idea*. It is not properly a *conception*; because a conception is not an idea at all, but a *habit*. But the repeated occurrence of a general idea and the experience of its *utility*, results in the formation or strengthening of that habit which is the conception; or if the conception is already a habit thoroughly compacted, the general idea is the *mark* of the habit. Some psychologists deny the existence of association by resemblance, or say that it is at bottom merely a special case of association by contiguity. To the arguments in defence of its fundamental character which are to be found in common books, I will add three. The first is that it is incredible that man is so constituted that no paths of nervous discharge between parts of the cortex are naturally more or less resistant than others. But those that are less resistant must correspond to natural associations, and ideas naturally associated will resemble one another. The second argument is that without association by resemblance there could be no general ideas and no resemblances. The third argument is this. Suppose I have long been puzzling over some problem, — say how to construct a really good typewriter. Now there are several ideas dimly in my mind from time, none of which taken by itself has any particular analogy with my grand problem. But someday these ideas, all present in consciousness together but yet all very dim deep in the depths of subconscious thought, chance to get joined together in a particular way such that the combination does present a close analogy to my difficulty. That combination almost instantly flashes out into vividness. Now it cannot be contiguity; for the combination is altogether a new idea. It never occurred to me before; and consequently cannot be subject to any *acquired habit*. It must be, as it appears to be, its *analogy*, or resemblance in form, to the nodus of my problem which brings it into vividness. Now what can that be but pure fundamental association by resemblance?

499.   On the other hand, the association, instead of being a natural disposition of mind, may be an acquired habit of mind. That supposes that similar ideas have been conjoined in experience until they have become associated. That is termed *association by contiguity*. Of course, psychologists have not been wanting who sought to show that there is no such thing as association by contiguity, or that it is merely a special case of association by resemblance. It is a long time since I read the work of Gay who first gave the idea of associationalism to Hartley. But I seem dimly to remember that he had a notion of that kind. A number of other principles of association have been proposed, such as contrast and causation. Association by contrast ought to be regarded as a case of association by resemblance, not in the narrow sense in which the reduction is often made, but by generalizing the conception of resemblance in accordance with the logic of relatives until it embraces all high degrees of logical relations between ideas. Contrast is a particular form, an especially prominent and familiar form, of what may be called *relational resemblance* by which I do not mean a resemblance of relations, but a connection of the kind which in the logic of relatives is shown to belong to the same class of relations to which the relation of resemblance belongs. Association by causation is an ill-defined conception embracing associations of different natures. But besides that reiterated coöccurrence which helps to consolidate an association by contiguity, another factor which plays a great part in accomplishing the association, is the experience that the combination of the ideas has important consequences. When we learn that white cats with blue eyes are deaf and have peculiar habits, such as that of following their masters like dogs, we no sooner see a white cat than we want to know what colored eyes she has. This may be called association by *relational contiguity*.

That is to say not only have the two ideas frequently been experienced together, but their union has often been accompanied in experience with a third idea of an interesting kind. Another kind of association which is very important is that which makes an idea *interesting*. I propose to term it *association by interest*. An idea occurs to us in such a way that it would, other things being equal, be very dim. For example, it may result from a fortuitous putting together of two other ideas both of which are sunk deep in the subconscious mind. But if the new idea happens to be *interesting*, it will promptly become vivid. Why is this? Clearly it is because the objective self-consciousness, or the idea which a man has of himself, consists in large measure of what may be roughly described as a composite of ideas of his aims and purposes, including all problems which exercise him. Now the separate components of this composite may for the most part be dim; but the total idea is perhaps the most vivid in consciousness at all times. Now an interesting idea is one which has an analogy, or resemblance in form, to this composite of the man's aims. It is, therefore, drawn into vividness by the vividness of that composite.

§6. LAW OF ACTION OF IDEAS

500. Let us now make an attempt to formulate the law of action of ideas. In the first place, an idea left to itself does not retain its vividness but sinks more and more into dimness. In the second place associated ideas in consciousness together soon undergo alterations of vividness, the dimmer ones becoming more vivid, and the more vivid ones dimmer, according to the strength of the associations. The dimmer idea never becomes more vivid than the more vivid idea had been before the change; but it may become more vivid than the idea originally the more vivid is after the change; for otherwise it would hardly be possible to explain idea chasing after idea. But in the third place the action of associative suggestion does not take place instantly as soon as the two ideas are in consciousness together. There are continual changes going on in the *connections* of ideas in consciousness; and the action of associative suggestion does not take place until chance has brought

the two ideas into suitable connection for acting upon one another. Thus, I stand before an emblem wondering what it means. It is vividly in my mind. Perhaps the meaning is dimly in my consciousness; but it is not until by the movements in consciousness, chance has thrown the idea of the emblem and the idea of its meaning into the right sort of connection, that they suddenly change in vividness, the idea of the emblem becoming much dimmer and that of its meaning much more vivid.

501.   In the fourth place, this interchange of vividness is accompanied by another event which takes place altogether outside my consciousness, though there is a sign of it in consciousness. Namely, the association between the two ideas becomes strengthened, in such a way that the more vivid idea becomes more likely to call up the less vivid one on another occasion. At the same time, in the fifth place, certain other associations become weakened.

502.   Now that the mental action, as so described, is upon the surface, at least, causational and not conservative is quite obvious. There is no reversibility in it, and the traces of anything like momentum are slight and doubtful. At the same time, it would be possible to suppose that it was a conservative action affected to such a degree by resistances, that the momentum had no sensible effect.

503.   The established cerebral theory will easily account for all the five features of mental action which I have mentioned; and that theory is favorable to the view that while the action is of a mixed nature, the non-conservative elements are the predominant ones. For there can hardly be a doubt that the peculiar properties of protoplasm depend upon the enormous complexity of its molecules, upon those molecules being frequently broken up and reunited in new connections, and upon the circumstance that in the quiescent state the molecules are in stationary motion, while in the active state they are partly broken up and the fragments are wandering. Now all this may be summarized by saying that its properties depend upon Bernoulli's law of high numbers, and every action depending upon that law is, so far as it is so dependent, purely causational and not conservative.

304

504. Although the cerebral theory is established and although it is of priceless value to psychology in its present stage of development, it by no means follows that it will never be superseded. That method may perhaps lead to a purely psychical way of investigating the mind. We must wait and see whether it will or not; but meantime for various reasons which I cannot now enter upon that is what I am inclined to expect.

§7. PHYSICS AND PSYCHICS

505. We have, then, these two modes of action, the conservative and the causational, the former rather the dominant one in pure physics, the latter dominant in psychics. Our logical impulse, which prompts us to try to understand the universe, and as an essential condition of doing so to bring all its action under a single principle, this impulse, I say, compels us to *hope* that it may in some way be shown either that all causational action is conservative at bottom or that all conservative action is causational at bottom.

506. But I am quite sure that, as far as I personally am concerned, if I had not been moved by any consideration which touched me more nearly than such a vast and shadowy hope can do, I never should have been moved to do all the hard work I have done for the last fifteen years in trying to reason this matter out. I must confess that for me a living motive must have smaller dimensions than that very general hope. But I am a physicist and a chemist, and as such eager to push investigation in the direction of a better acquaintance with the minute anatomy and physiology of matter. What led me into these metaphysical speculations, to which I had not before been inclined, I being up to that time mainly a student of the methods of science, was my asking myself, how are we ever going to find out anything more than we now [know] about molecules and atoms? How shall we lay out a broad plan for any further grand advance?

507. As a first step toward the solution of that question, I began by asking myself what were the means by which we had attained so much knowledge of molecules and ether as we already had attained. I cannot here go through the analysis,

although it is very interesting. But that knowledge has been based on the assumption that the molecules and ether are like large masses of ordinary matter. Evidently, however, that similarity has its limits. We already have positive proof that there are also wide dissimilarities; and furthermore it seems clear that nearly all that method could teach has been already learned.

508. We now seem launched upon a boundless ocean of possibilities. We have speculations put forth by the greatest masters of physical theorizing of which we can only say that the mere testing of any one of them would occupy a large company of able mathematicians for their whole lives; and that no one such theory seems to have an antecedent probability of being true that exceeds say one chance in a million. When we theorized about molar dynamics we were guided by our instincts. Those instincts had some tendency to be true; because they had been formed under the influence of the very laws that we were investigating. But as we penetrate further and further from the surface of nature, instinct ceases to give any decided answers; and if it did there would no longer be any reason to suppose its answers approximated to the truth. We thus seem to be reduced to this alternative. Either we must make some very broad generalization as to the character of Nature's ways, which may at least tell us that one theory about molecules and ether is better worth trying than another theory, or else we had better abandon altogether a line of inquiry, — I mean into the inmost constitution of matter, — which is likely to prove a mere waste of time.

509. But meantime our scientific curiosity is stimulated to the highest degree by the very remarkable relations which we discover between the different laws of nature, — relations which cry out for rational explanation. That the intensity of light should vary inversely as the square of the distance, is easily understood, although not in that superficial way in which the elementary books explain it, as if it were a mere question of the same thing being spread over a larger and larger surface. I cannot stop to give the true explanation, but I will just give you two hints. The first is that the basis of the measurement of light is the convention that we will call the light of two can-

dles double the light of one. The other hint is that according to the superficial explanation of the school-books, you would expect the brightness of the image of a star made by a perfect lens to be proportional to the area of the lens, while in point of fact it is proportional to the square of that area. But grant that the law of variation of light with the distance is known, what an extraordinary fact it is that the force of gravitation should vary according to the same law! When both have a law which appeals to our reasons as so extraordinarily simple, it would seem that there must be some *reason* for it. Gravitation is certainly not spread out on thinner and thinner surfaces. If anything is so spread it is the potential energy of gravitation. Now *that* varies not as the inverse square but simply [as] the distance. Then electricity repels itself according to the very same formula. Here is a fluid; for electricity is really something like a fluid. It is not a mode of motion. Here is a fluid repelling itself but not at all as a gas seems to repel itself, but following that same law of the inverse square. I have not time to instance other extraordinary relations between laws of nature. But I cannot refrain from alluding to that most extraordinary law of Mendeléef.

510.   According to the strictest principles of logic these relations call for explanation. In order to find such explanation, you must deduce the fundamental laws of the physical universe as necessary consequences of something. That is you must explain those laws altogether.

511.   Now were it merely a question of the *form* of the law, you might hope for a purely *rational* explanation, — something in Hegel's line, for example. But it is *not* merely that. Those laws involve *constants*. Light for example moves over 300,000,-000 centimetres *per* second. A mass at a distance of one centimetre from a gramme of matter receives in consequence of gravitation an increment of velocity toward that mass every second of . . .[12] centimetre per second. The explanation of the laws of nature must be of such a nature that it shall explain why these quantities should have the particular values they have. But these particular values have nothing rational about

[12] (Ed.) The dots indicate a blank in the manuscript, where presumably Peirce meant to write in the value of the gravitational constant. This value is approximately 6.7×10^{-8} in the centimeter-gram-second system of units.

them. They are mere arbitrary *Secondnesses*. The explanation cannot then be a purely rational one. And there are numberless other facts about nature which, if my logic is not quite at fault, absolutely and decisively refute the notion that there can be any purely rational explanation.

§8. EVOLUTION OF THE LAWS OF NATURE

512. What kind of an explanation can there be then? I answer, we may still hope for an evolutionary explanation. We may suppose that the laws of nature are results of an evolutionary process. In the course of this process of evolution, light, let us suppose, age by age moves faster and faster, and we have now arrived at the stage of the process in which it moves just so fast. Now logic does not demand any further explanation than that. The same applies to gravitation. You might ask me whether the relation between the velocity of light and the modulus of gravitation does not require explanation. I answer that it does not because the dimensions of the quantities are different. One involves the unit of mass and the other does not. But two universal constants are as many as can be allowed without explanation of their relations, except that there may be besides a constant of space.

513. By a process of reasoning, then, of the nature of which I thus give you some hint, though given in full it would be seen to be drawn from a great variety of different evidences, I reached the conclusion that a theory of the evolution of the laws of nature must be sought.[13]

514. But if the laws of nature are the result of evolution, this evolutionary process must be supposed to be still in progress. For it cannot be complete as long as the constants of the laws have reached no ultimate possible limit. Besides, there are other reasons for this conclusion. But if the laws of nature are still in process of evolution from a state of things in the infinitely distant past in which there were no laws, it must be that events are not even now absolutely regulated by law. It must be that just as when we attempt to verify any law of nature our observations show irregular departures from law owing

---

[13] (Ed.) Cf. [Bibliography] G–1891–1.

to our errors, so there are in the very facts themselves absolutely fortuitous departures from law trillions of trillions of times smaller no doubt, but which nevertheless must manifest themselves in some indirect way on account of their continual occurrence. I do not mean to say that it is a strictly necessary consequence that there should be this element of absolute chance in nature, and my first theory attempted to avoid it. But as I went on, I found other reasons to support this view of which I will endeavor to give you some idea in the next lecture.[14]

515.   But if the laws of nature are results of evolution, this evolution must proceed according to some principle; and this principle will itself be of the nature of a law. But it must be such a law that it can evolve or develope itself. Not that if absolutely absent it would create itself perhaps, but such that it would strengthen itself, and looking back into the past we should be looking back through times in which its strength was less than any given strength, and so that at the limit of the infinitely distant past it should vanish altogether. Then the problem was to imagine any kind of a law or tendency which would thus have a tendency to strengthen itself. Evidently it must be a tendency toward generalization, — a generalizing tendency. But any fundamental universal tendency ought to manifest itself in nature. Where shall we look for it? We could not expect to find it in such phenomena as gravitation where the evolution has so nearly approached its ultimate limit, that nothing even simulating irregularity can be found in it. But we must search for this generalizing tendency rather in such departments of nature where we find plasticity and evolution still at work. The most plastic of all things is the human mind, and next after that comes the organic world, the world of protoplasm. Now the generalizing tendency is the great law of mind, the law of association, the law of habit taking. We also find in all active protoplasm a tendency to take habits. Hence I was led to the hypothesis that the laws of the universe have been formed under a universal tendency of all things toward generalization and habit-taking.

[14] (Ed.) Presumably Lecture 8, "The Logic of Continuity." There is a manuscript, "The Logic of Continuity," in Widener IB3 which is very probably the lecture referred to; 6.185–213 are from this manuscript.

516. The next problem was to find a method of reasoning by which I could deduce with mathematical certainty the exact nature and formulæ of the laws which would be formed under the influence of such a tendency and having deduced them to compare them with nature and thus see whether the theory was tenable or not.

517. Now I have had some remarkable successes in this line; and have also been led to make some remarkable predictions which remain yet to be compared with observation. Of the method of reasoning I have used I shall give you some slight idea in the next lecture.[15]

§9. CHANCE AND LAW [16]

518. *Uniform* distribution presents to a superficial view diverse characters. There are just so many suicides every year; of children born every year just so many develope into giants and just as many into dwarfs. An insurance company stakes almost its existence upon the expectation that just so many losses will occur each year. The relation between temperature, pressure, and volume upon which the whole cosmos of business reposes, insofar as it depends on the regular working of steam-engines, is another case of a uniformity which is simply a necessary corollary of a fortuitous distribution. But in many cases of *uniform* distribution, so far as we can see, *fortuitous* distribution plays no part. Thus, the two kinds of electricity tend to unite in a certain fixed proportion. This is simply because one kind attracts what the other repels and these two forces vary with the distance in precisely the same way. Both are conservative forces; and the uniform distribution of the two electricities is due to the very peculiarly adjusted relation between the two conservative forces. In chemical combinations we have a very marked example of uniform distribution. We do not know by what sort of forces chemical compounds are held to-

[15] (Ed.) See the preceding footnote.

[16] (Ed.) This final section is the four missing manuscript pages referred to at 6.81n* (p. 60); these pages are now with the rest of the manuscript at Widener IB2–10. They are published here to fill the gap in "Causation and Force," 6.66–87, Lecture 4 of the Cambridge series, [Bibliography] G–1898–1. This lecture deals with some of the topics dicussed in "Habit," Sections 1–8 above.

gether. Even apart from the circumstance that some of the
most readily formed bodies, such as acetylene, are endothermic,
there are other considerations which show that those forces are
not altogether conservative. But the bonds of atoms and their
atomicities are sufficient warrant for the assertion that the
forces must be exceedingly complicated and specially related
to one another. I might say much more both about chemical
forces and about the conditions of uniform distribution in general; but in the limits of one lecture I think it best to confine
myself to the two clearer cases.

519. I have said that a uniformity, or regular law, may be
a mere consequence of a fortuitous distribution. But if you
examine any such case critically, you will find that after all,
this only results because of some regularity in the conditions.
Take, for example, Boyle's law that if the density of a gas is
doubled its pressure will be exactly doubled. This is because
if there are twice as many molecules in the space, twice as
many in a given time will pound upon the wall of the receptacle.
But this results not from fortuitous distribution alone, but from
fortuitous distribution conjoined with the circumstance that the
paths of the molecules are all very nearly rectilinear. I will not
stop to prove this, which you will find set forth both in Watson's
little treatise and in the more generally interesting volume of
Oscar Emil Meyer. Suffice it to say that it *is* an essential condition. Now this is something which, being true of *all* the molecules, is a regularity. The simplicity of the law is due to the
simplicity of this regularity. You will find, if you analyze the
problem, that it must always be the case when a regularity
results from a fortuitous distribution that some uniformity of
the objects of the collection must come into play, and further
that any simplicity the resulting law may exhibit must be due
to the simplicity of that uniformity.

520. On the other hand, in regard to fortuitous distribution,
while you may undoubtedly suppose that it arises simply from
the absence of any sufficient reason to the contrary, — not that
I accept the principle of sufficient reason as a general one by
any means, but in this case, it amounts merely to supposing the
fortuitous distribution is a pure First, without any cause or
reason whatsoever, — while this you may of course suppose,

yet if you suppose it to have been in any case a necessary result, this necessity certainly implies that some law of uniformity is at work, but for all that it will be quite evident that the uniformity has not *per se* of its own nature produced the irregularity, but that this irregularity is due to some other irregularity, some other fortuitous distribution, in the initial conditions.

521.   Thus it is that uniformity, or necessary law, can only spring from another law; while fortuitous distribution can only spring from another fortuitous distribution. Law begets law; and chance begets chance; and these elements in the phenomena of nature must of their very nature be primordial and radically distinct stocks. Or if we are to escape this duality at all, urged to do so by the principle of retroduction, according to which we ought to begin by pressing the hypothesis of unity as far as we can, the only possible way of doing so is to suppose that the first germ of law was an *entity*, which itself arose by chance, that is as a First. For it is of the nature of Chance to be First and that which is First is Chance; and fortuitous distribution, that is, utter irregularity, is the only thing which it is legitimate to explain by the absence of any reason to the contrary.

522.   These things having become clear to us, let us now, remembering that the whole aim of this discussion is to find some clue by which physical and psychical action may be unified, examine, a little, certain other features of the two classes of phenomena governed respectively by conservative forces and by the principle of causality, and see how bright or how darkling a light is shed upon them by what we have thus far made out.

523.   Looking first at conservative forces, we remark that they govern nothing but the space relations of particles. They are the law of the mutual reactions of particles in space. And the first fact that demands our attention is that, other things being equal, particles react upon one another more strongly the nearer they are to one another. How shall we explain this fact? We shall get the right hint if we ask ourselves what would happen in case all this were suddenly reversed and particles were to act most and most directly on those particles which were most distant from them.

CHAPTER 4

CONSCIOUSNESS

§1. CATEGORIES OF EXPERIENCE [1]

524.   If the whole business of mathematics consists in deducing the properties of hypothetical constructions, mathematics is the one science to which a science of logic is not pertinent. For nothing can be more evident than its own unaided reasonings. On the contrary logic is an experiential, or positive, science. Not that it needs to make any special observations, but it does rest upon a part of our experience that is common to all men. Pure deductive logic, insofar as it is restricted to mathematical hypotheses, is, indeed, mere mathematics. But when logic tells us that we can reason about the real world in the same way with security, it tells us a positive fact about the universe. As for induction, it is generally admitted that it rests upon some such fact. But all facts of this sort are irrelevant to the deduction of the properties of purely hypothetical constructions.

525.   But there is a part of the business of the mathematician where a science of logic is required. Namely, the mathematician is called in to consider a state of facts which are presented in a confused mass. Out of this state of things he has at the outset to build his hypothesis. Thus, the question of topical geometry is suggested by ordinary observations. In order definitely to state its hypothesis, the mathematician, be-

[1] (Ed.) From Section 2, "Some Logical Prolegomena," the final section of a manuscript, "On Topical Geometry, in General," Widener IA–2, undated, with added quotations in 534n4 and 535n6. A partial draft and a complete draft of Section 2 have a common first page. Paragraphs 524–529 are from the partial draft; paragraphs 530–538 are the last part of the complete draft.

fore he comes to his proper business, must define what continuity, for the purpose of topics, consists in; and this requires logical analysis of the utmost subtlety. Mathematicians still survive who are so little versed in reasoning as to deny that we can reason mathematically about infinity, although the hypothesis of an endless series of whole numbers involves infinity and the hypothesis of transcendental irrational quantities involves an infinity of another kind. If we cannot reason mathematically about infinity, *a fortiori* we cannot reason mathematically about continuity, and any exact mathematics of topical geometry becomes impossible. To clear up these difficulties, some consideration of logical matters is indispensable.

526. Logic is a branch of philosophy. That is to say it is an experiential, or positive science, but a science which rests on no special observations, made by special observational means, but on phenomena which lie open to the observation of every man, every day and hour. There are two main branches of philosophy, Logic, or the philosophy of thought, and Metaphysics, or the philosophy of being. Still more general than these is High Philosophy which brings to light certain truths applicable alike to logic and to metaphysics. It is with this high philosophy that we have at first to deal.

527. What is the *experience* upon which high philosophy is based? For any one of the special sciences, experience is that which the observational art of that science directly reveals. This is connected with and assimilated to knowledge already in our possession and otherwise derived, and thereby receives an interpretation, or theory. But in philosophy there is no special observational art, and there is no knowledge antecedently acquired in the light of which experience is to be interpreted. The interpretation itself is experience. Even logic, however, the higher of the two main branches of philosophy, draws a distinction between truth and falsehood. But in high philosophy, experience is the entire cognitive result of living, and illusion is, for its purposes, just as much experience as is real perception. With this understanding, I proceed to make evident the following proposition.

528. All the elements of experience belong to three classes, which, since they are best defined in terms of numbers, may be

termed *Kainopythagorean categories.*[2] Namely, experience is composed of

1st, *monadic experiences*, or *simples*, being elements each of such a nature that it might without inconsistency be what it is though there were nothing else in all experience;

2nd, *dyadic experiences*, or *recurrences*, each a direct experience of an opposing pair of objects;

3rd, *triadic experiences*, or *comprehensions*, each a direct experience which connects other possible experiences.

529. In order to prove this proposition I have, first, to invite every reader to note certain phenomena in experience and make certain simple generalizations from those observations; second, to point out in those generalized phenomena the essential characters in the above definitions of the categories; third, to point out certain other characteristics of those phenomena and show how they are related to the essential characters of the categories; fourth, to exemplify the wide range of each category in experience; fifth, to show by comparison of the characters already ascertained that none of the categories can be resolved into the others, but that all are distinct from one another; sixth, and most difficult, to prove that there can be no element in experience not included in the three categories.

530. A *quality* of feeling, say for example of [a] certain purple color, might be imagined to constitute the whole of some being's experience without any sense of beginning, ending, or continuance, without any self-consciousness distinct from the feeling of the color, without comparison with other feelings; and still it might be the very color we see. This is a conclusion which anybody can reach by comparing his different states of feeling; but we cannot actually observe a quality of feeling in its purity; it is always mixed with other elements which modify it greatly. Were a feeling thus to usurp the whole consciousness, it would necessarily be perfectly simple; for the perception of different elements in it is a comparison of feelings. Moreover, with us every feeling has its degree of vividness, which does not affect its quality, but is apparently the degree of disturbance it produces. It is necessary to speak vaguely,

---

[2] (Ed.) These are the psychological versions of Peirce's categories, First, Second, and Third, which are treated in general in [CP] I, Book III.

because it is not settled precisely what vividness consists in. But [were] the feeling uncomplicated by anything else, no particular degree of vividness would attach to it. The quality of feeling would then be the whole feeling. Qualities, then, constitute the first category. A quality of feeling is perfectly simple, in itself; though a quality thought over and thus mixed with other elements, may be compared with others and analyzed. A quality of feeling, in itself, is no object and is attached to no object. It is a mere tone of consciousness. But qualities of feeling may be attached to objects. A quality of feeling, in itself, has no generality; but it is susceptible of generalization without losing its character; and indeed all the qualities of feeling we are able to recognize are more or less generalized. In a mathematical hypothesis the qualities of feeling are so subordinate as to be scarcely noticeable.

531.   That we cannot have an experience of exertion without a direct experience therein of resistance to our exertion is plain. By an experience of exertion, I do not mean a consciousness of resolving to do something, nor the collection of our force preparatory to an effort, but merely what we experience in the very act of doing. This being understood, I contend that it is equally true that we cannot have an experience of being affected by anything without having therein a direct experience of our resisting the effect. Take hold of one end of a lexicon and lift it, while one edge remains on the table or floor. You experience its resistance. But when the centre of gravity has passed beyond the vertical plane of stationary edge, what you feel is that the dictionary is acting upon you. Yet the only difference is that different muscles are now called into play, which are elongating instead of contracting. Lay your forearm on the table and place the book on your palm. Though the sensation is somewhat different, you still have an experience of being overborne, and thus of holding out against the compression. A series of such experiments, with variations needless to describe, will convince the reader that there is a common character in the experience of acting upon anything by a muscular contraction and an experience of being acted on whether by a relaxation of a muscle or by a sensation received upon the organs of sense. That experience gives us at once a direct consciousness of something

inward and an equally direct consciousness of something outward. In fact, these two are one and the same consciousness.
They are inseparable. The same two-sided consciousness appears when by direct effort I bring to the surface of recollection a name that I dimly remember, and when I make distinct
to myself a confused conception.[3] If the purple color which
we just supposed made up the whole consciousness of a being
were suddenly to change, then, still supposing the idea of continuance is either absent or not prominent, that being will have
a two-sided consciousness. The sense of what has been will
be a rudimentary *ego*, the sense of what comes about will be a
rudimentary *non-ego*. For past experience is for each of us
ours, and that which the future brings is not ours, which becomes present only in the instant of assimilation. That being
could have no sense of change except by experiencing the two
colors together. The instant change would involve a sort of
shock consisting in the two-sided consciousness. This experience of *reaction* is the second Kainopythagorean category. It is
impossible to find any element of experience directly involving
two objects, and no more, — those two embraced in any third,
such as a pair, but standing in their naked otherness, — other
than an experience of reaction.

532. A reaction is something which occurs *hic et nunc*. It
happens but once. If it is repeated, that makes two reactions.
If it is continued for some time, that, as will be shown below,
involves the third category. It is an individual event, and I
shall show that it is the root of all logical individuality. A reaction cannot be generalized without entirely losing its character as a reaction. A generalized reaction is a law. But a law,
by itself without the addition of a living reaction to carry it
out on each separate occasion, is as impotent as a judge without
a sheriff. It is an idle formula entirely different from a reaction.
A reaction may be ever so conformable to law or reason, that
is, it may occur when law or reason calls for it. But, in itself,
as reaction it is arbitrary, blind, and brute exertion of force.
To express the fact that a reaction thus resists all generaliza-

[3] But I do not mean to say that bare striving usually does any more good in
these cases than in the case of such a physical difficulty as turning a key that
does not fit very well in its lock. If a moderate effort does not suffice, some contrivance has to be employed.

tion, I say that it is *anti-general*. In this respect it contrasts with a quality of feeling, which though not in itself general is susceptible of generalization without losing its character as quality of feeling. It is remarkable that Reaction, which is the Dyad category, should have an aggressive unity that Quality, the Monad category, does not exhibit. But the explanation of it is that the quality involves no reference to anything else and so is one without any special emphasis, since it could not be otherwise; while reaction consists in the congress of two things, that might not come together, and every concurrence of them makes a distinct reaction. It will be found that the third category also has a mode of unity which does not belong to either of the others.

533. A quality of feeling does not in itself involve any reaction. But an experience of reaction does involve two qualities of feeling. It consists in the conjunction of two qualities of feeling; and in this conjunction those two qualities of feeling become more than mere qualities. In being thus set over against one another they acquire the concreteness and actuality of feelings. The one purple color absorbing the entire consciousness of our supposed being was a mere tone of life. But when a sudden change occurs setting two against one another, they become objects.

534. Although in all direct experience of reaction, an *ego*, a something within, is one member of the pair, yet we attribute reactions to objects outside of us. When we say that a thing *exists*, what we mean is that it reacts upon other things.[4] That we are transferring to it our direct experience of reaction is

---

[4] (Ed.) "When the idea of space forms itself in our minds, or being inborn, connects itself with sensations, those things come to be regarded as near together which act strongly on one another, and are intimately related in regard to forces; while those things come to be regarded as remote which, as far as those forces of which we have any primitive experience are concerned, have little to do with one another. Hence, when gravitation was found to act at a distance, and even at vast distances, men were astounded; they thought it could not be. It seemed somehow to involve absurdity. The absurdity which was obscurely felt was that the idea [of] nearness was the idea of close connection; and therefore men felt that immediate connection supposed confinity. But that instinctive idea has been corrected. Any particle may be regarded as extending throughout space. It is where it acts. But it acts extremely little except in a very little space; and its place is peculiarly where it acts the most." From a fragment in Widener IA–8, undated.

shown by our saying that one thing *acts* upon another. It is our hypothesis to explain the phenomena, — a hypothesis, which like the working hypothesis of a scientific inquiry, we may not believe to be altogether true, but which is useful in enabling us to conceive of what takes place.

535. Now if we ask ourselves what else we observe in every experience (taking experience in its broadest sense to include experience of ideal worlds and of the real world as we interpret its phenomena) besides qualities and reactions, the answer will readily come that there remain the regularities, the continuities, the significances. These are essentially of one kind. That continuity is only a variation of regularity, or, if we please so to regard it, that regularity is only a special case of continuity, will appear below, when we come to analyze the conception of continuity. It is already quite plain that any continuum we can think of is perfectly regular in its way as far as its continuity extends. No doubt, a line may be say an arc of a circle up to a certain point and beyond that point it may be straight. Then it is in one sense continuous and without a break, while in another sense, it does not all follow one law. But in so far as it is continuous, it everywhere follows a law; that is, the same thing is true of every portion of it; while in the sense in which it is irregular its continuity is broken. In short, the idea of continuity is the idea of a homogeneity, or sameness, which is a regularity. On the other hand, just as a continuous line is one which affords room for any multitude of points, no matter how great,[5] so all regularity affords scope for any multitude of variant particulars; so that the idea [of] continuity is an extension of the idea of regularity. Regularity implies generality; [6] and generality is an intellectual relation essentially the

---

[5] (Ed.) Cf. 3.567, 4.639–640.

[6] (Ed.) "I begin by defining a *part* of any *whole*, in a sense of the [term] much wider [than] any in current use, though it is not obsolete in the vocabulary of philosophy. In this broadest sense, [it] is anything that is (1) other than its whole, and (2) . . . such that if the whole were really to be, no matter what else might be true, then the part must under all conceivable circumstances itself really be, in the same 'universe of discourse,' though by no means necessarily in the same one of those three Universes with which experience makes us all more or less acquainted. Thus, light is a *part* of vision. . . .

"A perfect continuum belongs to the genus, of a whole all whose parts without any exception whatsoever conform to one general law to which same law conform likewise all the parts of each single part. *Continuity* is thus a special

same as significance, as is shown by the contention of the nominalists that all generals are names. Even if generals have a
being independent of actual thought, their being consists in
their being possible objects of thought whereby particulars can
be thought. Now that which brings another thing before the
mind is a representation; so that generality and regularity are
essentially the same as significance. Thus, continuity, regularity, and significance are essentially the same idea with merely
subsidiary differences. That this element is found in experience
is shown by the fact that all experience involves time. Now
the flow of time is conceived as continuous. No matter whether
this continuity is a datum of sense, or a quasi-hypothesis imported by the mind into experience, or even an illusion; in any
case it remains a direct experience. For experience is not what
analysis discovers but the raw material upon which analysis
works. This element then is an element of direct experience.

536. It remains to be shown that this element is the third
Kainopythagorean category. All flow of time involves learning;
and all learning involves the flow of time. Now no continuum
can be apprehended except by a mental generation of it, by
thinking of something as moving through it, or in some way
equivalent to this, and founded upon it. For a mere dull staring
at a superficies does not involve the positive apprehension of
continuity. All that is given in such staring is a feeling which

---

kind of *generality*, or conformity to one Idea. More specifically, it is a *homogeneity*, or generality among all of a certain kind of parts of one whole. Still
more specifically, the characters which are the same in all the parts are a certain
kind of relationship of each part to all the coordinate parts; that is, it is a
regularity. The step of specification which seems called for next, as appropriate
to our purpose of defining, or logically analyzing the Idea of continuity, is that
of asking ourselves what kind [of] relationship between parts it is that constitutes the regularity a continuity; and the first, and therefore doubtless the
best answer for our purpose, not as the ultimate answer, but as the proximate
one, is that it is the relation or relations of *contiguity*; for continuity is unbrok-
enness (whatever that may be,) and this seems to imply a *passage* from one
part to a contiguous part. What is this 'passage'? This passage seems to be an
act of turning the attention from one part to another part; in short an actual
event in the mind. This seems decidedly unfortunate, since an event can only
take place in Time, and Time is a continuum; so that the prospect is that we
shall rise from our analysis with a definition of continuity in general in terms
of a special continuity. However, it is possible that this objection will disappear
as we proceed." From "Supplement. 1908 May 24," Widener IA–3, an addendum alternative to 4.642 ([Bibliography] G–1908–1b).

serves as a sign that the object might be apprehended as a continuum. Thus, all apprehension of continuity involves a consciousness of learning. In the next place, all learning is virtually
reasoning; that is to say, if not reasoning, it only differs there-
from in being too low in consciousness to be controllable and in
consequently not being subject to criticism as good or bad, —
no doubt, a most important distinction for logical purposes, but
not affecting the nature of the elements of experience that it
contains. In order to convince ourselves that all learning is virtually reasoning, we have only to reflect that the mere experience of a sense-reaction is not learning. That is only something
from which something can be learned, by interpreting it. The
interpretation is the learning. If it is objected that there must
be a first thing learned, I reply that this is like saying that there
must be a first rational fraction, in the order of magnitudes,
greater than zero. There is no minimum time that an experience of learning must occupy. At least, we do not conceive it
so, in conceiving time as continuous; for every flow of time, however short, is an experience of learning. It may be replied that
this only shows that not all learning is reasoning, inasmuch as
every train of reasoning whatever consists of a finite number
of discrete steps. But my rejoinder is that if by an argument
we mean an attempt to state a step in reasoning, then the simplest step in reasoning is incapable of being completely stated
by any finite series of arguments. For every step in reasoning
has a premiss, P, and a conclusion, C; and the reasoning consists in the perception that if P is found true as it has been
found true, then *must* C be always or mostly true; and this
"must" means that not only [is] C true (or probable) unless
P is false (or not found true in the way supposed) but that
every analogous premiss and conclusion are in the same relation. That is to say, in the reasoning we observe that P has a
certain general character and C is related to it in a certain
general way, and further that given any proposition whatever
of that general character, the proposition related to it in that
general way is true unless the former proposition is false;
whence it necessarily follows of C and P, that either the former
is true or the latter is false. But this is a second argument
involved in the reasoning. For the first argument was

P is true,
Hence, C must be true;

while the second argument is

P has a general character P' and C has a relation r to P;
But given any proposition having the character P', the proposition having the relation r to it is true unless the former is false;
Hence, C is true unless P is false.

Thus, every reasoning involves another reasoning, which in its turn involves another, and so on *ad infinitum*. Every reasoning connects something that has just been learned with knowledge already acquired so that we thereby learn what has been unknown. It is thus that the present is so welded to what is just past as to render what is just coming about inevitable. The consciousness of the present, as the boundary between past and future, involves them both. Reasoning is a new experience which involves something old and something hitherto unknown. The past as above remarked is the *ego*. My recent past is my uppermost *ego*; my distant past is my more generalized *ego*. The past of the community is *our ego*. In attributing a flow of time to unknown events we impute a quasi-*ego* to the universe. The present is the immediate representation we are just learning that brings the future, or non-ego, to be assimilated into the *ego*. It is thus seen that learning, or representation, is the third Kainopythagorean category.

537. There are no more Kainopythagorean categories than these three. For the first category is nonrelative experience, the second is experience of a dyadic relation, and the third is experience of a triadic relation. It is impossible to analyze a triadic relation, or fact about three objects, into dyadic relations; for the very idea of a compound supposes two parts, at least, and a whole, or three objects, at least, in all. On the other hand, every tetradic relation, or fact about four objects can be analyzed into a compound of triadic relations. This can be shown by an example. Suppose a seller, S, sells a thing, T, to a buyer, B, for a sum of money, M. This sale is a tetradic relation. But if we define precisely what it consists in, we shall find it to be a compound of six triadic relations, as follows:

1st, S is the subject of a certain receipt of money, R, in return for the performance of a certain act A_s;

2nd, This performance of the act A_s effects a certain delivery, D, according to a certain contract, or agreement, C;

3rd, B is the subject of a certain acquisition of good, G, in return for the performance of a certain act, A_b;

4th, This performance of the act A_b effects a certain payment, P, according to the aforesaid contract C;

5th, The delivery, D, renders T the object of the acquisition of good G;

6th, The payment, P, renders M the object of the receipt of money, R.

Or we may define a sale as the execution of contract of sale. The contract of sale has two clauses. The first clause provides for a giving and a receiving. The giving is by the seller of the commodity; the receiving is by the buyer of the same commodity. The second clause provides for a giving and a receiving. The giving is by the buyer of the price; the receiving is by the seller of the same price. The execution is of the first clause and of the second, etc. But I do not think this latter definition as good as the other, since it introduces several unnecessary elements and also covertly brings in four pentadic relations, such as the relation of the buyer to the first and second clauses of the contract and to the separate executions of them.

538. Let me now resume the argument. To begin with, it is to be remarked that I use the word "experience" in a much broader sense than it carries in the special sciences. For those sciences, experience is that which their special means of observation directly bring to light, and it is contrasted with the interpretations of those observations which are effected by connecting these experiences with what we otherwise know. But for philosophy, which is the science which sets in order those observations which lie open to every man every day and hour, experience can only mean the total cognitive result of living, and includes interpretations quite as truly as it does the matter of sense. Even more truly, since this matter of sense is a hypothetical something which we never can seize as such, free from all interpretative working over. Such being what is here meant

by experience, my argument is of the utmost simplicity. It consists merely in begging the reader to notice certain phenomena which he will find, I believe, in every corner of experience and to draw the simplest generalizations from them. The first phenomenon that I ask him to observe is, that he can detect elements in experience which are whatever they are each in its own simplicity. Namely, he will perceive that this is true of colors, smells, emotions, tones of mood, the characteristic flavors, if I may use this expression, attaching to certain ideas. Look, for instance, on anything yellow. That yellow quality is not in itself, as that mere quality, to be explained by anything else, or defined in terms of anything else; nor does it involve or imply anything else. This is surely evident. True, we know by experiment that a yellow color can be produced by mixing green and red light. But the yellow, as a quality of feeling, involves no reference to any other color. Every quality of feeling, as such, is perfectly simple and irrespective of anything else. The second phenomenon that I ask the reader to observe is that there are in experience occurrences; and in every experience of an occurrence two things are directly given as opposed, namely, what there was before the occurrence, which now appears as an *ego*, and what the occurrence forces upon the *ego*, a *non-ego*. This is particularly obvious in voluntary acts; but it is equally true of reactions of sense. If the latter are intense, or violent, the sense of reaction is particularly strong. There is a certain quality of feeling here, a brute arbitrariness, as I may call it, though it cannot be described any more than yellow can be described. But it is not this quality of feeling to which I wish to direct attention as peculiar, but the actual taking place. This actual taking place essentially involves two things, what there was before and what the occurrence introduces. I ask the reader to remark that such an occurrence cannot possibly be resolved into qualities of feeling. For in the first place, a quality of feeling is, in itself, simple and irrespective of anything else; so that anything compound necessarily involves something besides a quality of feeling. Secondly, a quality is merely something that *might* be realized, while an occurrence is something that *actually* takes place. The character of brute exertion that attaches to every occurrence is, no doubt, a quality of feeling; but experience of the occurrence itself, is something else. Such an element of experience I term a *reaction* in order to emphasize its essentially dual character. Thirdly, a reaction has an individuality. It happens only once. If it is repeated, the repetition is another occurrence, no matter how like the first it may be. It is anti-general. A quality, on the other hand, has no individuality. Two qualities are different only so far as they are unlike. Individuality is an aggressive unity, arising from an absolute refusal to be in any degree responsible for anything else. This a quality cannot have since it is too utterly irrespective of anything else even to deny it. A reaction, on the other hand, is an opposition, or pairedness of objects that are existentially correlative, neither existing except by virtue of this opposition.

§2. FORMS OF CONSCIOUSNESS [7]

539. I propose to review the ideas of the Nineteenth Century; and as an introduction to that review it will be well to glance at the general tendencies of the times in their influence upon human nature in general. In order to do that it will be convenient first to enumerate the departments of mental action.

540. Almost all the philosophers of this century have agreed to name Feeling, Knowledge, and Will, as the parts of the mind, or to speak more accurately as the three classes of states of mind. Few of those who make use of this enumeration pretend that it is exactly scientific; but it has served a good purpose. It is usually attributed to the Father of German philosophy, Immanuel Kant, who died in the last year of the last century. Kant borrowed it from his master Tetens; but in doing so he quite changed the boundaries of the department of *Feeling*. Take whatever is directly and immediately in consciousness at any instant,[8] just as it is, without regard to what it signifies, to

---

[7] (Ed.) An untitled manuscript, Widener IB1-2, undated. The quotations in 540n8 and 541n9 are from what appears to be an alternative partial draft, Widener IC1-a,b, undated. In this alternative draft it is stated that the paper was originally written to be read to a group that met Sunday afternoons. It is likely that these manuscripts were written about 1900; see paragraphs 539, 540 and 545 and [Bibliography] G-1901-5, but note that Kant died in 1804 and not "in the last year of the last century," as Peirce says in paragraph 540.

[8] (Ed.) "*Direct* in philosophical language without anything intervening.

what its parts are, to what causes it, or any of its relations to
anything else, and that is what Tetens means by Feeling; and
I shall invariably use the word in that same sense. For example, here we are in this pleasant room, sitting before the fire,
listening to my reading. Now take what is in your consciousness at any one single moment. There is in the first place a
general consciousness of life. Then, there is the collection of
little skin-sensations of your clothes. Then, there is the sense
of cheerfulness of the room. Then, there is a social consciousness, or feeling of sympathy with one another. Then, there is
the light. Then, there is the warmth of the fire. Then, there is
the sound of my voice, which in any one instant will merely
be a note. In addition, there [are] a hundred things in the
background of consciousness. This is the best way in which I
can describe what is in your consciousness in a single moment.
But it has taken me a considerable time to describe them. I
cannot, therefore, have described them as they are in your
mind; for precisely what I am trying to describe is the consciousness of a moment. By the very nature of language, I am
obliged to pick them to pieces to describe them. This requires
reflection; and reflection occupies time. But the consciousness
of a moment as it is in that very moment is not reflected upon,
and not pulled to pieces. As it is in that very moment, all these
elements of feeling are together and they are one undivided
feeling without parts. What I have described as elements of
the feeling are not really parts of the feeling as it is in the
very moment when it is present; they are what appears to have
been in it, when we reflect upon it, after it is past. As it is felt
at the moment itself these parts are not yet recognized, and
therefore they do not exist in the feeling itself. I have assured
myself that this is so, by frequent repetitions of the following
experiment. Namely, sitting in a perfectly dark room with my
eyes directed to a piece of paper upon which some pretty simple
figure had been drawn, I knew not what, I have caused the
paper to be instantaneously illuminated by a single electric

Thus this house directly abuts upon the street. I am talking to you directly.
Immediate involves the same idea carried further. It denies every kind of
separation by a boundary, by a difference of place or time. What is immediately
in consciousness is what consciousness is made of." A footnote from the alternative draft (see 539n7).

spark. The spark was practically instantaneous; but the impression upon the retina would last nearly a quarter of a second. But I always found I had to sit reflecting for several seconds before I could tell at all what I had seen. Undoubtedly, the feeling was actually present for a good quarter of a second; and it was followed by a vivid memory that for some seconds was, I will not say nearly as intense as the feeling itself, but yet very perfect for a memory. But until I had had time to pick the memory to pieces, I found I could not say what I had seen. After experimenting in this way for some time, I became struck with the fact that there was, after all, conclusive proof of the thing, without the experiment. In the very moment of receiving an impression, it is impossible that we should say what the parts of it are, because in order that we should do that we must attend to one part and another separately, and to carry the attention from one part to another requires time. The third of a second is sufficient time for me to say that I have seen a light, not felt a jab; for some reflection can be accomplished in a third of a second, or much less. For in watching a pendulum swing over twenty millimetres with a scale of millimetres behind it, I can accurately observe the extreme point of the swing to a millimetre and estimate to a tenth part the fraction of the millimetre, although the pendulum is not there for a twentieth of a second. Now this requires reflection. So that it is proved that a not very simple reflection can be performed in the twentieth part of a second. But reflection cannot be performed instantaneously; and the evidence is quite satisfactory that the feeling of a moment cannot be at all analyzed in that moment. I trust then that I have made clear what I mean, and what Tetens meant by Feeling. It is the consciousness of a moment as it is in its singleness, without regard to its relations whether to its own elements or to anything else. Of course, this feeling although it can exist in a moment, can also be protracted for some time. For example, if we are close to an engine with a powerful whistle, and this suddenly shrieks, the intensity of it seems to paralyze me; and for several seconds my mind seems to have hardly anything in it but that shriek. Even when our thoughts are active, at each instant we have a feeling; and in the midst of changes of thought not a whole feeling but an ele-

327

ment of feeling, which I shall also call a Feeling, may endure.
Kant, in order to make the enumeration of Tetens fit into his
own philosophical system, limited the word Feeling to feelings
of pleasure and pain; and the majority of philosophical writers
of this century have followed him in this. I think this has been
unfortunate, and has hindered the perception of the real relations of [the] triad.

541.   It may be asked where Tetens got his idea that Feelings, Cognitions or Knowledges, and Volitions or acts of willing
made up the mind. I have never seen this question answered.
Yet the answer is not far to seek. He took it from the ancient
writers upon rhetoric. For they instruct the orator to begin his
discourse by creating a proper state of feeling in the minds of
his auditors, to follow this with whatever he has to address to
their understandings, that is, to produce cognitions, and finally
to inflame them to action of the will. For the rhetoricians, therefore, the triad names three states of mind; and most of the psychologists of our century have considered Feeling, Cognition,
and Volition to be three general states of mind.[9]

542.   But in my opinion, by a slight modification the triad
may be made to stand for three radically different kinds of
elements of all consciousness, the only elements of consciousness, which are respectively predominant in the three whole
states of mind which are usually called Feeling, Knowing, and
Willing. It is thus raised from a mere loose grouping into a
scientific and fundamental analysis of the constituents of consciousness.

543.   The modification which I propose relates to the department to which *Sensation* is to be assigned. It will be best
to explain what I mean by *sensation*. If you look at a flame,
you observe that it is orange, and that orange color as it was
seen on that particular occasion and was attributed to a reality
then and there before you, and not called up in memory, was
a sensation. So if you hear a cry, whether it is real or a hallu-

[9] (Ed.) "No sharp line of demarcation can be drawn between different integral states of mind; certainly not between such states as feeling, knowing,
and willing. It is plain that we are actively knowing in all our waking minutes,
and actually feeling, too. If we are not always willing, we are, at least, at all
times consciously reacting against the outer world. Strümpell's celebrated experiment, fully confirmed by others, shows that as soon as outward stimuli are entirely removed, the person falls asleep." From the alternative draft (see 539n7).

cination, if you take it for a reality then and there present, every vowel and consonant of it is a separate sensation. But if it is only called up by your own act of imagination it is not a sensation. A sensation is not a feeling; but an element of feeling is one part of it. Here is a little bottle with some green spicular crystals in it. When I look at it, I experience a sensation of greenness. Were that greenness to fill my whole field of vision, while I became momentarily deaf, lost my skin-sensations, and my memory, it would be a total feeling. For it would be my life for the moment, and would not be attributed to anything in particular without me or within me. As it is, it is an element of my feeling while I am looking at the bottle. But to make up the sensation, along with this feeling there is a consciousness of being irresistibly compelled to see it when I look at it. I cast my eyes upon it, without any intention of imagining such a thing, and there it is more vivid than any imagination could be. The sight forces itself upon me. The sensation has two parts: first, the feeling, and second, the sense of its assertiveness, of my being compelled to have it. The consequence is that remembering a sensation is not at all the same thing as having it. For though there is some vestige of compulsiveness, even in the memory, it is not at all comparable to the compulsiveness of the actual sensation. But if I remember, or imagine a feeling, whatever I remember or imagine is a feeling, and I cannot remember or imagine or anywise represent to myself a feeling without having that very feeling then and there. All the existence a feeling can have is had the moment it is thought. But a sensation is not had until I am really acted upon by something out of my control. I have, thus, made clear, I hope, what I mean by a sensation. It is an event which has to happen at a particular moment. For that reason there is great need of a verb to correspond with the noun; and I shall use the expression to *sense* the greenness. It translates the German verb *empfinden*. The verb to *feel* is quite superfluous; for to think a feeling at all is to *feel* it. But the verb to *sense* is indispensable, because to actually *sense* a sensation is very different from remembering or imagining it. Now, it is usual to put sensation under the head of Knowledge. This may or may not be correct language; I do not propose to be led into any verbal dispute. But I refuse to classify sensation in that way, because I aim to enumerate the different kinds of elements of consciousness. Now, sensation contains two radically different kinds of consciousness. One part is feeling and the other part is the consciousness of being compelled to feel upon that particular occasion. This consciousness of compulsion has a general resemblance to the consciousness of willing. Willing is the consciousness of exerting a force upon something without the consciousness, or at least outside of that part of consciousness. But the consciousness of exerting force and the consciousness of suffering the effect of a force are one and inseparable. Suppose I try to exercise my strength in lifting a huge dumb-bell. If I strive to lift it, I feel that it is drawing my arm down. If I suffer no consciousness of having my arm pulled down, I can have no consciousness of exerting force in lifting the dumb-bell. To be conscious of exerting force and to be conscious [of] having force used upon me are the same consciousness. Hence, the compulsive element of sensation must be classed along with the consciousness of willing. Both are particular events which must happen at definite times; and to dream of exercising the will is as different from actually willing as dreaming of a sensation is from actually sensing. Feeling is neither over against me nor in me. If I have any momentary consciousness of self, that is a part of the feeling. So that I am, or at any rate my immediate self-consciousness is, a part of my total feeling. Any element of feeling has the same relation to self-consciousness that it has to any other element of the same total feeling; that is to say, it is quite independent of it. An element of Feeling is neither a part of self-consciousness nor is set up over against self-consciousness. But the consciousness of compulsion in sensation as well as the consciousness of willing necessarily involves self-consciousness and also the consciousness of some exterior force. The self and the not-self are separated in this sort of consciousness. The sense of reaction or struggle between self and another is just what this consciousness consists in. Hence, to give it a name, I propose to call it *altersense*. To avoid circumlocution, I will speak of the *altersense* element of sensation, as *Sensation* simply. Thus, *Altersense* has two varieties, Sensation and Will. The difference between them is that Sensation is an event in which a feeling is forced upon the mind; while Volition or Willing, is an event in which a desire is satisfied, that is, an intense state of feeling is reduced. In Sensation, a feeling is forced upon us; in Willing, feeling forces its way out from us.

544. The removal of sensation from the department of *cognition*, or Knowledge, leaves nothing remaining in that department except what are called Mediate Cognitions, that is, Knowledges through some third idea or process different from either the Knowing self or the Known object. For the sake of giving this Mediate Cognition, or rather the peculiar kind of element of consciousness it involves a single name, I will call it *medisense*, that is, the consciousness of a middle term, or process, by which something not-self is set up over against the consciousness. All consciousness of a process belongs to this *medisense*. It has several varieties. In the first place there is a separative process, the centrifugal tendency of thought, by which any idea by following out its own development becomes separated from those with which it is connected. We see this in attention. When we see the little bottle with green crystals, the green idea detaches itself from the remaining ideas, the spicular form, the being bunched together in a little tube, etc. and leads to a thought which is accurately expressed by the sentence "these crystals are green," where the green stands off from the remaining ideas which remain confused together. It is the liveliness of the green idea which brings this about. And in all cases it is the idea which has vigor which spontaneously detaches itself from the rest. We may call this variety of *medisense* by the name of *Abstraction*.

545. Before I go further, there are one or two points which require explanation. Everybody knows that recollections gradually become *"dim"*; and also that attention makes Feelings *"vivid,"* which before attention was applied to them were relatively "dim." This does not mean that we recollect a bright color as a dull color, or a loud sound as a faint sound; nor that attention makes an olive color seem an apple green or a whisper seem to be a bellow. It is several years since I was at Niagara Falls; but I have no doubt my recollection of the roar is of its being about as loud as it really is. I remember when

I returned from a long absence, I found my old room was much smaller than I had recollected it. The first cup of coffee I tasted more than fifty years ago seems to me of a higher flavor than any coffee in the world really is. Though my imagination is very much the reverse of a vivid one, I can carry colors in my mind with more than usual accuracy. Dim as my imaginations and memories are, they do not represent high colors by low colors. We must say then that feelings have two kinds of intensity. One is the intensity of the feeling itself,[10] by which loud sounds are distinguished from faint ones, luminous colors from dark ones, highly chromatic colors from almost neutral tints, etc. The other is the intensity of consciousness that lays hold of the feeling, which makes the ticking of a watch actually heard infinitely more vivid than a cannon shot remembered to have been heard a few minutes ago. I shall not stop to discuss the difficult question of what the distinction between those two kinds of intensity consists in, about which three or four opinions are held. I shall simply say that in my opinion the first kind of intensity, distinguishing bright colors from dim ones, is the intensity of feeling-consciousness; while the second kind, distinguishing sensation from imagination, is the intensity of *alter-sense* or of the assertiveness of the feeling. I shall call this second *vividness*.

546. Now, in order that you may understand what I am about to say, I must tell you about some experiments which I have conducted.[11] They have been several times repeated. But each series of experiments lasted for from three to five weeks, at a time when the weather was steady and my health or that of the subject of experiment was good; and I or he, as the case might be, took pains to lead a regular, cheerful life without agitation. The experiments would last for an hour, in some series for an hour and a half, at the same time every day. Extraordinary precautions were taken to have all the mental influences, light, warmth, etc. precisely the same every day, and the same throughout the time of experimentation. The attention would be exercised for seven minutes, in some series for ten; and then five minutes, sometimes three minutes,

---

[10] (Ed.) Peirce first had "One is an *objective* intensity" and then substituted "One is the intensity of the feeling itself." Cf. 555.

[11] (Ed.) Cf. 7.215.

rest would be taken of just the same kind, generally a little conversation about the experiments. A habit was acquired of making two different efforts of attention of just the same degree of effort of attention at every experiment. One of these would be a very light effort, the other a vigorous one. I did not assume that these two degrees of attention would remain exactly the same throughout the month, but I did assume, first, that they would not change extravagantly, and second, that if, say, six or eight kinds of experiments were made, each ten times every day, then on the average of the whole month, the degree of effort made would be the same in one kind of experiment as in another, especially when the subject could not tell which were which. In that way, I was able to produce a fixed average intensity of attention. That attention was directed to certain differences of sensation. The sensations were of two general kinds in different series, some being colors and others sensations of pressure. In each case, there was a very carefully devised apparatus for producing the precise sensations desired, and for measuring them. I may mention that my color-box cost me $2000. The pressure apparatus was cheap; but there no conceivable refinement was left out of account. I have mentioned that the sensations were measured. Now many psychologists deny that sensation can be measured. That is because they are not mathematicians, and are unacquainted with the mathematical theory of measurement; of which they have the crudest notions. I repeat that the sensations *were* scientifically measured, and on such a scale that zero meant no sensation. To show how accurate they were I may say that a piece of specially selected fuzzy black paper much blacker than black velvet was found to be 30 measurable degrees from absolute blackness. To get absolute blackness a closet about ten feet by ten was constructed and painted with lamp black in the inside. This was placed in a large hall with little light in it. Then, a small hole about the size of a cent in the thin wall of the closet when looked at from the outside appeared to be absolutely black. Now the experiments would be like this. The subject would put his eye to the eye-piece of the color-box and would see a small rectangle which at first sight would appear to be all one color. But after an effort of attention continuing from 5 seconds to a minute, he would see

333

that it was not all one color, that it was sharply divided into two parts whose colors were different. One part might be a very little yellower than the other. After he had exerted his attention for a certain number of seconds, the whole would disappear and he would tell a second person, the operator, what he thought he had seen, and would also give a number marking his degree of confidence that he had seen it. The operator would record the result, in absolute silence without the slightest sign and without being seen. A tap mechanically made of precisely the same intensity would inform the subject that another rectangle was to be seen, and he would say "tp" when he put his eye to the eye-piece. I need not describe exactly how the pressure-experiments were made.[12] As a result there would be several thousand experiments showing the effect of two degrees of attention exerted for several different lengths of time upon discriminating between sensations differing by several known amounts. The results of experiments would all be expressed in two sets [of] numbers, one showing the percentage of errors and the other the feeling of confidence, in the attempts at discrimination under different circumstances. Those numbers were then subjected to mathematical discussion, according to the established principles of such work; and from them a law was deduced. It was found that the feeling of confidence did not begin to show itself at all until the real power of discrimination had reached a considerable strength. There were a very large number of cases in which the confidence was *zero*, so that the answers given appeared to the subject to be mere random guesses. Yet a decided majority of them were, in all cases, correct. It was also found that during the period of attention, the difference of sensation was continually increasing in vividness. Sensations that differed less, no matter how little, could still be discriminated just as well as sensations that differed more, if the effort of attention were greater, or if it were longer continued. The law was so accurately fulfilled, that it was safe to infer that the point at which infinite attention would be required for the slightest preponderance of right answers over wrong ones was

[12] (Ed.) See Chapter 2, "Small Differences of Sensation," Book I, present volume.

just the point where the two sensations differed not at all. The difference of sensation for the discrimination of which no attention whatever would be required appeared to be infinite; though this result was less certain than the other.

547. The general upshot of all these experiments, together with others which I have not time to describe, was that when you ask yourself what is in your mind at any moment, and give yourself an answer, even after a searching scrutiny of the field of consciousness, you have not begun to tell yourself the whole truth. For it is one thing to feel a thing and it is another thing to have a reflex feeling, that *there is* a feeling; and my experiments conclusively show that the consciousness must reach a considerable vividness before the least reflex feeling of it is produced. That it is really felt is shown by the fact that a greater effort of attention would detect it. There is as it were, an upper layer of consciousness to which reflex consciousness, or self-consciousness, is attached. A moderate effort of attention for a second or two only brings a few items into that upper layer. But all the time the attention lasts, thousands of other ideas, at different depths of consciousness, so to speak, that is, literally, of different degrees of vividness, are moving upwards. These may influence our other thoughts long before they reach the upper layer of reflex consciousness. There are such vast numbers of ideas in consciousness of low degrees of vividness, that I think it may be true, — and at any rate is roughly true, as a necessary consequence of my experiments, — that our whole past experience is continually in our consciousness, though most of it sunk to a great depth of dimness. I think of consciousness as a bottomless lake, whose waters seem transparent, yet into which we can clearly see but a little way. But in this water there are countless objects at different depths; and certain influences will give certain kinds of those objects an upward impulse which may be intense enough and continue long enough to bring them into the upper visible layer. After the impulse ceases they commence to sink downwards.[13]

548. I have spoken [14] of the first kind of *medisense*, abstraction, which breaks one idea away from another. There is

[13] (Ed.) Cf. 553–554.
[14] (Ed.) In 544.

an opposite influence by which when one idea has its vividness increased it gives an upward impulse to a number of other ideas with which it is connected so that it forms one set with them. The law of this is often called the law of the association of ideas. That is well enough. But it is inaccurate to call this phenomenon *association*, as Germans especially often do. Association is a different thing.[15] More accurate German writers call the action of which we are now speaking *reproduction*. But even that is not free from objection. For the *idea* which receives an upward impulse, making it grow more vivid, was not necessarily ever so near the surface of consciousness before; or if it was, that circumstance has nothing to do with it. It is a great mistake to suppose that ideas only become associated into sets in the upper layer of consciousness, although such action is more lively there. Most English and American psychologists of today use the term *Reproduction*; but I prefer the older English word *Suggestion*, to which some of the very best writers still adhere. The only objection to it is that the word is used in another sense in reference to the phenomena of hypnotism.

549. What takes place in suggestion is that an idea when it rises gives an upward motion to all other ideas belonging to the same set. For example, if the idea of *husband* is mentioned, since husband and wife form a set, the idea of *wife* will receive an upward motion and a few minutes later when fatigue has caused the husband idea to commence sinking, that is to become dim, the *wife* idea will be uppermost. I will some other day talk to you about this action of suggestion.

550. At present I hurry on to the third form of *medisense* which is that of the formation of sets of ideas, or association proper. A great many associations of ideas are inherited. Others grow up spontaneously. The rest depend upon the principle that ideas once brought together into a set remain in that set. Many associations are merely accidental. A child acquires a distaste for a particular kind of food merely because it ate it when it was sick. The idea of that food and the feeling of sickness are brought into a set; and the consequence is that every time the idea of that food reaches a high degree of vivid-

---

[15] (Ed.) See Chapter 2, "Association," in the present book.

ness, the feeling of sickness gets a swift upward motion. Other associations cannot be called accidental because it was in the nature of things that they should appear in sets. Thus, light and warm get associated in our minds because they are associated in Nature.

551. There are no other forms of consciousness except the three that have been mentioned, Feeling, Altersense, and Medisense. They form a sort of system. Feeling is the momentarily present contents of consciousness taken in its pristine simplicity, apart from anything else. It is consciousness in its first state, and might be called *primisense*. *Altersense* is the consciousness of a directly present other or second, withstanding us. *Medisense* is the consciousness of a thirdness, or medium between primisense and altersense, leading from the former to the latter. It is the consciousness of a process of bringing to mind. Feeling, or *primisense*, is the consciousness of firstness; altersense is consciousness of otherness or secondness; medisense is the consciousness of means or thirdness. Of *primisense* there is but one fundamental mode. *Altersense* has two modes, Sensation and Will. *Medisense* has three modes, *Abstraction, Suggestion, Association*.[16]

552. The only element of the mind that this enumeration omits is the phenomenon of *Fatigue*. It is a highly important matter. Our mental life and health depend to a far greater extent than would at first be guessed upon the action of fatigue. But it finds no place in this system. The only defence that I can offer for this is that there is no direct consciousness of fatigue. Whether that is an adequate excuse or not, I am not yet quite decided.

§3. CONSCIOUSNESS AND REASONING [17]

553. We are going to shock the physiological psychologists, for once, by attempting, not an account of a hypothesis about the brain, but a description of an image which shall correspond, point by point, to the different features of the phenomena of consciousness. Consciousness is like a bottomless

---

[16] (Ed.) See further 7.276–278.

[17] (Ed.) Paragraph 553 is an undated fragment; paragraph 554 is from an alternative draft. Both are in Widener IC1–a,b.

lake in which ideas are suspended at different depths.[18] Indeed, these ideas themselves constitute the very medium of
consciousness itself.[19] Percepts alone are uncovered by the
medium. We must imagine that there is a continual fall of rain
upon the lake; which images the constant inflow of percepts in
experience. All ideas other than percepts are more or less deep,
and we may conceive that there is a force of gravitation, so that
the deeper ideas are, the more work will be required to bring
them to the surface. This virtual work, which the mathematicians call the 'potentials' of the particles, is the negative of
the 'potential energy'; and the potential energy is that feature
of the image which corresponds to the degree of vividness of
the idea. Or we may see that the potential, or depth, represents
the degree of energy of attention that is requisite to discern the
idea at that depth. But it must not be thought that an idea
actually has to be brought to the surface of consciousness before
it can be discerned. To bring it to the surface of consciousness
would be to produce a hallucination. Not only do all ideas
tend to gravitate toward oblivion, but we are to imagine that
various ideas react upon one another by selective attractions.
This images the associations between ideas which tend to
agglomerate them into single ideas. Just as our idea of spatial
distance consists in the sense of time that it would take with
a given effort to pass from one object to another, so the distance
between ideas is measured by the time it will take to unite
them. One tries to think of the French for *shark* or for *linch-
pin*. The time that it will take to recover the forgotten word
depends upon the force of association between the ideas of the
English and French words and upon circumstances which we
image by their *distance*. This, it must be confessed, is exceedingly vague; as vague as would be our notion of spatial

---

Paragraphs 555–558 are from Chapter I, "Of Reasoning in General," of the
"Short Logic," Widener IB2–10. This manuscript is dated c.1893 in [CP] II.
Paragraph 555 follows immediately after the last sentence of 2.443. The part of
the manuscript from which 555–558 and 2.444 are taken is not continuous;
paragraph 2.444 is from manuscript pages beyond 555–558, but the last paragraph of 2.444 is similar to 558.

[18] (Ed.) Cf. 547.

[19] (Ed.) "An idea is nothing but a portion of consciousness having in itself
no definite boundaries, except so far as it may be of a different quality from
contiguous ideas." Peirce's marginal comment.

distance if we lived in the body of an ocean, and were destitute of anything rigid to measure with, being ourselves mere portions of fluid.

554. Consciousness is rather like a bottomless lake in which ideas are suspended, at different depths. Percepts alone are uncovered by the medium. The meaning of this metaphor is that those which [are] deeper are discernible only by a greater effort, and controlled only by much greater effort. These ideas suspended in the medium of consciousness, or rather themselves parts of the fluid, are attracted to one another by associational habits and dispositions, — the former in association by contiguity, the latter in association by resemblance. An idea near the surface will attract an idea that is very deep only so slightly that the action must continue for some time before the latter is brought to a level of easy discernment. Meantime the former is sinking to dimmer consciousness. There seems to be a factor like momentum, so that the idea originally dimmer becomes more vivid than the one which brought it up. In addition, the mind has but a finite area at each level; so that the bringing of a mass of ideas up inevitably involves the carrying of other ideas down. Still another factor seems to be a certain degree of buoyancy or association with whatever idea may be vivid, which belongs to those ideas that we call purposes, by virtue of which they are particularly apt to be brought up and held up near the surface by the inflowing percepts and thus to hold up any ideas with which they may be associated. The control which we exercise over our thoughts in reasoning consists in our purpose holding certain thoughts up where they may be scrutinized. The levels of easily controlled ideas are those that are so near the surface as to be strongly affected by present purposes. The aptness of this metaphor is very great.

555. If the question is asked in what the processes of contemplation and of fixation of the attention consist, this question being psychological, it is necessary, before answering it, to describe some phenomena of the mind. Be it known, then, that consciousness, or feeling, has been ascertained by careful observations mathematically discussed to have the properties now

to be stated.[20] Feeling, by which is here meant that of which we are supposed to be immediately conscious, is subject to degrees. That is to say, besides the *objective intensity* which distinguishes a loud sound from a faint sound, there is a *subjective intensity* which distinguishes a lively consciousness of a sound, from a dull consciousness of it. Though the two kinds of intensity are apt to go together, yet it is possible for a person at the same time to recall the tick of a watch and the sound of a neighboring cannon, and to have a livelier consciousness of the former than of the latter, without however remembering the latter [as] a fainter sound than the former. Feelings of slight subjective intensity act upon one another, undergo transformations, and affect the emotions and the voluntary actions; although they do all this less decisively than they would do if they were more intense. They are also, *other things being equal*, much less under control than more subjectively intense feelings. This remark needs explanation. A feeling may be forced upon the mind through the senses, or by experience, directly or indirectly, and bear down the power of the will; and those feelings are the most subjectively intense we have. Why they should be so, will soon be explained.[21] But when a feeling is *not* thus forced upon us our being conscious of it sufficiently to attract attention makes it act more upon us, and at the same time enables us to affect its transformations, more than if it were scarcely perceptible. Now there are certain combinations of feelings which are specially interesting. These are those which tend toward a reaction between mind and body, whether in sense, in the action of the glands, in contractions of involuntary muscles, in coordinated voluntary deeds, or, finally, in discharges of an extraordinary kind of one part of the nerves upon another. Interesting combinations of ideas are more active than others, both in the way of suggestion, and in the way of subjective intensity. The action of thought is all the time going on, not merely in that part of consciousness which thrusts itself on the attention, and which is the most under discipline, but also in its deeply shaded parts, of which we are in some measure conscious but not sufficiently so to be strongly affected by what

[20] (Ed.) Cf. 546.
[21] (Ed.) No such explanation is given in the extant manuscript.

is there. But when in the uncontrolled play of that part of thought, an interesting combination occurs, its subjective intensity increases for a short time with great rapidity.[22] This is what constitutes the fixation of the attention. Contemplation consists in using our self-control to remove us from the forcible intrusion of other thoughts, and in considering the interesting bearings of what may lie hidden in the icon, so as to cause the subjective intensity of it to increase.

556. The observation of the icon may be ordinary direct observation, or it may be scientific observation aided by the apparatus of logical algebra and other technical means.

557. A third step in inference is performed upon the indices. Thus, an index may be dropped from consideration. If there are two selective indices, one universal, the other particular, and the latter selection is made last, the order of the selections can be reversed. But all these changes in the indices are justified only by considering icons. We may, therefore, say that excepting the colligation of different beliefs the whole of inference consists in *observation*, namely in the observation of icons. Even the colligations well up from the depths of consciousness in precisely the same manner as that in which the special features of icons are remarked.

558. Thus, all knowledge comes to us by observation, part of it forced upon us from without from Nature's mind and part coming from the depths of that inward aspect of mind, which we egotistically call *ours*; though in truth it is we who float upon its surface and belong to it more than it belongs to us. Nor can we affirm that the inwardly seen mind is altogether independent of the outward mind which is its Creator.

§4. WHAT IS THE USE OF CONSCIOUSNESS? [23]

559. In the last chapter,[24] I assumed the reader would occupy the position of Common Sense, which makes the real things in this world blind unconscious objects working by

[22] It may be remarked that this is a very temporary condition, and shortly after the interesting idea will be found to have a lower subjective intensity than it would have had if it had not been interesting.

[23] (Ed.) "What is the Use of Consciousness?" Chapter IV, c.1893, of *Grand Logic*, Widener IB2–1.

[24] (Ed.) "The Materialistic Aspect of Reasoning," 6.278–286.

mechanical laws together with a consciousness as idle spectator.
I pointed out that this spectator cannot have part or lot even
in the intelligence and purpose of the business; for intelligence
does not consist in feeling intelligently but in acting so that
one's deeds are concentrated upon a result.

560.　This makes the universe a muddle. According to it
consciousness is perfectly impotent and is not the original of
the material world; nor on the other hand can material forces
ever have given birth to feeling, for all they do is to accelerate
the motions of particles. Nay, that they should so much as
give rise to sensations in that consciousness is more than incomprehensible, it is manifestly impossible. There is no room
for reaction between mind and matter. The only consistent
position for such a philosophy is flatly to deny that there is any
such thing as consciousness. Even were that denial made, the
question would be insoluble — not for us merely, but in its
own nature, — how all the laws of mechanics came about, or
why they should have the curious relationships they exhibit.
Then, were that impossibility disregarded, just look out of
your window, reader, and see this world in all its infinite mani-
foldness, and say whether you are content to take it wholly un-
accounted for, as something that always has been, and always
has been as complex as it is now. For mechanical forces never
produce any new diversity, but only transform one diversity
into another diversity.

561.　The whole of this suicide of Common Sense results
from its incautious assumption that it is one thing to look red
or green and another thing to see red or green. Now metaphysicians never have agreed, or at least never have perceived
that they agreed, about anything; but I believe that every
man who has ever reflected deeply about knowledge has come
to the conclusion that there is something wrong about that
assumption.[25]

562.　Grant that that assumption is somehow wrong, though
we may not, at first, see how exactly, and the muddle begins
to clarify itself. The spectator is no longer on one side of the

---

[25] Take, for instance, that superlatively cunning defense of common sense,
the doctrine of immediate perception, — a doctrine so subtle that it has eluded
the grasp of many a fine logician, — and what is it, after all, but a confession
that to see and to be seen are one and the same fact.

footlights, and the world on the other. He is, in so far as he sees, at one with the poet of the piece. To act intelligently and to see intelligently become at bottom one. And in the matter of auditing the account of the universe, its wealth and its government, we gain the liberty of drawing on the bank of thought.

563.   This method promises to render the totality of things thinkable; and it is plain there is no other way of explaining anything than to show how it traces its lineage to the womb of thought.

564.   This is what is called Idealism. As soon, however, as we seek preciser statement, difficulties arise, — by no means insuperable ones, yet calling for patient study based upon a thorough understanding of logic. All this must be postponed. Yet one very obvious and easily answered objection may be noticed. It will be said that the identification of knowledge and being threatens to deprive us of our Ignorance and Error. Let me hasten to swear that no act of mine shall lay hands on those sacramenta.

§5. SYNECHISM AND IMMORTALITY [26]

565.   The word *synechism* is the English form of the Greek συνεχισμός, from συνεχής, continuous.[27] For two centuries we have been affixing -ist and -ism to words, in order to note sects which exalt the importance of those elements which the stem-words signify. Thus, *materialism* is the doctrine that matter is everything, *idealism* the doctrine that ideas are everything, *dualism* the philosophy which splits everything in two. In like manner, I have proposed to make *synechism* mean the tendency to regard everything as continuous.[28]

566.   For many years I have been endeavoring to develope this idea, and have, of late, given some of my results in the *Monist*.[29] I carry the doctrine so far as to maintain that con-

---

[26] (Ed.) "Immortality in the Light of Synechism," Widener IB3. "For the Open Court" is written on the manuscript. It is dated c.1892 on the basis of the bibliographic references in the article.

[27] (Ed.) Synechism is treated in detail in [CP] VI, Part B of Book I.

[28] The Greek word means continuity of parts brought about by surgery.

[29] (Ed.) [Bibliography] G–1891–1c (1892). This paper gives a definition of "synechism," 6.103.

tinuity governs the whole domain of experience in every element of it. Accordingly, every proposition, except so far as it relates to an unattainable limit of experience (which I call the Absolute,) is to be taken with an indefinite qualification; for a proposition which has no relation whatever to experience is devoid of all meaning.

567.   I propose here, without going into the extremely difficult question of the evidences of this doctrine, to give a specimen of the manner in which it can be applied to religious questions. I cannot here treat in full of the method of its application. It readily yields corollaries which appear at first highly enigmatic; but their meaning is cleared up by a more thoroughgoing application of the principle. This principle is, of course, itself to be understood in a synechistic sense; and, so understood, it in no wise contradicts itself. Consequently, it must lead to definite results, if the deductions are accurately performed.

568.   Thoroughgoing synechism will not permit us to say that the sum of the angles of a triangle exactly equals two right angles, but only that it equals that quantity plus or minus some quantity which is excessively small for all the triangles we can measure.[30] We must not accept the proposition that space has three dimensions as certainly strictly accurate; but can only say that any movements of bodies out of the three dimensions are at most exceedingly minute. We must not say that phenomena are perfectly regular, but only that the degree of their regularity is very high indeed.

569.   There is a famous saying of Parmenides $\check{\epsilon}\sigma\tau\iota$ $\gamma\grave{\alpha}\rho$ $\epsilon\hat{\iota}\nu\alpha\iota$, $\mu\eta\delta\grave{\epsilon}\nu$ δ' $o\grave{\upsilon}\kappa$ $\epsilon\hat{\iota}\nu\alpha\iota$, "being is, and not-being is nothing." This sounds plausible; yet synechism flatly denies it, declaring that being is a matter of more or less, so as to merge insensibly into nothing. How this can be appears when we consider that to say that a thing *is* is to say that in the upshot of intellectual progress it will attain a permanent status in the realm of ideas. Now, as no experiential question can be answered with absolute certainty, so we never can have reason to think that any given idea will either become unshakably established or be forever exploded.[31] But to say that neither of these two events

[30] (Ed.) Cf. Chapter 5, "On Non-Euclidean Geometry," [CP] VIII, Book I.
[31] (Ed.) Cf. 1.171.

will come to pass definitively is to say that the object has an imperfect and qualified existence. Surely, no reader will suppose that this principle is intended to apply only to some phenomena and not to others, — only, for instance, to the little province of matter and not to the rest of the great empire of ideas. Nor must it be understood only of phenomena to the exclusion of their underlying substrates. Synechism certainly has no concern with any incognizable; but it will not admit a sharp sundering of phenomena from substrates. That which underlies a phenomenon and determines it, thereby is, itself, in a measure, a phenomenon.

570. Synechism, even in its less stalwart forms, can never abide dualism, properly so called. It does not wish to exterminate the conception of twoness, nor can any of these philosophic cranks who preach crusades against this or that fundamental conception find the slightest comfort in this doctrine. But dualism in its broadest legitimate meaning as the philosophy which performs its analyses with an axe, leaving as the ultimate elements, unrelated chunks of being, this is most hostile to synechism. In particular, the synechist will not admit that physical and psychical phenomena are entirely distinct, — whether as belonging to different categories of substance, or as entirely separate sides of one shield, — but will insist that all phenomena are of one character, though some are more mental and spontaneous, others more material and regular. Still, all alike present that mixture of freedom and constraint, which allows them to be, nay, makes them to be teleological, or purposive.

571. Nor must any synechist say, "I am altogether myself, and not at all you." If you embrace synechism, you must abjure this metaphysics of wickedness. In the first place, your neighbors are, in a measure, yourself, and in far greater measure than, without deep studies in psychology, you would believe. Really, the selfhood you like to attribute to yourself is, for the most part, the vulgarest delusion of vanity. In the second place, all men who resemble you and are in analogous circumstances are, in a measure, yourself, though not quite in the same way in which your neighbors are you.

572. There is still another direction in which the barbaric

345

conception of personal identity must be broadened. A Brah-
manical hymn begins as follows: "I am that pure and infinite
Self, who am bliss, eternal, manifest, all-pervading, and who
am the substrate of all that owns name and form." This expresses more than humiliation, — the utter swallowing up of
the poor individual self in the Spirit of prayer. All communication from mind to mind is through continuity of being. A
man is capable of having assigned to him a *rôle* in the drama of
creation, and so far as he loses himself in that *rôle*, — no matter
how humble it may be, — so far he identifies himself with its
Author.

573. Synechism denies that there are any immeasurable
differences between phenomena; and by the same token, there
can be no immeasurable difference between waking and sleep-
ing. When you sleep, you are not so largely asleep as you fancy
that you be.

574. Synechism refuses to believe that when death comes,
even the carnal consciousness ceases quickly. How it is to
be, it is hard to say, in the all but entire lack of observational
data. Here, as elsewhere, the synechistic oracle is enigmatic.
Possibly, the suggestion of that powerful fiction "Dreams of
the Dead," recently published,[32] may be the truth.

575. But, further, synechism recognizes that the carnal
consciousness is but a small part of the man. There is, in the
second place, the social consciousness, by which a man's spirit
is embodied in others, and which continues to live and breathe
and have its being very much longer than superficial observers
think. Our readers need not be told how superbly this is set
forth in Freytag's *Lost Manuscript*.[33]

576. Nor is this, by any means, all. A man is capable of
a spiritual consciousness, which constitutes him one of the
eternal verities, which is embodied in the universe as a whole.
This as an archetypal idea can never fail; and in the world to
come is destined to a special spiritual embodiment.

577. A friend of mine, in consequence of a fever, totally
lost his sense of hearing. He had been very fond of music before his calamity; and, strange to say, even afterwards would

[32] (Ed.) Edward Stanton Huntington, *Dreams of the Dead*, by Edward
Stanton (pseud.), Boston, 1892. Cf. [Bibliography] N–1892–14.
[33] (Ed.) Gustav Freytag, *Die Verlorene Handschrift*, Leipzig, 1869.

love to stand by the piano when a good performer played. So then, I said to him, after all you can hear a little. Absolutely not at all, he replied; but I can *feel* the music all over my body. Why, I exclaimed, how is it possible for a new sense to be developed in a few months! It is not a new sense, he answered. Now that my hearing is gone I can recognize that I always possessed this mode of consciousness, which I formerly, with other people, mistook for hearing. In the same manner, when the carnal consciousness passes away in death, we shall at once perceive that we have had all along a lively spiritual consciousness which we have been confusing with something different.

578. I have said enough, I think, to show that, though synechism is not religion, but, on the contrary, is a purely scientific philosophy, yet should it become generally accepted, as I confidently anticipate, it may play a part in the onement of religion and Science.

§6. CONSCIOUSNESS AND LANGUAGE [34]

579. Philosophy is the attempt, — for as the word itself implies it is and must be imperfect — is the attempt to form a general informed conception of the *All*. All men philosophize; and as Aristotle says we must do so if only to prove the futility of philosophy. Those who neglect philosophy have metaphysical theories as much as others — only they [have] rude, false, and wordy theories. Some think to avoid the influence of metaphysical errors, by paying no attention to metaphysics; but experience shows that these men beyond all others are held in an iron vice of metaphysical theory, because by theories that they have never called in question. No man is so enthralled by metaphysics as the totally uneducated; no man is so free from its dominion as the metaphysician himself. Since, then,

[34] (Ed.) From Lecture XI of an incomplete series of lectures in Widener IB2–10. The editor has been unable to make a positive identification of these lectures, but the internal references and the general tone of the writing indicate that they are probably the manuscripts for the Lowell Institute lectures of 1866–67 ([Bibliography] G–1866–2a). On this basis Lecture XI is dated c.1867. In Widener IB2–10 these lectures are mixed with the manuscripts of a different series, which are probably those of the Harvard series of 1865–66, [Bibliography] G–1864–3.

everyone must have conceptions of things in general, it is most important that they should be carefully constructed.

580.   I shall enter into no criticism of the different methods of metaphysical research, but shall merely say that in the opinion of several great thinkers, the only successful mode yet lighted upon is that of adopting our logic as our metaphysics. In the last lecture,[35] I endeavored to show how logic furnishes us with a classification of the elements of consciousness. We found that all modifications of consciousness are inferences and that all inferences are valid inferences. At the same time we found that there were three kinds of inference: 1st, Intellectual inference with its three varieties Hypothesis, Induction and Deduction; 2nd, Judgments of sensation, emotions, and instinctive motions which are hypotheses whose predicates are unanalyzed in comprehension; and 3rd, Habits, which are Inductions whose subjects are unanalyzed in extension. This division leads us to three elements of consciousness: 1st, *Feelings* or Elements of comprehension; 2nd, *Efforts* or Elements of extension; and 3rd, *Notions* or Elements of information,[36] which is the union of extension and comprehension. I regret that the time does not permit me to dwell further upon this theory; but I wish to pass to a loftier and more practical question of metaphysics in order to put in a still stronger light the advantages of the study of logic. The question which I shall select is "what is man?" I think I may state the prevalent conception thus: Man is essentially a soul, that is, a thing occupying a mathematical point of space, not thought itself but the subject of inhesion of thought, without parts, and exerting a certain material force called volition. I presume that most people consider this belief as intuitive, or, at least, as planted in man's nature and more or less distinctly held by all men, always and everywhere.[37] On the contrary, the doctrine is a very modern one. All the ancients and many of the scholastics, held that man is compact of several souls; three was the usual number

[35] (Ed.) Lecture X. Only fragments of it have been found.

[36] (Ed.) Cf. 2.407ff.

[37] (Ed.) The following was pencilled in the margin with a line to indicate that it was to be inserted here:

"Most ignorant of what he's most assured
His glassy essence."

assigned, sometimes two, four, or five. Every attentive reader of St. Paul is aware that according to him, man has a three-fold being. We derive the notion of the soul's being single from Descartes. But with him, thought itself makes the man; whereas with us consciousness *is* not the man but is in man. Descartes, also, does not admit that the will of man exerts any force upon matter; as we mostly believe. In fact, the prevalent view of the present day is a heterogeneous hodgepodge of the most contradictory theories; its doctrines are borrowed from different philosophers while the premisses by which alone those philosophers were able to support their doctrines are denied; the theory thus finds itself totally unsupported by facts and in several particulars at war with itself. And this is admitted by most of those who have subjected it to rigid criticism.[38]

581.   One source of all this diversity of opinion, has been the want of an accurate discrimination between an inductive and a hypothetic explanation of the facts of human life. We have seen that every fact requires two kinds of explanation; the one proceeds by induction to replace its subject by a wider one, the other proceeds by hypothesis to replace its predicate by a deeper one.[39] We have seen that these two explanations never coincide, that both are indispensable, and that quarrels have sprung up even in physical science where there are so few disagreements in consequence of trying to make one theory perform both functions. Let us take care that we do not confound these two separate inquiries in reference to the soul. The hypothetic explanation will inform us of the causes or necessary antecedents of the phenomena of human life. These phenomena may be regarded internally or externally. Regarded internally they require an internal explanation by internal necessary antecedents, that is by *premisses*; and this explanation was given in the last lecture. If they are regarded externally or physically they require a physical explanation by physical antecedents, and this inquiry must be turned over unreservedly to the physiologists. They will find the truth of the matter,

[38] (Ed.)   Peirce here inserted "Upon the diversities of theories of the soul there are some pretty lines by Sir John Davies in his poem on Psychology" and referred to Sir William Hamilton's edition of Thomas Reid's *Works*, p. 203.

[39] (Ed.)   Induction and hypothesis are discussed in Book II of the present volume and at 2.508ff. (1867).

and we may rest satisfied that no explanation which is based squarely upon legitimate hypothesis from the facts of nature, can possibly conflict with a purely inductive explanation of man. It is true that the question for the physiologist is what are the physical antecedents of man's actions, that is what sort of an automaton is man; so that it is assumed as the condition of the problem that man is an automaton. For, automatism in this connection, consciousness being of course admitted, means nothing but regular physical antecedence; — implies only that nature is uniform; and this as we have seen is not a mere law of nature or fact of observation, but is a postulate of all thought, which no man consistently or persistently denies.[40] Yet this automatism seems, no doubt, to many to conflict with the notion of man as a RESPONSIBLE and IMMORTAL soul. But, then, we should remember that in our minds, the essential conceptions of responsibility and immortality are covered over with a mass of parasitical reflection derived from every philosophy and every religion of past time; so that if *we* cannot reconcile the doctrines of responsibility and immortality with the postulates of thought or with themselves, this is sufficiently accounted for by the obscurity and confusion of our notions on this subject, and we are by no means forced to adopt that which is the only other alternative and say that these doctrines are essentially false. These doctrines are a part of our religion; and one [of] them — if not both — are among its most precious consolations, which it would be difficult indeed to wring from the breast of a people which has entertained them for a thousand years. Talk as they please, of the weariness of unceasing day, of the balm of an eternal sleep, of the nobility lent to humanity by regarding it as capable of struggling and suffering for that which transcends its own responsibility and life-time; we still cling by nature original or acquired, to the dear hopes of our ancient religion. But while I have thought it proper to dwell for a moment upon the possibility of our being unable to reconcile responsibility and immortality with physical necessity, I must add that in fact we are not driven to that point, at all. On the contrary the philosophers of the Brownist school have

---

[40] (Ed.) Cf. 7.131–138, which are from Lecture IV of the same series (see 579n34).

shown uncontrovertibly that they are capable of being reconciled, and their arguments are very forcibly stated in an American work called Liberty and Necessity, written by Judge
[Henry] Carleton of Louisiana and published in Philadelphia
in 1857. There may be other modes of reconciling these conceptions [41] besides that which they have pointed out but still
they have shown that a rational reconciliation is possible.

582. Thus, the hypothetic explanation of human nature
stands by itself and will present no contradiction to the inductive explanation, which is what we desire when we ask what
is man? To what real kind does the thinking, feeling, and willing being belong? We know that externally considered man
belongs to the animal kingdom, to the branch of vertebrates,
and the class of mammals; but what we seek is his place when
considered internally, disregarding his muscles, glands, and
nerves and considering only his feelings, efforts, and conceptions.

583. We have already seen that every state of consciousness [is] an inference; so that life is but a sequence of inferences or a train of thought. At any instant then man is a
thought, and as thought is a species of symbol, the general
answer to the question what is man? is that he is a symbol.
To find a more specific answer we should compare man with
some other symbol.

584. I write here the word Six. Now let [us] ask ourselves
in what respects a man differs from that word. In the first
place, the body of man is a wonderful mechanism, that of the
word nothing but a line of chalk. In the second place, the
meaning of the word is very simple, the meaning of a man a
very Sphinx's question. These two differences are very obvious,
— they lie upon the surface. But what other difference is
there?

585. A man has consciousness; a word has not.[42] What do
we mean by consciousness, for it is rather an ambiguous term.
There is that emotion which accompanies the reflection that we
have animal life. A consciousness which is dimmed when animal life is at its ebb, in age or sleep, but which is not dimmed

[41] (Ed.) Cf. 5.339.
[42] (Ed.) Compare the following paragraphs with 5.313ff. (1868).

351

when the spiritual life is at its ebb; which is more lively the
better animal a man is, but is not so the better man he is.
You can all distinguish this sensation I am sure; we attribute
it to all animals but not to words, because we have reason to
believe that it depends upon the possession of an animal body.
And, therefore, this difference is included under the first that
we mentioned and is not an additional one. In the second
place, consciousness is used to mean the knowledge which we
have of what is in our minds; the fact that our thought is an
index for itself of itself on the ground of a complete identity
with itself. But so is any word or indeed any thing, so that
this constitutes no difference between the word and the man.
In the third place, consciousness is used to denote the *I think*,
the unity of thought; but the unity of thought is nothing but
the unity of symbolization; consistency, in a word — the implication of being — and belongs to every word whatever. It is
very easy to think we have a *clear* notion of what we mean by
consciousness, and yet it may be that the word excites no
thought but only a sensation, a mental word within us; and
then because we are not accustomed to allow the word written
on the board to excite that sensation, we may think we distinguish between the man and the word when we do not.

> "Most ignorant of what we're most assured
> Our glassy essence!"

586. Consciousness is, also, used to denote what I call
feeling; as by Mr. Bain whom I mention in order to say that he
recognizes the unity of sensation and emotion under this term
although he has not carried out the conception consistently.
Has that word feeling? Man, say the sensationalists, is a series
of feelings; at any one moment, then, *is a feeling*. How is it
with the word? Feelings, we all know, depend upon the bodily
organism. The blind man from birth has no such feelings as
red, blue, or any other colour; and without any body at all,
it is probable we should have no feelings at all; and the word
which has no animal body probably therefore has no animal
feelings, and of course if we restrict the word feeling to meaning animal feeling the word has no feelings. But has it not
something corresponding to feeling? Every feeling is cognitive

— is a sensation, and a sensation is a mental sign or word. Now the word has a word; it has itself; and so if man is an animal feeling, the word is just as much a written feeling.

587. But is there not this difference. Man's feelings are perceptions, he is affected by objects. He sees, hears, etc. A word does not. Yes; that is true, but perception, plainly, depends upon having an animal organism and therefore there is here no further difference beyond the obvious two mentioned at first. Yet even here, there is a correspondence between the word and the man. Perception is the possibility of acquiring information, of meaning more; now a word may learn. How much more the word *electricity* means now than it did in the days of Franklin; how much more the term planet means now than it did in the time [of] Hipparchus. These words have acquired information; just as a man's thought does by further perception. But is there not a difference, since a man makes the word and the word means nothing which some man has not made it mean and that only to that man? This is true; but since man can think only by means of words or other external symbols, words might turn round and say, You mean nothing which we have not taught you and then only so far as you address some word as the interpretant of your thought. In fact, therefore, men and words reciprocally educate each other; each increase of a man's information is at the same time the increase of a word's information and *vice versa*. So that there is no difference even here.

588. You see that remote and dissimilar as the word and the man appear, it is exceedingly difficult to state any essential difference between them except a physiological one. A man has a moral nature, a word apparently has none. Yet morals relate primarily to what we ought to do; and therefore as words are physiologically incapacitated to act we should not consider this as a separate point of distinction. But if we consider morality as the conformity to a law of fitness of things, — a principle of what is suitable in thought, not in order to make it true but as a prerequisite to make it spiritual, to make it rational, to make it more truly thought at all; we have something extremely analogous in the good grammar of a word or sentence. Good grammar is that excellence of a word by which

353

it comes to have a good conscience, to be satisfactory not merely [with] reference being had to the actual state of things which it denotes, not merely to the consequences of the act, but to it in its own internal determination. Beauty and truth belong to the mind and word alike. The third excellence is morality on the one hand, Grammar on the other.

589.   Man has the power of effort or attention; but as we have seen that this is nothing but the power of denotation, it is possessed by the word also.

590.   Perhaps the most marvellous faculty of humanity is one which it possesses in common with all animals and in one sense with all plants, I mean that of procreation. I do not allude to the physiological wonders, which are great enough, but to the fact of the production of a new human soul. Has the word any such relation as that of father and son? If I write "Let *Kax* denote a gas furnace," this sentence is a symbol which is creating another within itself. Here we have a certain analogy with paternity; just as much and no more as when an author speaks of his writings as his offspring, — an expression which should be regarded not as metaphorical but merely as general. Cuvier said that Metaphysics is nothing but Metaphor; an identity which is prettily typified in those acted charades, [in] the first of which two doctors come in at opposite sides of the stage, shake hands and go out for the first scene, then repeat the same thing for the second scene and again for the whole word; and then do the same thing three times for the three scenes of the second word; the two words are of course metaphysician and metaphor; and their identity suggests that the characters must have been the invention of some one who thought with Cuvier that Metaphysics is another term for Metaphor. If metaphor be taken literally to mean an expression of a similitude when the sign of predication is employed instead of the sign of likeness — as when we say this man *is* a fox instead of this man is like a fox, — I deny entirely that metaphysicians are given to metaphor; on the contrary, no other writers can compare with them for precision of language; but if Cuvier was only using a metaphor himself, and meant by metaphor broad comparison on the ground of characters of a formal and highly abstract kind, — then, indeed, meta-

physics professes to be metaphor — that is just its merit — as
it was Cuvier's own merit in Zoölogy. . . .

591.   Enough has now been said, I think, to show a true
analogy between a man and a word. I dare say this seems very
paradoxical to you; I remember it did to me, at first. But
having thought it over repeatedly, it has come to seem merest
truism. A man denotes whatever is the object of his attention
at the moment; he connotes whatever he knows or feels of this
object, and is the incarnation of this form or intelligible species;
his interpretant is the future memory of this cognition, his future
self, or another person he addresses, or a sentence he writes,
or a child he gets. In what does the identity of man consist
and where is the seat of the soul? It seems to me that these
questions usually receive a very narrow answer. Why we used
to read that the soul resides in a little organ of the brain no
bigger than a pin's head. Most anthropologists now more rationally say that the soul is either spread over the whole body
or is all in all and all in every part. But are we shut up in a box
of flesh and blood? When I communicate my thought and my
sentiments to a friend with whom I am in full sympathy, so
that my feelings pass into him and I am conscious of what he
feels, do I not live in his brain as well as in my own — most
literally? True, my animal life is not there but my soul, my
feeling thought attention are. If this be not so, a man is not
a word, it is true, but is something much poorer. There is a
miserable material and barbarian notion according to which
a man cannot be in two places at once; as though he were a
thing! A word may be in several places at once, Six Six, because its essence is spiritual; and I believe that a man is no
whit inferior to the word in this respect. Each man has an
identity which far transcends the mere animal; — an essence,
a *meaning* subtile as it may be. He cannot know his own
essential significance; of his eye it is eyebeam. But that he truly
has this outreaching identity — such as a word has — is the
true and exact expression of the fact of sympathy, fellow feeling — together with all unselfish interests — and all that makes
us feel that he has an absolute worth. Some one will ask me for
proof of this. It seems to me that I have already given both the
proof and the confirmation. The whole proof is very long but its

principal *lemmas* were these: 1st, "What is man?" is an inductive question in its present sense; 2nd, The inductive explanation is only the general expression of the phenomena, and makes no hypothesis; 3rd, Whatever man is he is at each instant; 4th, At each instant the only internal phenomena he presents are feeling, thought, attention; 5th, Feelings, thought, attention are all cognitive; 6th, All cognition is general, there is no intuition;[43] 7th, A general representation is a symbol; 8th, Every symbol has an essential comprehension which determines its identity. The confirmation I offered was the fact that man is conscious of his interpretant, — his own thought in another mind — I do not say immediately conscious — is happy in it, feels himself in some degree to be there. So that I believe that nothing but an undue ascendency of the animal life can prevent the reception of this truth.

592.   This essence of which I speak is not the whole soul of man; it is only his core which carries with it all the information which constitutes the development of the man, his total feelings, intentions, thoughts. When I, that is my thoughts, enter into another man, I do not necessarily carry my whole self, but what I do carry is the seed of [the] part that I do not carry — and if I carry the seed of my whole essence, then of my whole self actual and potential. I may write upon paper and thus impress a part of my being there; that part of my being may involve only what I have in common with all men and then I should have carried the soul of the race, but not my individual soul into the word there written. Thus every man's soul is a special determination of the generic soul of the family, the class, the nation, the race to which he belongs. . . .

593.   The principle that the essence of a symbol is formal, not material, has one or two important consequences. Suppose I rub out this word (Six) and write Six. Here is not a second word but the first over again; they are identical. Now can identity be interrupted or ought we to say that the word existed although it was unwritten? This word *six* implies that *twice three* is *five and one*. This is eternal truth; a truth which always is and must be; which would be though there were not six things in the universe to number, since it would still remain

[43] (Ed.) Cf. [Bibliography] G–1868–2a (5.213–263).

true that *five and one* would have been *twice three*. Now this *truth* is the word, six; if by six we mean not this chalk line, but that wherein *six, sex, ἕξ, sechs, zes, seis, sei* agree. Truth, it is said, is never without a witness; and, indeed, the fact itself — the state of things — is a symbol of the general fact through the principles of induction; so that the true symbol has an interpretant so long as it is true. And as it is identical with its interpretant, it always exists. Thus, the necessary and true symbol is immortal. And man must also be so, provided he is vivified by the truth. This is an immortality very different indeed from what most people hope for, although it does not conflict with the latter. I do not *know* that the Mohammedan paradise is not true, only I have no evidence that it is. Animal existence is certainly a pleasure, though some speak of being weary of it; but I think it is confessed by the most cultivated peoples that it is not immortal; otherwise, they would consider the brutes as immortal. Spiritual existence, such as a man has in him, whom he carries along with him in his opinions and sentiments; sympathy, love; this is what serves as evidence of man's absolute worth — and this is the existence which logic finds to be certainly immortal. It is not an impersonal existence; for personality lies in the unity of the *I think* — which is the unity of symbolization — the unity of consistency — and belongs to every symbol. It is not an existence, cut off from the external world, for feeling and attention are essential elements of the symbol itself. It is, however, a changed existence; one in which there are no longer any of the glories of hearing and vision, for sounds and colors require an animal eye; and in the same way all the feelings will be different.

594.   This immortality is one which depends upon the man's being a true symbol. If instead of *six*, we had written *Jove* we should have had a symbol which has but a contingent existence; it has no everlasting witness in the nature of things and will pass away or remain only in men's memories without exciting any response in their hearts. It is, indeed, true so far as it means a *supreme being*; its generic soul is true and eternal, but its specific and individual soul is but a shadow.

595.   Each man has his own peculiar character. It enters into all he does. It is in his consciousness and not a mere

357

mechanical trick, and therefore it is by the principles of the last lecture a cognition; but as it enters into all his cognition, it is a cognition of *things in general*. It is therefore the man's philosophy, his way of regarding things; not a philosophy of the head alone — but one which pervades the whole man. This idiosyncrasy is the idea of the man; and if this idea is true he lives forever; if false, his individual soul has but a contingent existence.

596. Gentlemen and ladies, I announce to you this theory of immortality for the first time. It is poorly said, poorly thought; but its foundation is the rock of truth. And at least it will serve to illustrate what use might be made by mightier hands of this reviled science, logic, *nec ad melius vivendum, nec ad commodius disserendum.*

CHAPTER 5

TELEPATHY AND PERCEPTION [1]

§1. TELEPATHY

597. A little passage at arms between a physicist of standing and a celebrated psychologist has lately focussed the public glance once more for a moment upon this subject.[2] The remarks of Prof. Trowbridge express, more or less successfully, the typical physicist attitude toward the hypothesis of telepathy and toward psychical research. I shall consider rather that typical attitude than the special points which this excellent physicist has made. For I was trained from boyhood in physics, have mostly associated with physicists, and fully share their prejudices, whether legitimate or illegitimate. Upon the formation of the Society for Psychical Research, I disapproved of physicists lending it their countenance, on the ground that in doing so they would be encouraging young men to devote the best years of their lives to an inquiry of little promise in which

---

[1] (Ed.) "Telepathy," including some alternative pages, Widener IC1–a,b, with deletions, and with an added quotation in 597n3. This manuscript is dated 1903 on the basis of the dates given in the next footnote, references to a manuscript on telepathy in the Peirce-James correspondence (James collection, Houghton Library), what appear to be James's handwritten comments in the margin of the first part of the manuscript, and a crossed-out date in the last section of the manuscript. This was a first draft from which Peirce intended to extract a magazine article.

Peirce divided the manuscript into six sections (with no titles); the sections of the present chapter are the same as Peirce's, but the titles have been supplied by the editor.

Cf. 6.548–587 and [Bibliography] G–1887–3 for other writings by Peirce on the subject of psychical research.

[2] (Ed.) John Trowbridge, "Telepathy," *The Nation* 76 (16 April 1903)308–309; and William James, "Telepathy Once More," *ibid.*, (23 April 1903)330.

those men would be in great danger of compromising themselves, since it would appear that they must either have some
positive result to defend after so much time had been spent
or else be reduced to a distressing acknowledgment of failure.
When the large book "Phantasms of the Living" appeared, I
wrote a long and minute criticism of it,[3] arguing that it only
showed that no scientific conclusion could be reached by the
examination of stories of sporadic and unanalyzed phenomena.
Thus I have little need of consulting with others to do full
justice to the typical physicist's disapproval of the hypothesis
and the methods of the telepathists. On the other hand, ever
since Wundt inaugurated the modern science of psychology
about 1862 (the date of the collected publication of his
Beiträge zur Theorie der Sinneswahrnehmung,) I have pursued that study both experimentally and speculatively, and am
thus better able than some physicists to appreciate the opinions of the psychologists.

598. Let me endeavor to explain the attitude of the physicist. Many people imagine that there is a certain class of
facts which it is repugnant to the physicist to acknowledge.
This is not so. If there were such a class of facts, the phenomena connected with radium would fall within it. Yet there has
been no disposition to ignore these phenomena. But the physicist recognizes that a phenomenon is of no use to him unless
both it and its conditions can be subjected to exact analysis.
Moreover, the only theories that can have any value for him
are those from which can be deduced exact predictions capable
of exact verification. As long as a fact stands isolated and
strange, it is next to impossible to make sure that it is a fact,
and quite impossible to render it useful to science. Physicists
are doubtless inclined to discredit facts of which they, as physi-

---

[3] (Ed.) [Bibliography] G–1887–3, "Criticism on 'Phantasms of the Living' . . ." In a fragment in Houghton Library, Peirce says: "Phenomena for
which psychical researchers invoke telepathy can be explained by unconscious
mental action, after severe scrutiny of testimony, and with aid from the doctrine of chances." Cf. [Bibliography] G–1887–3, p. 194. The fragment concludes, "Eight years ago on the appearance of the laborious work, Phantasms
of the Living, I examined the question with care, pronounced it very doubtful,
but provisionally rejected the whole theory. Reviewing the state of the question, this year, I find no decided change in either direction." This internal
reference dates the fragment as c.1895.

cists, could make no use. But that is a mere matter of personal *belief* with them. It cannot affect their conduct as physicists. Thus, in regard to aerolites, as long as there were merely scattered tales of stones having fallen from heaven at long intervals, although some of them were very strongly attested, as when a shower of them were dashed into a public square of Siena, it must be admitted that physicists of the very highest genius were too much inclined to pooh-pooh the matter. But this they did not do in their character as physicists, since there seemed to be no way by which a physicist could inquire into the matter. It was merely a "belief." One physicist, however, Chladni, bethought him to draw up a catalogue of all these tales, — using, not "post-card evidence," since post-cards were not yet in use, but testimonies that, taken singly, were mostly far from affording satisfactory scientific security. The result was that it appeared that stones fall from heaven every day (we now know that thousands fall daily). Thus, the subject became opened to scientific investigation, and the personal adverse "beliefs" of the physicists, gave way to the general acknowledgment that the fact had been established.

599. Suppose we knew nothing at all about electricity except for the stories of fire-balls. Then it could make no difference to physicists, as physical inquirers, whether those stories were true or not, since there would be no way by which further physical inquiry into their nature could be pursued. It would not be their concern, professionally; but personally their "belief" would mostly be that they were fancies.

600. The theory of telepathy is that in some cases one mind acts upon another, whether directly or not, at any rate by means fundamentally different from those that every-day experience renders familiar. As a scientific theory, this almost condemns itself. For to say that a phenomenon is fundamentally different from anything in ordinary experience is almost to say that it is of such a nature as to preclude the deduction from it of manifold exact predictions verifiable by ordinary perception. Pretty nearly the sole support claimed for this theory consists of certain tremendous experiences that are said to have happened to a minute fraction of mankind. If such be the only facts in the case, they are facts with which science can have

nothing to do, since science is the business of finding out Law, i.e., what always happens.

601. Suppose it were true that those marvellous stories proved the doctrine of telepathy; then what would it be that had been proved? Why, that very rarely mind acts upon mind in a way utterly unlike the normal way. This would be no contribution to science. It would, in the case supposed, have been ascertained that sometimes a marvel, an impenetrable mystery, occurs. The concern of science, however, is with intelligible facts. Science no more denies that there are miracles and mysteries than it asserts them. But it is a Postulate, — a hope, — of science and of all sound reasoning that *any given fact* to which our attention may be directed shall turn out to be intelligible.[4] It is justly held criminal for a commander-in-chief to "despair of the republic"; and it would be as monstrous for an inquirer to despair of the comprehensibility of his problem. The psychicists are fond of reminding us that the most familiar facts are full of mystery. So they are, in a metaphysical sense; and that is the very reason why the physicist eschews metaphysical inquiry and seeks to understand phenomena only in the sense of establishing their exact relations to one another. Hence, what is absolutely severed and sundered from the body of ordinary experience is absolutely beyond scientific comprehension.

602. Sharing these sentiments common to all physicists, when 'Phantasms of the Living' appeared, — that vast collection of well-sifted stories by which Messrs. Gurney, Myers, and Podmore endeavored to prove the theory of telepathy, — I felt that I would far sooner believe in spiritualism. For according to this latter theory, we *all* pass into another life; nor would this experience common to us all be much more wonderful than the development that we all undergo when the child becomes a grown person. If telepathy be a fact, why should it have the strange character of being excessively infrequent, so contrary to the ubiquity of all the other agencies of nature? One cannot suppose it otherwise than extremely infrequent without having long ago become well-known and beyond doubt. Nor have the psychicists succeeded in making out the slightest trace of it in

[4] (Ed.) Cf. 5.354ff., 2.654ff.

ordinary people. If, on the other hand, we suppose there are communications from the other world, there is nothing surprising in their being infrequent. For with what disgust and indifference must the departed spirit recall the pettiness and blindness of the ends, the villainy, meanness, and filth of the methods of the inhabitants of this [world], who, as he well sees, are at the bottom of their hearts glad to get rid of him, and who have to work out their own salvation without interference, — the nasty little imps.[5] Surely, the canyon that spiritualism has to suppose between the two worlds has a gentle slope compared with the abyss that telepathy opens in the midst of experience between the ordinary and extraordinary intercommunion between minds.

603. Messrs. Gurney, Myers, and Podmore in asking human reason to admit that a class of phenomena was sundered from ordinary experience vastly more than any phenomena had been believed to be, seemed to me to be all but asking reason to admit that its hope of understanding things, — its only aim, — was futile; and I was accordingly moved to write an elaborate criticism of their book to show that hallucinations were so very common, while hallucinations coincident with truth beyond the ken of sense were so very rare, after the suspicious cases had been weeded out, that these coincidences might very well be supposed to be fortuitous. At the same time, I essayed to determine by logical analysis what were the conditions to which a census of hallucinations must conform in order to afford sound support to the contention of the telepathists that the veridical [6] hallucinations were too numerous to be accounted chance coin-

[5] It would be different if the theory of Hobbes, LaRochefoucauld, and other thinkers in the boyhood of modern philosophy, were true, and man could not act otherwise than selfishly. But this theory which rests on a logical fallacy is supported by no fact and refuted by many.

[6] The word "veridical" was first made a term of art by Mr. Myers in the sense of coinciding with the truth, whether fortuitously or causedly. It is contrary to the ethics of terminology to change the meaning of a term of art without necessity. Its author has no more right to do so than anybody else. Yet in Baldwin's Dictionary, where accuracy of definition ought to have been the first consideration, Mrs. Sidgwick limits the term to that which is determined by a general cause to be true, with no hint that it had ever been used in any other sense. Looseness of speech and looseness of thought are wife and husband. I shall speak of the 'simply veridical' and the 'determinedly veridical,' in the wider and narrower senses.

cidences. The Society at once set about making a new census.
I wish I could pay them the compliment of averring that, in
doing so, they were influenced by my reasons or by any better
considered reasons. But I am obliged to say that they so far
failed to conform to the conditions which I had shown to be
requisite, — and in the direction of favoring their doctrine of
telepathy, — that now the question stands as it did before, a
question which each man will answer according to his predilec-
tions, whether these owe their birth to his general experience
of the ways of nature or to some episode of his private life.

§2. THE SCIENTIFIC ATTITUDE

604.   I am sorry. For the question at issue between the
physicist and the psychologist in the recent passage of arms was
how far the psychical researchers have the character of men of
science. Now however much ratiocinative analysis may help
toward a decision upon this point, the answer must ultimately
rest, like every other judgment concerning men's character,
upon the testimony of instinctive impressions; and one of my
purposes in this article is to render the testimony of my own
impressions upon the matter. Thus finding myself in a situation
that calls for truth-telling, truth will I tell, without exaggeration or extenuation, as accurately as I can, whatever it costs me.

605.   There are two qualifications which every true man of
science possesses, and which, if a man possesses them, he is
sure to develop into a scientific man in the course of time, if
he ought not fairly to be called such already. First, the dominant passion of his whole soul must be to find out the truth in
some department, regardless of what the color of that truth
may be. Secondly, he must have a natural gift for reasoning, for
severely critical thought. Perhaps a man who had drunk of the
fountain of perpetual youth need not, at the outset of his career,
possess either of those qualifications: he would infallibly become a man of science at last, because the incessant action of
experience would ultimately produce those two qualities in him.
For we see that, in a measure, that effect has been produced in
the course of history upon civilized man at large.

606.   In a measure, I say, for the love of truth is still far

from mighty; and a gift for reasoning is still as rare a talent as a gift for music. Most men are incapable of strong control over their minds. Their thoughts are such as instinct, habit, association suggest, mainly. Their criticism of their thoughts is confined to reconsideration and to asking themselves whether their ideas seem reasonable. I do not call this reasoning: I call it instinctive reflexion. For most purposes it is the best way to think; for instinct blunders far less than reason. Reasoners are in danger of falling into sophistry and pedantry. Our instinctive ways of thinking have become adapted to ordinary practical life, just as the rest of our physiology has become adapted to our environment. Wisdom lies in nicely discriminating the occasions for reasoning and the occasions for going by instinct. Some of my most valued friends have been almost incapable of reasoning; and yet they have been men of singularly sound judgment, penetrating and sagacious. So much more important is it, on the whole, to feel right than to reason deeply. But in science instinct can play but a secondary *rôle*. The reason of this is that our instincts are adapted to the continuance of the race and thus to individual life. But science has an indefinite future before it; and what it aims at is to gain the greatest possible advance in knowledge in five centuries or ten. Instinct not being adapted to this purpose, the methods of science must be artificial. As Professor Trowbridge hints, pure science has nothing to do with *belief*. What I *believe* is what I am prepared to go on today. Imagine a general besieging a city. He sits in his tent at night preparing the details of his plan of action for the morrow. He finds that what his orders ought to be and perhaps the whole fate of his army depend upon a certain question of topography concerning which he is in need of information. He sends for his best engineer officer, — a highly scientific man, — and asks how he is to ascertain the fact in question. The officer replies, "There is only one possible way of ascertaining that. So and so must be done." "How long will that take?" "Two or three months." The general dismisses the man of science, — as Napoleon dismissed Laplace, — and sends for another officer, not half so scientific, but good at guessing. What this officer shall say, the general will go by. He will adopt it as his belief.

607. Beyond the two general qualifications mentioned, every scientific man needs a special training in his particular branch of research; and moreover this branch will probably call for the possession of some special mental, physiological, and instrumental advantages for the acquisition of a special line of facts. I do not set down "power of observation" among the general qualifications, because this phrase covers a variety of capacities having nothing in common, of which a naturalist will want one, an astronomer another, a linguist a third, a psychologist a fourth, and so on. Besides, there has been some exaggeration about the observing powers of scientific men; and in that quality which the phrase seems best to fit, the power of noting one's precise sensations unaffected by any interpretation of them, the scientific men of most branches are decidedly inferior to the artists. I should not, therefore, attribute any very high importance to great general powers of observation as distinguishing men of science. But I must say that the best psychical researchers rank high in this respect as compared with scientific men generally.

608. In considering how far they possess the essential characters of scientists, I first note that amateurs, idlers, and people not extra wise naturally flock to the Society for Psychical Research and make up an even greater proportion of it than they do of other large scientific associations. But these are not the persons under consideration. It is only the men who have devoted all the strenuous energies of their lives to the work, some of whom have succumbed to the strain of it, whom I am to endeavor to class.

609. As to their devotion to truth, I have to remember that, as I have known them, they have been serious and foreseeing men who would not embark upon any enterprise without carefully reckoning up its contingencies. Therefore, at the moment when any one of those men deliberately devoted his life and his whole being to this inquiry, as several have done, he certainly had distinctly before his mind the following considerations:

that it would be hard and incessant work, mostly drudgery, requiring him to be occupied mostly with knaves and fools;

that it would cost him a great deal of money, considering all that it would prevent him from earning;

366

that it would never bring him much honor, but would put a certain stamp of obloquy upon him;

that even among the company of those who professed to love the truth, and who ought to press him to their hearts as a brother, there would be found in the more richly endowed sciences, individuals who would treat him in the narrowest and most despicable spirit of the east wind;

that after his whole life had been poured out into the inquiry, it was not unlikely that he might find that he had not found out anything.

610.   These considerations go to show that, whatever those men have been aiming at, they have aimed at in a single-hearted manner. Were they desirous of believing in the particular doctrine of telepathy, or were they bent on finding out the truth, whatever it might be?

611.   I cannot see that there is anything particularly comfortable about a belief in telepathy. To be sure, it cuts off, or greatly weakens, the force of such evidence as there might seem to be for spiritualism; and, no doubt, for many reflecting persons, the prospect of another life is rather unpleasant. But who will believe that the main motive of the telepathists has been to escape thoughts of another world? Such thoughts are not troublesome enough for that.

612.   I had a somewhat prolonged controversy with Edmund Gurney which was only interrupted by his death; and this brought me into fine touch with the spirit of the man. I was most strongly impressed with the purity of his devotion to truth. This impression has been thoroughly convincing in the cases of others whom I have met personally, but whom I do not name because they are still living.

613.   The power of reasoning of the leaders is certainly much above that of the average of men. It does not seem to me to have been altogether sufficient for their problem. The hypothesis of telepathy does not seem to me to have much merit, as a specimen of scientific method. I believe that if the researchers had been better reasoners they would not have spent so much time in sifting tales of extraordinary happenings but would rather have thrown their energies into an endeavor to connect the dubious extraordinary phenomena with ordinary

367

experience. In this direction, the little that they have done seems to me feeble and to show defect of analysis.

614. As for scientific training and special qualifications, the psychicists seem to me to have been amply provided with all that their method gave room for. Their exposure of several frauds has been neat and workmanlike, and they have made use of numbers as far as numbers have been applicable. Prof. Trowbridge complains that they make no measurements; and that coincides with my complaint that they have not sufficiently endeavored to bring their marvels into relation to ordinary experience. For, in order to do that, the phenomena would have had to be analyzed; and then, and not before, would measurements have been applicable. Prof. Trowbridge will not forget that in the early stages of physics, there were no measures. Galileo, Gilbert and others made considerable progress before they arrived at a stage at which they were able to make any measurements to speak of. But they did exhibit great skill in analyzing the phenomena; and I agree that the psychicists have not exhibited signal ability in doing that. It must be remembered, however, that they are only breaking ground in a perfectly virgin soil intractable and thicket-tangled. They are doing good honest work, not shrinking from labor, and proceeding intelligently, if not with high genius. The farm of physics has long been under cultivation, the costliest implements and the most refined methods are here in use. Here have come these new settlers, occupying land not easy to till and poor in resources. Come, let us turn up our noses at them, gossip about their suspicious ways, and let them feel the difference between them and us. Who knows whether they are honest?

§3. PERCEPTION

615. If there were only some way of reconciling the usual order of nature, as it is familiar to us, with the possibility of rare cases of quasi-vision beyond the ken of sense, then I grant that the testimonies adduced in "Phantasms of the Living" would suffice to render it extremely likely that such rare quasi-vision actually takes place. For, after all, the theory of chance coincidence puts a certain strain upon our instinct of receiving

testimony; and natural instinct is not a thing to be lightly disregarded.

616.   Is it quite certain that such an occasional, but very rare, determinedly veridical vision of things beyond the senses' ken would be altogether unlike every-day experience? As to that I have a suggestion to make.

617.   It is not uncommon to hear a man or woman say, "I believe what I see, and nothing more." But little cross-questioning would commonly be needed to show that it is an exaggeration. There are not many persons, even though they boast themselves to be materialists, who do not really believe much that they do not themselves think that they directly perceive by any sense, peripheral or visceral; — polonium, the sacred city of Thibet, George Washington, the glacial period, that motions will tomorrow conform to Newton's three laws. But I myself happen, in common with a small but select circle, to be a pragmatist, or "radical empiricist," [7] and as such, do not believe in anything that I do not (as I think) perceive: and I am far from believing in the whole of that.

618.   Only, the question arises, What do we perceive? It would not serve our turn to answer scholastically with an arbitrary definition which might be ill-considered. Let us rather set out from familiar instances, and having noticed what their relation is to the formation of scientific opinions, found upon that a definition which shall cover all that is so related to knowledge and shall cover nothing else.

619.   Let us say that, as I sit here writing, I see on the other side of my table, a yellow chair with a green cushion. That will be what psychologists term a "percept" (*res percepta*). They also frequently call it an "image." With this term I shall pick no quarrel. Only one must be on one's guard against a false impression that it might insinuate. Namely, an "image" usually means something intended to represent, — virtually professing to represent, — something else, real or ideal. So understood, the word "image" would be a misnomer for a percept. The chair I appear to see makes no professions of any kind, essentially embodies no intentions of any kind, does not stand for anything. It obtrudes itself upon my gaze; but not as

[7] (Ed.) See [CP] V, *Pragmatism and Pragmaticism.*

a deputy for anything else, not "as" anything. It simply knocks at the portal of my soul and stands there in the doorway.

620.   It is very insistent, for all its silence. It would be useless for me to attempt to pooh-pooh it, and say, "Oh come, I don't believe in the chair." I am forced to confess that it appears. Not only does it appear, but it disturbs me, more or less. I cannot think the appearance is not there, nor dismiss it as I would a fancy. I can only get rid of it by an exertion of physical force.

621.   It is a forceful thing. Yet it offers no reason, defence, nor excuse for its presence. It does not pretend to any right to be there. It silently forces itself upon me.

622.   Such is the percept. Now what is its logical bearing upon knowledge and belief. This may be summed up in three items, as follows:

1st, it contributes something positive. (Thus, the chair has its four legs, seat, and back, its yellow color, its green cushion, etc. To learn this is a contribution to knowledge.)

2nd, it *compels* the perceiver to acknowledge it.

3rd, it neither offers any reason for such acknowledgment nor makes any pretension to reasonableness. This last point distinguishes the percept from an axiom. I am a total disbeliever in axioms; but so far as the proposition, say, that a straight line is the shortest distance between two points even so much as *seems* to be self-evident, it seems to be *reasonable*. It is as founded in reason or in the nature of things, or as *founded* in something, that it recommends itself. The percept, on the contrary, is absolutely dumb. It acts upon us, it forces itself upon us; but it does not address the reason, nor *appeal* to anything for support.

623.   Let us say, then, that anything is, for the purposes of logic, to be classed under the species of perception wherein a positive qualitative content is forced upon one's acknowledgment without any reason or pretension to reason. There will be a wider genus of things *partaking* of the character of perception, if there be any matter of cognition which exerts a force upon us *tending* to make us acknowledge it without any *adequate* reason.

But in order fully to satisfy ourselves of the justice of classing in this species and in this genus all that I propose to refer to them, it is desirable to examine a little more closely the characters of the percept.

624. A visual percept obtrudes itself upon me in its entirety. I am not therein conscious of any mental process by which the image has been constructed. The psychologists, however, are able to give some account of the matter. Since 1709, they have been in possession of sufficient proof (as most of them agree,) that, notwithstanding its apparent primitiveness, every percept is the product of mental processes, or at all events of processes for all intents and purposes mental, except that we are not directly aware of them; and these are processes of no little complexity. The psychologists very reasonably argue that the first impressions made upon sense must have been feelings of sense qualities, — say colors, sounds, etc. — disconnected from one another, and not appearing to stand over against a self as objects; and it would seem that this must have been true of the *very* first impressions ever made upon sense in the history of mental development, however far the sense of the individual man of today may have been rendered capable of immediately apprehending the complex. But this is quite inferential. We are, of course, directly aware of positive sense-qualities in the percept (although in the percept itself they are in no wise separate from the whole object); but as for their being at first disconnected and not objectified, that is psychological theory.

625. Thus, two utterly different kinds of elements go to compose any percept. In the first place, there are the qualities of feeling or sensation, each of which is something positive and *sui generis*, being such as it is quite regardless of how or what anything else is. On account of this self-sufficiency, it is convenient to call these the elements of "Firstness." [8] In the percept, these elements of Firstness are perceived to be connected in definite ways. A visual percept of a chair has a definite shape. If it is yellow with a green cushion, that is quite different from being green with a yellow cushion. These connectives are directly perceived, and the perception of each of them is a perception at once of two opposed objects, — a double awareness. In

[8] (Ed.) The psychological versions of Peirce's categories of First, Second, and Third are discussed in 7.524–538, and the categories in general are treated in [CP] I.

respect to each of these connections, one part of the percept appears as it does *relatively to a second part*. Hence, it is convenient to call them elements of "Secondness." The vividness with which a percept stands out is an element of secondness; because the percept is vivid in proportion to the intensity of its effect upon the perceiver. These elements of secondness bring with them the peculiar singleness of the percept. This singleness consists in a double definiteness. For on the one hand, the percept contains no blank gaps which, in representing it, we are free to fill as we like. What I mean will be seen if we consider any knowledge we can have of the future. I heard somebody say that the Brooklyn bridge would fall some day. The only way in which he could even think he knew that would be by knowing that any bridge I might select that should be constructed in a certain way would fall. There is no such universality about the percept. It is quite individual. On the other hand, the definiteness of the percept is of a perfectly explicit kind. In any knowledge of the past something is, as it were, held in reserve. There is an indicated gap which we are not free to fill but which further information may fill. We know that the Sphinx was made by *some* king of Egypt. But what one? The percept, however, exhibits itself in full. These two kinds of definiteness, first, that the percept offers no range of freedom to anybody who may undertake to represent it, and secondly, that it reserves no freedom to itself to be one way or another way, taken together, constitute that utter absence of "range" which is called the *singularity*, or singleness, of the percept, the one making it individual and the other positive. The percept is, besides, whole and undivided. It has parts, in the sense that in thought it can be separated; but it does not represent itself to have parts. In its mode of being as a percept it is one single and undivided whole.

626. The percept is not the only thing that we ordinarily say we "perceive"; and when I professed to believe only what I perceived, of course I did not mean *percepts*, since percepts are not subjects of belief or disbelief. I meant *perceptual judgments*. Given a percept, this percept does not describe itself; for description involves analysis, while the percept is whole and undivided. But once having a percept, I may contemplate it,

372

and say to myself, 'That appears to be a yellow chair'; and our usual language is that we "perceive" it to be a yellow chair, although this is not a percept, but a judgment about a present percept.

627.   The perceptual judgment is all but in the same relation to knowledge and belief as is the percept. It is true that I may, by an effort of will, abstain from thinking about the color of the chair, so that the judgment 'the chair appears yellow' is not unconditionally forced upon me, and thus might seem not quite fully to partake of the character of perception. One can, however, escape the percept itself by shutting one's eyes. If one *sees*, one cannot avoid the percept; and if one *looks*, one cannot avoid the perceptual judgment. Once apprehended, it absolutely compels assent. Its defect in forcefulness is thus excessively slight and of no logical importance.

628.   To about the same degree its forcefulness falls short of the utter irrationality of that of the percept. The perceptual judgment professes to represent the percept. A logical defence of it would therefore have to be founded either on the percept as a premiss of that logical defence, or else on the percept as a fact represented by such premiss. But the percept cannot be a premiss, since it is not a proposition; and a statement of the character of the percept would have to rest on the perceptual judgment, instead of this on that. Thus, the perceptual judgment does not represent the percept *logically*. In what intelligible manner, then, does it represent the percept? It cannot be a *copy* of it; for, as will presently appear, it does not resemble the percept at all. There remains but one way in which it can represent the percept; namely, as an index, or true symptom, just as a weather-cock indicates the direction of the wind or a thermometer the temperature. There is no warrant for saying that the perceptual judgment actually *is* such an index of the percept, other than the *ipse dixit* of the perceptual judgment itself. And even if it be so, what is an index, or true symptom? It is something which, without any rational necessitation, is forced by blind fact to correspond to its object. To say, then, that the perceptual judgment is an infallible symptom of the character of the percept means only that in some unaccountable manner we find ourselves impotent to refuse our assent to it in

the presence of the percept, and that there is no appeal from it. Thus, the forcefulness of the perceptual judgment falls short of the pure unreasonableness of the percept only to this extent, that it does profess to represent the percept, while the perfection of the percept's surdity consists in its not so much as professing anything.

629.   The perceptual judgment, then, does not quite accurately fulfill the condition of forcefulness nor that of irrationality, as it should do to be strictly entitled to be considered a product of perception. But the differences are so minute and so unimportant logically that it will be convenient to neglect them. Perhaps I might be permitted to invent the term *percipuum* [9] to include both percept and perceptual judgment.

630.   I promised to show that a perceptual judgment is entirely unlike a percept. If it be true, as my analysis makes it to be, that a percept contains only two kinds of elements, those of firstness and those of secondness, then the great overshadowing point of difference is that the perceptual judgment professes to represent something, and thereby does represent something, whether truly or falsely. This is a very important difference, since the idea of representation is essentially what may be termed an element of "Thirdness," that is, involves the idea of determining one thing to refer to another. The element of secondness in the percept consists in one part being relative to another. But the percept presents itself ready made, and contains no idea of any state of things being brought about. There is a rigid mathematical demonstration (which I cannot give here) that the idea of Firstness, or that of a positive suchness, and the idea of Secondness, or that of one thing's referring to another, can in no way be combined so as to produce the idea of one thing A, referring to a second, B, in the very act of referring to a third, C.[10] This is the element of Thirdness, or mediation, which the conception of the representation *of* some-

---

[9] Formed from *percipio* on the analogy of *praecipuum* from *praecipio*. I am quite sure that it would be well if philosophers were bolder in forming new words instead of giving old ones so many meanings. What if we were to use words ending in *-cept* for different kinds of acquisition of cognition? There would be of good Latin words accept, antecept, decept, except, incept, intercept, occept, precept, suscept, besides many others quite supportable.

[10] (Ed.)   Cf. 7.537.

thing *to* somebody obviously involves. In a perceptual judgment the mind professes to tell the mind's future self what the character of the present percept is.[11] The percept, on the contrary, stands on its own legs and makes no professions of any kind.

631.   There are several other points of contrast between the perceptual judgment and the percept that are calculated to exhibit their disparateness. The judgment, "This chair appears yellow," separates the color from the chair, making the one predicate and the other subject. The percept, on the other hand, presents the chair in its entirety and makes no analysis whatever.

632.   We have seen that the "singularity" of the percept is a composite of two modes of definiteness. The first consists in this, that its faithful and full interpreter has no freedom allowed to him, but all is prescribed. But the perceptual judgment 'This chair appears yellow' has vaguely in mind a whole lot of yellow things, of which some have been seen, and no end of others may be or might be seen; and what it means to say is, 'Take any yellow thing you like, and you will find, on comparing it with this chair, that they agree pretty well in color.' It thus directly invites the exercise of a freedom of choice on the part of the interpreter (any one yellow thing answering as well as any other) which freedom the percept sternly and stupidly precludes.

633.   The other mode of definiteness of the percept consists in its being perfectly explicit. The perceptual judgment carelessly pronounces the chair yellow. What the particular shade, hue, and purity of the yellow may be it does not consider. The percept, on the other hand, is so scrupulously specific that it makes this chair different from every other in the world; or rather, it would do so if it indulged in any comparisons.

634.   It may be objected that the terms of the judgment resemble the percept. Let us consider, first, the predicate, 'yellow' in the judgment that 'this chair appears yellow.' This predicate is not the sensation involved in the percept, because it is general. It does not even refer particularly to this percept

---

[11] There is no objection to saying that 'The chair appears yellow' means 'The chair appears *to me* yellow'; but the reference to the future self is more pertinent.

but to a sort of composite photograph of all the yellows that have been seen. If it *resembles* the sensational element of the percept, this resemblance consists only in the fact that a new judgment will predicate it of the percept, just as this judgment does. It also awakens in the mind an imagination involving a sensational element. But taking all these facts together, we find that there is no relation between the predicate of the perceptual judgment and the sensational element of the percept, except forceful connections.

635. As for the subject of the perceptual judgment, as subject it is a sign. But it belongs to a considerable class of mental signs of which introspection can give hardly any account. It ought not to be expected that it should do so, since the qualities of these signs as objects have no relevancy to their significative character; for these signs merely play the part of demonstrative and relative pronouns, like "that," or like the A, B, C, of which a lawyer or a mathematician avails himself in making complicated statements. In fact, the perceptual judgment which I have translated into "that chair is yellow" would be more accurately represented thus: " ☞ is yellow," a pointing index-finger taking the place of the subject. On the whole, it is plain enough that the perceptual judgment is not a copy, icon, or diagram of the percept, however rough. It may be reckoned as a higher grade of the operation of perception.

636. In order not to prolong the discussion, I leave some possible objections to what I have said unanswered. The most serious of these is that a perceptual judgment may be revised; so that there is a certain check upon it. The examination of this point would be lengthy, and it does not seem to me likely to appear to anybody to be of fundamental importance. Full justice to it would involve complications which few would have the patience to follow.[12]

§4. A PROGRAMME

637. Having thus formed some acquaintance with the characteristics of perception, we go on to a line of thought of which the programme may be set down in advance.

[12] (Ed.) "It may be objected that a perceptual judgment is not so utterly beyond all control or check as I say; since it may be revised. I may negligently

638. No scientifically valuable classification can draw a line of demarcation between forms which differ indefinitely little. I shall begin by showing that this principle, which I shall refer to as the "serial principle," [13] obliges us to class as perceptions many ideas not popularly regarded as belonging to this class.

639. By the continued application of the same principle, I shall widen more and more our notion of what perception includes. In particular, I shall endeavor to bring into a clear light the truth that although what I have already said implies the truth of that doctrine of the direct, or "immediate," perception of the external world which is taught by the Aristotelians, by Kant, and by the philosophers of the Scotch school, yet we cannot refuse the name of perception to much which we rightly reject as unreal; as indeed, dreams and hallucinations are quite commonly classed as perceptions.

640. In this way, I shall lead up to the consideration of a certain group of ideas, — I beg permission to withhold the specification of what group it is, for the moment, — which ordinary instinctive language speaks of as perception, but which, as soon as one undertakes to be extra precise in one's speech, one usually never thinks of so classing; and I hope to give good reason for holding that, in this particular, instinct is right and pedantry wrong. Of this group of ideas, however, the great majority are illusory, the small minority determinedly veridical and not merely true by chance coincidence. The physicist would stultify himself if he were not the last of all men to call this into question.

641. With this group of ideas I proceed to compare the entire host of hallucinations, which there is no good reason to separate into the veridical and the non-veridical, and which there *is* good reason to account far more frequent than the census of

---

think 'this chair appears scarlet,' when if I had looked more carefully, I should have said 'it appears vermillion.' I reply that no doubt mistakes can arise from inadvertency; and possibly, in order to take due account of that phenomenon, some complication of my statement would be required. But it cannot be that, on this account, it is fundamentally wrong. A perceptual judgment can only refer to a single percept which can never re-exist; and if I judge that it appears red when it did not appear red, it must, at least, be acknowledged that it *appeared to appear* red. I do not think it worth while to follow out the objection further." From alternate pages of the manuscript (see 597n1).

[13] (Ed.) Cf. Peirce's doctrine of synechism, 7.565ff.

the Society for Psychical Research admits. They shade off into *bévues* of which ordinary people commit from one to dozens daily. In view of this comparison and of all the characteristics that have been developed of ordinary perceptions in their now enlarged domain, I shall inquire, to begin [at] the end, whether it will be more in accordance with general experience to expect that some fraction of hallucinations should have a pronounced tendency to being determinedly veridical or that none should be so. Thence I shall go on to the two questions that are really pertinent to the present positions of opinion,

first, whether, in case we were to admit, what is very far from commanding any reasonable assent, that all the stories which the telepathists consider marvellous and that are supported by testimony of real weight are real histories, there would be any ground for admitting a mode of communication between minds, in those cases, differing radically from modes that are ordinary;

secondly, whether it be consonant with ordinary experience to be so extremely sceptical about the determinedly veridical character of occasional visions of what is beyond the ken of the senses as the rank and file of the physicists are apt to be.

§5. THE PERCIPUUM

642. If there is any novelty in the suggestion I am about to make, — and I must confess I fear there is, — it lies only in the juxtaposition of ideas. The facts which I shall adduce are to the psychologist the merest commonplaces. In the classification of them I endeavor to eliminate the pedantries and formalisms which are retained in the books for convenience, but to which psychologists attach no particular importance; and this I do by the application of the above principle of forming almost continuous series, which principle is the principal clew of which the biological taxonomists, — the great masters of classification and of terminology, — are accustomed to avail themselves. Addressing, as I do, a reader who I dare say has read a book or two about psychology but who has not dwelt enough upon the subject to prevent his being impressed by the more tangible,

wooden, and dead ideas, — or corpses of ideas, — rather than
by the more elusive, fluid, and living ones, my principal care
will be to correct such notions. If the reader comes with a fresh
mind unsophisticated by any such reading, he will follow my
meaning all the easier.

643.   We know nothing about the percept otherwise than by
testimony of the perceptual judgment, excepting that we feel
the blow of it, the reaction of it against us, and we see the contents of it arranged into an object, in its totality, — excepting
also, of course, what the psychologists are able to make out
inferentially. But the moment we fix our minds upon it and
think the least thing about the percept, it is the perceptual
judgment that tells us what we so "perceive." For this and
other reasons, I propose to consider the percept as it is immediately interpreted in the perceptual judgment, under the name
of the "percipuum." The percipuum, then, is what forces
itself upon your acknowledgment, without any why or wherefore, so that if anybody asks you why you should regard it as
appearing so and so, all you can say is, 'I can't help it. That
is how I see it.' For example, one of the foolish questions with
which treatises on physics used to abound was why things look
right side up, when the images on the two retinas are upside
down; and sundry sapient reasons more or less abstruse were
given for their looking as they do. Now such arguments might
have proved that things really are right side up, or perhaps they
might have shown what physiological and psychical agencies
cause us to regard them as right side up; but if anybody were
to ask you why you *should* regard the visual images as right
side up like the things themselves, rather than upside down like
the optical images on the retinæ, how you were justified in doing
so, your only possible answer would be "They *do* look so, and
I cannot make them look otherwise," whether it is reasonable
for them to look so or not. Sometimes when I have been seated
in a railway-car that was stationary and another train has been
slowly passing by, I have been vexed at the unreasonableness
of its appearing to me that our train was moving and the other
train was at rest. I have reasoned with my perception. I have
asked, "Is there jarring such as there is when one is in a moving car?" No. "Is there any noise of the wheels?" No. "Is

379

there anything at all in the looks of either train that is more as if we were moving rather than they?" Quite the reverse. "Then why do I have the idea that that train is at rest and that we are moving?" There is no answer except that such is the percipuum, and I cannot help it.

644.   There is no difference between a real perception and a hallucination, taken in themselves; or if there be, it is altogether inconsiderable. The difference is that rational predictions based upon the hallucination will be apt to be falsified, — as for example, if the person having the hallucination expects another person to see the same thing; while truly sound predictions based on real perceptions are supposed *never* to be falsified, although we have no positive reason for assuming so much as that. But this difference between hallucinations and real perceptions is a difference in respect to the relations of the two cases to other perceptions: it is not a difference in the presentations themselves. For the purposes of physiological psychology it may be proper and needful to put them into different classes. That is a branch of science with which I am not concerned. But for logical purposes, that is, in regard to their relations to knowledge and belief, which is the concern of this whole paper, they should be regarded as one and the same phenomenon, in themselves.

645.   So likewise all hallucinations, the non-veridical, the fortuitously veridical, and the determinedly veridical, are, for our purposes, all one and the same phenomenon, in themselves.

646.   But this is not all. The serial principle will not permit us to draw a hard and fast line of demarcation between perception and imagination. Physiological psychology may be justified or compelled to separate them, for aught I know or care. But, in regard to their relation to knowledge and belief, the percipuum is nothing but an extreme case of the fancy.

647.   We all know, only too well, how terribly insistent perception may be; and yet, for all that, in its most insistent degrees, it may be utterly false, — that is, may not fit into the general mass of experience, but be a wretched hallucination. In other cases, the insistence of the percipuum may be something of a sham. That is, it may resist all unskillful attempts to overthrow it, be they ever so energetic; and yet when one

380

knows the right trick it will be curious to see how easily it is downed. For example, that moving train that appears stationary will not move however one may try to force it to do so. Yet if one only looks down and watches the wheels turn, in a very few seconds it will seem to start up. The percipuum, insistent as it is, is not nearly so persistent and thing-like as one is apt to think. There is a well-known outline figure of a straight flight of steps against a wall seen in perspective from the side. It is called 'Schroeder's Stair.' [14] When you look at it you seem to be looking at the stairs from above. You cannot conceive it otherwise. Continue to gaze at it, and after two or three minutes the back wall of the stairs will jump forward and you will now be looking at the under side of them from below, and again cannot see the figure otherwise. After a shorter interval, the upper wall, which is now nearer to you, will spring back, and you will again be looking from above. These changes will take place more and more rapidly, the aspect from above always lasting longer, until at length, you will find you can at will make it look either way. But put it aside for a quarter of an hour or less and you will find you have lost this power. Doubtless frequent repetition of the experiment would give one complete control over it. You will thus have converted an uncontrollable percipuum into a controllable imagination by a brief process of education. It is one of the recognized difficulties of all psycho-physical measurement that the faculties rapidly become educated to an extraordinary degree. Thus, contrast-colors, when properly exhibited, are incredibly vivid. One is not easily persuaded that they are not real. Yet the experimenter becomes, in time, almost incapable of perceiving them. This is a case in which the same educational course which gives control over appearances which sometimes do and sometimes do not accord with the mass of experiences, only serves to strengthen the forcefulness of those appearances which always do so accord.

648. It is a difficult question whether the serial principle permits us to draw sharp lines of demarcation between the percept and the near anticipation, or say the *antecept*, and

[14] It was discovered by H. G. F. Schroeder in 1858. Poggendorff Annalen CV, 298.

between the percept and the recent memory (may I be permitted to call this the *ponecept*, a distant and dubious memory
being perhaps quite another thing?), or whether the percept
is at once but an extreme case of an antecept and an extreme
case of a ponecept. Or rather, — I beg the reader's pardon for
my awkwardness of statement, — the precise question is not
about percept, antecept, and ponecept, but about percipuum,
antecipuum, and *ponecipuum*, the direct and uncontrollable
interpretations of percept, antecept, and ponecept. There can
surely be no objection to our beginning the discussion by asking
what the deliverance of a flow of time, say for example of the
motion of a shooting star, is concerning the matter; for this
inquiry cannot result in our knowing less about the main question than we did before. The psychologists think it will not
cause us to know any more, either; because the question is not
what the percipuum represents the nature of the transformations of antecipuum into percipuum and of percipuum into
ponecipuum to be, but what in fact they really are. It will be
observed that, in so putting the question, the psychologists are
assuming that time really is as our common-sense metaphysics,
or rather as their own interpretation of common-sense metaphysics, represents it to be. What they doubt is whether the
percipuum accords with the facts; that is, with their interpretation of the general mass of experience; or, since experience is
nothing but the interpretation of the percipua, what they doubt
is whether the percipuum accords with an interpretation of an
interpretation of itself, just as one asks whether the Greek
testament faithfully accords with the Authorized Version,
whether Jesus was a sound christian and could sign the thirty-
nine articles, whether Plato, Isocrates, Thucydides and the rest
of the prosaists of that period wrote good grammar, and the
like.[15] I fear I shall not be able to follow them far into this
deep and dark exploration.

649. If we wish to know what the percipuum of the course
of time is, all we have to do is to abstain from sophisticating it,
and it will be plain enough. No more than the present moment

---

[15] I myself was severely taken to task, sat upon, squelched, marked down to
my real insignificance, by an eminent French logician, for presuming to speak
disparagingly of so sublime a work of genius as the algebra of dual relatives,
this algebra happening to be a thing of my own invention.

directly confronts us. The future, however little future it may be, is known only by generalization. The past, however little past it may be, lacks the explicitness of the present. Nevertheless, in the present moment we are directly aware of the flow of time, or in other words that things can change.[16] Several other points are clearly delivered in the percipuum, but they are implied in what has been stated. Sundry schools of philosophy hold this testimony of the percipuum to be contrary to sound reason, and accordingly either set it down as false, or conclude that the facts really are absurd, or both. But it strikes me that while it is not the business of facts to conform to what M or N may approve as sound reasoning, it is the business of M's and N's logic to conform to facts.

650.   Fully to unfold all the implications of the deliverance of the percipuum so as to demonstrate the accuracy of the interpretation would require a small treatise, if written in the English style, or three stout octavos in German. But I will endeavor to summarize what the upshot of the discussion would be so as to render it tolerably perspicuous.

651.   Kant squarely hit the nail on the head when he said that every part of a lapse of time was a lapse of time. But here as in many parts of his philosophy, Kant did not quite understand himself, and imagined that in saying that every part of a time is a time he had only said that time was infinitely divisible.[17] . . .[18]

652.   But although Kant unwarily confused the idea that time, as "intuited" (to use his language, for he himself translates his *Anschauung* by the Latin *intuitus*), has no parts that are not themselves times with the very different idea that there *is* a way of dividing time so as never to reach an ultimate part (though such parts there may be), yet his reasoning, taken as a whole, is consistent only with the idea that time as intuited has no ultimate parts, or instants. That opinion I share, substituting the percipuum for his intuition. Thus, that which the

[16] (Ed.) Cf. 5.205, 6.109–110.

[17] In the *Monist* for July, 1892, I followed him in this misunderstanding, my notion of continuity at that date being far from clear.

(Ed.) Cf. 6.120ff.

[18] (Ed.) The editor has deleted a long passage on continuity, which presents material already covered in 6.120ff. and 6.174ff.

mathematicians call "continuity" becomes, for me, "pseudo-continuity."

653.   Of course, if there is no such thing as an absolute instant, there is nothing *absolutely present* either temporarily or in the sense of confrontation. In fact, we are thus brought close to the doctrine of Synechism, which is that elements of Thirdness cannot entirely be escaped. The present moment will be a lapse of time, highly confrontitial, when looked at as a whole, seeming absolutely so, but when regarded closely, seen not to be absolutely so, its earlier parts being somewhat of the nature of memory, a little vague, and its later parts somewhat of the nature of anticipation, a little generalized. It contains a central part which is still more present, still more confrontitial, but which presents the same features. There is nothing at all that is absolutely confrontitial; although it is quite true that the confrontitial is continually flowing in upon us.

654.   I aver, but do not show, that if my statement of what I call the essential part of the delivery of the percipuum be true to it, then the interpretation given is demonstrably the only one possible. But though I do not actually demonstrate it, I will mention some secondary features of the deliverance of the percipuum which strongly tend to confirm the interpretation.

655.   One such deliverance is that any multitude of changes not too great to be successive in any sense might take place in any lapse of time however short. Now two things are demonstrable (although again I withhold the demonstrations). One is that *no* multitude is so great as to prevent a collection of objects of that multitude from being linearly arranged.[19] The other is that there is no maximum multitude. It follows, then, from the deliverance just stated, that the possible mutually exclusive divisions of any time, however short, exceed all multitude. In that case, time can not only not have merely the pseudo-continuity of quantity, — since the multitude of quantities [20] is well-known to be only the second of an endless series of grades of infinite multitude, — but it cannot be composed of instants at all (as it might very well be and still enormously

[19] (Ed.)   Cf. 3.567, 4.639ff.
[20] (Ed.)   That is, real numbers.

exceed the differentiation of quantity) since the entire collection of such instants would have a multitude.

656.   Another plain deliverance of the percipuum is that moment melts into moment. That is to say, moments may be so related as not to be entirely separate and yet not be the same. Obviously, this would be so according to our interpretation. But if time consists of instants, each instant is exactly what it is and is absolutely not any other. In particular, any two real quantities differ by a finite amount.

657.   Still another deliverance of the percipuum is that every interval of time has a beginning and an end, an initial moment and a terminal moment; that is, a moment before which there is no moment of the interval and a moment after which there is no moment of the interval. This again is obviously true of our interpretation; and were the terminal moment thrown off, that is, not reckoned as belonging to the interval, still what was left would have a terminal moment. If only one moment were thrown off at the end, the new terminal moment would not be altogether different from what had been the terminal moment. Of course, the expression "only one moment" can only be understood in a relative sense. This precisely agrees with the percipuum, according to which if from a terminated line, the terminal point be thrown off, what remains still has a terminal which is substantially identical with the old terminal. I appeal to the reader's consciousness to say if that be not so. But if time is composed of instants, and the last instant of an interval be thrown off, the interval will be left *without any last*. For if it had any, then before the last was thrown off, there would be no instant between this original last and the instant which becomes the last after the throwing off. But to say that there is not a moment between any two distinct moments is too monstrously in conflict with the percipuum for any reasoning man to maintain. Such a notion would be exploded in a dozen ways.

658.   By this time, while I have not exhausted my stock of reasons for thinking that the deliverance of the percipuum concerning the flow of time must be interpreted as I say, yet I have said enough to convince any superior reasoner, — or as nearly to convince him as his caution will allow him to be con-

vinced until he has had time for reconsideration. Further
confirmation will soon appear; but we may turn now to the
question of whether the testimony of the percipuum is truthful
or not. It is obvious that a *percept* cannot be false, since it
makes no assertion and is not a proposition, whether indicative,
interrogative, optative, imperative, or in any mood whatever;
and few philosophers will today think otherwise. It is indeed
one of the stock remarks that even a hallucination is not false.
It would save me trouble in my present argumentation if I
could take that short cut to the truth; but I fear I cannot quite
do so.

659. We must enter for a few moments into the field of
metaphysics. For we are inquiring how things really are whatever we may think. What is reality? There would not be any
such thing as truth unless there were something which is as it
is independently of how we may think it to be.[21] That is the
reality, and we have to inquire what its nature is. We speak of
hard facts. We wish our knowledge to conform to hard facts.
Now, the "hardness" of fact lies in the insistency of the percept,
its entirely irrational insistency, — the element of Secondness
in it. That is a very important factor of reality. But this factor is not confined to the percept. We can know nothing about
the percept, — but only experience it in its totality, — except
through the perceptual judgment, and this likewise compels
acceptance without any assignable reason. This indefensible
compulsiveness of the perceptual judgment is precisely what
constitutes the cogency of mathematical demonstration. One
may be surprised that I should pigeon-hole mathematical demonstration with things unreasonably compulsory. But it is the
truth that the nodus of any mathematical proof consists precisely in a judgment in every respect similar to the perceptual
judgment except only that instead of referring to a percept
forced upon our perception, it refers to an imagination of our
creation. There is no more why or wherefore about it than
about the perceptual judgment, "This which is before my eyes
looks yellow." To show this I must take an example of a
mathematical proof; and for the reader's comfort I will take
an extremely simple one. At the same time it must be of as

[21] (Ed.) Cf. 8.12ff.

abstract a nature as possible, or it might be said that whether intuitional mathematics were perceptual or not, this was not the nature of all mathematics.

660.   I will start with the following premiss, which is true of whole numbers: If any predicate, P, be true of the number 0, *zero*, but not of all numbers, then there must be two numbers M and N such that N is next greater than M, and P, while true of M, is not true of N.

661.   From this I proceed to prove, first, that there is no number except zero that is not next greater than some number other than itself. For if there were any such number, call it A. Then the predicate "is not A" would be true of 0 (since A is supposed other than 0) but not of all numbers (since it would not be true of A). Yet there would be no number of which it would be true that it was not A while there was a number next greater than this number of which this was not true (since A is, by hypothesis, not next greater than any other number than itself).

662.   I will further prove from the same premiss that there is no number except zero that cannot be reached from zero by a finite multitude of successive steps, each passing from a number to [a] number next greater than it. By a "finite" multitude is meant the multitude of any collection [for which, that collection] being substituted for "Hottentot" in the following syllogism, this syllogism would be valid:

> Every Hottentot kills a Hottentot;
> No Hottentot is killed by more than one Hottentot;
> Therefore every Hottentot must be killed by a Hottentot.

663.   I will first demonstrate that if a single individual is joined to a finite collection, the collection will remain finite. For that purpose, I first remark that the premisses of the above syllogism say nothing about the individual differences of the single Hottentots; and therefore if a newcomer were substituted for one of the Hottentots and the conclusion logically followed from the premisses before the substitution, so they would after the substitution. (There are other ways of making this evident.) Now suppose the tribe were increased by a new man. If the collection thereby ceased to be finite, the premisses might

continue to be true of the new Hottentots (that is, of the tribe as so increased) and yet some man might escape being killed. We may suppose for convenience that this is the newcomer (since we have seen that a mere substitution as to who kills who makes no difference). Then no Hottentot kills the new-comer; but every Hottentot still kills some Hottentot. Hence he must kill one of the old Hottentots. So as before every old Hottentot kills an old Hottentot and the old Hottentots being a finite collection, every old Hottentot gets killed by an old Hottentot. But no man is killed by two different men; so that there is nobody for the newcomer to kill. Thus the premisses cannot be true of the increased collection unless the conclusion be true; which is as much as to say that the collection remains finite.

664.   Now, to return to the numbers, suppose there be such a number as I undertake to prove there is not. Call it A (or if there be more than one, call any one of them A). Let the predicate, P, be "is either zero or can be reached from zero by a finite collection of steps from [a] number to [a] next greater number." This predicate is true of zero, but not of A. Yet there is no number of which it is true and yet not of a next greater, since to suppose this would be to suppose a finite collection of steps would cease to be finite on the adjunction of one more. Thus the supposition that there is such a number as A is absurd, and the proposition is proved.

665.   These proofs are founded on nothing but an abstract proposition. But an abstract proposition is a subject for observation as much as anything else. The proofs consist in remarking implications which were not thought of in the proposition as first adopted. Our premiss said that no matter what predicate and what number be chosen, either that predicate is true of that number or not true of *zero* or else two numbers could be found of one of which, which was next greater than the other, the predicate would not be true while it would be true of the other. In thinking this, we did not think whether or not it was possible that there should be a number not greater than any other. But when this is suggested, we are led to remark that being not next greater than any number and yet not zero is itself a predicate and the negative of a predicate. This

is the kind of observation peculiar to mathematics, the looking at things substantively that have only been regarded transitively, or transitorily, the operation of abstraction.[22] How do we know that is a predicate? Precisely as we know that what is before our eyes is yellow. We can, after the fact, invent a formula to cover the case; but it will still leave something undefended. It is really a compulsion similar to that of the perceptual judgment with which we have to do.

Both the arguments happen to be stated in the form of the *reductio ad absurdum*, which is very appropriate to mathematics as bringing out its ultimately irrational character. But it is a mere form of statement. Every *reductio ad absurdum* can be stated as a direct argument. The reduction of the figures of [the] syllogism illustrates, if it does not virtually demonstrate, this truth.

666.   But it is not in respect to this immediate insistence alone that the real is as it is independently of how we think it to be. The future is real, as well as the present, in so far as it is predetermined; and who but a mad man will deny that it largely is predetermined, at least to some degree, if not irrevocably. Indeed, the tendency of modern philosophy has been to follow the stoical doctrine that the future is what it is to be, independently — of something; I do not think it is clearly said of what. The explanation of this state of mind, as far as the stoics were concerned, is not difficult. The early stoics in their efforts to make the universe comprehensible endeavored to discard elements of Thirdness, with a more or less unconscious feeling of Ockham's razor. The resulting hard dualism suited the hard lot of slaves and of the oppressed; and as time went on and this class and their descendants became more influential, a stern morality, which is essentially dualistic, naturally flourished amid the hideous riot of that age, while thirdness was utterly shoved into the background. The chief rival of stoicism, Epicureanism, sought to get along in its philosophy even without elements of secondness. About 1600, it was the scholastic realists who were the defenders of thirdness, and their dunsical opposition to the new learning and their dreadful corruption of

[22] (Ed.) Peirce's observational theory of mathematics is discussed also in various places in [CP] IV.

the university disgusted the new men. Hence the fight was between Gassendi, the Epicurean, and Descartes, the real though
unconscious stoic. I refuse to believe the future is entirely predetermined; but it certainly is so in great measure; and in so
far as it is so, it is independent of all that we can think, wish,
or do. It has the kind of compulsiveness that belongs to inductive reasoning, or experimental inquiry, really the most
mighty cogency there is. For experimental inquiry sets out
with a hypothesis; upon which it bases predictions as to the
issue of experiments, and it is left to the future experiment to
bring forth the conclusion from the womb of the future. This
factor of reality is specially prominent in the reality of personality. It is what the man is destined to do, what of the
future is wrapped up in him, that makes him what he is.

667. The difference between the insistency of what is before
us and the power of predestination is manifest enough. But
there is a third factor of reality, different from either of those.
The past also is real, — *something* in it, at least. The future
weeds it out; but the positive element is peculiar. Memory
would be nothing but a dream if it were not that predictions
are based on it that get verified. When we think how slight and
entangled must be the ultimate bits of feeling out of which
memory constructs her mosaic, we are compelled to liken it to
conjecture. It is a wonderful power of constructing quasi-con-
jectures or dreams that will get borne out by future experience.
The power of performing this feat, which is the power of the
past, is a gentle compulsiveness.

668. There are the three elements of reality: that by which
ideas spring up that have concealed within them an accord with
the mass of ideas; that by which one idea acts directly on another; that force from without that weeds out a part of the
ideas and strengthens the rest.

669. To state the matter otherwise: An idea, a surmise
springs up in my mind. It recommends itself to me more or
less forcibly as reasonable. The fact that it recommends itself
to me more or less surely warrants its pretty near accord with
what will recommend itself to reasonable minds as well as to
the quasi-mind behind the issues of the future. That idea acts
upon other ideas and absolutely forces me to say that it requires

certain things to happen in the future. The future events come to pass and in part negative my surmise, in part confirm it. I do not know what idea we can form of reality except that it is that threefold force; or what the real can be except that which the whole process tends, as we hope, to induce our thoughts to rest upon.

670.   Such being the nature of the real, since the percipuum confesses itself to contain a *soupçon* of memory, — that is, of conjecture, — as well as a *soupçon* of onsight, or watching to see if the future comes as expected, it must be confessed that according to the percipuum's own account of itself, not only may this or that percipuum be false, — and should be so regarded in the case of blunders, if not of hallucinations, — but it is even conceivable that all percipua should contain a false element, perpetually refuted by oncoming fresh percipua, although these fresh percipua perpetually introduce the like falsity anew.

671.   But it is remarkable that in case we do not accept the percipuum's own account of itself, but maintain that time is composed of absolute instants, then it would seem that there is nothing that empirical truth can mean except accordance with what is given in those instants, which in this case, in no way testify concerning one another or in any way refer to one another. If that be so, a percept must be absolutely true. Here, then, we have a witness who testifies, "There is a certain dose of falsity in my testimony, I know," and a large and influential party of philosophers who protest, "Oh, no such thing! Whatever you testify to is absolute truth."

672.   Suppose, however, that some fallacy lurks here, and that the doctrine of instantaneous consciousness does not logically require absolute assent to all the representations of perception. Still, it must be admitted that the only method of ascertaining the truth is to repeat this trio of operations: conjecture; deductions of predictions from the conjecture; testing the predictions by experimentation (not necessarily what is technically so called, but essentially the same thing, — trial).[23] We, thus, necessarily repose upon man's power of guessing the truth. Let him analyze the question as far as practicable;

___

[23] (Ed.) See Book II, "Scientific Method," in the present volume.

and give him guesses enough (not very many) upon each simple item and eventually he will guess right. Since we thus unavoidably assume that the mind has a certain power of evolving the truth from its own entrails, natural ideas, such as the deliverances of the percipua, have a right of precedence, and should be adhered to until fact flatly contradicts them. But thus far all the facts of observation are in remarkable accord with the deliverance of the percipuum as it is above stated.

673.   If my view is right, time is of the nature of a general. That is, it may be a day; and a day is, by virtue of there being a forenoon and an afternoon; and a forenoon or afternoon is, by virtue of the different hours; the hour, by virtue of its minutes; and so on endlessly. But you never can find an indivisible time.

674.   It is true that we may imagine a pendulous motion. The motion to the right ceases and the motion to the left begins. If the pendulum is an absolutely rigid body all whose parts are constrained to move in precisely the same way, then, were time composed of rational dates only, there need not be any date at which the right hand motion ended and the left hand motion began. In a true continuum there must be a common moment, but not an absolute instant, independent of all that is before and after. Looking at matters through the wrong end of a telescope, as it were, — that is, aggregating the parts, — there certainly is something in a moment altogether independent of past and future. But examining the moment under a microscope we find this independent element divided up into portions, less independent of one another. Finally, we come to this, that while there are elements of secondness, — of irrational compulsion — they flow in upon us continuously, thus being subjected from the very first to thirdness. Take away considerable time, — as a day; — and doubtless much therein happens that could not have been expected. But if we divide the day into hours, we find that much that was unexpected on the whole is no more than might have been anticipated from a part; and so we are led to say that the unexpected comes, not only in driblets, but in inappreciable flow.

675.   On the whole, then, the percipuum is not an absolute event. There is no span of present time so short as not to con-

tain something remembered, that is, taken as a reasonable conjecture, not without containing something expected for the
confirmation which we are waiting. The peculiar element of
the present, that it confronts us with ideas which it forces upon
us without reason, is something which accumulates in wholes
of time and dissipates the more minutely the course of time
is scrutinized.

676. There is no percipuum so absolute as not to be subject
to possible error.

677. The percipuum is a recognition of the character of
what is past, the percept which we think we remember. The interpretation is forced upon us; but no reason for it can be given.

678. But just so when we experience a long series of systematically connected phenomena, suddenly the idea of the
mode of connection, of the system, springs up in our minds, is
forced upon us, and there is no warrant for it and no apparent
explanation of how we were led so to view it. You may say
that we put this and that together; but what brought those
ideas out of the depths of consciousness? On this idea, which
springs out upon experience of part of the system we immediately build expectations of what is to come and assume the
attitude of watching for them.

679. It is in this way that science is built up; and science
would be impossible if man did not possess a tendency to conjecture rightly.

680. It is idle to say that the doctrine of chances would
account for man's ultimately guessing right. For if there were
only a limited number n of hypotheses that man could form,
so that $1/n$ would be the chance of the first hypothesis being
right, still it would be a remarkable fact that man only could
form n hypotheses, including in the number the hypothesis
that future experimentation would confirm. Why should man's
n hypotheses include the right one? The doctrine of chances
could never account for that until it was in possession of statistics of the hypotheses that are inconceivable by man. But even
that is not the real state of things. It is hard to say how many
hypotheses a physicist could conceive to account for a phenomenon in his laboratory. He might suppose that the conjunctions
of the planets had something to do with it, or some relation

393

between the phases of variability of the stars in ω *Centauri*, or the fact of the Dowager empress having blown her nose 1 day 2 hours 34 minutes and 56 seconds after an inhabitant of Mars had died. The truth is that very few hypotheses will appear to the physicist to be reasonable; and the one true hypothesis is usually of this small number. Why is that? It may be answered, very truly, that experience has taught us that astrology, correspondences, magic, and many hypotheses formerly considered reasonable are to be put aside. Yes, but if primitive man had not had, at the very outset, some decided tendency toward preferring truthful hypotheses, no length of time, — absolutely none, — would have been sufficient to educate him even to the state of mind of Aristotle in his Book of Physical Auscultations, ridiculous as all that now seems to us. No, it is absolutely necessary to admit some original connection between human ideas, and the events that the future was destined to unfold.

681. But that is something very like telepathy. What would telepathy amount to, if it were an established fact. It would then be proved that people not very infrequently have hallucinations, and that one hallucination out of a great number (but more frequently than chance coincidence could account for) coincides with subsequent experience to such a degree as to attract attention; for even if there really be telepathy we must suppose, from what we know of human nature, that the accordance with truth is apt to be greatly exaggerated. In this case, telepathy would be a phenomenon somewhat more remote from perception than the conjectures by which physicists so often hit upon the truth.

§6. CONCLUSION

682. Very well, then; what does all this rambling lead to? Nobody, of course, denies the *phenomena*, which the telepathists bring before us; that is to say, that such and such stories are told. The only question is whether they are to be accounted for by the operation of causes usually active in such phenomena.

683. The doctrine of telepathy is not established, nor far on the way toward establishment, as a scientific truth. For un-

derstood as the telepathists make a point of defining it, it denies the hope on which all science is based. If, however, we amend it, in order to avoid that positively anti-scientific character, what does it amount to? That very rarely a person at a distance from another has a hallucination or a positive conviction apparently irrational which represents something as having happened to that other person, and this turns out to be veridical with a frequency and to a degree which we know not how to explain, and which seems mysterious. But science can make no use of a proposition so vague as that. Where is the phenomenon, or the feature of a phenomenon, in which, if we examine closely, we shall not find much that our science cannot yet explain?

684. There is, however, no part of the work of science that ought to rank higher than that which brings a phenomenon to the cognizance of science. That sort of work, which Chladni did for the falling stones, is what the psychicists are endeavoring to do for veridical hallucinations and the like; and they will no doubt persevere until they succeed. I do not think they have displayed great genius for research; but they ought to be respected for the thorough single-heartedness, conscientiousness, and constancy with which they have pursued this purpose.

685. The general public has no accurate conception of what the work of a scientific investigator consists in; for the books of "popular science" give no idea of it. But the general public is no fool in judging of human nature; and the general public is decidedly of the opinion that there is such a thing as a scientific pedantry that swells with complaisance when it can sneer at popular observations, not always wisely. I must confess that in the past generations scientists of great eminence have sometimes been betrayed into this fault; but it will not be so hereafter. As for Sir William Crooks his most exquisite experimental researches were still in the future when he first displayed an openness of mind more admirable still. Neither Newcomb nor Langley was a worn-out and super-annuated physicist when he took a prominent position in the Psychical Research Society; neither had at that time achieved his most brilliant experimental triumphs.

686. What school of philosophers is it that attributes to

the human mind the most wonderful powers? One might guess that it would be the idealists and spiritualists; but strange to say it is those who boast themselves to be materialists and who insist that nothing is real except *mass* and *motion*. For in order to maintain that, they are obliged to say that *law* is nothing but a figment of the human mind. Now *law* can certainly not be jammed into the pigeon-hole of mass, nor into that of motion. That indeed is their real reason for making it a fiction. Now is it not of all things the most wonderful, that the mind should be able to create an idea for which there is no prototype in nature, nor anything in the least resembling it, and that by means of this utter fiction it should manage to predict the results of future experiments and by means of that power should during the nineteenth century have transformed the face of the globe? Telepathy, with its infrequency and usual deceptiveness (for there is no reason for separating veridical from non-veridical hallucinations, as phenomena essentially different,) would be an insignificant faculty in comparison.

687. For my part, I cannot accept such a theory. It attributes to man powers which he knows too well that he does not possess. It seems to me that the only admissible view is that the reasonableness, or idea of law, in a man's mind, being an idea by which objective predictions are effected, — for all physical theories originate in human conjectures, and experiment only lops off what is erroneous and determines exact values, — must be in the mind as a consequence of its being in the real world. Then the reasonableness of the mind and that of nature being essentially the same, it is not surprising that the mind, after a limited number of guesses, should be able to conjecture what the law of any natural phenomenon is. How far this power of conjecture may go we certainly do not know. We do know that it goes far enough to have enabled men to make already considerable progress in science. Whether or not it extends so far that very rarely one mind can know what passes in another at a distance, would seem to be a question to be investigated as soon as we can see our way to doing so intelligently. I do not believe that questions can be permanently settled by pooh-poohing one or another alternative.

688. It is curious to see how the materialists, — or those

who are flattered at being so called, — plume themselves on being free from "beliefs." Really, one would suppose they imagined it possible for a man to conduct his life on a basis of scientifically established doctrine. It is true that an engineer, civil, mechanical, electrical, or chemical, is able to do this in the present advanced state of science, so far as he has to deal with materials. But even a member of one of those four professions, the only ones that can be called thoroughly reduced to the applications of scientific principles, even he still finds that exact science fails him in dealing with men, — that is to say in considering the use to which his construction is to be put, in considering financial questions, in considering his relations to those who are to execute his plans. For everything else in life unscientific beliefs have to be relied upon for the present; and in particular, it is precisely what we are to *believe* about telepathy that we all are curious to know.[24]

[24] (Ed.) The manuscript breaks off shortly after this point.

INDEX OF PROPER NAMES *

* The numbers refer to paragraphs, not to pages.

INDEX OF PROPER NAMES

400

INDEX OF PROPER NAMES

INDEX OF SUBJECTS *

* The numbers refer to paragraphs, not to pages.

INDEX OF SUBJECTS

INDEX OF SUBJECTS

INDEX OF SUBJECTS

410

INDEX OF SUBJECTS

411

INDEX OF SUBJECTS

in suggestion 453
of ideas 392
see also Association
Simples 528, 530
Simplicity 92–96, 220, 538
of law 519
Singularity, of percept 625, 632
Sleep 573
in psychological classification 375
Society, in psychological classification 385
Solar system 180
Soul 580f, 591f, 594f
action of 410
and body 368
and mind 365
Space 486ff
dimensionality of 197, 568
measures of 305
relations of particles 523, 534n4
Species, in classification of science 374n10
Sphinx 425, 584, 625
Spiritualism 602, 611
Spiritualists 686
Spontaneity, in thought 389f
Standards
for long measure 306
of measurement 297f, 307f
Stars, magnitude of 258, 265
State
in measurement 285ff
ultimate 471ff
State number 292ff
Station number 297, 302
Stoicism 666
Succession, in induction 121ff
Suggestion 218, 377, 389, 391ff, 395ff, 433ff, 451ff, 495, 500, 548ff
see also Association
Surmise 36, 669
see also Abduction
Surprise, and explanation 188ff, 197
Syllogism 72, 662ff
in Aristotle 246, 249ff
Symbol
and consciousness 407
and nature of man 583, 590f, 593f
see also Sign
Symptom 356, 628
Synechism 653
and immortality 565–578

Synesthesia 377
Synthesis
in psychology 377
in understanding 198
System
idea of 678
in law of mind 467

Tact 256
Telepathy 35, 597–603, 610f, 613, 681, 683, 686, 688
in psychological classification 377
Terminology 494f, 642
ethics of 603n6
Testimony
instinct of receiving 615
method of treating 162ff, 224ff
of instinctive impressions 604
Theology, in development of performances 384
Theorem 204
of Cantor 209
Taylor's 263
Theorematic, in deduction 204, 223
Theory 93–96, 399, 410, 527
and practice 63, 453
cerebral 503ff
correction of 180
in abduction 218
in history of science 276
in physics 598
of balancing likelihoods 164–182
of errors 142f
of gases 216, 220ff
of light 116, 220
of pre-established harmony 368
of probability 177
of telepathy 600
physical 687
Thinking 328
individual 269
instinctive 606
scientific 494n9
see also Reasoning
Third, *and* Thirdness 532, 536, 551, 630, 653, 666, 674
and space 488f
see also Argument, Law, Thought
Thisness, and secondness 488
Thought 276ff, 326, 328, 331ff, 336ff, 355ff, 440
action of 555

Volume VIII

REVIEWS, CORRESPONDENCE, AND BIBLIOGRAPHY

PREFACE

When the first volume of the *Collected Papers* of Charles
Peirce was published in 1931, its Introduction predicted some
ten volumes in the series, those beyond the sixth being expected
to contain Peirce's "writings on physics and psychology, as
well as his reviews, letters, and biography." Footnotes to the
subsequent text even cited some of those last volumes. Nevertheless, it was only of the six volumes that the Introduction
spoke in the present tense, and these, under the editorship of
Drs. Charles Hartshorne and Paul Weiss, appeared as promised, ending with Volume VI in 1935. Selection, preparation,
and publication of further material was at that time impractical, and for the next twenty years the remaining papers in
Harvard's custody were accessible only to such scholars as
could consult them in Cambridge. In 1954, however, the Harvard Department of Philosophy was able to renew the enterprise. The Rockefeller Foundation granted to the University a
subvention for the costs of further editing, and the Department
was fortunate to enlist Professor Arthur W. Burks, of the University of Michigan, to perform that peculiarly exacting task.
The Department is glad of this occasion to acknowledge its
debt, and that of the scholarly community in general, both to
the Foundation and to Professor Burks, and to remind the
reader that since the expense of the further actual book-making
is defrayed from royalties from the earlier volumes, which
were subsidized by gifts of the late Professor James H. Woods
and anonymous friends, we are still their beneficiaries too.

The present publication comprises two volumes instead of
the four of the old estimate. Mr. Burks's Introduction, which
follows on page ix, indicates how nearly he is completing the
original plan. A substantial addition is his extraordinarily
searching bibliography, with its introduction comparing the
sum of published material with what still remains only in manuscript.

Besides joining in the editor's acknowledgements of those
who assisted him, the Department and Publishers thank the

Houghton Library for permission to print previously unpublished correspondence between Peirce and James, Edith Davidson Harris and the Hoose Library of Philosophy at the University of Southern California for permission to print a letter
from Peirce to William T. Harris, and the following for the use
of copyrighted material as indicated: Helen G. Baldwin, definitions from James Mark Baldwin's *Dictionary of Philosophy
and Psychology*, Vol. II; *The Nation*, several reviews; *Popular
Science Monthly*, Peirce's review of Pearson's *Grammar of Science*; Whitlock's, Inc., parts of two letters reprinted from Irwin
C. Lieb's *Charles S. Peirce's Letters to Lady Welby*; William
James, correspondence from Peirce to his father, William
James, and quotations from a Peirce manuscript, "Questions
on William James's Principles of Psychology," previously
printed in Ralph Barton Perry's *Thought and Character of
William James*.

Harvard University
August, 1957

CONTENTS

INTRODUCTION

The first six volumes of the series, *Collected Papers of Charles Sanders Peirce*, included Peirce's main writings in general philosophy, logic (deductive, inductive, and symbolic), pragmatism, and metaphysics. The present two volumes are a continuation of this series. Volume VII is organized in three books containing papers on experimental science, scientific method, and philosophy of mind, respectively. Volume VIII contains selections from Peirce's reviews and correspondence and a bibliography of his published works.

Since Book I of Volume VII, "Experimental Science," is the only book in the series not on philosophy, its inclusion may require special comment. Much of Peirce's life was devoted to experimental science. In fact, the only permanent position Peirce held was with the United States Coast Survey, where he was employed to do research in astronomy and geodetics. Though this position allowed him considerable time for philosophy, it is nevertheless true that for more than half of his mature life his main responsibility was to conduct scientific investigations.[1] His efforts in the physical sciences resulted in a large number of published papers, several of considerable length, as well as his only published book, *Photometric Researches*, 1878.[2] Moreover, Peirce's experimental work had an important influence on his philosophy. His pragmatic theory of meaning is a generalization from scientific practice, his laboratory experience having influenced his discovery of that theory (see

---

[1] He was employed by the Coast Survey from September 21, 1859, to June 1, 1860, and from July 1, 1861, to December 31, 1891.

[2] See the Bibliography in Vol. VIII, especially the years 1872 through 1886; Peirce produced little in the way of results for the Coast Survey after he moved to Milford, Pa., in the spring of 1887.

5.411–412). His indeterminism was connected with his work for the Coast Survey on precise measurement.[3] And his empirical investigations in psychology (see 7.21–35) influenced his theory of mind. Thus Peirce's scientific work played an important role in his life and in the formation of his philosophy, and it is for these reasons that we have reprinted his only published article in experimental psychology and two short pieces on gravity. We have limited ourselves to this small sample of his work in physical science because, though his astronomical researches showed originality and his gravimetric work was well respected by eminent men in geodetics, Peirce remained a minor figure in these fields.

The editors of the earlier volumes made some introductory remarks about the Peirce manuscripts and their policies in editing them (Vol. I, p. iv ff.). The present editor has continued their practice of publishing only parts of some of the works, omitting large portions altogether. He has also continued the policy of selecting or compiling a draft for publication whenever there were several drafts available. The justification for these procedures is to be found in certain aspects of the Peirce manuscripts. Many of the manuscripts are internally variable in quality: one frequently finds publishable sections in the midst of material which either is of little contemporary interest or presents ideas better treated in other manuscripts. Moreover, there are often alternative and sometimes incomplete versions of the same work to choose from; and in some cases no final version is discernible. The editor must then make selections and, if necessary, piece together drafts from the hodgepodge of partial drafts. These characteristics are so typical that any satisfactory edition of Peirce's papers must contain a great deal of fragmentary material.

The present editor has also continued the plan of organization pursued in the previous volumes, breaking up manuscripts, books, and series of articles, and arranging the resultant ma-

---

[3] Cf. 6.44, 6.46. Peirce's most original contribution to geodetics was the discovery of a new source of error in gravity measurement; this is described at 7.1–12. Peirce also did research for the Coast Survey on standards of measurement.

terials primarily by subject matter rather than chronologically. Though this plan tends to bring together under one heading passages on a given topic, it makes Peirce's writings appear to be more disorganized than they actually are. To mitigate this shortcoming, there is included in Volume VIII as complete a bibliography of Peirce's published works as the editor could compile. This bibliography is arranged for the most part chronologically, with a connected series of articles, parts of a single manuscript, or a series of lectures grouped together under one listing. The bibliography will also assist the reader in locating any published works not reprinted in this series.

The chapter and section headings have been chosen by the editor; when these are the same as Peirce's, the footnotes so indicate. Editorial alterations are enclosed in brackets, and the editor's footnotes are indicated by "(Ed.)." Peirce's punctuation, spelling, and underlining for emphasis have, in general, been retained. Obvious errors, however, have been corrected; and where clarity of presentation has required them, minor changes have been made in format, capitalization, abbreviations, italicizing of titles, etc., without any indication. Likewise, questions of manuscript interpretation which made no significant difference in the meaning have been settled without any indication.

The editor wishes to thank the Rockefeller Foundation and the Department of Philosophy of Harvard University for their aid in the preparation and publication of these two volumes. While giving him the kindest and fullest assistance, both left him completely free in his work and have no responsibility for any shortcomings in it. The editor is also grateful for a grant for editorial assistance from the Horace H. Rackham School of Graduate Studies of the University of Michigan.

For assistance in locating and evaluating various Peirce materials, the editor is personally indebted to William Alston, Jackson Cope, Carolyn Eisele, Mrs. E. L. C. Hales, Murray Murphey, W. E. Schlaretzki, James F. Sheridan, Manley Thompson, and Philip Wiener; to the previous editors, Charles Hartshorne and Paul Wiess; and especially to Max Fisch, who also read the manuscript and made many valuable suggestions. In all cases the final decision as to what materials were to be

included was made by the editor, and the responsibility for the
choices is his alone.

The editor expresses his deep thanks to Grace L. Wood, who
assisted greatly in the preparation of the bibliography and did
much of the editorial work for the volumes, and to his wife,
Alice, for her helpful advice.

Arthur W. Burks

Ann Arbor, Michigan

Book I

REVIEWS

CHAPTER 1

JOHN VENN, *THE LOGIC OF CHANCE*[1]

1. Here is a book which should be read by every thinking man. Great changes have taken place of late years in the philosophy of chances. Mr. Venn remarks, with great ingenuity and penetration, that this doctrine has had its realistic, conceptualistic, and nominalistic stages. The logic of the Middle Ages is almost coextensive with demonstrative logic; but our age of science opened with a discussion of probable argument (in the *Novum Organum*), and this part of the subject has given the chief interest to modern studies of logic. What is called the doctrine of chances is, to be sure, but a small part of this field of inquiry; but it is a part where the varieties in the conceptions of probability have been most evident. When this doctrine was first studied, probability seems to have been regarded as something inhering in the singular events, so that it was possible for Bernouilli to enounce it as a *theorem* (and not merely as an identical proposition), that events happen with frequencies proportional to their probabilities. That was a realistic view. Afterwards it was said that probability does not exist in the singular events, but consists in the degree of credence which ought to be reposed in the occurrence of an event. This is conceptualistic. Finally, probability is regarded as the ratio of the number of events in a certain part of an aggregate of them to the number in the whole aggregate. This is the nominalistic view.

2. This last is the position of Mr. Venn and of the most advanced writers on the subject. The theory was perhaps first

[1] (Ed.) Review of John Venn's *The Logic of Chance, An Essay on the Foundations and Province of the Theory of Probability, with especial Reference to its Application to Moral and Social Science* (London and Cambridge, 1866), *The North American Review* 105 (July 1867) 317–321. This is Peirce's earliest full statement of his theory of probability; cf. 3.19 (1867). His later views are discussed in [CP] II, Book III, and [CP] VII, Book II.

put forth by Mr. Stuart Mill; but his head became involved in clouds, and he relapsed into the conceptualistic opinion. Yet the arguments upon the modern side are overwhelming. The question is by no means one of words; but if we were to inquire into the manner in which the terms *probable*, *likely*, and so forth, have been used, we should find that they always refer to a determination of a genus of argument. See, for example, Locke on the Understanding, Book IV. ch. 14, §1. There we find it stated that a thing is probable when it is supported by reasons *such as* lead to a true conclusion. These words *such as* plainly refer to a genus of argument. Now, what constitutes the validity of a genus of argument? The necessity of thinking the conclusion, say the conceptualists. But a madman may be under a necessity of thinking fallaciously, and (as Bacon suggests) all mankind may be mad after one uniform fashion. Hence the nominalist answers the question thus: A genus of argument is valid when from true premises it will yield a true conclusion — invariably if demonstrative, generally if probable. The conceptualist says, that probability is the degree of credence which *ought* to be placed in the occurrence of an event. Here is an allusion to an entry on the debtor side of man's ledger. What is this entry? What is the meaning of this *ought*? Since probability is not an affair of morals, the *ought* must refer to an alternative to be avoided. Now the reasoner has nothing to fear but error. Probability will accordingly be the degree of credence which it is necessary to repose in a proposition in order to escape error. Conceptualists have not undertaken to say what is meant by "degree of credence." They would probably pronounce it indefinable and indescribable. Their philosophy deals much with the indefinable and indescribable. But propositions are either absolutely true or absolutely false. There is nothing *in the facts* which corresponds at all to a degree of credence, except that a genus of argument may yield a certain proportion of true conclusions from true premises. Thus, the following form of argument would, in the long run, yield (from true premises) a true conclusion two thirds of the time: —

> A is taken at random from among the B's;
> ⅔ of the B's are C;
> ∴ A is C.

4

3. Truth being, then, the agreement of a representation with its object, and there being nothing *in re* answering to a degree of credence, a modification of a judgment in that respect cannot make it more true, although it may indicate the proportion of *such* judgments which are true *in the long run*. That is, indeed, the precise and only use or significance of these fractions termed probabilities: they give security in the long run. Now, in order that the degree of credence should correspond to any truth in the long run, it must be the representation of a general statistical fact, — a real, objective fact. And then, as it is the fact which is said to be probable, and not the belief, the introduction of "degree of credence" at all into the definition of probability is as superfluous as the introduction of a reflection upon a mental process into any other definition would be, — as though we were to define man as "that which (if the essence of the name is to be apprehended) ought to be conceived as a rational animal."

4. To say that the conceptualistic and nominalistic theories are both true at once, is mere ignorance, because their numerical results conflict. A conceptualist might hesitate, perhaps, to say that the probability of a proposition of which he knows absolutely nothing is ½, although this would be, in one sense, justifiable for the nominalist, inasmuch as one half of all possible propositions (being contradictions of the other half) are true; but he does not hesitate to assume events to be equally probable when he does not know anything about their probabilities, and this is for the nominalist an utterly unwarrantable procedure. A probability is a statistical fact, and cannot be assumed arbitrarily. Boole first did away with this absurdity, and thereby brought the mathematical doctrine of probabilities into harmony with the modern logical doctrine of probable inference. But Boole (owing to the *needs* of his calculus) admitted the assumption that simple events whose probabilities are given are independent, — an assumption of the same vicious character. Mr. Venn strikes down this last remnant of conceptualism with a very vigorous hand.

5. He has, however, fallen into some conceptualistic errors of his own; and these are specially manifest in his "applications to moral and social science." The most important of these is contained in the chapter "on the credibility of extraordinary

5

stories"; but it is defended with so much ingenuity as almost to give it the value of a real contribution to science. It is maintained that the credibility of an extraordinary story depends either entirely upon the veracity of the witness, or, in more extraordinary cases, entirely upon the *a priori* credibility of the story; but that these considerations cannot, under any circumstances, be combined, unless arbitrarily. In order to support this opinion, the author invents an illustration. He supposes that statistics were to have shown that nine out of ten consumptives who go to the island of Madeira live through the first year, and that nine out of ten Englishmen who go to the same island die the first year; what, then, would be the just rate of insurance for the first year of a consumptive Englishman who is about to go to that island? There are no certain data for the least approximation to the proportion of consumptive Englishmen who die in Madeira during the first year. But it is certain that an insurance company which insured only Englishmen in Madeira during the first year, or only consumptives under the same circumstances, would be warranted (a certain moral fact being neglected) in taking the consumptive Englishman at its ordinary rate. Hence, Mr. Venn thinks that an insurance company which insured all sorts of men could with safety and fairness insure the consumptive Englishman either as Englishman or as consumptive.[2] Now, the case of an extraordinary story is parallel to this: for such a story is, 1st, told by a certain person, who tells a known proportion of true stories, — say nine out of ten; and, 2d, is of a certain sort (as a fish story), of which a known proportion are true, — say one in ten. Then, as much as before, we come out right, in the long run, by considering such a story under either of the two classes to which it belongs. Hence, says Mr. Venn, we

---

[2] This is an error. For supposing every man to be insured for the same amount, which we may take as our unit of value, and adopting the notation,

(c,e) = number of consumptive Englishmen insured.

$(c,\bar{e})$ = " " consumptives not English insured.

$(\bar{c},e)$ = " " not consumptive English insured.

x = unknown ratio of consumptive English who *do not die* in the first year. The amount paid out yearly by the company would be, in the long run,

$$\frac{1}{10}(c,\bar{e}) + \frac{9}{10}(\bar{c},e) + x(c,e),$$

and x is unknown. This objection to Venn's theory may, however, be waived.

must repose such belief in the story as the veracity of the witness alone, or the antecedent probability alone, requires, or else arbitrarily modify one or other of these degrees of credence. In examining this theory, let us first remark, that there are two principal phrases in which the word probability occurs: for, first, we may speak of the probability of an event or proposition, and then we express ourselves incompletely, inasmuch as we refer to the frequency of true conclusions in the genus of arguments by which the event or proposition in question may have been inferred, without indicating what genus of argument that is; and, secondly, we may speak of the probability that any individual of a certain class has a certain character, when we mean the ratio of the number of those of that class that have that character to the total number in the class. Now it is this latter phrase which we use when we speak of the probability that a story of a certain sort, told by a certain man, is true. And since there is nothing in the data to show what this ratio is, the probability in question is unknown. But a "degree of credence" or "credibility," to be logically determined, must, as we have seen, be an expression of probability in the nominalistic sense; and therefore this "degree of credence" (supposing it to exist) is unknown. "We know not what to believe," is the ordinary and logically correct expression in such cases of perplexity.

6. Credence and expectation cannot be represented by single numbers. Probability is not always known; and then the probability of each degree of probability must enter into the credence. Perhaps this again is not known; then there will be a probability of each degree of probability of each degree of probability; and so on. In the same way, when a risk is run, the expectation is composed of the probabilities of each possible issue, but is not a single number, as the Petersburg problem shows. Suppose the capitalists of the world were to owe me a hundred dollars, and were to offer to pay in either of the following ways: 1st, a coin should be pitched up until it turned up heads (or else a hundred times, if it did not come up heads sooner), and I should be paid two dollars if the head came up the first time, four if the second time, eight if the third time, etc.; or, 2d, a coin should be turned up a hundred times, and I should receive two dollars for every head. Each of

7

these offers would be worth a hundred dollars, *in the long run*;
that is to say, if repeated often enough, I should receive on
the average a hundred dollars at each trial. But if the trial
were to be made but once, I should infinitely prefer the second
alternative, on account of its greater security. Mere certainty is
worth a great deal. We wish to know our fate. How much it is
worth is a question of political economy. It must go into the
market, where its worth is what it will fetch. And since security
may be of many kinds (according to the distribution of the
probabilities of each sum of money and of each loss, in prospect), the value of the various kinds will fluctuate among one
another with the ratio of demand and supply, — the demand
varying with the moral and intellectual state of the community,
— and thus no single and constant number can represent the
value of any kind.

CHAPTER 2

FRASER'S EDITION OF
THE WORKS OF GEORGE BERKELEY [1]

§1. INTRODUCTION

7.   This new edition of Berkeley's works is much superior
to any of the former ones. It contains some writings not in any
of the other editions, and the rest are given with a more carefully
edited text. The editor has done his work well. The introductions to the several pieces contain analyses of their contents which will be found of the greatest service to the reader.
On the other hand, the explanatory notes which disfigure every
page seem to us altogether unnecessary and useless.

8.   Berkeley's metaphysical theories have at first sight an
air of paradox and levity very unbecoming to a bishop. He
denies the existence of matter, our ability to see distance, and
the possibility of forming the simplest general conception;
while he admits the existence of Platonic ideas; and argues the
whole with a cleverness which every reader admits, but which
few are convinced by. His disciples seem to think the present
moment a favorable one for obtaining for their philosophy a
more patient hearing than it has yet got. It is true that we of
this day are sceptical and not given to metaphysics, but so,
say they, was the generation which Berkeley addressed, and for
which his style was chosen; while it is hoped that the spirit of
calm and thorough inquiry which is now, for once, almost the
fashion, will save the theory from the perverse misrepresenta-

---

[1] (Ed.) Review of Alexander Campbell Fraser's *The Works of George Berkeley, D.D., formerly Bishop of Cloyne: including many of his Writings hitherto
unpublished,* four volumes (Clarendon Press, Oxford, 1871), *The North American
Review* 113 (Oct. 1871) 449–472.
   Cf. Peirce's review of the 1901 edition, [Bibliography] N–1901–10.

tions which formerly assailed it, and lead to a fair examination of the arguments which, in the minds of his sectators, put the truth of it beyond all doubt. But above all, it is anticipated that the Berkeleyan treatment of that question of the validity of human knowledge and of the inductive process of science, which is now so much studied, is such as to command the attention of scientific men to the idealistic system. To us these hopes seem vain. The truth is that the minds from whom the spirit of the age emanates have now no interest in the only problems that metaphysics ever pretended to solve. The abstract acknowledgment of God, Freedom, and Immortality, apart from those other religious beliefs (which cannot possibly rest on metaphysical grounds) which alone may animate this, is now seen to have no practical consequence whatever. The world is getting to think of these creatures of metaphysics, as Aristotle of the Platonic ideas: τερετίσματα γάρ ἐστι, καὶ εἰ ἔστιν, οὐδὲν πρὸς τὸν λόγον ἐστίν. The question of the grounds of the validity of induction has, it is true, excited an interest, and may continue to do so (though the argument is now become too difficult for popular apprehension); but whatever interest it has had has been due to a hope that the solution of it would afford the basis for sure and useful maxims concerning the logic of induction, — a hope which would be destroyed so soon as it were shown that the question was a purely metaphysical one. This is the prevalent feeling, among advanced minds. It may not be just; but it exists. And its existence is an effectual bar (if there were no other) to the general acceptance of Berkeley's system. The few who do now care for metaphysics are not of that bold order of minds who delight to hold a position so unsheltered by the prejudices of common sense as that of the good bishop.

9. As a matter of history, however, philosophy must always be interesting. It is the best representative of the mental development of each age. It is so even of ours, if we think what really is our philosophy. Metaphysical history is one of the chief branches of history, and ought to be expounded side by side with the history of society, of government, and of war; for in its relations with these we trace the significance of events for the human mind. The history of philosophy in the British Isles is a subject possessing more unity and entirety within it-

self than has usually been recognized in it. The influence of
Descartes was never so great in England as that of traditional
conceptions, and we can trace a continuity between modern
and mediaeval thought there, which is wanting in the history
of France, and still more, if possible, in that of Germany.

10. From very early times, it has been the chief intellectual
characteristic of the English to wish to effect everything by
the plainest and directest means, without unnecessary contrivance. In war, for example, they rely more than any other
people in Europe upon sheer hardihood, and rather despise
military science. The main peculiarities of their system of
law arise from the fact that every evil has been rectified as it
became intolerable, without any thoroughgoing measure. The
bill for legalizing marriage with a deceased wife's sister is
yearly pressed because it supplies a remedy for an incon-
venience actually felt; but nobody has proposed a bill to legal-
ize marriage with a deceased husband's brother. In philosophy,
this national tendency appears as a strong preference for the
simplest theories, and a resistance to any complication of the
theory as long as there is the least possibility that the facts
can be explained in the simpler way. And, accordingly, British
philosophers have always desired to weed out of philosophy all
conceptions which could not be made perfectly definite and
easily intelligible, and have shown strong nominalistic tendencies since the time of Edward I., or even earlier. Berkeley
is an admirable illustration of this national character, as well
as of that strange union of nominalism with Platonism, which
has repeatedly appeared in history, and has been such a stum-
bling-block to the historians of philosophy.

11. The mediaeval metaphysic is so entirely forgotten, and
has so close a historic connection with modern English philosophy, and so much bearing upon the truth of Berkeley's doctrine,
that we may perhaps be pardoned a few pages on the nature of
the celebrated controversy concerning universals. And first let
us set down a few dates. It was at the very end of the eleventh
century that the dispute concerning nominalism and realism,
which had existed in a vague way before, began to attain extraordinary proportions. During the twelfth century it was the
matter of most interest to logicians, when William of Cham-
peaux, Abélard, John of Salisbury, Gilbert de la Porrée, and

11

many others, defended as many different opinions. But there
was no historic connection between this controversy and those
of scholasticism proper, the scholasticism of Aquinas, Scotus,
and Ockam. For about the end of the twelfth century a great
revolution of thought took place in Europe. What the influences
were which produced it requires new historical researches to
say. No doubt, it was partly due to the Crusades. But a great
awakening of intelligence did take place at that time. It requires, it is true, some examination to distinguish this particular movement from a general awakening which had begun a
century earlier, and had been growing ever since. But now
there was an accelerated impulse. Commerce was attaining
new importance, and was inventing some of her chief con-
veniences and safeguards. Law, which had hitherto been utterly barbaric, began to be a profession. The civil law was adopted
in Europe, the canon law was digested; the common law took
some form. The Church, under Innocent III., was assuming
the sublime functions of a moderator over kings. And those
orders of mendicant friars were established, two of which did
so much for the development of the scholastic philosophy. Art
felt the spirit of a new age, and there could hardly be a greater
change than from the highly ornate round-arched architecture
of the twelfth century to the comparatively simple Gothic of
the thirteenth. Indeed, if any one wishes to know what a
scholastic commentary is like, and what the tone of thought
in it is, he has only to contemplate a Gothic cathedral. The
first quality of either is a religious devotion, truly heroic. One
feels that the men who did these works did really believe in religion as we believe in nothing. We cannot easily understand
how Thomas Aquinas can speculate so much on the nature of
angels, and whether ten thousand of them could dance on a
needle's point. But it was simply because he held them for
real. If they are real, why are they not more interesting than
the bewildering varieties of insects which naturalists study; or
why should the orbits of double stars attract more attention
than spiritual intelligences? It will be said that we have no
means of knowing anything about them. But that is on a par
with censuring the schoolmen for referring questions to the
authority of the Bible and of the Church. If they really believed in their religion, as they did, what better could they do?

12

And if they found in these authorities testimony concerning angels, how could they avoid admitting it. Indeed, objections of this sort only make it appear still more clearly how much those were the ages of faith. And if the spirit was not altogether admirable, it is only because faith itself has its faults as a foundation for the intellectual character. The men of that time did fully believe and did think that, for the sake of giving themselves up absolutely to their great task of building or of writing, it was well worth while to resign all the joys of life. Think of the spirit in which Duns Scotus must have worked, who wrote his thirteen volumes in folio, in a style as condensed as the most condensed parts of Aristotle, before the age of thirty-four. Nothing is more striking in either of the great intellectual products of that age, than the complete absence of self-conceit on the part of the artist or philosopher. That anything of value can be added to his sacred and catholic work by its having the smack of individuality about it, is what he has never conceived. His work is not designed to embody *his* ideas, but the universal truth; there will not be one thing in it however minute, for which you will not find that he has his authority; and whatever originality emerges is of that inborn kind which so saturates a man that he cannot himself perceive it. The individual feels his own worthlessness in comparison with his task, and does not dare to introduce his vanity into the doing of it. Then there is no machine-work, no unthinking repetition about the thing. Every part is worked out for itself as a separate problem, no matter how analogous it may be in general to another part. And no matter how small and hidden a detail may be, it has been conscientiously studied, as though it were intended for the eye of God. Allied to this character is a detestation of antithesis or the studied balancing of one thing against another, and of a too geometrical grouping, — a hatred of posing which is as much a moral trait as the others. Finally, there is nothing in which the scholastic philosophy and the Gothic architecture resemble one another more than in the gradually increasing sense of immensity which impresses the mind of the student as he learns to appreciate the real dimensions and cost of each. It is very unfortunate that the thirteenth, fourteenth, and fifteenth centuries should, under the name of Middle Ages, be con-

founded with others, which they are in every respect as unlike as the Renaissance is from modern times. In the history
of logic, the break between the twelfth and thirteenth centuries is so great that only one author of the former age is
ever quoted in the latter. If this is to be attributed to the
fuller acquaintance with the works of Aristotle, to what, we
would ask, is this profounder study itself to be attributed,
since it is now known that the knowledge of those works was
not imported from the Arabs? The thirteenth century was realistic, but the question concerning universals was not as much
agitated as several others. Until about the end of the century,
scholasticism was somewhat vague, immature, and unconscious
of its own power. Its greatest glory was in the first half of the
fourteenth century. Then Duns Scotus,[2] a Briton (for whether
Scotch, Irish, or English is disputed), first stated the realistic
position consistently, and developed it with great fulness and
applied it to all the different questions which depend upon it.
His theory of "formalities" was the subtlest, except perhaps
Hegel's logic, ever broached, and he was separated from nominalism only by the division of a hair. It is not therefore
surprising that the nominalistic position was soon adopted by
several writers, especially by the celebrated William of Ockam,
who took the lead of this party by the thoroughgoing and
masterly way in which he treated the theory and combined
it with a then rather recent but now forgotten addition to the
doctrine of logical terms. With Ockam, who died in 1347,
scholasticism may be said to have culminated. After him the
scholastic philosophy showed a tendency to separate itself
from the religious element which alone could dignify it, and
sunk first into extreme formalism and fancifulness, and then
into the merited contempt of all men; just as the Gothic architecture had a very similar fate, at about the same time, and for
much the same reasons.

§2. FORMULATION OF REALISM

12. The current explanations of the realist-nominalist controversy are equally false and unintelligible. They are said
to be derived ultimately from Bayle's Dictionary; at any rate,

[2] Died 1308.

14

they are not based on a study of the authors. "Few, very few, for a hundred years past," says Hallam, with truth, "have broken the repose of the immense works of the schoolmen." Yet it is perfectly possible so to state the matter that no one shall fail to comprehend what the question was, and how there might be two opinions about it. Are universals real? We have only to stop and consider a moment what was meant by the word *real*, when the whole issue soon becomes apparent. Objects are divided into figments, dreams, etc., on the one hand, and realities on the other. The former are those which exist only inasmuch as you or I or some man imagines them; the latter are those which have an existence independent of your mind or mine or that of any number of persons. The real is that which is not whatever we happen to think it, but is unaffected by what we may think of it.[3] The question, therefore, is whether *man, horse,* and other names of natural classes, correspond with anything which all men, or all horses, really have in common, independent of our thought, or whether these classes are constituted simply by a likeness in the way in which our minds are affected by individual objects which have in themselves no resemblance or relationship whatsoever. Now that this is a real question which different minds will naturally answer in opposite ways, becomes clear when we think that there are two widely separated points of view, from which *reality*, as just defined, may be regarded. Where is the real, the thing independent of how we think it, to be found? There must be such a thing, for we find our opinions constrained; there is something, therefore, which influences our thoughts, and is not created by them. We have, it is true, nothing immediately present to us but thoughts. These thoughts, however, have been caused by sensations, and those sensations are constrained by something out of the mind. This thing out of the mind, which directly influences sensation, and through sensation thought, because it *is* out of the mind, is independent of how we think it, and is, in short, the real. Here is one view of reality, a very familiar one. And from this point of view it is clear that the nominalistic answer must be given to the question concerning universals. For, while from this standpoint it may be admitted to be true as a rough statement that

[3] (Ed.) Cf. 5.311.

15

one man is like another, the exact sense being that the realities
external to the mind produce sensations which may be embraced
under one conception, yet it can by no means be admitted
that the two real men have really anything in common, for to
say that they are both men is only to say that the one mental
term or thought-sign "man" stands indifferently for either of
the sensible objects caused by the two external realities; so
that not even the two sensations have in themselves anything
in common, and far less is it to be inferred that the external
realities have. This conception of reality is so familiar, that
it is unnecessary to dwell upon it; but the other, or realist conception, if less familiar, is even more natural and obvious. All
human thought and opinion contains an arbitrary, accidental
element, dependent on the limitations in circumstances, power,
and bent of the individual; an element of error, in short. But
human opinion universally tends in the long run to a definite
form, which is the truth. Let any human being have enough
information and exert enough thought upon any question,
and the result will be that he will arrive at a certain definite
conclusion, which is the same that any other mind will reach
under sufficiently favorable circumstances. Suppose two men,
one deaf, the other blind. One hears a man declare he means
to kill another, hears the report of the pistol, and hears the
victim cry; the other sees the murder done. Their sensations
are affected in the highest degree with their individual peculiarities. The first information that their sensations will
give them, their first inferences, will be more nearly alike, but
still different; the one having, for example, the idea of a man
shouting, the other of a man with a threatening aspect; but
their final conclusions, the thought the remotest from sense,
will be identical and free from the one-sidedness of their idiosyncrasies. There is, then, to every question a true answer, a
final conclusion, to which the opinion of every man is constantly
gravitating. He may for a time recede from it, but give him
more experience and time for consideration, and he will finally
approach it. The individual may not live to reach the truth;
there is a residuum of error in every individual's opinions. No
matter; it remains that there is a definite opinion to which the
mind of man is, on the whole and in the long run, tending. On
many questions the final agreement is already reached, on all it

16

will be reached if time enough is given. The arbitrary will or other individual peculiarities of a sufficiently large number of minds may postpone the general agreement in that opinion indefinitely; but it cannot affect what the character of that opinion shall be when it is reached. This final opinion, then, is independent, not indeed of thought in general, but of all that is arbitrary and individual in thought; is quite independent of how you, or I, or any number of men think.[4] Everything, therefore, which will be thought to exist in the final opinion is real, and nothing else. What is the POWER of external things, to affect the senses? To say that people sleep after taking opium because it has a soporific *power*, is that to say anything in the world but that people sleep after taking opium because they sleep after taking opium? To assert the existence of a power or potency, is it to assert the existence of anything actual? Or to say that a thing has a potential existence, is it to say that it has an actual existence? In other words, is the present existence of a power anything in the world but a regularity in future events relating to a certain thing regarded as an element which is to be taken account of beforehand, in the conception of that thing? If not, to assert that there are external things which can be known only as exerting a power on our sense, is nothing different from asserting that there is a general *drift* in the history of human thought which will lead it to one general agreement, one catholic consent. And any truth more perfect than this destined conclusion, any reality more absolute than what is thought in it, is a fiction of metaphysics. It is obvious how this way of thinking harmonizes with a belief in an infallible Church, and how much more natural it would be in the Middle Ages than in Protestant or positivist times.

13. This theory of reality is instantly fatal to the idea of a thing in itself, — a thing existing independent of all relation to the mind's conception of it. Yet it would by no means forbid, but rather encourage us, to regard the appearances of sense as only signs of the realities. Only, the realities which they represent would not be the unknowable cause of sensation, but *noumena*, or intelligible conceptions which are the last products of the mental action which is set in motion by sensation. The matter of sensation is altogether accidental; precisely the same

[4] (Ed.) Cf. 5.311.

information, practically, being capable of communication through different senses. And the catholic consent which constitutes the truth is by no means to be limited to men in this earthly life or to the human race, but extends to the whole communion of minds to which we belong, including some probably whose senses are very different from ours, so that in that consent no predication of a sensible quality can enter, except as an admission that so certain sorts of senses are affected. This theory is also highly favorable to a belief in external realities. It will, to be sure, deny that there is any reality which is absolutely incognizable in itself, so that it cannot be taken into the mind. But observing that "the external" means simply that which is independent of what phenomenon is immediately present, that is of how we may think or feel; just as "the real" means that which is independent of how we may think or feel *about it*; it must be granted that there are many objects of true science which are external, because there are many objects of thought which, if they are independent of that thinking whereby they are thought (that is, if they are real), are indisputably independent of all *other* thoughts and feelings.

14. It is plain that this view of reality is inevitably realistic; because general conceptions enter into all judgments, and therefore into true opinions. Consequently a thing in the general is as real as in the concrete. It is perfectly true that all white things have whiteness in them, for that is only saying, in another form of words, that all white things are white; but since it is true that real things possess whiteness, whiteness is real. It is a real which only exists by virtue of an act of thought knowing it, but that thought is not an arbitrary or accidental one dependent on any idiosyncrasies, but one which will hold in the final opinion.

15. This theory involves a phenomenalism. But it is the phenomenalism of Kant, and not that of Hume. Indeed, what Kant called his Copernican step was precisely the passage from the nominalistic to the realistic view of reality. It was the essence of his philosophy to regard the real object as determined by the mind. That was nothing else than to consider every conception and intuition which enters necessarily into the experience of an object, and which is not transitory and acciden-

18

tal, as having objective validity. In short, it was to regard the reality as the normal product of mental action, and not as the incognizable cause of it.

16.   This realistic theory is thus a highly practical and common-sense position. Wherever universal agreement prevails, the realist will not be the one to disturb the general belief by idle and fictitious doubts. For according to him it is a consensus or common confession which constitutes reality. What he wants, therefore, is to see questions put to rest. And if a general belief, which is perfectly stable and immovable, can in any way be produced, though it be by the fagot and the rack, to talk of any error in such belief is utterly absurd. The realist will hold that the very same objects which are immediately present in our minds in experience really exist just as they are experienced out of the mind; that is, he will maintain a doctrine of immediate perception. He will not, therefore, sunder existence out of the mind and being in the mind as two wholly improportionable modes. When a thing is in such relation to the individual mind that that mind cognizes it, it is in the mind; and its being so in the mind will not in the least diminish its external existence. For he does not think of the mind as a receptacle, which if a thing is in, it ceases to be out of. To make a distinction between the true conception of a thing and the thing itself is, he will say, only to regard one and the same thing from two different points of view; for the immediate object of thought in a true judgment *is* the reality. The realist will, therefore, believe in the objectivity of all necessary conceptions, space, time, relation, cause, and the like.

17.   No realist or nominalist ever expressed so definitely, perhaps, as is here done, his conception of reality. It is difficult to give a clear notion of an opinion of a past age, without exaggerating its distinctness. But careful examination of the works of the schoolmen will show that the distinction between these two views of the real — one as the fountain of the current of human thought, the other as the unmoving form to which it is flowing — is what really occasions their disagreement on the question concerning universals. The gist of all the nominalist's arguments will be found to relate to a *res extra animam*, while the realist defends his position only by assuming that the immediate object of thought in a true judgment is real. The no-

tion that the controversy between realism and nominalism had anything to do with Platonic ideas is a mere product of the imagination, which the slightest examination of the books would suffice to disprove. But to prove that the statement here given of the essence of these positions is historically true and not a fancy sketch, it will be well to add a brief analysis of the opinions of Scotus and Ockam.

§3. SCOTUS, OCKAM, AND HOBBES

18.   Scotus sees several questions confounded together under the usual *utrum universale est aliquid in rebus.* In the first place, there is the question concerning the Platonic forms. But putting Platonism aside as at least incapable of proof, and as a self-contradictory opinion if the archetypes are supposed to be strictly universal, there is the celebrated dispute among Aristotelians as to whether the universal is really in things or only derives its existence from the mind. Universality is a relation of a predicate to the subjects of which it is predicated. That can exist only in the mind, wherein alone the coupling of subject and predicate takes place. But the word *universal* is also used to denote what are named by such terms as *a man* or *a horse*; these are called universals, because a man is not necessarily this man, nor a horse this horse. In such a sense it is plain universals are real; there really is a man and there really is a horse. The whole difficulty is with the actually indeterminate universal, that which not only is not necessarily *this*, but which, being one single object of thought, is predicable of many things. In regard to this it may be asked, first, is it necessary to its existence that it should be in the mind; and, second, does it exist *in re*? There are two ways in which a thing may be in the mind, — *habitualiter* and *actualiter*. A notion is in the mind *actualiter* when it is actually conceived; it is in the mind *habitualiter* when it can directly produce a conception. It is by virtue of mental association (we moderns should say), that things are in the mind *habitualiter*. In the Aristotelian philosophy, the intellect is regarded as being to the soul what the eye is to the body. The mind *perceives* likenesses and other relations in the objects of sense, and thus

20

just as sense affords sensible images of things, so the intellect affords intelligible images of them. It is as such a *species intelligibilis* that Scotus supposes that a conception exists which is in the mind *habitualiter*, not *actualiter*. This *species* is in the mind, in the sense of being the immediate object of knowledge, but its existence in the mind is independent of *consciousness*. Now that the *actual* cognition of the universal is necessary to its existence, Scotus denies. The subject of science is universal; and if the existence of [the] universal were dependent upon what we happened to be thinking, science would not relate to anything real. On the other hand, he admits that the universal must be in the mind *habitualiter*, so that if a thing be considered as it is independent of its being cognized, there is no universality in it. For there is *in re extra* no one intelligible object attributed to different things. He holds, therefore, that such natures (i.e. sorts of things) as a *man* and a *horse*, which are real, and are not of themselves necessarily *this* man or *this* horse, though they cannot exist *in re* without being some particular man or horse, are in the *species intelligibilis* always represented positively indeterminate, it being the nature of the mind so to represent things. Accordingly any such nature is to be regarded as something which is of itself neither universal nor singular, but is universal in the mind, singular in things out of the mind. If there were nothing in the different men or horses which was not of itself singular, there would be no real unity except the numerical unity of the singulars; which would involve such absurd consequences as that the only real difference would be a numerical difference, and that there would be no real likenesses among things. If, therefore, it is asked whether the universal is in things, the answer is, that the nature which in the mind is universal, and is not in itself singular, exists in things. It is the very same nature which in the mind is universal and *in re* is singular; for if it were not, in knowing anything of a universal we should be knowing nothing of things, but only of our own thoughts, and our opinion would not be converted from true to false by a change in things. This nature is actually indeterminate only so far as it is in the mind. But to say that an object is in the mind is only a metaphorical way of saying that it stands to the intellect in the relation of known to knower. The truth is, therefore, that that real nature which

21

exists *in re*, apart from all action of the intellect, though in it-self, apart from its relations, it be singular, yet is actually universal as it exists in relation to the mind. But this universal only differs from the singular in the manner of its being conceived (*formaliter*), but not in the manner of its existence (*realiter*).

19.   Though this is the slightest possible sketch of the realism of Scotus, and leaves a number of important points unnoticed, yet it is sufficient to show the general manner of his thought and how subtle and difficult his doctrine is. That about one and the same nature being in the grade of singularity in existence, and in the grade of universality in the mind, gave rise to an extensive doctrine concerning the various kinds of identity and difference, called the doctrine of the *formalitates*; and this is the point against which Ockam directed his attack.

20.   Ockam's nominalism may be said to be the next stage in English opinion. As Scotus's mind is always running on forms, so Ockam's is on logical terms; and all the subtle distinctions which Scotus effects by his *formalitates*, Ockam explains by implied syncategorematics (or adverbial expressions, such as *per se*, etc.) in terms. Ockam always thinks of a mental conception as a logical term, which, instead of existing on paper, or in the voice, is in the mind, but is of the same general nature, namely, a *sign*. The conception and the word differ in two respects: first, a word is arbitrarily imposed, while a conception is a natural sign; second, a word signifies whatever it signifies only indirectly, through the conception which signifies the same thing directly. Ockam enunciates his nominalism as follows: "It should be known that *singular* may be taken in two senses. In one sense, it signifies that which is one and not many; and in this sense those who hold that the universal is a quality of mind predicable of many, standing however in this predication, not for itself, but for those many (i.e. the nominalists), have to say that every universal is truly and really singular; because as every word, however general we may agree to consider it, is truly and really singular and one in number, because it is one and not many, so every universal is singular. In another sense, the name *singular* is used to denote whatever is one and not many, is a sign of something which

22

is singular in the first sense, and is not fit to be the sign of many. Whence, using the word *universal* for that which is not one in number, — an acceptation many attribute to it, — I say that there is no universal; unless perchance you abuse the word and say that *people* is not one in number and is universal. But that would be puerile. It is to be maintained, therefore, that every universal is one singular thing, and therefore there is no universal except by signification, that is, by its being the sign of many." [5] The arguments by which he supports this position present nothing of interest.[6] Against Scotus's doctrine that universals are without the mind in individuals, but are not really distinct from the individuals, but only formally so, he objects that it is impossible there should be any distinction existing out of the mind except between things really distinct. Yet he does not think of denying that an individual consists of matter and form, for these, though inseparable, are really distinct things; though a modern nominalist might ask in what sense things could be said to be distinct independently of any action of the mind, which are so inseparable as matter and form. But as to *relation*, he most emphatically and clearly denies that it exists as anything different from the things related; and this denial he expressly extends to relations of agreement and likeness as well as to those of opposition. While, therefore, he admits the real existence of qualities, he denies that these real qualities are respects in which things agree or differ; but things which agree or differ agree or differ in themselves and in no respect *extra animam*. He allows that things without the mind are similar, but this similarity consists merely in the fact that the mind can abstract one notion from the contemplation of them. A resemblance, therefore, consists solely in the property of the mind by which it naturally imposes one mental sign upon the resembling things. Yet he allows there is something in the things to which this mental sign corresponds.

[5] (Ed.) See William Ockham, *Summa Logicae, Pars Prima*, Philotheus Boehner, ed., St. Bonaventure, New York, 1951, p. 44; cf. Ernest A. Moody, *The Logic of William of Ockham*, Sheed and Ward, Inc., New York, 1935, footnotes pp. 81–82, for a somewhat different version of this passage.

[6] The *entia non sunt multiplicanda præter necessitatem* is the argument of Durand de St. Pourcain. But any given piece of popular information about scholasticism may be safely assumed to be wrong.

21. This is the nominalism of Ockam so far as it can be sketched in a single paragraph, and without entering into the complexities of the Aristotelian psychology nor of the *parva logicalia*. He is not so thoroughgoing as he might be, yet compared with Durandus and other contemporary nominalists he seems very radical and profound. He is truly the *venerabilis inceptor* of a new way of philosophizing which has now broadened, perhaps deepened also, into English empiricism.

22. England never forgot these teachings. During that Renaissance period when men could think that human knowledge was to be advanced by the use of Cicero's Commonplaces, we naturally see little effect from them; but one of the earliest prominent figures in modern philosophy is a man who carried the nominalistic spirit into everything — religion, ethics, psychology, and physics, the *plusquam nominalis*, Thomas Hobbes of Malmesbury. His razor cuts off, not merely substantial forms, but every incorporeal substance. As for universals, he not only denies their real existence, but even that there are any universal conceptions except so far as we conceive names. In every part of his logic, names and speech play an extraordinarily important part. Truth and falsity, he says, have no place but among such creatures as use speech, for a true proposition is simply one whose predicate is the name of everything of which the subject is the name. "From hence, also, this may be deduced, that the first truths were arbitrarily made by those that first of all imposed names upon things, or received them from the imposition of others. For it is true (for example), that *man is a living creature*, but it is for this *reason* that it pleased men to impose both those names on the same thing." [7] The difference between true religion and superstition is simply that the state recognizes the former and not the latter.

23. The nominalistic love of simple theories is seen also in his opinion, that every event is a movement, and that the sensible qualities exist only in sensible beings, and in his doctrine that man is at bottom purely selfish in his actions.

24. His views concerning matter are worthy of notice, because Berkeley is known to have been a student of Hobbes, as

[7] (Ed.) *The English Works of Thomas Hobbes of Malmesbury*, Sir William Molesworth, ed., Vol. I, London, 1839, p. 36.

Hobbes confesses himself to have been of Ockam. The following paragraph gives his opinion: —

"And as for that matter which is common to all things, and which philosophers, following Aristotle, usually call *materia prima*, that is, *first matter*, it is not a body distinct from all other bodies, nor is it one of them. What then is it? A mere name; yet a name which is not of vain use; for it signifies a conception of body without the consideration of any form or other accident except only magnitude or extension, and aptness to receive form and other accident. So that whensoever we have use of the name *body in general*, if we use that of *materia prima*, we do well. For when a man, not knowing which was first, water or ice, would find out which of the two were the matter of both, he would be fain to suppose some third matter which were neither of these two; so he that would find out what is the matter of all things ought to suppose such as is not the matter of anything that exists. Wherefore *materia prima* is nothing; and therefore they do not attribute to it form or any other accident, besides quantity; whereas all singular things have their forms and accidents certain.

"*Materia prima* therefore is body in general, that is, body considered universally, not as having neither form nor any accident, but in which no form nor any other accident but quantity are at all considered, that is, they are not drawn into argumentation." — p. 118.[8]

25. The next great name in English philosophy is Locke's. His philosophy is nominalistic, but does not regard things from a logical point of view at all. Nominalism, however, appears in psychology as sensationalism; for nominalism arises from taking that view of reality which regards whatever is in thought as caused by something in sense, and whatever is in sense as caused by something without the mind. But everybody knows that this is the character of Locke's philosophy. He believed that every idea springs from sensation and from his (vaguely explained) reflection.

[8] (Ed.) *The English Works of Thomas Hobbes of Malmesbury*, Sir William Molesworth, ed., Vol. I, London, 1839, pp. 118–119.

§4. BERKELEY'S PHILOSOPHY

26.　Berkeley is undoubtedly more the offspring of Locke than of any other philosopher. Yet the influence of Hobbes with him is very evident and great; and Malebranche doubtless contributed to his thought. But he was by nature a radical and a nominalist. His whole philosophy rests upon an extreme nominalism of a sensationalistic type. He sets out with the proposition (supposed to have been already proved by Locke), that all the ideas in our minds are simply reproductions of sensations, external and internal. He maintains, moreover, that sensations can only be thus reproduced in such combinations as might have been given in immediate perception. We can conceive a man without a head, because there is nothing in the nature of sense to prevent our seeing such a thing; but we cannot conceive a sound without any pitch, because the two things are necessarily united in perception. On this principle he denies that we can have any abstract general ideas, that is, that universals can exist in the mind; if I think of a man it must be either of a short or a long or a middle-sized man, because if I see a man he must be one or the other of these. In the first draft of the Introduction of the Principles of Human Knowledge, which is now for the first time printed, he even goes so far as to censure Ockam for admitting that we can have general terms in our mind; Ockam's opinion being that we have in our minds conceptions, which are singular themselves, but are *signs* of many things.[9] But Berkeley probably knew only of Ockam from hearsay, and perhaps thought he occupied a position like that of Locke. Locke had a very singular opinion on the subject of general conceptions. He says: —

"If we nicely reflect upon them, we shall find that general

[9] The sole difference between Ockam and Hobbes is that the former admits the universal signs in the mind to be natural, while the latter thinks they only follow instituted language. The consequence of this difference is that, while Ockam regards all truth as depending on the mind's naturally imposing the same sign on two things, Hobbes will have it that the first truths were established by convention. But both would doubtless allow that there is something *in re* to which such truths corresponded. But the sense of Berkeley's implication would be that there are no universal thought-signs at all. Whence it would follow that there is no truth and no judgments but propositions spoken or on paper.

26

ideas are fictions, and contrivances of the mind, that carry difficulty with them, and do not so easily offer themselves as we are apt to imagine. For example, does it not require some pains and skill to form the general idea of a triangle (which is none of the most abstract, comprehensive, and difficult); for it must be neither oblique nor rectangle, neither equilateral, equicrural, nor scalenon, but all and none of these at once? In effect, is something imperfect that cannot exist, an idea wherein some parts of several different and inconsistent ideas are put together." [10]

27. To this Berkeley replies: —

"Much is here said of the difficulty that abstract ideas carry with them, and the pains and skill requisite in forming them. And it is on all hands agreed that there is need of great toil and labor of the mind to emancipate our thoughts from particular objects, and raise them to those sublime speculations that are conversant about abstract ideas. From all which the natural consequence should seem to be, that so difficult a thing as the forming of abstract ideas was not necessary to communication, which is so easy and familiar to all sort of men. But we are told, if they seem obvious and easy to grown men, it is only because by constant and familiar use they are made so. Now, I would fain know at what time it is men are employed in surmounting that difficulty [and furnishing themselves with those necessary helps for discourse]. It cannot be when they are grown up, for then it seems they are not conscious of such painstaking; it remains, therefore, to be the business of their childhood. And surely the great and multiplied labor of framing abstract notions will be found a hard task at that tender age. Is it not a hard thing to imagine that a couple of children cannot prate together of their sugar-plums and rattles, and the rest of their little trinkets, till they have first tacked together numberless inconsistencies, and so formed in their minds abstract general ideas, and annexed them to every common name they make use of?" [11]

[10] (Ed.) See *An Essay Concerning Human Understanding* by John Locke, edited by Alexander Campbell Fraser, Vol. II, Clarendon Press, Oxford, 1894, p. 247, §9.

[11] (Ed.) In the work under review this passage from the introduction to

28.   In his private note-book Berkeley has the following: —

"*Mem*. To bring the killing blow at the last, e.g. in the matter of abstraction to bring Locke's general triangle in the last." [12]

There was certainly an opportunity for a splendid blow here, and he gave it.

29.   From this nominalism he deduces his idealistic doctrine. And he puts it beyond any doubt that, if this principle be admitted, the existence of matter must be denied. Nothing that we can know or even think can exist without the mind, for we can only think reproductions of sensations, and the *esse* of these is *percipi*. To put it another way, we cannot think of a thing as existing unperceived, for we cannot separate in thought what cannot be separated in perception. It is true, I can think of a tree in a park without anybody by to see it; but I cannot think of it without anybody to imagine it; for I am aware that I am imagining it all the time. Syllogistically: trees, mountains, rivers, and all sensible things are perceived; and anything which is perceived is a sensation; now for a sensation to exist without being perceived is impossible; therefore, for any sensible thing to exist out of perception is impossible. Nor can there be anything out of the mind which *resembles* a sensible object, for the conception of likeness cannot be separated from likeness between ideas, because that is the only likeness which can be given in perception. An idea can be nothing but an idea, and it is absurd to say that anything inaudible can resemble a sound, or that anything invisible can resemble a color. But what exists without the mind can neither be heard nor seen; for we perceive only sensations within the mind. It is said that *Matter* exists without the mind. But what is meant by matter? It is acknowledged to be known only as *supporting* the accidents of bodies; and this word 'supporting' in this connection is a word without meaning. Nor is there any necessity for the hypothesis of external bodies. What we observe is that we have ideas. Were there any use in supposing external

"A Treatise Concerning the Principles of Human Knowledge" is to be found in Vol. I, p. 146, §14. The portion in brackets was omitted by Peirce without notice.

[12] (Ed.) In the work under review this passage is in "Commonplace Book of Occasional Metaphysical Thoughts," Vol. IV, p. 448.

28

things it would be to account for this fact. But grant that bodies exist, and no one can say how they can possibly affect the mind; so that instead of removing a difficulty, the hypothesis only makes a new one.

30.   But though Berkeley thinks we know nothing out of the mind, he by no means holds that all our experience is of a merely phantasmagoric character. It is not all a dream; for there are two things which distinguish experience from imagination: one is the superior vividness of experience; the other and most important is its connected character. Its parts hang together in the most intimate and intricate conjunction, in consequence of which we can infer the future from the past. "These two things it is," says Berkeley, in effect, "which constitute reality. I do not, therefore, deny the reality of common experience, although I deny its externality." Here we seem to have a third new conception of reality, different from either of those which we have insisted are characteristic of the nominalist and realist respectively, or if this is to be identified with either of those, it is with the realist view. Is not this something quite unexpected from so extreme a nominalist? To us, at least, it seems that this conception is indeed required to give an air of common sense to Berkeley's theory, but that it is of a totally different complexion from the rest. It seems to be something imported into his philosophy from without. We shall glance at this point again presently. He goes on to say that ideas are perfectly inert and passive. One idea does not make another and there is no power or agency in it. Hence, as there must be some cause of the succession of ideas, it must be *Spirit*. There is no *idea* of a spirit. But I have a consciousness of the operations of my spirit, what he calls a *notion* of my activity in calling up ideas at pleasure, and so have a relative knowledge of myself as an active being. But there is a succession of ideas not dependent on my will, the ideas of perception. Real things do not depend on my thought, but have an existence distinct from being perceived by me; but the *esse* of everything is *percipi*; therefore, *there must be some other mind wherein they exist*. "As sure, therefore, as the sensible world really exists, so sure do there an infinite omnipotent Spirit who contains and supports it." [13] This puts the keystone

[13] (Ed.) In the work reviewed this passage from "The Second Dialogue be-

29

into the arch of Berkeleyan idealism, and gives a theory of the relation of the mind to external nature which, compared with the Cartesian Divine Assistance, is very satisfactory. It has been well remarked that, if the Cartesian dualism be admitted, no divine *assistance* can enable things to affect the mind or the mind things, but divine power must do the whole work. Berkeley's philosophy, like so many others, has partly originated in an attempt to escape the inconveniences of the Cartesian dualism. God, who has created our spirits, has the power immediately to raise ideas in them; and out of his wisdom and benevolence, he does this with such regularity that these ideas may serve as signs of one another. Hence, the laws of nature. Berkeley does not explain how our wills act on our bodies, but perhaps he would say that to a certain limited extent we can produce ideas in the mind of God as he does in ours. But a material thing being only an idea, exists only so long as it is in some mind. Should every mind cease to think it for a while, for so long it ceases to exist. Its permanent existence is kept up by its being an idea in the mind of God. Here we see how superficially the just-mentioned theory of reality is laid over the body of his thought. If the reality of a thing consists in its harmony with the body of realities, it is a quite needless extravagance to say that it ceases to exist as soon as it is no longer thought of. For the coherence of an idea with experience in general does not depend at all upon its being actually present to the mind all the time. But it is clear that when Berkeley says that reality consists in the connection of experience, he is simply using the word *reality* in a sense of his own. That *an object's independence of our thought about it* is constituted by its connection with experience in general, he has never conceived. On the contrary, that, according to him, is effected by its being in the mind of God. In the usual sense of the word *reality*, therefore, Berkeley's doctrine is that the reality of sensible things resides only in their archetypes in the divine mind. This is Platonistic, but it is not realistic. On the contrary, since it places reality wholly out of the mind in the cause of sensations, and since it denies reality (in the

---

tween Hylas and Philonous" is in Vol. I, p. 304. There the passage reads: "As sure, therefore, as the sensible world really exists, so sure is there an infinite omnipresent Spirit, who contains and supports it."

true sense of the word) to sensible things in so far as they are sensible, it is distinctly nominalistic. Historically there have been prominent examples of an alliance between nominalism and Platonism. Abélard and John of Salisbury, the only two defenders of nominalism of the time of the great controversy whose works remain to us, are both Platonists; and Roscellin, the famous author of the *sententia de flatu vocis*, the first man in the Middle Ages who carried attention to nominalism, is said and believed (all his writings are lost) to have been a follower of Scotus Erigena, the great Platonist of the ninth century. The reason of this odd conjunction of doctrines may perhaps be guessed at. The nominalist, by isolating his reality so entirely from mental influence as he has done, has made it something which the mind cannot conceive; he has created the so often talked of "improportion between the mind and the thing in itself." And it is to overcome the various difficulties to which this gives rise, that he supposes this *noumenon*, which, being totally unknown, the imagination can play about as it pleases, to be the emanation of archetypal ideas. The reality thus receives an intelligible nature again, and the peculiar inconveniences of nominalism are to some degree avoided.

31.   It does not seem to us strange that Berkeley's idealistic writings have not been received with much favor. They contain a great deal of argumentation of doubtful soundness, the dazzling character of which puts us more on our guard against it. They appear to be the productions of a most brilliant, original, powerful, but not thoroughly disciplined mind. He is apt to set out with wildly radical propositions, which he qualifies when they lead him to consequences he is not prepared to accept, without seeing how great the importance of his admissions is. He plainly begins his principles of human knowledge with the assumption that we have nothing in our minds but sensations, external and internal, and reproductions of them in the imagination. This goes far beyond Locke; it can be maintained only by the help of that "mental chemistry" started by Hartley. But soon we find him admitting various *notions* which are not *ideas*, or reproductions of sensations, the most striking of which is the notion of a cause, which he leaves himself no way of accounting for experientially. Again, he lays down the principle that we can have no ideas in which the sensations are

reproduced in an order or combination different from what could have occurred in experience; and that therefore we have no abstract conceptions. But he very soon grants that we can consider a triangle, without attending to whether it is equilateral, isosceles, or scalene; and does not reflect that such exclusive attention constitutes a species of abstraction. His want of profound study is also shown in his so wholly mistaking, as he does, the function of the hypothesis of matter. He thinks its only purpose is to account for the production of ideas in our minds, so occupied is he with the Cartesian problem. But the real part that material substance has to play is to account for (or formulate) the constant connection between the accidents. In his theory, this office is performed by the wisdom and benevolence of God in exciting ideas with such regularity that we can know what to expect. This makes the unity of accidents a rational unity, the material theory makes it a unity not of a *directly* intellectual origin. The question is, then, which does experience, which does science decide for? Does it appear that in nature all regularities are directly rational, all causes final causes; or does it appear that regularities extend beyond the requirement of a rational purpose, and are brought about by mechanical causes. Now science, as we all know, is generally hostile to the final causes, the operation of which it would restrict within certain spheres, and it finds decidedly an other than directly intellectual regularity in the universe. Accordingly the claim which Mr. Collyns Simon, Professor Fraser, and Mr. Archer Butler make for Berkeleyanism, that it is especially fit to harmonize with scientific thought, is as far as possible from the truth. The sort of science that his idealism would foster would be one which should consist in saying what each natural production was made for. Berkeley's own remarks about natural philosophy show how little he sympathized with physicists. They should all be read; we have only room to quote a detached sentence or two: —

"To endeavor to explain the production of colors or sound by figure, motion, magnitude, and the like, must needs be labor in vain. . . . In the business of gravitation or mutual attraction, because it appears in many instances, some are straightway for pronouncing it *universal*; and that to attract and be attracted by every body is an essential quality inherent in all bodies whatever. . . . There is nothing necessary or essential in the case, but it depends entirely on the will of the Governing Spirit, who causes certain bodies to cleave together or tend towards each other according to various laws, whilst he keeps others at a fixed distance; and to some he gives a quite contrary tendency, to fly asunder just as he sees convenient. . . . First, it is plain philosophers amuse themselves in vain, when they inquire for any natural efficient cause, distinct from *mind* or *spirit*. Secondly, considering the whole creation is the workmanship of a *wise and good Agent*, it should seem to become philosophers to employ their thoughts (contrary to what some hold) about the final causes of things; and I must confess I see no reason why pointing out the various ends to which natural things are adapted, and for which they were originally with unspeakable wisdom contrived, should not be thought one good way of accounting for them, and altogether worthy of a philosopher." — Vol. I. p. 466.[14]

32. After this how can his disciples say *"that the true logic of physics is the first conclusion from his system"*!

33. As for that argument which is so much used by Berkeley and others, that such and such a thing cannot exist because we cannot so much as frame the idea of such a thing, — that matter, for example, is impossible because it is an abstract idea, and we have no abstract ideas, — it appears to us to be a mode of reasoning which is to be used with extreme caution. Are the facts such, that if we could have an idea of the thing in question, we should infer its existence, or are they not? If not, no argument is necessary against its existence, until something is found out to make us suspect it exists. But if we ought to infer that it exists, if we only could frame the idea of it, why should we allow our mental incapacity to prevent us from adopting the proposition which logic requires? If such arguments had prevailed in mathematics (and Berkeley was equally strenuous in advocating them there), and if everything about negative quantities, the square root of *minus*, and infinitesimals, had been excluded from the subject on the ground that we can form

[14] (Ed.) In the work reviewed this passage from "A Treatise Concerning the Principles of Human Knowledge," Part I, is in Vol. I, p. 208 (§102), p. 210 (§106), and pp. 210–211 (§107).

no idea of such things, the science would have been simplified no doubt, simplified by never advancing to the more difficult matters. A better rule for avoiding the deceits of language is this: Do things fulfil the same function practically? Then let them be signified by the same word. Do they not? Then let them be distinguished. If I have learned a formula in gibberish which in any way jogs my memory so as to enable me in each single case to act as though I had a general idea, what possible utility is there in distinguishing between such a gibberish and formula and an idea? Why use the term *a general idea* in such a sense as to separate things which, for all experiential purposes, are the same? [15]

34.   The great inconsistency of the Berkeleyan theory, which prevents his nominalistic principles from appearing in their true colors, is that he has not treated mind and matter in the same way. All that he has said against the existence of matter might be said against the existence of mind; and the only thing which prevented his seeing that, was the vagueness of the Lockian *reflection*, or faculty of internal perception. It was not until after he had published his systematic exposition of his doctrine, that this objection ever occurred to him. He alludes to it in one of his dialogues, but his answer to it is very lame. Hume seized upon this point, and, developing it, equally denied the existence of mind and matter, maintaining that only appearances exist. Hume's philosophy is nothing but Berkeley's, with this change made in it, and written by a mind of a more sceptical tendency. The innocent bishop generated Hume; and as no one disputes that Hume gave rise to all modern philosophy of every kind, Berkeley ought to have a far more important place in the history of philosophy than has usually been assigned to him. His doctrine was the half-way station, or necessary resting-place between Locke's and Hume's.

35.   Hume's greatness consists in the fact that he was the man who had the courage to carry out his principles to their utmost consequences, without regard to the character of the conclusions he reached. But neither he nor any other one has set forth nominalism in an absolutely thoroughgoing manner;

---

[15] (Ed.) This is an early anticipation of Peirce's pragmatism, which is discussed in detail in [CP] V, *Pragmatism and Pragmaticism*. See especially 5.402, 5.453, 5.504n1 (p. 353). Cf. also 7.360.

and it is safe to say that no one ever will, unless it be to reduce it to absurdity.

36. We ought to say one word about Berkeley's theory of vision. It was undoubtedly an extraordinary piece of reasoning, and might have served for the basis of the modern science. Historically it has not had that fortune, because the modern science has been chiefly created in Germany, where Berkeley is little known and greatly misunderstood. We may fairly say that Berkeley taught the English some of the most essential principles of that hypothesis of sight which is now getting to prevail, more than a century before they were known to the rest of the world. This is much; but what is claimed by some of his advocates is astounding. One writer says that Berkeley's theory has been accepted by the leaders of all schools of thought! Professor Fraser admits that it has attracted no attention in Germany, but thinks the German mind too *a priori* to like Berkeley's reasoning. But Helmholtz, who has done more than any other man to bring the empiricist theory into favor, says: "Our knowledge of the phenomena of vision is not so complete as to allow only one theory and exclude every other. It seems to me that the choice which different *savans* make between different theories of vision has thus far been governed more by their metaphysical inclinations than by any constraining power which the facts have had." [16] The best authorities, however, prefer the empiricist hypothesis; the fundamental proposition of which, as it is of Berkeley's, is that the sensations which we have in seeing are signs of the relations of things whose interpretation has to be discovered inductively. In the enumeration of the signs and of their uses, Berkeley shows considerable power in that sort of investigation, though there is naturally no very close resemblance between his and the modern accounts of the matter. There is no modern physiologist who would not think that Berkeley had greatly exaggerated the part that the muscular sense plays in vision.

37. Berkeley's theory of vision was an important step in the development of the associationalist psychology. He thought all our conceptions of body and of space were simply reproductions in the imagination of sensations of touch (including the muscular sense). This, if it were true, would be a most surprising

[16] (Ed.) See Helmholtz's *Treatise on Physiological Optics*, §33.

case of mental chemistry, that is of a sensation being felt and yet so mixed with others that we cannot by an act of simple attention recognize it. Doubtless this theory had its influence in the production of Hartley's system.

Hume's phenomenalism and Hartley's associationalism were put forth almost contemporaneously about 1750. They contain the fundamental positions of the current English "positivism." From 1750 down to 1830 — eighty years — nothing of particular importance was added to the nominalistic doctrine. At the beginning of this period Hume was toning down his earlier radicalism, and Smith's theory of Moral Sentiments appeared. Later came Priestley's materialism, but there was nothing new in that; and just at the end of the period, Brown's Lectures on the Human Mind. The great body of the philosophy of those eighty years is of the Scotch common-sense school. It is a weak sort of realistic reaction, for which there is no adequate explanation within the sphere of the history of philosophy. It would be curious to inquire whether anything in the history of society could account for it. In 1829 appeared James Mill's Analysis of the Human Mind, a really great nominalistic book again. This was followed by Stuart Mill's Logic in 1843. Since then, the school has produced nothing of the first importance; and it will very likely lose its distinctive character now for a time, by being merged in an empiricism of a less metaphysical and more working kind. Already in Stuart Mill the nominalism is less salient than in the classical writers; though it is quite unmistakable.

§5. SCIENCE AND REALISM

38.   Thus we see how large a part of the metaphysical ideas of today have come to us by inheritance from very early times, Berkeley being one of the intellectual ancestors whose labors did as much as any one's to enhance the value of the bequest. The realistic philosophy of the last century has now lost all its popularity, except with the most conservative minds. And science as well as philosophy is nominalistic. The doctrine of the correlation of forces, the discoveries of Helmholtz, and the hypotheses of Liebig and of Darwin, have all that character of explaining familiar phenomena apparently of a peculiar kind

by extending the operation of simple mechanical principles, which belongs to nominalism. Or if the nominalistic character of these doctrines themselves cannot be detected, it will at least be admitted that they are observed to carry along with them those daughters of nominalism, — sensationalism, phenomenalism, individualism, and materialism. That physical science is necessarily connected with doctrines of a debasing moral tendency will be believed by few. But if we hold that such an effect will not be produced by these doctrines on a mind which really understands them, we are accepting this belief, not on experience, which is rather against it, but on the strength of our general faith that what is really true it is good to believe and evil to reject. On the other hand, it is allowable to suppose that science has no essential affinity with the philosophical views with which it seems to be every year more associated. History cannot be held to exclude this supposition; and science as it exists is certainly much less nominalistic than the nominalists think it should be. Whewell represents it quite as well as Mill. Yet a man who enters into the scientific thought of the day and has not materialistic tendencies, is getting to be an impossibility. So long as there is a dispute between nominalism and realism, so long as the position we hold on the question is not determined by any proof *indisputable*, but is more or less a matter of inclination, a man as he gradually comes to feel the profound hostility of the two tendencies will, if he is not less than man, become engaged with one or other and can no more obey both than he can serve God and Mammon. If the two impulses are neutralized within him, the result simply is that he is left without any great intellectual motive. There is, indeed, no reason to suppose the logical question is in its own nature unsusceptible of solution. But that path out of the difficulty lies through the thorniest mazes of a science as dry as mathematics. Now there is a demand for mathematics; it helps to build bridges and drive engines, and therefore it becomes somebody's business to study it severely. But to have a philosophy is a matter of luxury; the only use of that is to make us feel comfortable and easy. It is a study for leisure hours; and we want it supplied in an elegant, an agreeable, an interesting form. The law of natural selection, which is the precise analogue in another realm of the law of supply and demand, has the most immediate effect in fostering the other faculties of the understanding, for the men of mental power succeed in the struggle for life; but the faculty of philosophizing, except in the literary way, is not called for; and therefore a difficult question cannot be expected to reach solution until it takes some practical form. If anybody should have the good luck to find out the solution, nobody else would take the trouble to understand it. But though the question of realism and nominalism has its roots in the technicalities of logic, its branches reach about our life. The question whether the *genus homo* has any existence except as individuals, is the question whether there is anything of any more dignity, worth, and importance than individual happiness, individual aspirations, and individual life. Whether men really have anything in common, so that the *community* is to be considered as an end in itself, and if so, what the relative value of the two factors is, is the most fundamental practical question in regard to every public institution the constitution of which we have it in our power to influence.

CHAPTER 3

JOSIAH ROYCE, *THE RELIGIOUS ASPECT OF PHILOSOPHY* [1]

§1. THE CONCEPT OF REALITY

39.   Dr. Royce has produced a work which will form a good introduction to Hegel. His language and his thought are equally lucid and within the capacity of ordinary minds, — his style is animated and readable, and in passages rises without effort to true philosophical eloquence. His method is a dialectic one; that is to say, it proceeds by the criticism of opinions, first, destructively to absolute scepticism, and then finds hidden in that scepticism itself the highest truth. It differs, however, very decidedly from the dialectic of Hegel, — and in its simplicity and general tone reminds us rather of the reasoning of Plato.

40.   But before we examine the method, let us glance at the philosophical upshot of the book. This is, that the reality of whatever really exists consists in the real thing being thought by God.[2] Ordinary people think that things exist by the *will*

---

[1] (Ed.) Review of Josiah Royce's *The Religious Aspect of Philosophy* (Houghton Mifflin Company, Boston, 1885, 484 pp.), hereafter referred to as [RAP], from a manuscript in Houghton Library. The first three pages (half-sheets) of this manuscript are missing and there is no explicit statement in the remainder that this is a review of [RAP], but all of the quotations from the work under review have been located there.

In a letter to James, dated 28 October 1885 (James Collection, Houghton Library), Peirce says that he wrote a review of Royce's book for Youmans, who would not take it. (E. L. Youmans and W. J. Youmans edited *Popular Scientific Monthly* at this time. Peirce refers to this journal in the text below.) The dates of the letter and [RAP] establish the date of the review as c.1885. It is the case, however, that some of the pages and many of the corrections in the manuscript are in a different ink and finer handwriting from the others, and hence they may be of a somewhat different date.

[2] (Ed.) [RAP] Ch. X, "Idealism."

of God; and if thought be taken in so wide a sense as to include volition, they have no difficulty in admitting the proposition which Dr. Royce has borrowed from Hegel and Schelling. But ordinary people say that not merely the real but all that can possibly enter into the mind of man must be within the thought of God in some sense; so that it must be some particular kind of divine thought which constitutes reality; and that particular kind of thought must be distinguished by a volitional element. In short, ordinary people make at once the very same criticism that the profoundest students of philosophy have made, namely, that the Hegelian school overlooks the importance of the will as an element of thought.

41. A certain writer has suggested that reality, the fact that there is such a thing as a true answer to a question, consists in this: that human inquiries, — human reasoning and observation, — tend toward the settlement of disputes and ultimate agreement in definite conclusions which are independent of the particular stand-points from which the different inquirers may have set out; so that the real is that which any man would believe in, and be ready to act upon, if his investigations were to be pushed sufficiently far.[3] Upon the luckless putter-forth of this opinion Dr. Royce is extremely severe. He will not even name him (perhaps to spare the family), but refers to him by various satirical nick-names, especially as *"Thrasymachus,"*[4] — a foolish character introduced into the Republic and another dialogue of Plato for the purpose of showing how vastly such an ignorant pretender to philosophy is inferior to Socrates (that is, to Plato himself) in every quality of mind and heart, and especially in good manners. But I must with shame confess that if I understand what the opinion of this poor, Royce-forsaken Thrasymachus is, I coincide with it exactly. I ask any man, Suppose you could be miraculously assured that a certain answer to any question that interests you would be the one in which, were your life and mental vigor to be indefinitely prolonged, you must eventually rest, would you not cease all inquiries at once, and be content with that answer now, as being the very thing you had been striving after? This question Dr. Royce answers explicitly in the negative. "No barely possible

[3] (Ed.) Cf. 5.311ff.
[4] (Ed.) [RAP] 393–394, 426ff.

judge," he says, "who *would* see the error, *if* he were there, will do for us." [5] Yet if I were to represent Dr. Royce as preferring to believe for a little while that which a certain Being — no matter who — imagines, rather than to come at once to the belief to which investigation is destined at last to carry him, I should probably be doing him injustice; because I suppose he would say that the thing which God imagines, and the opinion to which investigation would ultimately lead him, in point of fact, coincide. If, however, these two things coincide, I fail to understand why he should be so cruel to the childish Thrasymachus; since after all there is no real difference between them, but only a formal one, — each maintaining as a theorem that which the other adopts as a definition. As was just remarked, the Hegelian school does not sufficiently take into account the volitional element of cognition. Dr. Royce admits in words that belief is what a man will act from; but he does not seem to have taken the truth of this proposition home to him, or else he would see that the whole end of inquiry is the settlement of belief; so that a man shall not war against himself, nor undo tomorrow that which he begins to do today. Dr. Royce's main argument in support of his own opinion, to the confusion of Thrasymachus, is drawn from the existence of error. Namely, the subject of an erroneous proposition could not be identified with the subject of the corresponding true proposition, except by being completely known, and in that knowledge no error would be possible. The truth must, therefore, be present to the actual consciousness of a living being. This is an argument drawn from Formal logic, for Formal logic it is which inquires how different propositions are made to refer to the same subject, and the like. German metaphysics has, since Kant, drawn its best arguments from Formal logic; and it is quite right in doing so, for the conceptions which are proved to be indispensable in Formal logic, must have been already rooted in the nature of the mind when reasoning first began, and are, so far, *a priori*. But one would surely have supposed that when the German philosophers were thus drawing their arguments from formal logic, they would have postponed their venturesome flights into the thin air of theology and the vacuum of pure reason, until they had carefully tried the strength of every part

[5] (Ed.) [RAP] 427.

of that logical machine on which they were to depend. Instead of that, they have left the great work of creating a true system of formal logic to English authors, who, while they have done most excellent work, have (with the insignificant exception of the present writer) been quite indifferent to the transcendental bearings of their results. Kant gives a half dozen only of his brief pages to the development of the system of logic upon which his whole philosophy rests; and though many valuable treatises on the science have appeared in Germany, there is hardly one of them which is not more or less marred by some arrant absurdity, acknowledged to be so by all the others; Grassmann and Schroeder alone pursuing the one method which will yield positive results properly secured against error. We must not, therefore, wonder that Dr. Royce's argument from formal logic overlooks one of the most important discoveries that have lately resulted from the study of that exact branch of philosophy. He seems to think that the real subject of a proposition can be denoted by a general term of the proposition; that is, that precisely what it is that you are talking about can be distinguished from other things by giving a general description of it. Kant already showed, in a celebrated passage of his cataclysmic work, that this is not so; and recent studies in formal logic [6] have put it in a clearer light. We now find that, besides general terms, two other kinds of signs are perfectly indispensable in all reasoning. One of these kinds is the *index*, which like a pointing finger exercises a real physiological *force* over the attention, like the power of a mesmerizer, and directs it to a particular object of sense.[7] One such index at least must enter into every proposition, its function being to designate the subject of discourse. Now observe that Dr. Royce does not merely say that there are no means by which an erroneous proposition can be produced; what he says is that the conception of an erroneous proposition (without an actual including consciousness) is absurd. If the subject of discourse had to be distinguished from other things, if at all, by a general term, that is, by its peculiar characters, it would be quite true that

---

[6] *Mitchell* in Logical Studies by members of the Johns Hopkins University, and *Peirce* in the American Journal of Mathematics, vol. vii.
  (Ed.) These items are listed at [Bibliography] G–1883–7 and G–1885–3.
[7] (Ed.) Cf. 2.248 and elsewhere in [CP] II.

its complete segregation would require a full knowledge of its characters and would preclude ignorance. But the index, which in point of fact alone can designate the subject of a proposition, designates it without implying any characters at all. A blinding flash of lightning forces my attention and directs it to a certain moment of time with an emphatic "Now!" Directly following it, I may judge that there will be a terrific peal of thunder, and if it does not come I acknowledge an error. One instant of time is, in itself, exactly like any other instant, one point of space like any other point; nevertheless dates and positions can be approximately distinguished. And how are they so distinguished? By *intuition* says Kant; perhaps not in so many words; but it is because of this property that he distinguishes Space and Time from the general conceptions of the understanding and sets them off by themselves under the head of intuition. But I should prefer to say that it is by volitional acts that dates and positions are distinguished. The element of feeling is so prominent in sensations, that we do not observe that something like Will enters into them, too. You may quarrel with the word *volition* if you like; I wish I had a more general one at my hand. But what I mean is that that strong, clear, and voluntary consciousness in which we act upon our muscles is nothing more than the most marked variety of a kind of consciousness which enters into many other phenomena of our life, a consciousness of duality or dual consciousness. Feeling is simple consciousness, the consciousness that can be contained within an instant of time, the consciousness of the excitation of nerve-cells; it has no parts and no unity.[8] What I call volition is the consciousness of the discharge of nerve-cells, either into the muscles, etc., or into other nerve-cells; it does not involve the sense of time (i.e. not of a continuum) but it does involve the sense of action and reaction, resistance, externality, otherness, pair-edness. It is the sense that something has hit me or that I am hitting something; it might be called the sense of collision or clash. It has an outward and an inward variety, corresponding to Kant's outer and inner sense, to will and self-control, to nerve-action and inhibition, to the two logical types A:B and A:A. The capital error of Hegel which permeates his

---

[8] (Ed.) Feeling and volition are instances of Peirce's categories of First and Second, respectively. See [CP] I, VII.

whole system in every part of it is that he almost altogether ignores the Outward Clash.[9] Besides the lower consciousness of feeling and the higher consciousness of nutrition, this direct consciousness of hitting and of getting hit enters into all cognition and serves to make it mean something real. It is formal logic which teaches us this; not that of a Whateley or a Jevons, but formal logic in its new development, drawing nutriment from physiology and from history without leaving the solid ground of logical forms.

42. An objection different from that of Dr. Royce might be raised. Namely it might be asked *how* two different men can know they are speaking of the same thing. Suppose, for instance, one man should say a flash of lightning was followed by thunder and another should deny it. How would they know they meant the same flash? The answer is that they would compare notes somewhat as follows. One would say, "I mean that very brilliant flash which was preceded by three slight flashes, you know." The second man would recognize the mark, and thus by a probable and approximate inference they would conclude they meant the same flash.

43. Dr. Royce in describing the opinion of Thrasymachus has selected the expression "a *barely* possible judge." [10] Is there not an ambiguity in this mode of speech which is unfair to Thrasymachus? The final opinion which would be sure to result from sufficient investigation may possibly, in reference to a given question, never be actually attained, owing to a final extinction of intellectual life or for some other reason. In that sense, this final judgment is not *certain* but only possible. But when Dr. Royce says "bare possibility is blank nothingness," [11] he would seem to be speaking of mere logical possibility, and not a possibility which differs but a hair's breadth from entire certainty. Let us consider what probability there is that a given question, say one capable of being answered by *yes* or *no*, will never get answered. Let us reason upon this matter by inductive logic. Dr. Royce and his school, I am well aware, consider inductive reasoning to be radically vicious;

---

[9] "We must be in contact with our subject-matter," says he in one place, whether it be by means of our external senses, *or, what is better*, by our profounder mind and our innermost self-consciousness.

[10] (Ed.) Italics not in [RAP]; cf. 41.

[11] (Ed.) [RAP] 430.

so that we unhappily cannot carry them along with us. (They often deny this, by the way, and say they rest entirely on experience. This is because they so overlook the Outward Clash, that they do not know what experience is. They are like Roger Bacon, who after stating in eloquent terms that all knowledge comes from experience, goes on to mention spiritual illumination from on high as one of the most valuable kinds of experiences.) But they will not succeed in exploding the method of modern science; and there is no reason why those who believe in induction at all, should not be willing to apply it to the subject now in hand. In the first place, then, upon innumerable questions, we have already reached the final opinion. How do we know that? Do we fancy ourselves infallible? Not at all; but throwing off as probably erroneous a thousandth or even a hundredth of all the beliefs established beyond present doubt, there must remain a vast multitude in which the final opinion has been reached. Every directory, guide-book, dictionary, history, and work of science is crammed with such facts. In the history of science, it has sometimes occurred that a really wise man has said concerning one question or another that there was reason to believe it never would be answered. The proportion of these which have in point of fact been conclusively settled very soon after the prediction has been surprisingly large. Our experience in this direction warrants us in saying with the highest degree of empirical confidence that questions that are either practical or could conceivably become so are susceptible of receiving final solutions provided the existence of the human race be indefinitely prolonged and the particular question excite sufficient interest. As for questions which have no conceivable practical bearings, as the question whether force is an entity, they mean nothing and may be answered as we like, without error.[12] We may take it as certain that the human race will ultimately be extirpated; because there is a certain chance of it every year, and in an indefinitely long time the chance of survival compounds itself nearer and nearer zero. But, on the other hand, we may take it as certain that other intellectual races exist on other planets, — if not of our solar system, then of others; and also that innumerable new intellectual races have yet to be developed; so that on the whole, it may be re-

[12] (Ed.) Pragmatism is treated in [CP] V.

garded as most certain that intellectual life in the universe will never finally cease. The problem whether a given question will ever get answered or not is not so simple; the number of questions asked is constantly increasing, and the capacity for answering them is also on the increase. If the rate of the latter increase is greater than that of the [former] the probability is unity that any given question will be answered; otherwise the probability is *zero*. Considerations too long to be explained here lead me to think that the former state of things is the actual one. In that case, there is but an infinitesimal proportion of questions which do not get answered, although the multitude of unanswered questions is forever on the increase. It plainly is not fair to call a judgment which is certain to be made a "barely possible" one. But I will admit (if the reader thinks the admission has any meaning, and is not an empty proposition) that some finite number of questions, we can never know which ones, will escape getting answered forever. Nor must I forget that I have not given the reader my proof that of the questions asked at any time the proportion that will never be answered is infinitesimal; so that he may be in doubt upon this point. That is not a thing to be regretted; for scepticism about the reality of things, — provided it be genuine and sincere, and not a sham, — is a healthful and growing stage of mental development. Let us suppose, then, for the sake of argument, that some questions eventually get settled, and that some others, indistinguishable from the former by any marks, never do. In that case, I should say that that conception of reality was rather a faulty one, for while there is a real so far as a question that will get settled goes, there is none for a question that will never be settled; for an unknowable reality is nonsense. The nonidealistic reader will start at this last assertion; but consider the matter from a practical point of view. You say that real things are manifested by their effects. True; for example, if the timbers of my house are inwardly rotting, it will some day fall down, and thus there will be a practical effect for me, whether I know the beams be rotten or not. Well, but if all the effects consistently point to the theory that the beams are rotting, it will come to be admitted at last that they are so; and if nothing is ever settled about the matter, it will be because the phenomena do not consistently point to any theory; and in that case there is a want of that "uniformity of nature" (to use a popular but very loose expression) which constitutes reality, and makes it differ from a dream. In that way, if we think that some questions are never going to get settled, we ought to admit that our conception of nature as absolutely real is only partially correct. Still, we shall have to be governed by it practically; because there is nothing to distinguish the unanswerable questions from the answerable ones, so that investigation will have to proceed as if all were answerable. In ordinary life, no matter how much we believe in questions ultimately getting answered, we shall always put aside an innumerable throng of them as beyond our powers. We shall not in our day seek to know whether the centre of the sun is distant from that of the earth by an odd or an even number of miles on the average; we shall act as if neither man nor God could ever ascertain it. There is, however, an economy of thought, in assuming that it is an answerable question. From this practical and economical point of view, it really makes no difference whether or not all questions are actually answered, by man or by God, so long as we are satisfied that investigation has a universal tendency toward the settlement of opinion; and this I conceive to be the position of Thrasymachus.

44. If there be any advantage to religion in supposing God to be omniscient, this sort of scepticism about reality can do no practical harm. We can still suppose that He knows all that there is of real to be known. On the theory of Dr. Royce, the real existence of God would consist in his imagining or positing Himself; it would thus be, according to him, of the same nature as the reality of anything else. For my part, I hold another theory, which I intend to take an early opportunity of putting into print.[13] I think that the existence of God, as well as we can conceive of it consists in this, that a tendency toward ends is so necessary a constituent of the universe that the mere action of chance upon innumerable atoms has an inevitable teleological result. One of the ends so brought about is the development of intelligence and of knowledge; and therefore I should say that God's omniscience, humanly conceived, consists in the fact that knowledge in its development leaves no question unanswered. The scepticism just spoken of

[13] (Ed.) Cf. [CP] V, Book II, "Religion."

would admit this omniscience as a regulative but not a speculative conception. I believe that even that view is more religiously fruitful than the opinion of Dr. Royce.

§2. COMMENTS ON ROYCE'S PHILOSOPHY

45. Let us now turn to the examination of Dr. Royce's peculiar method of reasoning; for that is always the most important element in every system of philosophy. His work is divided into a brief introduction and two books, the first entitled "The Search for a Moral Ideal"; the second "The Search for a Religious Truth." These titles seem to me to point, at the outset, to a fault of method. The pursuit of a conscience, if one hasn't one already, or of a religion, which is the subjective basis of conscience, seems to me an aimless and hypochondriac pursuit. If a man finds himself under no sense of obligation, let him congratulate himself. For such a man to hanker after a bondage to conscience, is as if a man with a good digestion should cast about for a regimen of food. A conscience, too, is not a theorem or a piece of information which may be acquired by reading a book; it must be bred in a man from infancy or it will be a poor imitation of the genuine article. If a man has a conscience, it may be an article of faith with him, that he should reflect upon that conscience, and thus it may receive a further development. But it never will do him the least good to get up a make-believe scepticism and pretend to himself not to believe what he really does believe. In point of fact, every man born and reared in a christian community, however little he may believe the dogmas of the Church, does find himself believing with the strongest conviction in the moral code of christendom. He has a horror of murder and incest, a disapproval of lying, etc., which he cannot escape from. The modern dialectician (if he will pardon a touch of exaggeration) would have such a man say to himself, Now I am going to be sceptical, but only provisionally so, in order to return to my faith with renewed conviction! But the whole history of thought shows that men cannot doubt at pleasure or merely because they find they have no positive reason for the belief they already hold. Reasons concern the man who is coming to believe, not the man who believes already. It has often been remarked

that metaphysics is an imitation of mathematics; and it may be added that the philosophic doubt is an imitation of the absurd procedure of elementary geometry, which begins by giving worthless demonstrations of propositions nobody ever questions. When Hegel tells me that thought has three stages, that of naïve acceptance, that of reaction and criticism, and that of rational conviction; in a general sense, I agree to it. And a down-right living scepticism without *arrière-pensée*, may be beneficial. It is not perhaps easy to see why an imaginary scepticism might not sometimes serve the same purpose; but experience shows that in questions of magnitude men haven't imagination enough to put themselves in the true doubter's shoes. But be that as it may, the idea that the mere reaction of assent and doubt, the mere play of thought, the heat-lightning of the brain, is going to settle anything in this real world to which we appertain, — such an idea only shows again how the Hegelians overlook the facts of volitional action and reaction in the development of thought. I find myself in a world of forces which act upon me, and it is they and not the logical transformations of my thought which determine what I shall ultimately believe.

46.   Dr. Royce seems to hold that at least in the philosophy of morals and religion a mere contemplation of our own crude beliefs will lead us to absolute scepticism and that then a mere contemplation of our own absolute scepticism will lead us back to rational conviction. Neither I nor the readers of the Popular Science Monthly can possibly believe that, in advance. But let us see how the method will work when applied to the discussion of ethics.

47.   The moral stand-point from which every man with a christian training sets out, even if he be a dogmatic atheist, is pretty nearly the same. He has a horror of certain crimes and a disapproval of certain lesser sins. He is also more or less touched with the spirit of christian love, which he believes should be his beacon, and which in point of fact, by its power in his heart, shall and will govern him in all questions of disputed morals. More or less, in all of us, this sentiment replaces and abolishes conscience; like Huckleberry Finn, we act from christian charity without caring very much whether conscience approves of the act or not.

49

This is the state of mind of the ordinary man or woman who will open Dr. Royce's book. And now Dr. Royce proposes that this person shall ask himself the question, what validity or truth is there in the distinction of right and wrong. To me, it plainly appears that such a person, if he have a clear head, will at once reply, right and wrong are nothing to me except so far as they are connected with certain rules of living by which I am enabled to satisfy a real impulse which works in my heart; and this impulse is the love of my neighbor elevated into a love of an ideal and divine humanity which I identify with the providence that governs the world. But Dr. Royce says that different people will answer the question in different ways; some will take the position of the 'moral realist' and say that moral distinctions are founded on some matter of fact (say a decree from Sinai), while others will take the position of the 'moral idealist' and say that these distinctions are founded on an inward sentiment, — an ideal.[14] Two such persons come into collision; they find by mutual criticism that both positions are unsatisfactory; external fact can only determine what *is*, not what *ought* to be; while inward sentiment cannot be a resting-place, because it is only individual caprice and has no authority for another man. From this criticism the only outcome is ethical scepticism.

48. This is a fair specimen of Dr. Royce's logical method, which is a mere apotheosis of the dilemma, as the great instrument of thought. As compared with syllogistic method of the middle ages (which survives in certain quarters, yet) it is certainly wonderfully superior; but as compared with the mathematical reasoning upon which modern science is built, it is inefficacious and restricted.

49. In the particular case in hand, it appears to me that the ordinary christian does not find himself caught in Dr. Royce's dilemma at all. He is a moral idealist; yet far from being shaken by the spectacle of different men having different passions, he feels that every man may come to the same passion which animates him by a mere enlargement of his horizon, and that his is the only sentiment in which all others may be reconciled. For altruism is but a developed egoism; that same sensitiveness which in its lowest state is selfishness, first transforms

[14] (Ed.) [RAP] 21ff.

itself into *esprit de corps* or collective selfishness; then, passing from feeling for others collectively to feeling for them individually, it becomes philanthropy, pity, sympathy tossed hither and thither rudderless on the ocean of human misery; finally, steadying itself by the conception of an ideal humanity and a divine providence, it passes into christian charity, which gathers up all selfishnesses and all pities and is ready to give each its due measure.

50. The author having stated the above argument with admirable clearness, fills a hundred pages with a perhaps not altogether necessary, though a charmingly written and highly interesting elaboration and illustration of it. He here passes in review a goodly number of the ethical theories which have been proposed at different times. After the Sophists, Plato, Aristotle, and the Stoics, he criticizes what he conceives to be the ethics of Jesus.[15] Every christian will tell him that he makes the mistake of viewing that as a *theory* or speculation which is really a spiritual *experience*; — another example of his neglect of the volitional element. For instance, he asks, "If I feel not the love of God, how prove to me that I ought to feel it?"[16] The answer to that need not be pointed out.

51. In what he says about Herbert Spencer, he seems to forget that Mr. Spencer is not addressing a body of moral sceptics but readers animated by the sentiments which, in our day, animate every man who reads at all.[17]

52. At last he takes up the thread of his argument as follows. The conflict between moral realism and idealism can only lead to moral scepticism. Now what is this scepticism? It is the contemplation of two opposing aims. Here he adduces the testimony of modern psychologists to show that we cannot think of willing without actually willing. (But for all that, I fancy I notice a difference sometimes in cold weather between thinking of willing to take my morning dash of cold water and actually willing to take it.) Scepticism, then, shares at once these opposing aims, or strives to share them. It has thus itself an aim, namely, to reconcile opposing aims. So absolute moral

---

[15] (Ed.) [RAP] Ch. III.

[16] (Ed.) [RAP] 48. The full statement in [RAP] is: " 'If I feel not the love of God,' the objector will say, 'how prove to me that I ought to feel it?' "

[17] (Ed.) [RAP] 82ff.

scepticism is self-destructive. "Possibly this result may be somewhat unexpected," [18] says our author. Not at all unexpected to one who does not believe in the dialectical method. You started with a hypochondriac hankering after an aim; and now you have acquired it. *Eurekas*! Well, what is it, this aim which you have at last got? Why, to have an aim! But that is nothing but the old nonsensical longing with which you set out. Like Kant's dove, you have been winging [in] a vacuum, without remarking that you never advanced an inch. I do not misrepresent the author. "For behold," he says, "made practical, brought down from its lonesome height, my Ideal very simply means the Will to direct my acts *towards* the attainment of universal Harmony." [19] But this, I must insist, was obviously implied in the original fantastic desire to have an aim. When I say that this is a fantastic desire, I do not of course mean to deny that there may be such an operation as the *choice of an aim*, if by that aim he meant a secondary or derived one; but I do say that it is absurd to speak of choosing an original and ultimate aim. That is something which, if you haven't it, you have nothing to do but wait till the grace of God confers it on you. I should think, however, that were it once admitted to be a rational performance to go ahunting for an ultimate aim or end, the first preliminary would be to recognize the axiom that such an end must have unity, after which the hunt might begin. But Royce, calling this axiom the 'ideal of ideals,' [20] as it certainly is, in a sense, exclaims 'Here I have the aim I wanted, and the hunt is over.' If one might be permitted to enliven a dry subject with a little folly, I should say that it reminded me of the surveyor Phoenix, who after purchasing 365 solar compasses and a vast amount of other paraphernalia, in order to ascertain the distance between San Francisco and the Mission of Dolores, stepped into a grocery and inquired how far it was, and returned "much pleased at so easily acquiring so much valuable information." If Dr. Royce merely means that it can be shown that a man who fancies he has no moral ideal really has one, I heartily grant it; and I will further admit that dialectic is the proper instrument to show this. But then

[18] (Ed.) [RAP] 138.
[19] (Ed.) [RAP] 140–141.
[20] (Ed.) [RAP] 144.

a very lowly kind of dialectic will do; and a rather more definite ideal may be pointed out.

53. The rest of Book I is occupied, as it seems to me, with illicitly slipping some content into an empty formula. Much of this part of the book is splendidly said. But other passages seem to me to preach, in a way quite uncalled for by the premises, an ethics of the evil eye. "It is well that we should feel . . . joy whenever pride has a fall. . . . In all such ways . . . we must show *no mercy*." [21] "When the hedonist gives us his picture of a peaceful society, where, in the midst of [universal] good humor, his ideal, the happiness of everybody concerned, is steadfastly pursued, we find ourselves disappointed and contemptuous. . . . Who cares whether that [really] wretched set . . . think themselves happy or not?" [22] "The appearance of anybody who pretends to be content with himself must be the signal not for admiration at the sight of his success, but for a good deal of contempt" [23] etc. Some of the students to whom this ethics is taught at Harvard may upon reflection think that christian charity is not so much lower a frame of mind after all.

54. In Book II, Dr. Royce undertakes, by the same dialectic procedure to establish the existence of a God. Space does not permit me to enter into a criticism of the second book; nor is it necessary, for it consists only of an application of the same method to a subject to which dialectics is far less suited. Besides, to the reader who has had the kindness and the resolution to follow me to this point I can say, 'You are the man to enjoy Dr. Royce's own book, which I can promise you you shall find, in comparison with [the] harsh and crabbed matter you have been reading here, to be "as musical as is Apollo's lute." '

[21] (Ed.) "Therefore it is well that we should feel not a selfish but a righteous joy whenever pride has a fall, whenever the man who thinks that he is something discovers of a truth that he is nothing. . . . In all such ways we must ask and we must show no mercy, save when these keen pains . . ." [RAP] 181–182.

[22] (Ed.) [RAP] 187. The words in brackets are in [RAP], but were omitted by Peirce without notice.

[23] (Ed.) ". . . whereas the rule of life for one's own person is simply to get all the satisfaction that one can, the appearance of anybody else who pretends to be content with *himself* must be the signal not for admiration at the sight of his success, but for a good deal of contempt." [RAP] 196–197.

CHAPTER 4

WILLIAM JAMES, *THE PRINCIPLES OF PSYCHOLOGY*

§1. REVIEW IN THE NATION [1]

55.   Upon this vast work no definitive judgment can be passed for a long time; yet it is probably safe to say that it is the most important contribution that has been made to the subject for many years.   Certainly it is one of the most weighty productions of American thought.   The directness and sharpness with which we shall state some objections to it must be understood as a tribute of respect.

56.   Beginning with the most external and insignificant characters, we cannot much admire it as a piece of bookmaking; for it misses the unity of an essay, and almost that of a connected series of essays, while not attaining the completeness of a thorough treatise.   It is a large assortment of somewhat heterogeneous articles loosely tied up in one bag, with tendencies towards sprawling.

57.   With an extraordinarily racy and forcible style, Prof. James is continually wresting words and phrases of exact import to unauthorized and unsuitable uses.   He indulges himself with idiosyncrasies of diction and tricks of language such as usually spring up in households of great talent.   To illustrate what we mean, we will open one of the volumes at random, and we come upon this: "A statement *ad hominem* meant as part of a reduction to the absurd." [2]   Now a *reductio ad absurdum* is a species of demonstration, and as such can contain no

---

[1] (Ed.)   The review of William James's *The Principles of Psychology* (American Science Series, Advanced Course, Henry Holt and Company, 1890), 2 vols. Paragraphs 55–61, *The Nation* 53 (2 July 1891) 15; paragraphs 62–71, *The Nation* 53 (9 July 1891) 32–33.

[2] (Ed.)   Vol. I, p. 368.

argumentum ad hominem, which is merely something a man is obliged by his personal interests to admit. On the next page, we read: "This dynamic (we had almost written dynamitic) way of representing knowledge." On the next page: "They talk as if, with this miraculous tying or 'relating,' the Ego's duties were done." It is the same with the technical terms of psychology. Speaking of certain theories, our author says they "carry us back to times when the soul as vehicle of consciousness was not discriminated, as it now is, from the vital principle presiding over the formation of the body." [3] How can anybody write so who knows the technical meaning of *vehicle*? On the same page occurs this phrase, "If unextended, it is absurd to speak of its having space relations at all," which sounds like a general attack on the geometry of points.

58. Prof. James's thought is highly original, or at least novel; but it is originality of the destructive kind. To prove that we do not know what it has been generally supposed that we did know, that given premises do not justify the conclusions which all other thinkers hold they do justify, is his peculiar function. For this reason the book should have been preceded by an introduction discussing the strange positions in logic upon which all its arguments turn. Even when new theories are proposed, they are based on similar negative or sceptical considerations, and the one thing upon which Prof. James seems to pin his faith is the general incomprehensibility of things. He clings as passionately to that as the old lady of the anecdote did to her total depravity. Of course, he is materialistic to the core — that is to say, in a methodical sense, but not religiously, since he does not deny a separable soul nor a future life; for materialism is that form of philosophy which may safely be relied upon to leave the universe as incomprehensible as it finds it. It is possible that Prof. James would protest against this characterization of his cast of mind. Brought up under the guidance of an eloquent apostle of a form of Swedenborgianism,[4] which is materialism driven deep and clinched on the inside, and educated to the materialistic profession, it can only be by great natural breadth of mind that he can know what materialism is,

[3] (Ed.) Vol. I, p. 215.
[4] (Ed.) Cf. Peirce's review of a book by James's father on Swedenborg, [Bibliography] G–1870–2.

by having experienced some thoughts that are not materialistic. He inclines towards Cartesian dualism, which is of the true strain of the incomprehensibles and modern materialism's own mother. There is no form of idealism with which he will condescend to argue. Even evolutionism, which has idealistic affinities, seems to be held for suspect. It is his *métier* to subject to severe investigation any doctrine whatever which smells of intelligibility.

59. The keynote of this is struck in the preface, in these words:

"I have kept close to the point of view of natural science throughout the book. Every natural science assumes certain data uncritically, and declines to challenge the elements between which its own 'laws' obtain, and from which its deductions are carried on. Psychology, the science of finite individual minds, assumes as its data (1) *thoughts and feelings*, and (2) a *physical world* in time and space with which they coexist and which (3) *they know*. Of course these data themselves are discussable; but the discussion of them (as of other elements) is called metaphysics, and falls outside the province of this book. This book, assuming that thoughts and feelings exist, and are the vehicles of knowledge, thereupon contends that Psychology, when she has ascertained the empirical correlation of the various sorts of thought and feeling with definite conditions of the brain, can go no farther — can go no farther, that is, as a natural science. If she goes farther, she becomes metaphysical. All attempts to *explain* our phenomenally given thoughts as products of deeper-lying entities (whether the latter be named 'Soul,' 'Transcendental Ego,' 'Ideas,' or 'Elementary Units of Consciousness') are metaphysical. This book consequently rejects both the associationist and the spiritualist theories; and in this strictly positivistic point of view consists the only feature of it for which I feel tempted to claim originality." [5]

60. This is certainly well put — considered as prestigiation. But when we remember that a natural science is not a person, and consequently does not "decline" to do anything, the argument evaporates. It is only the students of the science who can "decline," and they are not banded together to repress

[5] (Ed.) Vol. I, pp. v–vi.

any species of inquiry. Each investigator does what in him lies; and declines to do a thousand things most pertinent to the subject. To call a branch of an inquiry "metaphysical" is merely a mode of objurgation, which signifies nothing but the author's personal distaste for that part of his subject. It does not in the least prove that considerations of that sort can throw no light on the questions he has to consider. Indeed, we suspect it might be difficult to show in any way that any two branches of knowledge should be allowed to throw no light on one another. Far less can calling one question scientific and another metaphysical warrant Prof. James in "consequently *rejecting*" certain conclusions, against which he has nothing better to object. Nor is it in the least true that physicists confine themselves to such a "strictly positivistic point of view." Students of heat are not deterred by the impossibility of directly observing molecules from considering and accepting the kinetical theory; students of light do not brand speculations on the luminiferous ether as metaphysical; and the substantiality of matter itself is called in question in the vortex theory, which is nevertheless considered as perfectly germane to physics. All these are "attempts to explain phenomenally given elements as products of deeper-lying entities." In fact, this phrase describes, as well as loose language can, the general character of scientific hypotheses.

61. Remark, too, that it is not merely nor chiefly the "soul" and the "transcendental ego" for which incomprehensibles he has some tenderness, that Prof. James proposes to banish from psychology, but especially *ideas* which their adherents maintain are direct data of consciousness. In short, not only does he propose, by the simple expedient of declaring certain inquiries extra-psychological, to reverse the conclusions of the science upon many important points, but also by the same negative means to decide upon the character of its data. Indeed, when we come to examine the book, we find it is precisely this which is the main use the author makes of his new principle. The notion that the natural sciences accept their data *uncritically* we hold to be a serious mistake. It is true, scientific men do not subject their observations to the kind of criticism practised by the high-flying philosophers, because they do not believe that method of criticism sound. If they really believed in

idealism, they would bring it to bear upon physics as much as possible. But in fact they find it a wordy doctrine, not susceptible of any scientific applications. When, however, a physicist has to investigate, say, such a subject as the scintillation of the stars, the first thing he does is to subject the phenomena to rigid criticism to find whether these phenomena are objective or subjective, whether they are in the light itself, or arise in the eye, or in original principles of mental action, or in idiosyncrasies of the imagination, etc. The principle of the uncritical acceptance of data, to which Prof. James clings, practically amounts to a claim to a new kind of liberty of thought, which would make a complete rupture with accepted methods of psychology and of science in general. The truth of this is seen in the chief application that has been made of the new method, in the author's theory of space-perception. And into the enterprise of thus revolutionizing scientific method he enters with a light heart, without any exhaustive scrutiny of his new logic in its generality, relying only on the resources of the moment. He distinctly discourages a separate study of the method. "No rules can be laid down in advance. Comparative observations, to be definite, must usually be made to test some preëxisting hypothesis; and the only thing then is to use as much sagacity as you possess, and to be as candid as you can." [6]

62.   We have no space for any analysis of the contents of this work, nor is that necessary, for everybody interested in the subject must and will read the book. It discusses most of the topics of psychology in an extremely unequal way, but always interesting and always entertaining. We will endeavor to give a fair specimen of the author's critical method (for the work is essentially a criticism and exposition of critical principles), with a running commentary, to aid a judgment. For this purpose we will select a short section entitled "Is Perception Unconscious Inference?" [7] Perception in its most characteristic features is, of course, a matter of association in a wide sense of that term. If two spots of light are thrown upon the wall of a dark room so as to be adjacent, and one of these is made red while the

[6] (Ed.) Vol. I, p. 194.
[7] (Ed.) Vol. II, pp. 111–114. Cf. 5.115, 5.181ff.

other remains white, the white one will appear greenish by contrast. If they are viewed through a narrow tube, and this is moved so that the red spot goes out of view, still the white one will continue to look green. But if the red light, now unseen, be extinguished and we then remove the tube from the eye, so as to take a new look, as it were, the apparent greenness will suddenly vanish. This is an example of a thousand phenomena which have led several German psychologists to declare that the process of perception is one of reasoning in a generalized sense of that term.

63.   It is possible some of the earlier writers held it to be reasoning, strictly speaking. But most have called it "unconscious inference," and unconscious inference differs essentially from inference in the narrow sense, all our control over which depends upon this, that it involves a conscious, though it may be an indistinct, reference to a genus of arguments. These German writers must also not be understood as meaning that the perceptive process is any more inferential than are the rest of the processes which the English have so long explained by association — a theory which until quite recently played little part in German psychology. The German writers alluded to explain an ordinary suggestion productive of belief, or any cognition tantamount to belief, as inference conscious or unconscious, as a matter of course. As German writers are generally weak in their formal logic, they would be apt to formulate the inference wrongly; but the correct formulation is as follows:

64.   A well-recognized kind of object, M, has for its ordinary predicates P_1, P_2, P_3, etc., indistinctly recognized.

The suggesting object, S, has these same predicates, P_1, P_2, P_3, etc.

Hence, S is of the kind M.

65.   This is hypothetic inference in form. The first premise is not actually thought, though it is in the mind habitually. This, of itself, would not make the inference unconscious. But it is so because it is not recognized as an inference; the conclusion is accepted without our knowing how. In perception, the conclusion has the peculiarity of not being abstractly thought, but actually seen, so that it is not exactly a judgment, though it is tantamount to one. The advantage of this method of explaining the process is conceived to be this: To explain

any process not understood is simply to show that it is a special case of a wider description of process which is more intelligible. Now nothing is so intelligible as the reasoning process. This is shown by the fact that all explanation assimilates the process to be explained to reasoning. Hence, the logical method of explaining the process of association is looked upon as the most perfect explanation possible. It certainly does not exclude the materialistic English explanation by a property of the nerves. The monist school, to which the modern psychologists mostly belong, conceives the intellectual process of inference and the process of mechanical causation to be only the inside and outside views of the same process. But the idealistic tendency, which tinctures almost all German thought not very recent, would be to regard the logical explanation as the more perfect, under the assumption that the materialistic explanation requires itself ultimately to be explained in terms of the reasoning process. But Prof. James is naturally averse to the logical explanation. Let us see, then, how he argues the point. His first remark is as follows:

"If every time a present sign suggests an absent reality to our mind, we make an inference; and if every time we make an inference, we reason, then perception is indubitably reasoning."

66. Of course, every psychological suggestion is regarded as of the general nature of inference, but only in a far more general sense than that in which perception is so called. This should be well known to Prof. James, and he would have dealt more satisfactorily with his readers if he had not kept it back. Namely, perception attains a virtual judgment, it subsumes something under a class, and not only so, but virtually attaches to the proposition the seal of assent — two strong resemblances to inference which are wanting in ordinary suggestions. However, Prof. James admits that the process *is* inference in a broad sense. What, then, has he to object to [in] the theory under consideration?

67.

"Only one sees no room in it for any unconscious part. Both associates, the present sign and the contiguous things which it suggests, are above board, and no intermediary ideas are required."

60

Here are two errors. In the first place, "unconscious inference" does not, either with other logicians or with the advocates of the theory in question, mean an inference in which any proposition or term of the argument is unconscious, any more than "conscious inference" implies that both premises are conscious. But unconscious inference means inference in which the reasoner is not conscious of making an inference. He may be conscious of the premise, but he is not conscious that his acceptance of the conclusion is inferential. He does not make that side-thought which enters into all inference strictly so called: "and so it would be in every analogous case (or in most cases.)" There is no doubt, therefore, that ordinary suggestion, regarded as inference, is of the unconscious variety. But Prof. James further forgets his logic in hinting, what he soon expresses more clearly, that such an inference is to be regarded as a mere "immediate inference," because it has no middle term. We might suppose he had never heard of the *modus ponens*, the form of which, A and B being any proposition, is

> If A, then B;
> But A:
> Hence, B.

Those who think a light is thrown upon the ordinary process of suggestion by assimilating it to reasoning, assimilate it to the *modus ponens*. The proposition "If A, then B," is represented by the association itself, which is not present to consciousness, but exists in the mind in the form of a habit, as all beliefs and general propositions do. The second premise A is the suggesting idea, the conclusion B is the suggested idea.

68.   Already quite off the track, our author now plunges into the jungle in this fashion:

"Most of those who have upheld the thesis in question have, however, made a more complex supposition. What they have meant is that perception is a *mediate* inference, and that the middle term is unconscious. When the sensation which I have called 'this' is felt, they think that some process like the following runs through the mind:

> 'This' is M;
> but M is A;
> therefore 'this' is A."

61

Those who have upheld the thesis are not in dispute among themselves, as represented. They make no supposition throughout not admitted by all the world. To represent any process of inference now as a *modus ponens*, now as a syllogism with a middle term, is not necessarily taking antagonistic views. As for the syllogism given, it is the weakest mode of supporting the thesis, far more open to attack than the form first given above. But Prof. James makes no headway, even against this. He says:

"Now there seems no good grounds for supposing this additional wheelwork in the mind. The classification of '*this*' as M is itself an act of perception, and should, if all perception were inference, require a still earlier syllogism for its performance, and so backwards *ad infinitum*."

69. Not one of the authors whom we have consulted makes the M entirely unconscious; but Prof. James says they do. If so, when he insists that "this is M" is an act of perception, he must mean some ultra-Leibnitzian *unconscious* perception! Has he ever found the German authors maintaining that that kind of perception is inferential? If not, where is his *regressus ad infinitum*? What those authors do say is that M, and with it the two premises, are thrown into the background and shade of consciousness; that "this is M" is a perception, sometimes in the strict sense, sometimes only in that sense in which perception embraces every sensation. They do not hold sensation to be inferential, and consequently do not suppose a *regressus ad infinitum*. But even if they did, there would be no *reductio ad absurdum*, since it is well known to mathematicians that any finite interval contains an infinite number of finite intervals; so that supposing there is no finite limit to the shortness of time required for an intellectual process, an infinite number of them, each occupying a finite time, may be crowded into any time, however short.

70. The Professor concludes:

"So far, then, from perception being a species of reasoning, properly so called, both it and reasoning are coördinate varieties of that deeper sort of process known psychologically as the association of ideas, and — "

We break the sentence, which goes on to something else, in order to remark that "a species of reasoning properly so called" must be a slip of the pen. For otherwise there would be an *ignoratio elenchi*; nobody ever having claimed that perception is inference in the strict sense of conscious inference. Instead of "a species of reasoning properly so called," we must read "reasoning in a generalized sense." Remembering also that Prof. James began by insisting on extending the controversy to association in general, we may put association in place of perception, and thus the conclusion will be, "so far from association being reasoning in a generalized sense, reasoning is a special kind of association." Who does not see that to say that perception and reasoning are coördinate varieties of association, is to say something in entire harmony with the thesis which Prof. James is endeavoring to combat? To resume:

71.
"— physiologically as the law of habit in the brain. To call perception unconscious reasoning is thus either a useless metaphor or a positively misleading confusion between two different things."

Here the section ends, and in these last words, for the first time in the whole discussion, the real question at issue is at length touched, and it is dismissed with an *ipse dixit*. There is no room for doubt that perception and, more generally, associative suggestion, may truthfully be considered as inference in a generalized sense; the only question is whether there is any use in so considering them. Had Prof. James succeeded in establishing his *regressus ad infinitum*, he would have refuted himself effectually, since it would then have been shown that an important consequence, not otherwise known, had been drawn from the theory. As it is, he says nothing pertinent either pro or con. But a little before, when an unconscious predication was called perception, was this perception "properly so called"? And if not, was calling it by that name a "useless metaphor," or was it a "positively misleading confusion between two different things"?

§2. QUESTIONS ON WILLIAM JAMES'S
THE PRINCIPLES OF PSYCHOLOGY [8]

72. Qu: 3 *p. 66*. "The cortex is the sole organ of consciousness in man." The reasoning seems pretty loose for settling all the important positions implied in this statement. What is consciousness anyway?

73. Qu: 5 *p. 80*. Is not the conscious element of any conception, — as Kant would say, its *matter*, — pretty accidental and unimportant? It must, no doubt, be there, but will not anything there do? Shall we not take *tongue* sensations as the skeleton or *corpus* of our conception of language, etc.?

74. Qu: 12 *p. 137*. ["Psychology is a mere natural science, accepting certain terms uncritically as her data, and stopping short of metaphysical reconstruction. Like physics, she must be *naïve*; and if she finds that in her very peculiar field of study ideas *seem* to be causes, she had better continue to talk of them as such. She gains absolutely nothing by a breach with common-sense in this matter, and she loses, to say the least, all naturalness of speech."] Had physics taken the course you wish psychology to take would she not have stuck to the idea of explaining everything by hot and cold, moist and dry? Is not the lesson of physics rather not to attack the most difficult problems first?

75. Qu: 14 *p. 144*. ["But if pleasures and pains have no efficacy, one does not see (without some such *à priori* rational harmony as would be scouted by the 'scientific' champions of the automaton-theory) why the most noxious acts, such as burning, might not give thrills of delight, and the most necessary ones, such as breathing, cause agony."] Why would it

[8] (Ed.) "Questions on William James's Principles of Psychology," Widener IC1a. This manuscript is dated c.1891 since it was probably written when Peirce composed his review (see 55n1). The questions are numbered from 1 to 44, with two questions bearing the number 40. All the questions concern Vol. I of the two volume work; where necessary, the editor has inserted in brackets the relevant passages. The questions published here are on the following chapters: 3 and 5 are on Ch. II, "The Functions of the Brain"; 12 and 14, Ch. V, "The Automaton-Theory"; 21, 22, 23, 29, and 30, Ch. VIII, "The Relations of Minds to other Things"; and 31, 32, 33, 36, 41, and 42, Ch. IX, "The Stream of Thought." [Bibliography] M–14a quotes some of the questions not printed here.

not be equally logical to say, "if pleasures and pains have no efficacy, one does not see why men should not shun the pleasurable as much as the painful." But the obvious answer would be, *because, as this fact shows, pleasure and pain are more than pure monadic feelings.* Is not this the answer to the question that *is* put?

76.   Qu: 21 *p. 215.* ["The truth is that if the thinking principle is extended we neither know its form nor its seat; whilst if unextended, it is absurd to speak of its having any space-relations at all. Space-relations we shall see hereafter to be *sensible* things. The only objects that can have mutual relations of position are objects that are perceived coexisting in the same felt space. A thing not perceived at all, such as the inextended soul must be, cannot coexist with any perceived objects in this way. No lines can be felt stretching from it to the other objects. It can form no terminus to any space-interval. It can therefore in no intelligible sense enjoy position. Its relations cannot be spatial, but must be exclusively cognitive or dynamic, as we have seen. So far as they are dynamic, to talk of the soul being 'present' is only a figure of speech. Hamilton's doctrine that the soul is present to the whole body is at any rate false: for cognitively its presence extends far beyond the body, and dynamically it does not extend beyond the brain."] The two centres of gyration of a reversible pendulum are *unextended points.* No lines can be felt stretching from them to other objects. They form no termini to any space-interval. Will you then say they "can have no mutual relations of position," or that "in no intelligible sense can they 'enjoy' position"?

77.   Qu: 22 *p. 215.* Is anything "present" in space except in the sense of being in dynamic reaction with other objects in space? If so, in what does the figure of speech consist?

78.   Qu: 23 *p. 215.* There is an attempt in the last sentence of the text of this page (and the idea has been vaguely running along) to establish a great contrast between the mode of the mind's *cognitive* reactions with things and its *dynamic* reactions. The former is direct, or there is, at least, no sense in calling it indirect. The latter is direct only with the brain, and mainly indirect. Is this tenable? The soul reacts dynamically with the future, cognitively with the past. Both are mediate. In

65

the immediate present, volition and experience are indistinguishable, are they not? What is the distinction that can exist in that instant? If I am right here, is there not a pretty accurate correspondence between our dealings with the Future and the Past, as far as mediacy is concerned, at any rate?

79. Qu: 29 *p. 222.* ["Through feelings we become acquainted with things, but only by our thoughts do we know about them. Feelings are the germ and starting point of cognition, thoughts the developed tree."] "Through feelings we become acquainted with things." This seems to me to be at the root of a good deal of bad metaphysics. On the contrary, the feelings are matters of indifference (in their qualities). It is by the *reactions* of ourselves upon things and of their parts on one another that we become acquainted with things, as it seems to me.

80. Qu: 30 *p. 222.* Is this classification of "mental states" as feelings and thoughts sufficiently scientific? Is it not better to adopt the *logical* division not of "mental states" but of mental elements, into feeling-qualities, reactions (volition and experience), and habit-taking?

81. Qu: 31 *p. 226.* "No thought even comes into direct sight of a thought in another personal consciousness than its own. Absolute insulation, irreducible pluralism, is the law." Is not the direct contrary nearer observed facts? Is not this pure metaphysical speculation? You think there *must* be such isolation, because you confound thoughts with feeling-qualities; but all observation is against you. There are some small particulars that a man can keep to himself. He exaggerates them and his personality sadly.

82. Qu: 32 *p. 226.* ["It seems as if the elementary psychic fact were not *thought* or *this thought* or *that thought*, but *my thought*, every thought being *owned*. Neither contemporaneity, nor proximity in space, nor similarity of quality and content are able to fuse thoughts together which are sundered by this barrier of belonging to different personal minds. The breaches between such thoughts are the most absolute breaches in nature. Everyone will recognize this to be true, so long as the existence of *something* corresponding to the term 'personal mind' is all that is insisted on, without any particular view of its nature being implied. On these terms the personal self rather than the

66

thought might be treated as the immediate datum in psychology."] Everybody will admit a personal self exists in the same sense in which a snark exists; that is, there is a phenomenon to which that name is given. It is an illusory phenomenon; but still it is a phenomenon. It is not quite *purely* illusory, but only *mainly* so. It is true, for instance, that men are *selfish*, that is, that they are really deluded into supposing themselves to have some isolated existence; and in so far, they *have* it. To deny the reality of personality is not anti-spiritualistic; it is only anti-nominalistic. It is true that there are certain phenomena, really quite slight and insignificant, but exaggerated, because they are connected with the tongue, which may be described as personality. The agility of the tongue is shown in its insisting that the world depends upon it. The phenomena of personality consist mainly in ability to hold the tongue. This is what the tongue brags so about.[9]

83. But all this business will appear dark and mysterious until the three categories are mastered and applied.[10]

84. Meantime, physicians are highly privileged that they can ask to see people's tongues; for this is inspecting the very organ of personality. It is largely because this organ is so sensitive that personality is so vivid. But it is more because it is so agile and complex a muscle. Its muscular habits are the basis of personality, which need not be lodged in the brain. The inhibition however which makes the strong personality comes from some exterior ganglion, no doubt.

85. This is a specimen of how other "thoughts" ought to be conceived. They are readily adoptable habits, taken, lost, replaced continually, and felt, no matter how. Mostly no doubt lodged in nerve matter, but not necessarily so.

86. The cases of double personality show that the cunning right hand can in a measure replace the tongue. But till a personality can control the tongue, it is very obscure. The principal personality resides there. Its superiority is shown by this that if cut out the person soon gets along and talks very well, with the remaining fragments. Farmers sometimes slit the

---

[9] (Ed.) Cf. 5.313ff.

[10] (Ed.) The psychological versions of Peirce's categories of First, Second, and Third are discussed in 7.524–538, and the categories in general are treated in [CP] I. See also 5.290.

tongues of self milking cows. But they soon learn to make use of the slit tongue just the same. So if a man's right hand is cut off, it is marvellous how much he can do with the stump. But the hand altogether lacks the extreme subtilty of the tongue. The school-boy writes with his tongue. That is the tongue teaching the fingers language. Some people roll up their tongues, or bite them, or shove them down when they do something sly or tricky. Some people stick them into their cheeks. These are the gestures of pure egotism. The tobacco chewer shifts his quid when he betrays his vanity.

All animals capable of domestication have good tongues.

87. Qu: 33 *p. 231*. ["Are not the sensations we get from the same object, for example, always the same? Does not the same piano-key, struck with the same force, make us hear in the same way? Does not the same grass give us the same feeling of green, the same sky the same feeling of blue, and do we not get the same olfactory sensation no matter how many times we put our nose to the same flask of cologne? It seems a piece of metaphysical sophistry to suggest that we do not; and yet a close attention to the matter shows that *there is no proof that the same bodily sensation is ever got by us twice.*

"What is got twice is the same OBJECT. We hear the same *note* over and over again; we see the same *quality* of green, or smell the same objective perfume, or experience the same *species* of pain."] Is it not plain that two feelings cannot be compared as they are as pure feelings? If so can a "likeness" between two feelings possibly consist in anything but their being naturally associated? That granted, is it not certain that feelings ever so much alike *do*, in that only possible sense, recur? As for *sameness*, this is a relation which by its nature is restricted to individuals. Feelings are in so far the same as they are alike.

88. Qu: 36 *p. 235*. I should be glad to know what possible relevancy all that has been so skillfully said about the total states of mind, that its commonplace is forgotten, has with the proposition that no two ideas can ever be exactly the same. This seems perfectly absurd. The essence of thought lies in the law of relationship that it implies. Do you mean to say that I never can have again my present view of the essence of the system of whole numbers? *That* is what it means to say I have the same idea I had yesterday.

89.   Qu: 41 *p. 243*. [*"Let us call the resting-places the 'substantive parts,' and the places of flight the 'transitive parts,' of the stream of thought*. It then appears that the main end of our thinking is at all times the attainment of some other substantive part than the one from which we have just been dislodged. And we may say that the main use of the transitive parts is to lead us from one substantive conclusion to another."] This is one of the finest, if not the finest, passage in the whole book. It is a direful pity the author could not have sufficient acquaintance with the history of words, and of knowledge of their importance, to avoid two of the most objectionable terms he could possibly have selected, for the trade marks of his invention. Why could he not have said "transitory" [11] instead of taking a word already over burdened with ambiguities. Not that still better terms might not have been discovered. As for "substantive," it wouldn't have been much worse if he had called it "absolute." . . .

90.   Qu: 42 *p. 244*. ["Let anyone try to cut a thought across in the middle and get a look at its section, and he will see how difficult the introspective observation of the transitive tracts is. The rush of the thought is so headlong that it almost always brings us up at the conclusion before we can arrest it."]   To cut a thought across and look at the section requires no introspection. It is one of the principal methods in mathematics, which is in no degree introspective. Treating operations as quantities is one of a hundred familiar examples.

[11] (Ed.) This word is not clearly legible in the manuscript. Cf. [Perry] II, 413–416.

CHAPTER 5

ON NON-EUCLIDEAN GEOMETRY [1]

91. Lobachevski's little book, 'Geometrische Untersuchungen,' marks an epoch in the history of thought, that of the overthrow of the axioms of geometry. The philosophical consequences of this are undoubtedly momentous, and there are thinkers who hold that it must lead to a new conception of nature, less mechanical than that which has guided the steps of science since Newton's discovery. The book has been published many years — in fact, the essence of it was set forth before 1830; so long does it take a pure idea to make its way, unbacked by any interest more aggressive than the love of truth. In this case, the idea is lucid, easy, and convincing. Nobody with enough mathematical capacity to be able to understand the first book of geometry need fear the least difficulty in mastering Lobachevski's tract; and really it is high time that every thinking man and woman should know what is in it.

92. In the pre-Lobachevskian days, elementary geometry was universally regarded as the very exemplar of conclusive reasoning carried to great lengths. It had been the ideal of speculative thinkers in all ages. Metaphysics, indeed, as an historical fact, has been nothing but an attempt to copy, in thinking about substances, the geometer's reasoning about shapes. This is shown by the declarations of Plato and others, by the spatial origin of many metaphysical conceptions and of the terms appropriated to them, such as *abstract, form, analogy,*

---

[1] (Ed.) Paragraphs 91–96 are the review of Nicholaus Lobatchewsky's *Geometrical Researches on the Theory of Parallels* (translated by George Bruce Halsted, Austin, 1891), *The Nation* 54(11 Feb 1892)116, with an added quotation in 93n2.

Paragraphs 97–99 are from an undated manuscript, "The Non Euclidean Geometry made Easy," Widener IA–2.

Cf. 1.130, 3.134n1, 3.557.

etc., and by the love of donning the outer clothing of geometry, even when no fit for philosophy. For instance, one of the remarkable features of geometry is the small number of premises from which galaxies of theorems result; and accordingly it has been an effort of almost all metaphysicians to reduce their first principles to the fewest possible, even if they had to crowd disparate thoughts into one formula. It did not seem to occur to them that since a list of first principles is a work of analysis, it would not be a small number of elementary propositions so much as a large number that would bespeak its thoroughness. Admiration for the elements of geometry was not, however, confined to metaphysicians. Euclid's treatise was acknowledged by all kinds of minds to be all but absolutely perfect in its reasoning, and the very type of what science should aim at as to form and matter.

93. In the empyrean of geometry there was but one little speck — the theory of parallels. Euclid had had a difficulty in proving the sum of the angles of a triangle to be not less than two right angles. His treatment of the subject betrays a very profound study of it; for instead of slipping over the difficulty unaware, as forty-nine out of fifty mathematicians would have done, instead of even bringing the necessary assumption to a persuasive shape, he takes as his fifth postulate (or 11th axiom, in incorrect editions) a proposition that begs the question in the frankest manner — namely, if two straight lines in a plane are met by a third making the sum of the inner angles on one side of this third less than two right angles, then these two lines will meet on that side if sufficiently produced. Innumerable attempts were made to demonstrate this; but, at length, the efforts of Legendre and others made it pretty clear that this proposition could be deduced only from some other nearly equivalent. The least unsatisfactory assumption ever proposed was that of Playfair, that if of three unlimited straight lines lying in one plane two intersect, the third must cross one or both. It was at this point that Lobachevski cut the knot by supposing Euclid's postulate untrue, and showing that the result was a perfectly consistent system of geometry which may, for all we can yet observe, be the system of nature.[2] All this time, Euclid's proof

---

[2] (Ed.) Peirce worked on the problem of determining which geometry holds of physical space. ". . . the physical geometry of celestial triangles needs exam-

(Elements, Bk. I., props. 16 and 17) of what substantially amounts to the proposition, that the sum of the three angles of a triangle is *not greater* than two right angles, was regarded as perfect. It was not till 1854 that Riemann first discovered that, though accepted for two thousand years as conclusive (and it stands to-day unchanged in almost all the text-books), this pretended proof is really quite fallacious. It is plain that it is so, because it uses no premises not as true in the case of spherical as in that of plane triangles; and yet the conclusion drawn from those premises is known to be false of spherical triangles.[3]

94. The truth is, that elementary geometry, instead of being the perfection of human reasoning, is riddled with fallacies, and is thoroughly unmathematical in its method of development. It has in some measure confused all mathematics, by leaving unnoticed most of the really fundamental propositions, while raising to an undue rank certain others almost arbitrarily selected. It leads young men into bad logical ways; and it causes pupil and teacher to think that whoever has difficulty with this sophisticated logic is wanting in aptitude for the apprehension of mathematics. The study of geometry ought to begin with the theory of perspective. Let a man be supposed to stand on an unbroken sandy plain. Let him fix a needle upon a post, and set up a plate of glass in a steady position, and draw a perspective picture upon the glass by placing his eye so as to bring the needle-point over each point in the sand to be represented and marking it on the glass in the same line of sight. The horizon is where the lines of sight just skim the surface of the rounded

---

ination, in order to ascertain whether the constant of space may not have a sensible magnitude. I have undertaken such an examination. I began by forming a list of all possible methods of determining this quantity by means of the following observations: 1st, the parallaxes of stars; 2nd, the numbers of stars of each parallax; 3rd, the proper motions of stars; 4th, the numbers of stars of different proper motions; 5th, the spectroscopic determinations of the motions of stars in the line of sight; 6th, the magnitudes of stars; 7th, the numbers of stars of each magnitude. My list of possible methods was long. All of them, it is true, involved some hypothetical element; but that is true of any research, whatever, into the value of a physical quantity; and it is possible so to modify the methods that the hypotheses that appear the most dangerous may probably be eliminated. I applied several methods: they seemed to indicate a hyperbolic space with a constant far from insignificant." From an undated fragment, Widener IA–7.

[3] (Ed.) Cf. *The Thirteen Books of Euclid's Elements*, edited by Thomas L. Heath, Second Edition (Dover, 1956), Vol. I, p. 280.

earth. These lines of sight form a cone, and their perspective representation will be the section of this cone by the plane of the glass. But for simplicity let it be supposed that the earth is flat and indefinitely extended, so that the *plain* is also a *plane*, and an unbounded one. Then every straight line in the sand will have a straight line for its picture, for all the lines of sight from the needle-point to points in that straight line will lie in one plane; and this plane will cut the plane of the glass in a straight line.

95. Lobachevski and Riemann cast no manner of doubt upon the geometry of perspective, so far as this is confined to questions of incidence and coincidence. But when it comes to the measurement of distances and angles, their objections begin. According to the Euclidean notions, the infinitely distant parts of an unbounded plane would be represented in perspective by a straight horizon or vanishing line. But Lobachevski says we cannot be sure that this line would be straight, that maybe it would be a hyperbola like the perspective of the terrestrial horizon; and, in fact, the straight line being only a special case of the hyperbola, it is proper to say that such is its form. Riemann, however, points out that we cannot even be sure there would be any such line at all, for we cannot be sure that space has any infinitely distant parts, since it may be that if we were to move off in any direction in a straight line, we might find that, after traversing a sufficient distance, we had got around to our starting-point again.

96. Prof. Halsted's translation (which, while our notice has been waiting, has reached, we are glad to see, a fourth edition) is excellent; his useful bibliography of non-Euclidean geometry was already well known. We could only wish there were a more copious appendix. The work of Lobachevski, though simple and convincing, is not what would now be considered a scientific presentation of the subject, and is open to a good deal of criticism. A new synthetic exposition is much needed, and might well accompany a collection of the contributions of Lobachevski, Bolyai, Riemann, Cayley, Klein, and Clifford.

———————

97. We have an *opinion* or natural idea of space, which by some kind of evolution has come to be very closely in accord

with observations. But we find in regard to our natural ideas, in general, that while they do accord in some measure with fact, they by no means do so to such a point that we can dispense with correcting them by comparison with observations.

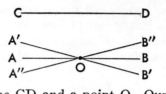

98. Given a line CD and a point O. Our natural (Euclidean) notion is that

1st there is a line AB through O in the plane OCD which will not meet CD at any finite distance from O.

2nd that if any line A'B' or A''B'' through O in the plane OCD be inclined by any finite angle, however small, to AB, it will meet CD at some finite distance from O.

99. Is this natural notion *exactly* true?

A. This is not certain.

B. We have no probable reason to believe it so.

C. We *never* can have positive evidence lending it any degree of likelihood. It *may* be disproved in the future.

D. It may be true, perhaps. But since the chance of this is as $1 : \infty$ or $\frac{0}{1}$, the logical presumption is, and must ever remain, that it is not true.

E. If there is some influence in evolution tending to adapt the mind to nature, it would probably not be completed yet. And we find other natural ideas require correction. Why not this, too? Thus, there is some reason to think this natural idea is *not* exact.

F. I have a theory which fits all the facts as far as I can compare them, which would explain how the natural notion came to be so closely approximate as it is, and how space came to have the properties we find it has. According to this theory, this natural notion would not be exact.

To give room for the non-Euclidean geometry, it is sufficient to admit the first of these propositions.

CHAPTER 6

JOSIAH ROYCE, *THE WORLD AND THE INDIVIDUAL*

§1. FIRST SERIES: THE FOUR HISTORICAL CONCEPTIONS OF BEING [1]

100.   We can do no more than explain in untechnical language what this important book is about. Its purpose is to say what it is that we aim at when we make any inquiry or investigation — not what our ulterior purpose may be, nor yet what our special effort is in any particular case, but what the direct and common aim of all search for knowledge is. This is a question of fact. Prof. Royce has clothed the matter in such academical guise that a reader untrained in philosophy might suppose it was a mere dispute about a definition, and therefore a profitless discussion; but, stripping off technicalities, we find this question of fact beneath them.

101.   The only opinion on this subject generally held at this day that Prof. Royce considers to be essentially different from his own, is one which may be attributed to Bishop Berkeley more justly than to any other individual. It is the opinion of Possible Experience. Though this has taken slightly different shapes with different thinkers, it will suffice, in order to explain the purport of Prof. Royce's book, to state it in one of its forms. The answer, then, generally given, or virtually given, to the question what any inquiry is instituted for, is approximately that it is intended to settle doubt on the subject. Did Sir Philip

---

[1] (Ed.) Paragraphs 100–107 are the review of Josiah Royce's *The World and the Individual*: Gifford Lectures delivered before the University of Aberdeen, First Series: The Four Historical Conceptions of Being (Macmillan, 1900, 588 pp.), *The Nation* 70 (5 April 1900) 267.

Paragraphs 108–116 are a review of the same work, Widener IV, dated c.1900 on the basis of the dates of the book and the published review.

Francis write the Junius letters? I can imagine, as the hand-writing experts say, that he did. I can imagine, as most of the recent inquirers say, that he did not. I feel no compulsion to attach either idea to my mental representation of the historic world. There are some images which I am forced, whether I would or no, to attach to mental objects — such as a dark skin and jealousy to Othello. The course of life has developed certain compulsions of thought which we speak of collectively as Experience. Moreover, the inquirer more or less vaguely identifies himself in sentiment with a Community of which he is a member, and which includes, for example, besides his momentary self, his self of ten years hence; and he speaks of the resultant cognitive compulsions of the course of life of that community as Our Experience. He says "we" find that terrestrial bodies have a component acceleration towards the earth of 980 centimetres per second, though neither he nor many of his acquaintances have ever made the experiment.

102. Now, such being his state of mind, two hopes motive his inquiry: the first is, that the course of "our" experience may ultimately compel the attachment of a settled idea to the mental subject of the inquiry; and the second is, that the inquiry itself may compel him to think that he anticipates what that destined ultimate idea is to be.[2]

103. Such, approximately, is the ordinary opinion of Possible Experience, in one of its modes of statement. According to it every inquiry is directed toward the resultant of certain compulsions; and, therefore, so far as a sense of compulsion is an immediate knowledge of something outside of self, exerting a brute force on self, this opinion is that every inquiry relates to a brute something without the mind. It was substantially on this ground that Kant opposed the anti-materialism of Berkeley. But, regarded from another side, this opinion is that the only object to which inquiry seeks to make our opinion conform is itself something of the nature of thought; namely, it is the predestined ultimate idea, which is independent of what you, I, or any number of men may persist, for however long, in thinking, yet which remains thought, after all. The whole course of life within which the experiential compulsions appear is a purely psychical development. For the gist of the opin-

[2] (Ed.) Cf. 5.357.

ion is that the flow of time consists in a continual assimilation into "our" inwardness, the Past, of a non-ego that is nothing but the ego that is to be — the Future. The Past acts upon the Future intelligibly, logically. But those blind compulsions are glimpses of an unknown object. Now, the unknown, according to this theory, is nothing but what is bound, as our hope is, to emerge in the future. Those blind compulsions, then, can be regarded as actions of the future on the past. From that point of view, it is seen that they can but be brute and blind, and, further, that in the course of time they must be seen to rationalize themselves and fall into place as the cognition develops.

104. To Prof. Royce's thinking, this opinion is unsatisfactory. He finds four faults with it, and sets them before us with his own argumentative lucidity and admirable mastery of the subject. Of the nature of three of them — that the opinion under examination makes the object of knowledge to be no more than a "would-be"; that its "experience" is no experience for an inquirer; that it seats an abstraction on a throne of reality — we can here find room for no clearer hint than those phrases may convey. Whatever solid skeleton the three objections may clothe is pretty much the same as that of the fourth and strongest, that if the non-ego to which the inquirer seeks to make his ideas conform is merely an idea in the future, that future idea must have for its object an idea future to it, and so on *ad infinitum*. There is no escaping the admission that the ultimate end of inquiry — the essential, not ulterior end — the mould to which we endeavor to shape our opinions, cannot itself be of the nature of an opinion. Could it be realized, it would rather be like an insistent image, not referring to anything else, and in that sense concrete. Passing from the consideration of a single inquiry to that of the aggregate of all possible inquiries, the phantom ultimate issue of them all would be the real universe. To be that, however, it must include the mental world as well as the physical, and must set forth to itself all laws and modes of conception. It must, above all, exhibit to itself the whole course of time, with that process of complete rationalization of ideas upon the assumption of which the very hypothesis of a fated ultimate destination of opinion is based. It must, therefore, be conceived as a perfect rational

77

consciousness. In short, it is such a conception of Deity (necessarily a one-sided one) as considerations limited to the Theory of Cognition could reasonably be expected to yield.

105. This inevitable outcome of the doctrine of Possible Experience is the very same goal, roughly speaking, to which Prof. Royce's explorations have brought him, too, by a path nearly parallel to that for which we have set up a sign-post for whoever may care to follow it out, though the hedgerows of thought may prevent the traveller over the one from being aware how close he is to the other. Prof. Royce reaches his conclusion by analyzing the nature of the purpose of an idea. Now this same conception of the purpose of an idea ought equally to be seized as the guiding thread to the doctrine of Possible Experience, although Prof. Royce believes his position to be quite foreign, even hostile, to that. One divergence is, that where another thinker might speak of a hope, as we have done above, Prof. Royce would substitute a *reductio ad absurdum* of the contrary opinion — a diminution of man's natural sublime attitude to a sorry "A is A." Fortunately the logic of those arguments is never impeccable, so that the hopes retain their matter and are not reduced to mere formulae.

106. Two other views are examined. One is that of cognitive Dualism, which Professor Royce calls by the objectionable name Realism (as if the Dualists alone admitted outward realities). The other is that of Mysticism, which is less an opinion than an attitude of mind, of which Professor Royce gives an exceedingly penetrating analysis. There is a long and technical supplementary essay on the One, the Many, and the Infinite, which is very important.

107. The dress of the book is as charming as that of one so sure of being long and often perused ought to be.

———————◆———————

108. Does the reader dabble in metaphysics? If he does, we make no sort of doubt that his opinions on such matters are nearer correct than those of any other human being; for we have talked with a hundred metaphysicians without ever yet meeting one who was not vastly superior to all the rest. So, *a fortiori*, the same superiority must be enjoyed by the gracious reader. But *present company excepted*, we do not know that

there lives a second metaphysician as strong as Prof. Royce. It need scarcely be said that no other theoretical science is at all comparable with philosophy in respect to the deep and large reading that its study absolutely makes exigent, lacking which the most splendid natural powers will leave their possessor a mere child in this science. For it is humanly impossible to know whither a given proposition in philosophy will inevitably lead without tracing out its historic development. Nor for this purpose will mere information suffice. It is requisite to enter into the range of ideas and spirit of each doctrine and thoroughly to assimilate it. In other sciences, only the true theories require close attention; but in philosophy the false ones are even more important, since it is precisely the thin and light soil of one-sided and extreme opinions that is easiest turned over to bring up the absurdities that lurk beneath the surface of their assumptions. Perhaps the greatest difficulty of the study arises from the circumstance that in youth one lacks the patience to sit down and soak one's mind in views from which one entirely dissents; so that by the time the preparation for original work is accomplished, the *élan* and agility of intellect that are nowhere more needed have been lost in the wear of advancing age. Now Royce has not only read all the great systems but he shows a truly admirable power of throwing himself into the mind of each philosopher and of appreciating with the greatest nicety just how each thinker has thought. The present volume contains a striking illustration of this in an exposition of the central position of Brahminic mysticism. It is a revelation almost too complete for the author's purpose, in that it comes perilously near to persuading the reader that that which the mystic affirms is undeniably true, and may almost indispose him to listen to its refutation.

109. The scientific world has now expended more than two centuries of concerted endeavor in the attempt to explain the phenomena of nature by means of the attractions and repulsions of discrete particles, and it is beginning to look strongly as if that hypothesis were insufficient. Some of the best authorities, for instance, now profess to demonstrate that phenomena as relatively simple as those of the elasticity of solid bodies cannot be so explained. Accordingly, new hypotheses infinitely more difficult to deal with are getting proposed, such as that

the universe is filled with a homogeneous fluid whose vortices constitute ordinary matter. It would be a pity, would it not, to turn the speculative energy of the world into such a channel only to find, at the expiration of two centuries, or more likely five, that it had a foolish hypothesis from which little or nothing ought ever to have been expected. If we only had at our command at this moment a really scientific logic and metaphysics, which might serve as guides in the choice of a hypothesis, such a doctrine might at this time be of the utmost service to science. But unfortunately the profounder sects of philosophy have sprung out of theology. Their adherents are tainted with the vicious intellectual diathesis of the seminaries. No class of persons above day-laborers has less comprehension of what science really is. As for mathematics, which ought to be the log-line and binnacle of the metaphysician, they are afraid to touch it, or when they do so venture, only make themselves ridiculous. This is particularly unfortunate because the main Hegelian idea is virtually an attempt to introduce the conception of continuity into philosophical doctrine, a conception which the mathematicians, on their side, have been engaged, since the birth of the differential calculus, in endeavoring to render distinct, hitherto without complete success; so that could a concerted assault be made upon it from opposite sides, it might be greatly to the advantage of both assailants. Now Prof. Royce is doing good service toward bringing this about, since, while he enjoys the esteem and sympathy of the theological metaphysicians, he is thoroughly alive to the ideas of science, and is thoroughly versed in all the more philosophical part of modern mathematical speculation. A "Supplementary Essay," appended to these lectures shows this very clearly. Meantime, in respect to that subtlety which seizes with accuracy upon the precise essence of a philosophical problem and disembarrasses it from all irrelevant considerations, which is the prime quality of a metaphysical mind, it may well be doubted whether any of the great figures of the history of philosophy have exhibited greater power than our American Plato.

110. It is now time to indicate what we venture to conceive to be Prof. Royce's greatest fault as a philosophical thinker. Metaphysicians have always taken mathematics as their exemplar in reasoning, without remarking the essential difference

between that science and their own. Mathematical reasoning has for its object to ascertain what would be true in a hypothetical world which the mathematician has created for himself, — not altogether arbitrarily, it is true, but nevertheless, so that it can contain no element which he has not himself deliberately introduced into it.[3] All that his sort of reasoning, therefore, has to do is to develop a preconceived idea; and it never reaches any conclusion at all as to what is or is not true of the world of existences. The metaphysician, on the other hand, is engaged in the investigation of matters of fact, and the only way to matters of fact is the way of experience. The only essential difference between metaphysics and meteorology, linguistics, or chemistry, is that it does not avail itself of microscopes, telescopes, voyages, or other means of acquiring recondite experiences, but contents itself with ascertaining all that can be ascertained from such experience as every man undergoes every day and hour of his life.[4] All other differences between philosophy and the special sciences are mere consequences of this one. It follows, that deductive, or mathematical, reasoning, although in metaphysics it may oftener "take the stage" than in the drama of special research, yet after all, has precisely the same *rôle* to enact, and nothing more. All genuine advance must come from real observation and inductive reasoning. Yet Dr. Royce cannot free himself from the Hegelian notion that the one satisfactory method in philosophy is to examine an opinion and to detect in it some hidden denial of itself, — which is nothing but the *reductio ad absurdum*. Strange that that method of reasoning to which mathematicians are often forced to resort, but which they always dislike because it does not exhibit the *rationale* of the proposition it proves, should by philosophers be made the standard of excellence. Such refutations in metaphysics are most frequently downright fallacies due to the loose habits of thinking prevalent in the theological seminaries. When their plight is not quite as bad as that, the very fact that the contradiction has to be sought in some obscure corner of the opinion refuted, shows that this opinion only needs to be modified in an inessential detail in order to escape the refutation. In the rare instances in which

[3] (Ed.) Cf. 3.363 and elsewhere in [CP] III.
[4] (Ed.) Cf. 6.2.

such refutations are really decisive, what happens is, that the refuter, without himself remarking it, slips into his reasoning some experiential fact. If, before publishing his proof, he were to search out that fact and bring it forward explicitly, he would not only make his reasoning more truly logical, though no longer purely deductive, but he would also render it infinitely more persuasive. For very seldom is anybody really convinced by the Socratic style of dialectic. Rather point out to a man a new fact, or one that he had overlooked; and then he himself, seeing it to be pertinent, will straightway begin to revise his opinion. The volume before us contains a remarkable illustration of this *penchant* of Prof. Royce in a proposed refutation of the opinion that, not merely is the element of existence a brute and non-intellectual element, but further that there exist things and facts about them which are as they are irrespective of any reason or idea. That this opinion can very readily be disposed of nobody knows better than Dr. Royce. But he is not satisfied with any mode of disproving it other than a *reductio ad absurdum*; and in order to effect the refutation in that way, he forces upon the notion of independence (or being irrespective of reason) elements that nobody who holds the opinion to be disproved will, for a moment, admit that it involves. With that hint, we refer the reader to Lecture III in the book itself.

111.   The main purpose of this volume is to show the inadequacy of the doctrine that whatever we know is either a direct experience or a possibility of experience, — a doctrine that Berkeley, more than any other person, introduced into philosophy and upon which Kant built his system of critic, — and further to propose in place of this doctrine a substitute [which], while Dr. Royce would certainly not claim it to be altogether novel, is undoubtedly a distinct improvement upon previous conceptions. Everybody who has reflected deeply upon the Berkeleyan principle must have seen that it leaves something to be desired. It will aid the reader to understand precisely what Dr. Royce's work is designed to effect, and how far it does actually effect it, if we state that doctrine of Possible Experience in one of its more modern forms.

112.   Remembering, then, that philosophy is a science based upon everyday experience, we must not fall into the absurdity

of setting down as a datum and starting-point of philosophy any abstract and simple idea, as Hegel did when he began his logic with pure Being; but we must set out from ideas familiar and complex, as Hegel began his greater masterpiece by considering a man sitting under a tree in a garden in the afternoon. We must not begin by talking of pure ideas, — vagabond thoughts that tramp the public roads without any human habitation, — but must begin with men and their conversation. We are familiar with the phenomenon of a man's expressing an opinion, sometimes decidedly, often otherwise. Perhaps it will be a mere suggestion, a mere question. Any such suggestion that may be expressed and understood relates to some common experience of the interlocutors, or, if there is a misunderstanding, they may think they refer to some common experience when, in fact, they refer to quite different experiences. A man reasoning with himself is liable to just such a misunderstanding. About this common experience the speaker has something to suggest which is supposed to be new to his auditor. Now this suggestion will be found inductively, by the examination of instances, to consist invariably in this, that if the auditor or any other man will act in a certain way, more or less vaguely described, he will find that common experience to connect itself with a new experience after a fashion analogous to other connections of experiences, which have made this mode of connection familiar to both parties. For example, if example be needed, suppose a man to go out of his house at night and see the light of a distant fire in the sky. He meets a neighbor and remarks, "There is a fire." [5] If he had only said "a fire exists," he would have conveyed next to no meaning at all. Not quite no meaning, since the remark would even so refer to that universe that is familiarly known to both men. But in saying "There is a fire," he refers to the common experience of that very place and time, and virtually says that if the second person will raise his eyes and look about him, he will find the common experience of that place and time to connect itself with the experience of a light as of a fire, the mode of connection being the familiar one that the speaker indicated. Let us take another example. Let the second man, having seen the fire, ask "Would you say, now, that that fire was about three

[5] (Ed.) This expression is indexical; cf. 2.305ff.

miles away?" This virtually suggests that if the first man or any other man will fill his purse, and take ship, and go to Westminster, and break into the houses of parliament, and bring away the standard yard, and lay it down repeatedly on the ground from where the two stand to where the fire is, and utter the cardinal numbers in their order as the successive layings down proceed, or if he will perform any other experiment virtually amounting to that, then the last number uttered might be 5280, and if it should prove to be a number near to that, he might not be surprised. Extensive experience leads us to expect that if an experiment virtually amounting to that were tried a hundred times, different numbers would be obtained which would cluster about one of them, and that among a million trials the clustering would be still more marked, according to a law well-known to mathematicians. It is possible, no doubt, that if our experience were still more extensive, we should find that if the experiment were tried, say, more than a billion times, then a new phenomenon would emerge and the oftener it was tried the *less* marked might grow the clustering. Our *hope*, however, in endeavoring to make a measurement extremely precise, is that there is a certain value toward which the resultant of all the experiments would approximate more and more, without limitation. Having that hope, the Berkeleyan theory is, that whenever we endeavor to state the distance, all that we aim at is to state as nearly as possible what that ultimate result of experience would be. We do not aim at anything quite beyond experience, but only at the limiting result toward which all experience will approximate, — or, at any rate, *would* approximate, were the inquiry to be prosecuted without cessation. And the theory is that so it is with all attempts at knowing anything more than what we immediately experience. This might be called the doctrine of the Non-relativity of Knowledge, since it eliminates any non-notional correlate of knowledge.

113. Prof. Royce seems to think that this doctrine is unsatisfactory because it talks about what would be,[6] although the event may never come to pass. It may be he is right in this criticism; yet to our apprehension this "would be" is readily resolved into a hope for *will be*. For what we mean by saying that any event, B, *would* happen under conditions, A, that are

[6] (Ed.) Cf. 1.420, 2.661–668, 4.580, 5.453, 5.467, 5.528, 6.327.

never fulfilled, is that the ultimate opinion which will, as we hope, actually be attained concerning any given question (though not in any finite time concerning *all* questions), will accept certain general laws from which a formal logical consequence will be that conditions, A, in any other world in which they may be fulfilled will, those laws still obtaining, involve the happening of the event, B. In short, we have only to conceive that the ultimate opinion about those general laws is attained before the attainment of the ultimate opinion that the condition, A, is never anywhere fulfilled. Let us not, then, too hastily accede to that criticism. On the other hand, it would be difficult to resist the criticism that the theory is unsatisfactory because it talks too exclusively of what *will be*. It is obvious that this *will be* is the very heart of the theory. The familiar notion of the flow of time is one of the most important data of metaphysical experience. In the special sciences facts are set over against theories, because it is the business of those sciences to connect the special phenomena which they discover with the general experience they derive from other sources. But philosophy embraces all experience. Its direct data are the familiar phenomena found everywhere which, from the point of view of psychology are quasi-theories, that is, are supposed to be worked up by the mind from simple elements that are not at all familiar to us, or even for the most part observable by themselves. It is of no consequence to the metaphysician whether psychology may teach that our sensations actually have a flow in time or whether we are only conscious in a series of detached instants, like the separate pictures of a zoëtrope. Whether Prof. Royce be right or wrong in asserting that we have an immediate consciousness of a finite span of time is equally unimportant.[7] The only important thing here is our metaphysical phenomenon, or familiar notion, that the past is a matter for knowledge but not for endeavor, that the future is an object that we may hope to influence, but which cannot affect us except through our anticipations, and that the present is a moment immeasurably small through which, as their limit, past and future can alone act upon one another. Whether this be an illusion or not, it is the phenomenon of which the metaphysician has to give an account. Now the Berkeleyan idea, when we come to reflect

[7] (Ed.) This question is further discussed in the following section.

85

upon it, amounts to this, that past experience is in some sense, my *ego*, that future experience is my sole *non-ego*, continually being assimilated by the *ego* through the present, and that that in this future *non-ego* which is destined at last to remain un-revoked in the *ego* is the only exemplar to which we desire that our ideas should conform.

114.   Prof. Royce admits, as we think justly, that this doc-trine of Possible Experience is true as far as it goes. But still he holds it to be unsatisfactory; and so it is, inasmuch as it re-gards time as a mere order of succession and fails to do justice to the *continuity* of the flow, which makes of all time an individ-ual object. That time is not a mere order of succession among a multitude of instants is shown by the following considerations. Any multitude of instants, however great, will find room for their succession in any lapse of time; so that if time were the mere order among a multitude of instants, that multitude would have to be a maximum than which no multitude could be greater. But it can be proved that there is no such maximum multitude. Consequently, there is more in time than any or all multitudes.[8] Time is such, says Kant, that every part of it has similar parts, — a proposition very different from merely saying that time is infinitely divisible, though Kant himself did not perceive the distinction. This continuity, or similarity of parts in respect to having parts, necessarily makes time an individual whole (though precisely how we lack space to explain); and thus it is that we shall never have a satisfactory account of what we virtually aim at in seeking to know, until we recognize the individual character of the object of search.

115.   This individual character is what Prof. Royce de-sires to bring out by his new definition of the object.[9] He reaches this aspect of the matter through the conception of Purpose. Every idea he says has its purpose, which he calls its "internal meaning." We wish that in place of the vague word "idea," he had substituted *judgment* or *virtual judgment*; for

[8] (Ed.) Cf. 4.639.

[9] But we must say that his attempt at defining an individual is surprisingly feeble; nor is this the only fault of this kind the book contains. But the truth is that the intellectual life of Harvard has, ever since Dr. Walker's death, been languishing more and more for want of a good sharp logician. To one who visits it once in every four or five years this is more noticeable than to a man living there.

since he is considering cognition in its truth or falsity, and only judgments have truth or falsity, he would thus have made himself more explicit and clear. Reality belongs primarily to *facts*, and attaches to *things* only as elements of facts. A judgment asserts that certain consequences would result from more or less vaguely indicated lines of action, which would be so many experiments. Now by the internal meaning or purpose of an idea Prof. Royce, if we rightly gather his intention, understands all the experiments which would verify it. We can hardly believe that he is so entirely won over to the extreme pragmatism of his colleague, James, as to hold that Doing is the ultimate purpose of life. Nor is this necessary; for the purpose of an experiment is to learn, and the performance of it is only a means to that end. This internal meaning calls, then, for more and more definiteness without cessation; and the limit toward which it thus tends but never fully attains is the knowledge of an individual, in short, of God. All this part of the discussion is susceptible of much improvement, which will come when the idea of continuity has been more fully analyzed. But, as it stands, it is a very notable contribution to the *prima philosophia*; and we need not say that in the book itself the thought shines out far more brightly and vivifyingly than it can shine through the cranny of our poor notice of it.

116. One word about the appearance of the book. The press-work is not quite uniform. Some pages are splendid. Others have greyish areas. The shape of the page is singularly pleasing, and we have been led to compare it with other serious octavos, in search of some reason for the sense of pleasure it imparts. We find that in English octavos, not mathematical, the diagonal of the rectangle of solid text divides the right angle between the vertical and horizontal edges into $\frac{1}{3}$ and $\frac{2}{3}$, or 30° and 60°. In American octavos, which are perhaps a little handsomer in shape, the same slope drawn from a bottom corner will intersect the opposite vertical edge half way between the text and the running title. Mathematical octavos are made broader, in order to accommodate long formulae; and they are far more pleasing in appearance. Now it is well-known that owing to the lesser strength of the muscles that cause the vertical motions of the eyeball, a rectangle that looks square really has a height less than its breadth by about one tenth part. In

order, therefore, to find the ratio of height to breadth in a rectangle whose diagonal shall seem to the eye to divide the right angle into a third and a two-thirds, we must take 9/10 of the tangent of 60°, which gives 1.559. In this pleasing page of Royce's volume, we find the height of the solid text is 1.556 times the breadth, which agrees as closely as the measurement can be made. Two diagonals drawn across the page in pencil will seem to make two equilateral triangles.

§2. SECOND SERIES: NATURE, MAN, AND THE MORAL ORDER [10]

117.   Professor Royce's second and concluding volume discusses questions of intimate interest to everybody. It is more persuasive than the first, of which it enhances the significance. The design of the whole now comes out — to introduce into the Hegelian philosophy of religion such rectifications as must result from recognition of scientific conceptions worked out

[10] (Ed.) Paragraphs 117 (in part), 120 (in part), and 126–130 are from the review of Josiah Royce's *The World and the Individual*: Gifford Lectures [on Natural Religion] delivered before the University of Aberdeen, Second Series: Nature, Man, and the Moral Order (Macmillan, 1901, 480 pp.), *The Nation* 75 (31 July 1902) 94–96, with added quotations in the present footnote. Paragraphs 117 (in part), 118–119, 120 (in part), 121–125, and 131 are from various partial drafts of this review, Widener IV, dated c.1902 on the basis of the dates of the book and of the published review, with added quotations in 117n12 and 122n19.

In a letter to James dated 25 November 1902 (James Collection, Houghton Library) Peirce remarks: "As for the *Nation*, I get $250 a year from it on which we live; and therefore I cannot speak above a whisper about it. But the way my bits (bad enough, at best) are cut is awful. I was really wounded at the way all the praise was cut out of my notice of Royce."

In a letter to "My dear Prof. Royce," dated 27 May 1902, Widener VB2a, Peirce says: "I am going to try to say what should be said of your second Volume in the *Nation*. I shall send Garrison something which is too long for anybody to read and too short to express what I try to cram into it; and Garrison will cut it down so as to leave what will strike the afternoon businessman on his way uptown hanging on to a strap, as smartly said, and whether or not it will mean anything to you I can't say. So in case it shouldn't get said there, as I hope it will, I will say *hic et nunc* that the volume has cut off a big piece of the road that it remains for Philosophy to travel before she will join company with the rest of the peaceable sciences. That junction must be made or Philosophy is a humbug. Your best years of philosophic reflection are still before you. The time is ripe and you are the very man to accomplish the great achievement of covering that distance. Yet you could not do it with your present views of logic, antagonistic to all that is possible for progressive science. My entreaty is that you will study logic."

during the century now completing itself since that philosophy first appeared. Of these new conceptions, some are psychological, some logical; but the chief of them are the new mathematical ideas which cluster about that of an infinite multitude. Mathematicians, perhaps, still linger on the stage, who, in their best days, used to be quite positive that one cannot reason mathematically about infinity, and used to feel, like the old lady about her total depravity, that, this cherished inability being taken away, the bottom would fall out of the calculus. Such notions are obsolete. Various degrees of infinity are to-day conceived with perfect definiteness; and the utter misapprehension of the metaphysicians about it, above all of Hegel, glares. As a first serious attempt to apply to philosophical subjects the exactitude of thought that reigns in the mathematical sciences, and this, not on the part of some obscure recluse whose results do not become known to the public, but on that of an eminent professor in a great university, to whom the world is disposed to listen with attention, Royce's "The World and the Individual" will stand a prominent milestone upon the highway of philosophy.[11] Agitating problems to which no man can be indifferent, offering us, at any rate, a sublime conception of the relation of man to God, a fit trellis for [a] vine of religion that might appease the longings of the heart in life and in the hour of death, it is a book about which little fuller information is proper here than concerning any ordinary essay in ontology. . . .[12]

118. Metaphysics is not yet a subject concerning which

[11] (Ed.) The remainder of this paragraph and the following two paragraphs are from manuscript (see 117n10).

[12] (Ed.) The closing paragraph of the letter to Royce, 27 May 1902 (see 117n10), reads: "Underneath your logic which I cannot approve there is a nearly parallel stream of thought perfectly sound and in fact without doubt this was really what has kept you straight so that, — of course, I am saying what *seems to me*, — the affirmatory clauses of your conclusions are approximately right. Your statement of the relation of the individual to God is sublime and fit to satisfy the soul in life and in the hour of death. It must stand for age after age. My feeling is that the individual just fills his little place in the revelation of the universal and except for the sake of what fragment of universal meaning he bears is no account. Like the word 'to' which fills out 'Be or not be' and so helps the effect of the drama of Hamlet. If there is so much glee in heaven over one sinner that repenteth, what must be the deep ineffable felicity to Carnegie of picking up a newspaper in the elevated and so saving his copper. Individuals are cells."

Cf. [Bibliography] M–16a, pp. 300–301.

magisterial judgments can be wise; but surveying its present
situation from the standpoint of a greater respect for physical
science than for theology, and for the objective style of thought
of the English with its faint traditional odor of scholasticism
rather than for German subjectivity, the reviewer has been
brought to believe that metaphysics has at length reached a
point in its disorderly march at which it can now discern,
through the haze upon the distant hill, the place at which it
is destined to join company with the orderly army of science.
Surely, that reunion must take place sometime. All human research must come to be conducted upon some unitary plan.
The pendulum of dispute may swing long; but we must hope
it will at last come to rest. To workers for that end this book
is an encouraging signal. For only let exact diagrammatic conceptions, like those of mathematics, once take the place of the
vague discourse that has prevailed in modern philosophy since
it threw off those wholesome obligations of debate (which kept
the scholastics to precise points and insured their precise arguments' meeting precise criticism), and what more will be needed
to make metaphysics a science? One vital condition must be
satisfied. The scientific man hangs upon the lips of nature, in
order to learn wherein he is ignorant and mistaken: the whole
character of the scientific procedure springs from that disposition. The metaphysician begins with a resolve to make out the
truth of a foregone conclusion that he has really never doubted
for an instant. Hegel was frank enough to avow that so it was
in his case. His "voyage of discovery" was undertaken in order
to recover the very fleece that it professed to bring home. The
development of the metaphysician's thought is a continual
breeding in and in; its destined outcome, sterility. The experiment was fairly tried with Hegelianism through an entire generation of Germans. The metaphysician is a worshipper of his
own prepossessions. As Royce expresses it, he is intent upon
developing his own purpose. The scientific man is eager to
submit himself, his ideas, and his purpose, to the Great Power
which, no doubt, penetrates his own being, but is yet all but
wholly external to him and beyond anything that his poor present notion could ever, of itself, develope unfructified. The Absolute Knowledge of Hegel is nothing but G. W. F. Hegel's
idea of himself; and it has not taught him the very first true

lesson in philosophy, that "whoever shall choose to seek his own purpose and idea shall miss it, and whoever shall abandon his own purpose and idea to adopt the purpose and idea of the Author of nature shall accomplish that, and his own long-abandoned purpose and idea along with it." If the idealist school will add to their superior earnestness the diligence of the mathematician about details, one will be glad to hope that it may be they who shall make metaphysics one of the true sciences. Prof. Royce himself has yet his best years of philosophical reflexion before him. The time seems all but ripe for the achievement of this great benefit to mankind; and he beyond any other now living seems to be the man fit for the undertaking. But it cannot be brought to accomplishment until Hegel is *aufgehoben*, with his mere rotation on his axis. Inquiry must react against experience in order that the ship may be propelled through the ocean of thought. . . .

119. Prof. Royce's theory, roughly sketched, is this. "An Idea is any state of mind that has a conscious meaning." As for the 'meaning,' logicians have recognized since Abélard's day and earlier that there is one thing which any sign, external or internal, stands for, and another thing which it signifies; its denoted breadth, its "connoted" depth. They have further generally held, in regard to the most important signs, that the depth, or signification, is intrinsic, the breadth extrinsic. Prof. Royce applying this doctrine to Ideas, notices their Internal Meaning and their External Meaning. He conceives of the internal meaning in a peculiar way. Another writer, a quarter of a century ago, laid down this maxim: "Consider what effects that might conceivably have practical bearings, we conceive the object of our conception to have. Then our conception of those effects is the *whole* of our conception of the object." [13] In the same pragmatistic spirit, Prof. Royce holds that the Internal Meaning of an idea is a Purpose, obscurely recognized in consciousness, partially fulfilled in being recognized but mainly unfulfilled and ill-understood in itself. The external meaning lies in the fulfillment of the purpose. In the opinion [of] some students who have succeeded in rendering the doctrines of logic more precise than they used to be, it is better to divide the difficulty of defining the meaning of an "idea," by

[13] (Ed.) 5.402; italics not in the text quoted.

first analyzing the nature of a sign in general. For an "idea," as having a meaning, is of the nature of a sign. After the general nature of a sign is once mastered, the problem of determining in what the meaning of an idea consists will evidently be stripped of a portion of its difficulty, and, as it turns out, of the greater portion. But in analyzing the general nature of a sign, it will be needful, to distinguish radically different kinds of signs. A sign may serve as a sign simply because it happens to resemble its object.[14] This resemblance will, then, constitute its internal meaning. But it cannot be said to have any external meaning, since it does not profess to represent anything; for if it did, that would be a manner of signifying its object, not consisting in merely resembling it. There are other signs which become such by virtue of being really connected with their objects.[15] Such is a symptom of disease, or the letters attached to parts of a diagram. The external meaning of such a sign is its most prominent feature. Its internal meaning may be vanishingly small, as in the case of the letters on the diagram, without ever utterly disappearing. There is, however, a third totally different order of signs, which become such, not by virtue of any character of their own as things, nor by virtue of any real connection with their objects, but simply by virtue of being represented to be signs.[16] Thus, the word 'cuckoo' does present a resemblance to the bird; but its onomatopoeia is a mere accident of its origin. It is further most used when cuckoos, or some effects of cuckoos, are really present; but that slight real connection with the birds is insignificant. It is constituted a name for the genus of birds exclusively by the circumstance that an English-speaking hearer of the word will so understand it. Such signs may have little or much internal meaning and external meaning but they have a third kind of meaning which consists in the character of the interpretant signs which they determine. This is their principal meaning. What Prof. Royce calls an "idea" is a sign of this class. For when he defines an idea as a state of mind which consciously "means" something, the whole context shows, as he would admit, that it "means" something in the sense of intending or pur-

---

[14] (Ed.) Peirce generally calls such signs "icons"; see [CP] II.

[15] (Ed.) These are generally called "indices" by Peirce; see [CP] II.

[16] (Ed.) These are generally called "symbols" by Peirce; see [CP] II.

posing something. Now a purposive state of mind is one that signifies something by virtue of intending to be interpreted in a deed. Therefore, although an idea certainly has its internal and its external meaning, yet its principal meaning is of a different kind from either of those.

120.   That the object of an idea, then, its external meaning, is of the nature of a sign could hardly be gainsaid. But Professor Royce finds it not only a sign but an idea; not only one idea but a "concrete" idea in the Hegelian sense, and that, not relatively, but perfectly, and so of the nature of life; and not only life, but an entire life. "The Being of the real object of which you now think, means a life that expresses the fulfilment of just your present plan." [17] We omit an inadmissible qualification [18] and remark that Prof. Royce's theory even if it were proved would not afford the slightest rational assurance that there is any such thing as a reality. In that respect it is, however, no worse than other theories, except in professing to be better.

121.   An arbitrary feature of the theory, and a most regrettable blemish, where the author, too, parts company with Hegel, is that he insists that the object of an idea must be something other, — or as he writes it, Other, — than the idea itself. Not having space to criticize this, we shall simply ignore it in the further account. . . .

122.   But how, it will be asked, can the meaning of a single idea be an entire life? An idea being a state of mind involving a purpose not fully realized, its internal meaning being that purpose so far as it is defined, we can understand that that purpose becomes more and more definite, until, being a sincere purpose, free from *arrière-pensée*, at the moment when it becomes in all respects determinate, it is transformed into an act. . . . But how can it become a complete life? The answer to this is very simple. Royce evidently thinks that a purpose cannot be fully definite, until all the circumstances of the entire life are taken into account; so that, however meagre the in-

[17] (Ed.) The preceding part of this paragraph is from *The Nation*; the following part and subsequent paragraphs are from the manuscripts (see 117n10).

[18] (Ed.) *The World and the Individual*, First Series, p. 359. The full statement reads: "And the Being of the real object of which you now think means a life that expresses the fulfilment of just your present plan, in the greatest measure in which your plan itself is logically capable of fulfilment."

ternal meaning of an idea may be, as long as it remains general and "abstract," yet when that internal meaning is fully accomplished by its becoming in every respect determined, the external meaning will cover the whole life of the individual. Certainly, it is conceivable that such might be the result; but to prove that such would be the result, a far more exact examination of the question would be requisite than the author attempts. There is another difficulty which he removes very happily. How, he supposes his reader to ask, can an idea, which is so microscopic a part of a life, contain within its implication a distinct feature corresponding to every feature of the entire life of which it is only a part? Here, he resorts to Gauss's conception of an *Abbild*, which has played so important a part in mathematics. That is to say, he likens the idea representing the entire life to a map of a country lying upon the ground in that country. Imagine that upon the soil of England, there lies somewhere a perfect map of England, showing every detail, however small. Upon this map, then, will be shown that very ground where the map lies, with the map itself in all its minutest details. There will be a part fully representing its whole, just as the idea is supposed to represent the entire life. On that map will be shown the map itself, and the map of the map will again show a map of itself, and so on endlessly. But each of these successive maps lies well inside the one which it immediately represents. Unless, therefore, there is a hole in the map within which no point represents a point otherwise unrepresented, this series of maps must all converge to a single point which represents itself throughout all the maps of the series. In the case of the idea, that point would be the self-consciousness of the idea. Since an idea is a state of mind with a conscious purpose, it obviously must be self-conscious.[19] Here,

[19] (Ed.) The first paragraph of the letter to Royce, 27 May 1902 (see 117n10 and 117n12), contains the following statement: "Perhaps the most suggestive phrase in your book is your 'dynamo of ideas.' Imagine each ether to be composed of atoms which are vortices in another ether of similar constitution and if the velocity of transmission increases as from sound to light, the whole endless series might be traversed in a fraction of a second, with purely dynamical causation, passing then into an endless series of soul-ethers under causation purely final or formal. No matter how improbable such [a] hypothesis, its mere possibility refutes the principal argument for 'Parallelism.' That is, it shows that though matter cannot act *immediately* upon mind or t'other way it may act all the same upon it. That self-control, self consciousness, involve endless

therefore, is a beautiful and needed, though not complete, confirmation of the idea's really being so related to the entire life. Singularly enough, however, for some reason, Prof. Royce here draws back and supposes the analogy with the map to break down in this respect. . . .

123. It will be perceived that, according to Prof. Royce's theory, if an idea fails of being a Self, it is only because it is general and not fully determined. Its implicit or germinal inward meaning is a little Self representing the entire man as its external meaning. In a similar way, the Self of the man is perhaps included within a larger Self of the community. On the other hand, the man's Self embraces intermediate selves, the domestic Self, the Self of business, the better Self, the evil spirit that sometimes possesses him. Here the author draws support from the psychological doctrine of what he calls the "time-span," a doctrine which, so far as it has really been placed beyond doubt, amounts to little more than that our image of the events of the few seconds last past is, or is very like, a direct perception, while our representation of what happened a minute ago partakes far less of the perceptive character.[20] The phenomenon had already been seized upon by sev-

---

series is clear. There are other *modes* of application, not merely other applications." Cf. 7.370.

The following is the closing paragraph of a letter to "My dear Professor Royce," dated 28 May 1902, Widener VB2a: "I wish you would tell me precisely why it is that you object to making anything its own purpose, or the sign of itself. It seems to me clear that that is just what consciousness is; and if that were admitted, the obstacle to the introduction of higher ideas, which we have but of which you admit no realization in God, would be removed."

[20] (Ed.) In one of the partial drafts (see 117n10), Peirce says in this connection: "Abridge our theory as we may and must, there is one detail which it will not do to omit. That is the use which is made of the psychological doctrine of the 'time span.' That singularly accurate observer, Thomas Reid, whose lessons have not yet been thoroughly learned by psychologists, seems to have been the first distinctly to recognize that we have something very like a direct perception of duration or, at least, of motion; and he drew the needful distinction between the lapse of time during the act of perception and the lapse of time represented in the percept. There are sundry unsettled questions, such as whether there is any consciousness in an instant of time and whether the time that is directly perceived seems to be present or not, but the best modern psychologists even from their precursor, Herbart, and more and more yearly since James's great work, recognize that our image of the last six to twelve seconds past is almost or quite of the nature of a percept, while the remoter past and the future are represented in a more mediated way. One opinion which has been put forward and which seems, at any rate, to be tenable and to harmonize

eral idealistic writers as affording a refutation of dualism; but the large calibre of Royce's thought cannot be better appreciated than by comparing their style of putting the phenomenon to the service of metaphysics with his.

124.   He imagines that greater selves will naturally have vastly longer time-spans than lesser selves. Now a consciousness whose time-span was a thousandth of a second or a thousand years would not ordinarily be recognized by us, as observers of its external manifestations, as being a consciousness, at all. The time-span of the All-seeing must cover all time; and thus foreknowledge and freewill become more clearly reconcilable after the fashion of Boethius, St. Augustine, and others.

125.   Every reality, then, is a Self; and the Selves are intimately connected, as if they formed a continuum. Each one is, so to say, a delineation, — with mathematical truth, incongruous as the metaphor is, we may say that each is a quasi-map of the organic aggregate of all the Selves, which is itself a Self, the Absolute Idea of Hegel, or God. It is a flagrant offence to use this name in philosophy. It is like inviting a man to see the body of his wife dissected. There is also a pretension in it that the philosophy of religion can be religion. But things shocking to right feeling are sometimes necessary in philosophy, as they are in science. It will be observed that if the Selves did form a continuum, each would be distinguished by its own point of Self-consciousness. This would not generally be the same as the point of self-consciousness of an idea within self, since each idea is distinguished by its own exclusive self-consciousness. The systems of delineation must be different. Here we see an inadequacy in the metaphor of the map; for what, more than anything else, makes my ideas mine is that they appeal to me, and are, or tend to become, represented in my general consciousness as representations. But, of course, the map-metaphor must be inadequate, since a map wants several of the essential characters of the class of signs to which

---

with the modern logico-mathematical conceptions, is that our image of the flow of events receives, in a strictly continuous time, strictly continual accessions on the side of the future, while fading in a gradual manner on the side of the past, and that thus the absolutely immediate present is gradually transformed by an immediately given change into a continuum of the reality of which we are thus assured. The argument is that in this way, and apparently in this way only, our having the idea of a true continuum can be accounted for."

ideas belong. Again, in the map the boundaries of the selves are somewhat indeterminate; each must embrace no more nor less than a complete map of the whole surface; but the boundary of any one can be considered to be drawn in any way which fulfills this condition, the boundaries of the others being drawn accordingly, just as on the Mercator's chart, which gives an endless series of representations of the whole globe, any one line from pole to pole may be taken as the boundary of the globe as represented in each chart. But the boundaries between Selves are not so indeterminate, because all that is in one Self appeals by a continuum of representations to that Self's self-consciousness. It will be necessary, therefore, to replace the idea of a map by that of a continuum of maps overlying one another. A map is a section of a projection of which the surface mapped is another section. The projection itself is a sheaf of lines which diverge from one point. Instead of saying that a Self is a map, a more adequate metaphor would call it a projection of the reality, of which projection any one idea of the Self is a section. At any rate, it is plain that the map-metaphor requires deep emendation in order to answer the purposes of philosophy. At the same time, it is a considerable aid even as it is; and the initiating of the introduction of such exact ideas into philosophy is one of the momentous events in its history.[21]

126. All reasoning goes upon the assumption that there is a true answer to whatever question may be under discussion, which answer cannot be rendered false by anything that the disputants may say or think about it; and further, that the denial of that true answer is false.[22] This makes an apparent difficulty for idealism. For if all reality is of the nature of an actual idea, there seems to be no room for possibility or any lower mode than actuality, among the categories of being. (Hegel includes modality only in his Subjective Logic.) But what, then, can be the mode of being of a representation or meaning unequivocally false? For Hegel, the false is the bad, that which is out of harmony with its own essence; and since, in his view, contradiction is the great form of activity of the

---

[21] (Ed.) The following paragraphs are from *The Nation* (see 117n10).

[22] (Ed.) Cf. 5.384 and Chapter 2 on *The Works of George Berkeley* in the present book.

world, he has no difficulty in admitting that an idea may be
out of harmony with itself. Prof. Royce, however, seems almost to resent the idea that anybody could suppose that he
denied the validity of the distinction of truth and falsehood.
He is fairly outspoken in pronouncing sundry doctrines false
(a word Hegel hardly uses), even if we do not quite hear his
foot come down; and nothing does he hold more false than the
usual form of stating the distinction now in question, namely,
that a true proposition corresponds to a *real matter of fact*,
by which is meant a state of things, definite and individual,
which *does not consist merely in being represented (in any particular representation) to be as it is*. For example, if I dream
that I find I can float in the air, this matter of dream is not
matter of fact, for the reason that the only sense in which I can
float in the air is that so my dream represented the matter.
Now Prof. Royce offers to demonstrate by necessary reasoning
that the statement — or, as he expresses it, that "to be real
means to be independent of ideas which relate to that being" [23]
— is false. His argument to this effect will serve as a sufficiently characteristic, but rather favorable sample of his general style of argumentation.

127.   Having given us to understand that he is going to disprove the proposition, he opens his argumentation by declaring that he does not know what the proposition means. Thereupon, he proceeds to propound a general maxim of procedure
for all cases in which one has to refute a proposition without
knowing what it means. It is to begin by assigning to it its
"most extreme form." This certainly does not signify the most
extremely defensible meaning, but rather the most extremely indefensible meaning that the language will bear. The proposition having been refuted in this extreme sense, it will only be
necessary afterwards to argue that other interpretations make
no essential difference. This maxim, one would suppose, would
prove very serviceable to anybody who should have any large
amount of that sort of refutation to perform. In accordance
with this maxim, Prof. Royce begins by assuming that realists
hold that no idea in the slightest degree determines the real

---

[23] (Ed.) ". . . to be real means to be independent of ideas which, while
other than a given real being, still relate to that being." *The World and the
Individual*, First Series, pp. 92–93.

object of it, whether causally or in any other manner. Whether this does not overstep the limits of admissible interpretation, seeing that a realist who meant this would deny that any promise can really be kept, or that any purpose can influence the real result, the reader must say. At any rate, it would not seem to be a difficult position to refute.

128. Now in order that he may get the realist where he wants him, there are two acknowledgments which Professor Royce endeavors to extort from him. To bring him to the first, the author assumes the principle that all causal action is reciprocal, or of the nature of reaction. This is evidently contrary to popular opinion, which holds that while the past has exerted some efficient causality upon the future, the future cannot have any *effect*, in the strict sense of that word, upon the past; and that while the future may have influenced the past by final, or ideal, causation, the past cannot possibly influence the future as the aim of the future. The reader may judge whether a realist of so extreme a type as that which Professor Royce has set up would or would not admit that the real object of an idea cannot have influenced the idea, in the absence of any attempt on the part of Professor Royce to prove his general principle of reciprocity. If he would not, old-fashioned logic (which Hegelians, it is true, hold in high contempt) would pronounce the attempted demonstration to be a bald *petitio principii*.

129. In order to extract the second acknowledgment from the realist, Professor Royce produces an argument which would seem to have as much force for one kind of realist as for another. He supposes two objects, B and R, to be related to one another as the realist supposes the Being, or the real object of an idea, and the Representation, in the form of an idea of that object, to be related; and he undertakes to define the relation between them. "The definition in question," he says, "is, as a mere abstract statement, easy." [24] One would think so. The realist simply says that B is not constituted by its being represented in R; that is, he says that the fact that B is as it is, would be logically consistent with R's representing it to be otherwise. But in place of this easily comprehensible relation, what fantastic attempt do we find at the definition that

[24] (Ed.) *The World and the Individual*, First Series, p. 118.

was pronounced to be so easy! Professor Royce will have it
that the realist holds that the relation is such that no matter
how R may be metamorphosed, it is logically possible for B to
remain unchanged. In such a sense, what two things in the
world are independent? Change the problematic madness of
Hamlet into the pacification of the Philippines, and it will become logically inconsistent with the continuance of great disturbances there. But change the doubtful *representation* by
Shakspere that the fictitious Hamlet was unhinged into the
representation that the Philippines were pacificated in 1901,
and it will not have the slightest logical consequence for the
real state of things. The truth is, that Professor Royce is blind
to a fact which all ordinary people will see plainly enough; that
the essence of the realist's opinion is that it is one thing to *be*
and another thing to *be represented*; and the cause of this
cecity is that the Professor is completely immersed in his absolute idealism, which precisely consists in denying that distinction. It is his element, and there is total reflection at its surface. That, however, is what Professor Royce asks the realist
to admit as a premise. The conclusion which he deduces from
it is that if B is linked as cause to any determination of R,
there must be a *tertium quid* by the mediation of which the
causation takes place. Now the premise is absurd; and the
formal rule is that from an absurd premise every conclusion
must be allowed to be logical; that is to say, it is needless to
dispute its logicality, the premise being false. The argument,
therefore, cannot be called formally bad; nor can we object
that a few lines below, in a restatement of the conclusion, B's
being linked as cause gets changed into B's having any causal
or other linkage.

130.   Professor Royce, armed with his wrong definition of
realism, goes on to a dilemma to show that, whether the realist
says that real things are one or are many, he equally involves
himself in contradiction. But, although the characteristics of
his style of argumentation become even more prominent in that
dilemma, the exigencies of space forbid our following him
further. But we should like to say one word to this powerful
and accurate thinker who has been so completely led astray in
his argumentation by his Hegelian logic: Absolute idealism
depends, as Hegel saw that it did, upon assuming that position

at the outset. If your refutation of realism is addressed to students who are already absolute idealists at heart, we will not undertake to say whether it will be serviceable for the development of that doctrine, or not. But if it is addressed to realists themselves, it must conform to the logical principles recognized by realists, or be nugatory. Now you know very well that realists do not admit that matter of fact can be apodeictically demonstrated. You ought to know, and surely you do know, that if you drive them into a corner, they will simply modify their admissions so far as may be necessary to avoid self-contradiction, and that from the very nature of apodeictic proof it is absolutely impossible to close off such escape in arguing about matter of fact. The history of the doctrine of parallels illustrates what logic shows to be necessarily the state of the case.[25] But the question of realism is a question of hard fact, if ever there was a hard fact; and therefore your method must be revolutionized if you are ever to convince any master of logic.[26]

131. Now let us address a few words to the author. A healthy religious spirit will not allow its religion to be disturbed by all the philosophy in the world. Nevertheless, a philosophy of religion deeply concerns us all. It is not a religious, but an intellectual need to bring our ideas into some harmony. Prof. Royce has inaugurated a vast reform, affecting not only the philosophy of religion but every department of metaphysics, and consisting in sweeping away all the vaguenesses and vagaries that now prevail in that science and replacing them by such exact ideas as Weierstrass and Cantor have begun to introduce into mathematics. No other man in the world, prominently before the public, is half so capable of working this matter out as he. What he has done is merely a preliminary essay. It is a pity that it fills a thousand pages. We want another book of about the same size; only instead of being written in the loose form of lectures, we want it to be a condensed and severe treatise, in which the innumerable vague and unsatisfactory points of the present exposition shall be minutely examined, in which *all* the new conceptions of multitude and continuity, and not merely that of the endless series, shall be applied not merely in the single narrow way in which that one is here applied, but

[25] (Ed.) Cf. Chapter 5, "On Non-Euclidean Geometry," in the present book.
[26] (Ed.) The following paragraph is from manuscript (see 117n10).

in every way, not merely to the one matter to which it is here
applied but to every subject of metaphysics from top to bottom, together with whatsoever other exact diagrammatic conceptions can be produced, and the whole reasoning, so far as it
is demonstrative, be rendered diagrammatic,[27] and so far as it
relates to questions of fact be made scientific. To illustrate
what various applications may be made of the idea of the endless series, it may be noted that admitting the actuality of this,
it does not follow that because A (or mind) cannot act directly
upon B (or matter), . . . A cannot act upon B without the
intervention of a *tertium quid*.[28] The bearing of this simple
remark upon the theory of Parallelism and upon the philosophy of conduct is dynamitic.[29] This is the work which it is
Prof. Royce's duty to give to the world, and the world's
bounden duty to aid Royce to produce, no matter how many
dimes, cents, and dollars it may cost.

[27] (Ed.) Cf. [CP] IV, Book II, "Existential Graphs."
[28] (Ed.) Cf. 8.168.
[29] (Ed.) Cf. 122n19.

CHAPTER 7

KARL PEARSON, *THE GRAMMAR OF SCIENCE* [1]

§1. THE JUSTIFICATION OF SCIENTIFIC RESEARCH

132.   If any follower of Dr. Pearson thinks that in the observations I am about to make I am not sufficiently respectful to his master, I can assure him that without a high opinion of his powers I should not have taken the trouble to make these annotations, and without a higher opinion still, I should not have used the bluntness which becomes the impersonal discussions of mathematicians.

133.   An introductory chapter of ethical content sounds the dominant note of the book. The author opens with the declaration that our conduct ought to be regulated by the Darwinian theory. Since that theory is an attempt to show how natural causes tend to impart to stocks of animals and plants characters which, in the long run, promote reproduction and thus insure the continuance of those stocks, it would seem that making Darwinism the guide of conduct ought to mean that the continuance of the race is to be taken as the *summum bonum*, and '*Multiplicamini*' as the epitome of the moral law. Professor Pearson, however, understands the matter a little differently, expressing himself thus: "The sole reason [for encouraging] any form of human activity . . . lies in this: [its] exist-

---

[1] (Ed.) Paragraphs 132–152 are the review, "Pearson's Grammar of Science, Annotations on the First Three Chapters" (second edition, Adams and Charles Black, London, 1900, 548 pp.), *The Popular Science Monthly* 58(Jan 1901)296–306, with added quotations in 136n3 and 138n4. Paragraphs 153–156 and 136n3 are from a partial draft of this review, Widener IV, dated c.1900 on the basis of the dates of the book and the published review.

Cf. Peirce's review of the first edition, [Bibliography] N–1892–10 and the brief notice of the second edition, [Bibliography] N–1900–12.

ence tends to promote the welfare of human society, to increase social happiness, or to strengthen social stability. In the spirit of the age we are bound to question the value of science; to ask in what way it increases the happiness of mankind or promotes social efficiency." [2]

134.   The second of these two statements omits the phrase, 'the welfare of human society,' which conveys no definite meaning; and we may, therefore, regard it as a mere diluent, adding nothing to the essence of what is laid down. Strict adhesion to Darwinian principles would preclude the admission of the 'happiness of mankind' as an ultimate aim. For on those principles everything is directed to the continuance of the stock, and the individual is utterly of no account, except in so far as he is an agent of reproduction. Now there is no other happiness of mankind than the happiness of individual men. We must, therefore, regard this clause as logically deleterious to the purity of the doctrine. As to 'social stability,' we all know very well what ideas this phrase is intended to convey to English apprehensions; and it must be admitted that Darwinism, generalized in due measure, may apply to English society the same principles that Darwin applied to breeds. A family in which the standards of that society are not traditional will go under and die out, and thus 'social stability' tends to be maintained.

135.   But against the doctrine that social stability is the sole justification of scientific research, whether this doctrine be adulterated or not with the utilitarian clause, I have to object, first, that it is historically false, in that it does not accord with the predominant sentiment of scientific men; second, that it is bad ethics; and, third, that its propagation would retard the progress of science.

136.   Professor Pearson does not, indeed, pretend that that which effectually animates the labors of scientific men is any desire 'to strengthen social stability.' Such a proposition would be too grotesque. Yet if it was his business, in treating of the grammar of science, to set forth the legitimate motive to research — as he has deemed it to be — it was certainly also his business, especially in view of the splendid successes of science, to show what has, in fact, moved such men. They have, at

[2] (Ed.) *The Grammar of Science*, p. 8; the brackets are Peirce's.

all events, not been inspired by a wish either to 'support social stability' or, in the main, to increase the sum of men's pleasures. The man of science has received a deep impression of the majesty of truth, as that to which, sooner or later, every knee must bow.[3] He has further found that his own mind is suffi-

[3] (Ed.) "The scientific man is deeply impressed with the majesty of truth, as something reasonable or intelligible which is bound sooner or later to force itself upon every mind. It is not too much to say that he worships the divine majesty of the power of reasonableness behind the fact. From that sentiment springs his ardent desire to further the discovery of truth. If he cannot discover it himself he wishes to lay a sure foundation from which some successor may come to the truth; — and the more far-reaching and general the particular question that he aims [at], the more it inspires him. It may be that all that he himself expects to ascertain is a minute fact, — say the parallax of a star. But he anticipates that this fact along with many others will ultimately lead to a great discovery. Will not every scientific researcher acknowledge the substantial accuracy of this statement of his motive?

"That it is a better motive than that which Prof. Pearson gives as the 'sole reason' for encouraging any form of human activity is easily shown. Every object which ever has been proposed as desirable in itself without any ulterior reason belongs to one or other of three classes. Namely it either consists

A. in superinducing upon feeling a particular quality, say pleasure; or

B. in extending the existence of some well-known thing, whether one's own life, or some known Creed or community, or what not, — or

C. in furthering the realization of some ideal description of a state of things.

"The desire for the stability of a particular social organization, say that of Great Britain, is a motive belonging to class B. The desire to further the discovery of truth, by whomsoever may be in a condition to discover it, belongs to class C. So also does the utilitarian end with which Prof. Pearson, following Herbert Spencer, adulterates his Darwinism; for it is highly unjust to confuse utilitarianism with simple hedonism of the pursuit of pleasure. That love for an individual thing, such as the British community, which is necessarily full of faults, is a less rational motive than the desire to realize an ideal state of things is almost too plain for argument. But it may be observed that if pleasure ought to be desired for itself, it is because it is desired; and whether that is a good reason or not, it is a reason; so that it cannot be said that pleasure ought to be desired without any reason. And if we ought to desire the extended existence of any particular object, it must be because that object has some good character, so that again there is a reason. In order to judge of the desire for the realization of a universal ideal, it is necessary to distinguish the character of that ideal; and here again there are three classes:

I. The ideal is one which recommends itself to immediate feeling. Such is the utilitarian ideal of the greatest pleasure of the greatest number. But if pleasure itself is good only for a reason, so *à fortiori* is such a generalization of it.

II. The ideal is a generalization of some familiar kind of good; such as the government of altruistic motives, or a state of society in which nothing is wasted. But if such characters are good, it must be because of some feature which renders them so. Besides, they would cease to be good if carried too far.

III. The ideal is one whose character cannot be known in advance, so that it can only be defined as the result, whatever it may be, of a process recognized as productive of good.

105

ciently akin to that truth, to enable him, on condition of submissive observation, to interpret it in some measure. As he
gradually becomes better and better acquainted with the character of cosmical truth, and learns that human reason is its
issue and can be brought step by step into accord with it, he
conceives a passion for its fuller revelation. He is keenly aware
of his own ignorance, and knows that personally he can make
but small steps in discovery. Yet, small as they are, he deems
them precious; and he hopes that by conscientiously pursuing
the methods of science he may erect a foundation upon which
his successors may climb higher. This, for him, is what makes
life worth living and what makes the human race worth perpetuation. The very being of law, general truth, reason — call
it what you will — consists in its expressing itself in a cosmos
and in intellects which reflect it, and in doing this progressively;
and that which makes progressive creation worth doing — so
the researcher comes to feel — is precisely the reason, the law,
the general truth for the sake of which it takes place.

137.   Such, I believe, as a matter of fact, is the motive which
effectually works in the man of science. That granted, we have
next to inquire which motive is the more rational, the one just
described or that which Professor Pearson recommends. The
ethical text-books offer us classifications of human motives.
But for our present purpose it will suffice to pass in rapid
review some of the more prominent ethical classes of motives.

138.   A man may act with reference only to the momentary
occasion, either from unrestrained desire, or from preference for
one desideratum over another, or from provision against future
desires, or from persuasion, or from imitative instinct, or from
dread of blame, or in awed obedience to an instant command;
or he may act according to some general rule restricted to his
own wishes, such as the pursuit of pleasure, or self-preserva-

---

"In order to judge of this third kind of ideal, it is requisite again to sub-
divide. Any such ideal belongs to one or other of three classes, as follows:

i. The natural development of feeling may be recognized as good and its
ultimate dictum as the ideal. This is sentimentalism. But if the natural man
is so good, it is by virtue of a contingent fact, which constitutes a reason for it.

ii. A developmental process of the world of experience may be recognized
as good and its ultimate limit as the ideal.

iii. Reasoning may be recognized as good, and the reasonable as the
ideal." From the partial draft (see 132n1).

tion, or good-will toward an acquaintance, or attachment to home and surroundings, or conformity to the customs of his tribe, or reverence for a law; or, becoming a moralist, he may aim at bringing about an ideal state of things definitely conceived, such as one in which everybody attends exclusively to his own business and interest (individualism), or in which the maximum total pleasure of all beings capable of pleasure is attained (utilitarianism), or in which altruistic sentiments universally prevail (altruism), or in which his community is placed out of all danger (patriotism), or in which the ways of nature are as little modified as possible (naturalism); or he may aim at hastening some result not otherwise known in advance than as that, whatever it may turn out to be, to which some process seeming to him good must inevitably lead, such as whatever the dictates of the human heart may approve (sentimentalism), or whatever would result from every man's duly weighing, before action, the advantages of his every purpose (to which I will attach the nonce-name *entelism*, distinguishing it and others below by italics), or whatever the historical evolution of public sentiment may decree (*historicism*), or whatever the operation of cosmical causes may be destined to bring about (evolutionism); or he may be devoted to truth, and may be determined to do nothing not pronounced reasonable, either by his own cogitations (rationalism), or by public discussion (dialecticism), or by crucial experiment; or he may feel that the only thing really worth striving for is the generalizing or assimilating elements in truth, and that either as the sole object in which the mind can ultimately recognize its veritable aim (educationalism), or that which alone is destined to gain universal sway (pancratism), or, finally, he may be filled with the idea that the only reason that can reasonably be admitted as ultimate is that living reason for the sake of which the psychical and physical universe is in process of creation (*religionism*).[4]

[4] (Ed.) In a letter of 14 July 1905 with the salutation, "My dear Russell," Widener VB2a, Peirce says: "Decidedly I must send you my article of Jan 1901 [the present review]. Your *summum bonum*, 'life,' is probably at bottom about the same as mine, though I view it more concretely. I look upon creation as going on and I believe that such vague idea as we can have of the power of creation is best identified with the idea of theism. So then the ideal would be to be fulfilling our appropriate offices in the work of creation. Or to come

139.   This list of ethical classes of motives may, it is hoped, serve as a tolerable sample upon which to base reflections upon the acceptability as ultimate of different kinds of human motives; and it makes no pretension to any higher value. The enumeration has been so ordered as to bring into view the various degrees of generality of motives. It would conduce to our purpose, however, to compare them in other respects. Thus, we might arrange them in reference to the degree to which an impulse of dependence enters into them, from express obedience, generalized obedience, conformity to an external exemplar, action for the sake of an object regarded as external, the adoption of a motive centering on something which is partially opposed to what is present, the balancing of one consideration against another, until we reach such motives as unrestrained desire, the pursuit of pleasure, individualism, sentimentalism, rationalism, educationalism, religionism, in which the element of otherness is reduced to a minimum. Again, we might arrange the classes of motives according to the degree in which immediate qualities of feeling appear in them, from unrestrained desire, through desire present but restrained, action for self, action for pleasure generalized beyond self, motives involving a retro-consciousness of self in outward things, the personification of the community, to such motives as direct obedience, reverence, naturalism, evolutionism, experimentalism, pancratism, religionism, in which the element of self-feeling is reduced to a minimum. But the important thing is to make ourselves thoroughly acquainted, as far as possible from the inside, with a variety of human motives ranging over the whole field of ethics.

140.   I will not go further into ethics than simply to remark that all motives that are directed toward pleasure or self-satisfaction, of however high a type, will be pronounced by every experienced person to be inevitably destined to miss the satisfaction at which they aim. This is true even of the highest of such motives, that which Josiah Royce develops in his 'World and Individual.' [5] On the other hand, every motive involving

---

down to the practical, every man sees some task cut out for him. Let him do it, and feel that he is doing what God made him in order that he should do."

The letter was written to Francis C. Russell, a Chicago attorney and friend.

[5] (Ed.) Cf. Peirce's review of this work, Chapter 6 in the present book.

dependence on some other leads us to ask for some ulterior reason. The only desirable object which is quite satisfactory in itself without any ulterior reason for desiring it, is the reasonable itself. I do not mean to put this forward as a demonstration; because, like all demonstrations about such matters, it would be a mere quibble, a sheaf of fallacies. I maintain simply that it is an experiential truth.

141.   The only ethically sound motive is the most general one; and the motive that actually inspires the man of science, if not quite that, is very near to it — nearer, I venture to believe, than that of any other equally common type of humanity. On the other hand, Professor Pearson's aim, 'the stability of society,' which is nothing but a narrow British patriotism, prompts the *cui bono* at once. I am willing to grant that England has been for two or three centuries a most precious factor of human development. But there were and are *reasons* for this. To demand that man should aim at the stability of British society, or of society at large, or the perpetuation of the race, as an *ultimate* end, is too much. The human species will be extirpated sometime; and when the time comes the universe will, no doubt, be well rid of it. Professor Pearson's ethics are not at all improved by being adulterated with utilitarianism, which is a lower motive still. Utilitarianism is one of the few theoretical motives which has unquestionably had an extremely beneficial influence. But the greatest happiness of the greatest number, as expounded by Bentham, resolves itself into merely superinducing the quality of pleasure upon men's immediate feelings. Now, if the pursuit of pleasure is not a satisfactory ultimate motive for me, why should I enslave myself to procuring it for others? Leslie Stephen's book was far from uttering the last word upon ethics; but it is difficult to comprehend how anybody who has read it reflectively can continue to hold the mixed doctrine that no action is to be encouraged for any other reason than that it either tends to the stability of society or to general happiness.

142.   Ethics, as such, is extraneous to a Grammar of Science; but it is a serious fault in such a book to inculcate reasons for scientific research the acceptance of which must tend to lower the character of such research. Science is, upon the whole, at present in a very healthy condition. It would not re-

main so if the motives of scientific men were lowered. The worst feature of the present state of things is that the great majority of the members of many scientific societies, and a large part of others, are men whose chief interest in science is as a means of gaining money, and who have a contempt, or half-contempt, for pure science. Now, to declare that the sole reason for scientific research is the good of society is to encourage those pseudo-scientists to claim, and the general public to admit, that they, who deal with the applications of knowledge, are the true men of science, and that the theoreticians are little better than idlers.

143.   In Chapter II., entitled 'The Facts of Science,' we find that the 'stability of society' is not only to regulate our conduct, but, also, that our opinions have to be squared to it. In section 10 we are told that we must not believe a certain purely theoretical proposition because it is 'anti-social' to do so, and because to do so 'is opposed to the interests of society.' As to the 'canons of legitimate inference' themselves, that are laid down by Professor Pearson, I have no great objection to them. They certainly involve important truths. They are excessively vague and capable of being twisted to support illogical opinions, as they are twisted by their author, and they leave much ground uncovered. But I will not pursue these objections. I do say, however, that truth is truth, whether it is opposed to the interests of society to admit it or not — and that the notion that we must deny what it is not conducive to the stability of British society to affirm is the mainspring of the mendacity and hypocrisy which Englishmen so commonly regard as virtues. I must confess that I belong to that class of scallawags who purpose, with God's help, to look the truth in the face, whether doing so be conducive to the interests of society or not. Moreover, if I should ever attack that excessively difficult problem, 'What is for the true interest of society?' I should feel that I stood in need of a great deal of help from the science of legitimate inference; and, therefore, to avoid running round a circle, I will endeavor to base my theory of legitimate inference upon something less questionable — as well as more germane to the subject — than the true interest of society.

§2. NATURAL LAW

144. The remainder of this chapter on the 'Facts of Science' is taken up with a theory of cognition, in which the author falls into the too common error of confounding psychology with logic. He will have it that knowledge is built up out of sense-impressions — a correct enough statement of a conclusion of psychology. Understood, however, as Professor Pearson understands and applies it, as a statement of the nature of our logical data, of 'the facts of science,' it is altogether incorrect. He tells us that each of us is like the operator at a central telephone office, shut out from the external world, of which he is informed only by sense-impressions. Not at all! Few things are more completely hidden from my observation than those hypothetical elements of thought which the psychologist finds reason to pronounce 'immediate,' in his sense.[6] But the starting point of all our reasoning is not in those sense-impressions, but in our percepts. When we first wake up to the fact that we are thinking beings and can exercise some control over our reasonings, we have to set out upon our intellectual travels from the home where we already find ourselves. Now, this home is the parish of percepts. It is not inside our skulls, either, but out in the open. It is the external world that we directly observe. What passes within we only know as it is mirrored in external objects. In a certain sense, there is such a thing as introspection; but it consists in an interpretation of phenomena presenting themselves as external percepts. We first see blue and red things. It is quite a discovery when we find the eye has anything to do with them, and a discovery still more recondite when we learn that there is an *ego* behind the eye, to which these qualities properly belong. Our logically initial data are percepts. Those percepts are undoubtedly purely psychical, altogether of the nature of thought. They involve three kinds of psychical elements, their qualities of feelings, their reaction against my will, and their generalizing or associating element. But all that we find out afterward. I see an inkstand on the table: that is a percept. Moving my head, I get a different percept of the inkstand. It coalesces with the other. What I

---

[6] (Ed.) Cf. 5.213ff., [Bibliography] G–1868–2.

call the inkstand is a generalized percept, a quasi-inference from percepts, perhaps I might say a composite-photograph of percepts. In this psychical product is involved an element of resistance to me, which I am obscurely conscious of from the first. Subsequently, when I accept the hypothesis of an inward subject for my thoughts, I yield to that consciousness of resistance and admit the inkstand to the standing of an external object. Still later, I may call this in question. But as soon as I do that, I find that the inkstand appears there in spite of me. If I turn away my eyes, other witnesses will tell me that it still remains. If we all leave the room and dismiss the matter from our thoughts, still a photographic camera would show the inkstand still there, with the same roundness, polish and transparency, and with the same opaque liquid within. Thus, or otherwise, I confirm myself in the opinion that its characters are what they are, and persist at every opportunity in revealing themselves, regardless of what you, or I, or any man, or generation of men, may think that they are. That conclusion to which I find myself driven, struggle against it as I may, I briefly express by saying that the inkstand is a *real* thing. Of course, in being real and external, it does not in the least cease to be a purely psychical product, a generalized percept, like everything of which I can take any sort of cognizance.

145.   It might not be a very serious error to say that the facts of science are sense-impressions, did it not lead to dire confusion upon other points. We see this in Chapter III.,[7] in whose long meanderings through irrelevant subjects, in the endeavor to make out that there is no rational element in nature, and that the rational element of natural laws is imported into them by the minds of their discoverers, it would be impossible for the author to lose sight entirely of the bearing of the question which he himself has distinctly formulated, if he were not laboring with the confusing effects of his notion that the data of science are the sense-impressions. It does not occur to him that he is laboring to prove that the mind has a marvelous power of creating an element absolutely supernatural — a power that would go far toward establishing a dualism quite antagonistic to the spirit of his philosophy. He evidently imagines that those who believe in the reality of law, or the rational

[7] (Ed.) The title of Chapter III is "The Scientific Law."

element in nature, fail to apprehend that the data of science are of a psychical nature. He even devotes a section to proving that natural law does not belong to things-in-themselves, as if it were possible to find any philosopher who ever thought it did. Certainly, Kant, who first decked out philosophy with these chaste ornaments of things-in-themselves, was not of that opinion; nor could anybody well hold it after what he wrote. In point of fact, it is not Professor Pearson's opponents but he himself who has not thoroughly assimilated the truth that everything we can in any way take cognizance of is purely mental. This is betrayed in many little ways, as, for instance, when he makes his answer to the question, whether the law of gravitation ruled the motion of the planets before Newton was born, to turn upon the circumstance that the law of gravitation is a formula expressive of the motion of the planets 'in terms of a purely mental conception,' as if there could be a conception of anything not purely mental. Repeatedly, when he has proved the content of an idea to be mental, he seems to think he has proved its object to be of human origin. He goes to no end of trouble to prove in various ways, what his opponent would have granted with the utmost cheerfulness at the outset, that laws of nature are rational; and, having got so far, he seems to think nothing more is requisite than to seize a logical maxim as a leaping pole and lightly skip to the conclusion that the laws of nature are of human provenance. If he had thoroughly accepted the truth that all realities, as well as all figments, are alike of purely mental composition, he would have seen that the question was, not whether natural law is of an intellectual nature or not, but whether it is of the number of those intellectual objects that are destined ultimately to be exploded from the spectacle of our universe, or whether, as far as we can judge, it has the stuff to stand its ground in spite of all attacks. In other words, is there anything that is really and truly a law of nature, or are all pretended laws of nature figments, in which latter case, all natural science is a delusion, and the writing of a grammar of science a very idle pastime?

146. Professor Pearson's theory of natural law is characterized by a singular vagueness and by a defect so glaring as to remind one of the second book of the *Novum Organum* or of some strong chess-player whose attention has been so riveted

113

upon a part of the board that a fatal danger has, as it were, been held upon the blind-spot of his mental retina. The manner in which the current of thought passes from the woods into the open plain and back again into the woods, over and over again, betrays the amount of labor that has been expended upon the chapter. The author calls attention to the sifting action both of our perceptive and of our reflective faculties. I think that I myself extracted from that vein of thought pretty much all that is valuable in reference to the regularity of nature in the POPULAR SCIENCE MONTHLY for June, 1878, (p. 208).[8] I there remarked that the degree to which nature seems to present a general regularity depends upon the fact that the regularities in it are of interest and importance to us, while the irregularities are without practical use or significance; and in the same article I endeavored to show that it is impossible to conceive of nature's being markedly less regular, taking it, 'by and large,' than it actually is. But I am confident, from having repeatedly returned to that line of thought that it is impossible legitimately to deduce from any such considerations the unreality of natural law. 'As a pure suggestion and nothing more,' toward the end of the chapter, after his whole plea has been put in, Dr. Pearson brings forward the idea that a transcendental operation of the perceptive faculty may reject a mass of sensation altogether and arrange the rest in place and time, and that to this the laws in nature may be attributable — a notion to which Kant undoubtedly leaned at one time. The mere emission of such a theory, after his argument has been fully set forth, almost amounts to a confession of failure to prove his proposition. Granting, by way of waiver, that such a theory is intelligible and is more than a nonsensical juxtaposition of terms, so far from helping Professor Pearson's contention at all, the acceptance of it would at once decide the case against him, as every student of the *Critic of the Pure Reason* will at once perceive. For the theory sets the rationality in nature upon a rock perfectly impregnable by you, me or any company of men.

147. Although that theory is only problematically put forth by Professor Pearson, yet at the very outset of his argumentation he insists upon the relativity of regularity to our faculties,

[8] (Ed.) 6.405ff.

as if that were in some way pertinent to the question. "Our law of tides," he says, "could have no meaning for a blind worm on the shore, for whom the moon had no existence." [9] Quite so; but would that truism in any manner help to prove that the moon was a figment and no reality? On the contrary, it could only help to show that there may be more things in heaven and earth than your philosophy has dreamed of. Now the *moon*, on the one hand, and the *law of the tides*, on the other, stand in entirely analogous positions relatively to the remark, which can no more help to prove the unreality of the one than of the other. So, too, the final decisive stroke of the whole argumentation consists in urging substantially the same idea in the terrible shape of a syllogism, which the reader may examine in section 11. I will make no comment upon it.

148.   Professor Pearson's argumentation rests upon three legs. The first is the fact that both our perceptive and our reflective faculties reject part of what is presented to them, and 'sort out' the rest. Upon that, I remark that our minds are not, and cannot be, positively mendacious. To suppose them so is to misunderstand what we all mean by truth and reality. Our eyes tell us that some things in nature are red and others blue; and so they really are. For the real world is the world of insistent generalized percepts. It is true that the best physical idea which we can at present fit to the real world, has nothing but longer and shorter waves to correspond to red and blue. But this is evidently owing to the acknowledged circumstance that the physical theory is to the last degree incomplete, if not to its being, no doubt, in some measure, erroneous. For surely the completed theory will have to account for the extraordinary contrast between red and blue. In a word, it is the business of a physical theory to account for the percepts; and it would be absurd to accuse the percepts — that is to say, the facts — of mendacity because they do not square with the theory.

149.   The second leg of the argumentation is that the mind projects its worked-over impressions into an object, and then projects into that object the comparisons, etc., that are the results of its own work. I admit, of course, that errors and delusions are everyday phenomena, and hallucinations not rare. We have just three means at our command for detecting any

[9] (Ed.) *The Grammar of Science*, p. 85.

unreality, that is, lack of insistency, in a notion. First, many ideas yield at once to a direct effort of the will. We call them *fancies*. Secondly, we can call in other witnesses, including ourselves under new conditions. Sometimes dialectic disputation will dispel an error. At any rate, it may be voted down so overwhelmingly as to convince even the person whom it affects. Thirdly, the last resort is prediction and experimentation. Note that these two are equally essential parts of this method, which Professor Pearson keeps — I had almost said sedulously — out of sight in his discussion of the rationality of nature. He only alludes to it when he comes to his transcendental 'pure suggestion.' Nothing is more notorious than that this method of prediction and experimentation has proved the master-key to science; and yet, in Chapter IV.,[10] Professor Pearson tries to persuade us that prediction is no part of science, which must only describe sense-impressions. (A sense-impression cannot be described.) He does not say that he would permit generalization of the facts. He ought not to do so, since generalization inevitably involves prediction.

150.   The third leg of the argumentation is that human beings are so much alike that what one man perceives and infers another man will be likely to perceive and infer. This is a recognized weakness of the second of the above methods. It is by no means sufficient to destroy that method, but along with other defects it does render resort to the third method imperative. When I see Dr. Pearson passing over without notice the first and third of the only three possible ways of distinguishing whether the rationality of nature is real or not, and giving a lame excuse for reversing the verdict of the second, so that his decision seems to spring from antecedent predilection, I cannot recommend his procedure as affording such an exemplar of the logic of science as one might expect to find in a grammar of science.

151.   An ignorant sailor on a desert island lights in some way upon the idea of the parallelogram of forces, and sets to work making experiments to see whether the actions of bodies conform to that formula. He finds that they do so, as nearly as he can observe, in many trials invariably. He wonders why inanimate things should thus conform to a widely general in-

[10] (Ed.) The title of Chapter IV is "Cause and Effect — Probability."

116

tellectual formula. Just then, a disciple of Professor Pearson lands on the island and the sailor asks him what he thinks about it. "It is very simple," says the disciple, "you see you made the formula and then you projected it into the phenomena." *Sailor*: What are the phenomena? *Pearsonist*: The motions of the stones you experimented with. *Sailor*: But I could not tell until afterward whether the stones had acted according to the rule or not. *Pearsonist*: That makes no difference. You made the rule by looking at some stones, and all stones are alike. *Sailor*: But those I used were very unlike, and I want to know what made them all move exactly according to one rule. *Pearsonist*: Well, maybe your mind is not in time, and so you made all the things behave the same way at all times. Mind, I don't say it is so; but it may be. *Sailor*: Is that all you know about it? Why not say the stones are made to move as they do by something *like* my mind?

152. When the disciple gets home, he consults Dr. Pearson. "Why," says Dr. Pearson, "you must not deny that the facts are really concatenated; only there is no rationality about that." "Dear me," says the disciple, "then there really is a concatenation that makes all the component accelerations of all the bodies scattered through space conform to the formula that Newton, or Lami, or Varignon invented?" "Well, the formula is the device of one of those men, and it conforms to the facts." "To the facts its inventor knew, and also to those he only predicted?" "As for prediction, it is unscientific business." "Still the prediction and the facts predicted agree." "Yes." "Then," says the disciple, "it appears to me that there really is in nature something extremely like action in conformity with a highly general intellectual principle." "Perhaps so," I suppose Dr. Pearson would say, "but nothing in the least like rationality." "Oh," says the disciple, "I thought rationality was conformity to a widely general principle."

———————◆———————

153. To sum up my objections. Prof. Pearson mistakes sense-impressions, which are psychological inferences, for the logical data, and is thus led to confuse his thought in this chapter with matters totally irrelevant to the question which he clearly puts. He fancies that his antagonists fail to appre-

hend the psychical side of the subject; but in fact it is he himself who has not thoroughly assimilated the truth that everything that we can in any way take cognizance of is purely mental. This is a truth, because every object of thought is either a percept or a generalization, that is, an inference from percepts. I am conscious that my meaning here is but vaguely expressed, because I use the word "generalization" in a generalized sense. Unfortunately, I cannot explain myself without tedious developments of exact logic into which I cannot here enter. Meantime, though my meaning can, perhaps, be but dimly apprehended, still it can be sufficiently understood for the purpose in hand. Prof. Pearson, not having fully assimilated the truth that every object is purely mental or psychical, thinks that when he has shown that the content of natural law is intellectual, he is entitled to conclude that it is of human origin. But every scientific research goes upon the assumption, the hope, that, in reference to its particular question, there is some true answer. That which that truth represents is a reality. This reality being cognizable and comprehensible, is of the nature of thought. Wherein, then, does its reality consist? In the fact that, though it has no being out of thought, yet it is as it is, whether you or I or any group of men think it to be so or not. The question of whether Hamlet was insane is the question whether Shakespeare conceived him to be insane. Consequently, Hamlet is a figment and not a reality. But as to the inkstand being on my table, though I should succeed in persuading myself and all who have seen it that it is a mere optical illusion, yet there will be a limit to this, and by the photographic camera, the balance, new witnesses, etc., it will, at last, I guess, force its recognition upon the world. If so, it has the characteristic which we call reality. There is a blind force about the inkstand by which it crowds its way into our universe in spite of all we can do. Prof. Pearson has no difficulty in showing, what his opponents are eager to have him commit himself to, that law is of an intellectual or rational nature; but he slides swiftly and lightly over the passage from that position to its having been introduced into the object by the scientist's own mind. But here is the whole question. Is law real or is it figment? Psychical of course it is; for every thing we can cognize is purely psychical. Intellectual or rational it plainly is. But the question is whether it is among those intellectual objects that are destined ultimately to be exploded from the spectacle of the universe, or whether, as far as we can judge, it has the force to stand its ground indefinitely. It seems clear, to begin with, that to prove law a figment would be to prove all science to be a delusion and a Grammar of Science an idle pastime. Prof. Pearson is very likely quite right when, in a later chapter, he suggests that the law of the parallelogram of forces is not perfectly true. His reasons have great weight. I, for my part, do not believe that any law is perfectly satisfied. If I am right in this, the reality of law is diminished; but it is not thereby abolished. But my argument to show that law is reality and not figment, — is in nature independently of any connivance of ours, — is that predictions are verified. Nobody will maintain that these verifications are chance coincidences. Nor can Prof. Pearson explain how Newton and Laplace have been influential in producing eclipses at the moments they were called for by theory. He does not attempt it. He tells us he admits that phenomena are "concatenated," but that he can see in that nothing that, in any intelligible sense, can be called rational. Here again, I take issue. "Concatenation" is not a fair word in this connection. For "concatenation" implies contiguity in some sense, through which some unintelligible action and reaction can take place. But the different cases in which a law is verified are not connected by contiguity but by resemblance, and that of a very abstract kind. Their connection consists merely in this, that wherever it may be that a certain very broad but definite resemblance occurs, there also resemblance in another definite respect occurs. Now how would you define a reason if not as a very broad definite character which makes us expect the occurrence of another definite character? If Prof. Pearson does not accept this statement, then, since he maintains that there is nothing at all mysterious about law, it was his business to say how he proposed to account for what he very ill describes as the concatenation of sense-impressions, that is to say, the conformity of widely scattered phenomena to the predictions of the scientist. Not to account for it at all, is simply to leave it as a conformity to a rational formula, and therefore as a real reasonableness in nature.

119

154.   From most of the other chapters in the book I should altogether dissent, and most especially from the account of probability in Chapter IV. But I shall, at this time, notice only two small points connected with the above remarks.

155.   In Chapter IV., Prof. Pearson declares that the sole business of science is to describe past experience and not at all to predict the future. This is entirely contrary to the universal opinion of men of science, in whose eyes prediction is the seal of success. Neither can it please those who have been led to expect from the introductory chapter that science would be of some practical service. It would be a maxim utterly blighting to all further progress of science, were it accepted, since it is only by predictions that men are led to devise new experiments. According to this doctrine, scientists should print their notebooks, and do no more. But evidently, science has, not so much to describe experience, as to generalize it. To generalize it is to comprehend it. Moreover, generalization refuses to limit itself to the past, but involves virtual prediction.

156.   In the same chapter, the author says that the *why* of things remains a mystery. He quotes with approval a sentence from Kirchhoff's *Mechanik* to the effect that dynamics is the description, in the simplest terms, of motions. This, except for its indeterminacy, is well enough. But he omits to mention that Kirchhoff goes on to say that what Force is must remain a mystery. But according to my notions there can be no mystery in the universe, in the sense of a real fact to which no approach to knowledge can ever be gained. For a reality is an idea that insists upon proclaiming itself, whether we like it or not. There may be a question that no amount of research can ever answer. If so, there is a *lacuna* in the completeness of reality. But these things usually called mysteries are simply cases in which questions cannot be answered for the reason that no definite meaning can be attached to them. If, for example, we know exactly under what circumstances bodies are accelerated, and what the resulting changes of velocity and position are, you must say definitely what further experience you wish to predict before you talk about a mystery.

CHAPTER 8

REVIEW OF A BOOK ON ETHICS [1]

157. Professor Mezes of the University of Texas has been known to the general public as a scholar of Howison, and as one of the four authors of the sympotic book, 'The Conception of God.' He there produced upon us a mixed impression, for his intellect seemed not to have quite so keen an edge as is called for in philosophy; and yet here and there conceptions appeared so simple and obvious, and yet so novel, that one ransacked one's memory in the endeavor to recall any anticipation of the remark. Much the same impression is renewed by the present book. Hard work and solid has been put into it; and, of course, the harvest must have proportionate value. Parts of the treatise are admirably worked out, and are, at any rate, instructive, even if their conclusions are rejected. But hard work is not all that is required in dealing with such a subject.

158. In aim and method the present work is fully as original as it ought to be. The author belongs to that school of ethics which is probably nearest right — that is to say, to the school which makes tribal tradition a main factor of morality, and which is thus enabled to frame an evolutionary theory of it. But although the author is thus in the van of ethical exploration, a certain old-fashioned and conservative color — attributable, perhaps, to temperament and Texan environment — strongly tinges his theory. Now, conservatism in morals is most needful in practice, and, of course, is theoretically defensible.[2] But that

---

[1] (Ed.) Review of Sidney Edward Mezes' *Ethics: Descriptive and Explanatory* (Macmillan, 1901, 435 pp.), *The Nation* 73(24 Oct 1901)325–326, with an added quotation in 158n3 from an alternative draft, Widener IV, dated 1901 on the basis of the dates of the book and the published review.

[2] (Ed.) Cf. 1.661ff.

defence itself is not conservative: on the contrary, it is ration-
alistic; and in pure theory, especially in a theory of aims, conservatism is irrational and out of place. The writer effects a
reconciliation of his conservatism (which is very likely unconscious) with his advanced views by exaggerating more than
usual a prevalent tendency which we venture to think that the
majority of philosophers of our day carry too far — we mean
the tendency to base everything in philosophy upon the psychical sciences. The immense success of scientific psychology
during the last forty years has very naturally given it a weight
in men's minds that ought not in philosophy to be accorded to
any merely special science, which is precisely what psychology
has all along been striving and struggling to be.[3] On the contrary, it is now generally admitted that psychology, like general physics, necessarily takes for granted a *Weltanschauung*
or outline system of metaphysics. Now, metaphysics can have
no satisfactory grounding except upon a scientific logic; and
logic rests on ethics to a degree that few are aware of. So if
there be no other basis for ethics than psychology, which is a
third story above it, the whole erection floats on air. Ethics
as a positive science must rest on observed facts. But it is quite
a different thing to make it rest on special scientific observation, and still more so to base it upon scientific conclusions.
The only solid foundation for ethics lies in those facts of every-

---

[3] (Ed.) "The immense success of scientific psychology during the last forty
years has naturally given it a weight that a merely special science, which is precisely what it has all along been aiming to be, ought not to have in philosophy.
The special sciences must be built upon philosophy; and consequently if philosophy has no deeper support than a special science, the whole rests on air. The
first duty of ethics is to show us what we really do desire and are willing to
accept as good, without any ulterior reason. This is a question of fact, and
the solution of the problem must be based upon experience. But it is no recondite scientific experience which is wanted; but what is well-known and accepted
by all men, philosophers, scientific men, and all others, unanimously. It is not
a question of how the mind acts. On the contrary, it is only after the moralist
has shown us what is our ultimate aim that the logician can tell how we
ought to think in order to conform to that end. It is only on a scientific logic
that a trustworthy metaphysics can be erected; and that the psychologist does
and must take a metaphysics for granted is now generally admitted. Thus, the
fundamental part, at least, of ethics — what might be called pure ethics, —
ought to precede psychology. Prof. Mezes, however, is not content even to
base ethics upon psychology, but must needs go to the still more special science
of anthropology to find a support for it." From the alternative draft (see
157n1).

day life which no skeptical philosopher ever yet really called in question.

159. Now, Mr. Mezes is so far from taking this view that he maintains that the whole business of the moralist consists in saying what men mean by morality, in describing what they hold to be moral, and in explaining how they come to do so. This is a most interesting and valuable study, but it is ethical anthropology, not pure ethics; and to limit ethics in this way is to be faithless to the first duty of a moralist, as such. "Ethical writers do not in any proper sense," he says, meaning that they overstep the bounds of their province when they do, "judge conduct or issue pronouncements as to what is right or wrong. Their more modest task is to discover and record men's genuine judgments as to what is right or wrong." [4] Let us see how this view of ethics works. A judge, let us suppose, has brought before him a case in which a man has suffered injury for which he claims damages of another. Whether damages ought to be paid in such a case is often, we know, a delicate and puzzling question. We will follow Professor Mezes in using a much too simple illustration, which ought to puzzle nobody. "Take," he says, "the case where A's cattle break out of their enclosure, in spite of A's having used all the care he reasonably could have used, or could learn to use, and destroy B's valuable crop in an adjoining field." [5] This case (or rather another far more difficult) puzzles the judge, and he takes it under advisement. He naturally looks into works on ethics, and, finding nothing pertinent in modern books, is driven to the scholastic treatises. Now, there is nothing in the whole scholastic logic more justly an object of derision for any modern thinker than its weak confusion of thought in its doctrine of causes; nor in that whole doctrine is there any more manifest absurdity than the distinction between a *proximate* and a *remote* cause. When we meet with an application of it in the scholastic commentary on the Sentences, it stands out as so much more nonsensical than the rest as to be comical; but that anybody should be made to suffer because of any consequence of such metaphysical jargon is outrageous flippancy. Yet it is just this outrage that the judge is driven to commit, or to pretend to commit, because

[4] (Ed.) *Ethics*, p. 7.
[5] (Ed.) *Ethics*, p. 34.

the ethical writers have not expounded right and wrong in a sufficiently luminous and reasonable form.

160.   Professor Mezes follows them. He maintains that A, the owner of the cattle, ought to reimburse B for the injury done by them to his crop, because A is the *proximate cause* of B's suffering. If he would not follow the decisions of Texas courts as the ultimate evidence concerning right and wrong, he could not fail to see that the real reason why the judge awards damages to B is that to allow a private person to undertake a business humanly sure in the long run to injure his neighbors (and all the more so if he "cannot learn to use" suitable preventive measures), and then to allow him to pocket all the profits, and make his neighbors pay for incidental losses, would be to bring himself and his court into public contempt and into no little danger. That was the judge's real reason. But in days gone by (perhaps not yet in Texas) if a judge could decide a case justly, and yet by a process of metaphysical reasoning the less intelligible the better, he was regarded with awe by the vulgar; and that was one motive for his seizing upon that argument when he could get no modern light.

161.   One of the distinctive features of Professor Mezes's book is a seventy-page chapter on Justice, in which legal decisions are followed, often in a way which will be repugnant to right-minded readers, and yet not so exclusively that the chapter can be said to constitute an exposition of the traditional legal conception of justice. Professor Mezes defines ultimate good as "the welfare of all sentient beings," but he is doubtful whether it is worth while to have any regard for the welfare either of *bacilli* (are these sentient beings in Texas?) or of criminals of all classes. The last exclusion is characteristic, we are sorry to say. But when we ask what he means by "welfare," in place of a *definition*, nothing is vouchsafed but a *division* of "welfare," in which there are two or three dozen items, such as "easy activity," "sense of personal attractiveness," "sense of solvency," "satisfaction from social standing," "sense of divine favor," "national pride," "self-control," "a body of well-poised spontaneous activities," "systematic ideas of rights and duties," "sagacity." [6] There are those who will think that

⁶ (Ed.) *Ethics*, Chapter XV, "Welfare," pp. 383–409; see especially "Table of Components of Individual Welfare," p. 400.

all this is on a pretty low plane, and we do not see much in the
list about the welfare of earthworms, etc., notwithstanding
the insistence upon "all sentient beings."

162.   The best thing in the book is the psychological analysis of conscience, which is decidedly noticeable. We could
hardly have expected the terminology to be reformed. The
scholastic writers mark two things which they distinguish by
the terms *synderesis* and *conscience* (the latter nearly in the
sense in which it is a household word). The interest of progress
in ethical discussion calls upon us to come to agreement about
the use of technical terms. But each of us is attached to his
own habit, and will not surrender it unless it can be shown
clearly to violate a law to which he has given in his allegiance.
A code of rules is needed, in framing which we cannot do
better than to be guided by the taxonomists, who have had,
of all men, most experience in dealing with similar difficulties.
If we do that, our first rule, subject, perhaps, to a few general
but well-defined classes of exceptions (the fewer the better),
will certainly be that every technical term of philosophy ought
to be used in that sense in which it first became a technical term
of philosophy. This will, generally speaking, result in the greatest accord between the language of philosophy and the vernacular, of which the word *conscience* will be an example. As for
that other thing which a good many moralists call conscience,
some other name ought to be given to it, preferably a new word.
At any rate, not *synderesis*, of which the original meaning, we
are convinced, is not that which Siebeck assigns to it. Professor
Mezes, whose definitions are mostly of doubtful accuracy, distinguishes between conscience about others' acts and conscience
about one's own. But a stay-at-home conscience does the most
to render earth habitable.

163.   As we rise from the reading of the whole book, we find
ourselves saying, If *this* is what morality is, we are disposed to
sympathize with Henry James, the elder, in his very limited
respect for morality.

CHAPTER 9

J. M. BALDWIN, *DICTIONARY OF PHILOSOPHY AND PSYCHOLOGY*, VOL. II [1]

164. Many evidences of different kinds reach us of the good service that this work is already rendering, notwithstanding the imperfections inevitable in any such composite book, and notwithstanding its lack of those formal perfections and uniformities upon which our American dictionaries and cyclopaedias are apt to insist to the neglect of the weightier matters of the law, to the point of leaving them dry, innutritious, and unvitalizing. Professor Baldwin, in the preface of this concluding volume (of the Dictionary proper), puts forth more an excuse than a defence for one of the few features of it that have been disapproved in almost every quarter; urging that the diminutive biographical notices which he has scattered through the vocabulary are that half-loaf that is said to be better than no bread. This hardly meets the stricture commonly made, which was to the effect that the entire omission of these supererogatory crumbs would have left room that might either have been filled to better purpose, or to better purpose have lightened the avoirdupois of the volumes.

165. But a more interesting question suggests itself. Upwards of seventy of the most reputable philosophers [2] whose services a distinguished editor could secure, have here set down their opinions upon the special points of philosophy of which they are reputed best qualified to treat. They have not argued

---

[1] (Ed.) Paragraphs 164–166 and 167 (in part) are from the review of James Mark Baldwin's *Dictionary of Philosophy and Psychology*, Vol. II (Macmillan, 1902, 892 pp.), *The Nation* 76(11 June 1903)482. Paragraphs 167 (in part) and 168–170 are from an alternative draft, Widener IV, dated c.1903 on the basis of the dates of the book and of the published review.

[2] (Ed.) Peirce was one of the contributors; cf. [Bibliography] G–1901–6.

their doctrines, since this is a dictionary, not a cyclopaedia; but they have defined them. All the principal groups of schools are more or less represented in the assemblage of contributors; even the idealists, whose showing is probably the least adequate. One naturally peruses their utterances to see what impression one can derive from them as to the prevalent tendencies of philosophy at the opening of the twentieth century; for surely this is an aspect under which it may be hoped that this dictionary will never lose its interest.

166. The most prominent of the philosophical signs of the times, as here displayed — so it strikes us, at least — is the manifest strenuous endeavor of the students of every department of philosophy to impart a "scientific" character each to his own particular branch, *i.e.*, to make it conform to the conditions which have caused the success of the modern acknowledged sciences. The progress is satisfactory. At least one branch of psychology has already taken its place among the special sciences, whose array others are well upon the way toward joining. The movement is not confined to psychology. There is much of a scientific character in ethics; and the critical part of logic has, in some hands at least, come to submit itself to the same criteria as those that have long been acknowledged in science. There seems every reason for hope concerning metaphysics and other branches.

167. Another mark of our philosophy is the disposition to make psychology the key to philosophy — categories, aesthetics, ethics, logic, and metaphysics. Something of this has existed since Descartes; but since about 1863 every student of philosophy, even though he be one of those who consider the present psychological tendency excessive, has placed a new and higher estimate than before upon the scientific value of psychology. Here was seen one science, than which no branch of philosophy, in the days when men disputed about the *primum cognitum*, was more enveloped in metaphysical fog, which yet almost suddenly, that mist lifting, had come out bright and clear as a June forenoon. How could it but happen, as it certainly did, that men should think that the best way to resolve any problem of philosophy would be to reduce it to a question of psychology? The future must determine precisely what the value of this method may be. It has its opponents. For some

years after the movement once became general, no strong voice was raised against it; and ten or fifteen years ago psychologists of the first rank could dream of establishing the truths of their science without any metaphysical assumptions whatsoever. Some writers use such language even yet; but careful examination has convinced the better part that even physics has its metaphysical postulates, and that psychology is peculiarly dependent upon them.[3] That being the case, some writers urge that if psychology needs to rest upon metaphysics, and metaphysics upon logic, especially if, as some contend, logic rests upon ethics, then to found ethics, logic, and metaphysics in their turn upon a basis of psychology, this self-supporting cycle would rest on nothing. The reply is that the philosophical sciences will support each other, like two drunken sailors. Suffice it to say that the mutual support theory and with it the theory that psychology is the proper foundation for philosophy are not now without vigorous opponents.

168. A third symptom of the philosophy of the day is a reaction against the general agnostic tendency of a generation ago. Many are beginning to feel that the only possible justification for a hypothesis is that it renders the facts comprehensible, and that to suppose them absolutely incomprehensible (which is what the doctrine of the Unknowable comes to) is not rendering them comprehensible. This seems to point toward some new incarnation of the idea of the old philosophy of common sense. In this connection it may be noticed that the theory of psychophysical parallelism is distinctly losing followers. Minds cannot reconcile themselves to the notion that consciousness stands and idle spectator of human conduct. Besides, the new logic of quantity, which Cantor, Whitehead and others have made irrefragable, shows that even though matter acts directly only upon matter and thought acts directly only upon thought, and though there be no *tertium quid*, it by no means follows that thought does not act upon matter nor that matter does not act upon thought. What if it should turn out that the atoms of matter were vortices of an ether, which ether is itself comprised of atoms each a vortex of an ether's ether; and so on *ad infinitum*; and what if mind had a similar con-

[3] (Ed.) The remainder of the review is from parts of the manuscript, rearranged by the editor.

stitution? It then might happen that upon an endless series of physical operations occurring in a fraction of a second should ensue a beginningless series of mental operations. Now it is to no purpose to say that this is improbable. If it is possible, as it certainly is, that suffices to show that mind and matter might, without contradiction, interact, although each could directly act only upon its own kind of substance. To the same general tendency belongs an opinion, now very common, that it is unscientific to inquire whether there be a God; the only rational question being what sort of God there is. With this is naturally associated the further opinion that instead of its being shallow philosophy to suppose an "anthropomorphic" God, if by "anthropomorphic" be meant *mental*, it is far more consonant with the method of science to formulate the problem by asking what sort of a mind God is; and if we cannot in some measure understand God's mind, all science, it is said with some color of justice, must be a delusion and a snare.

169. There is one more lineament of contemporary philosophy which, trivial as it may seem, is worth mention when a dictionary is our theme. It is that the days of literary style in philosophy seem to be numbered. The philosophy of the future must, like the other sciences, be put forth chiefly in the form of memoirs; and it is a truism to say that a memoir written in an ornate style would be as ridiculous as if it were in rhyming pentameters. From this follows another truism, that there is a good style and a bad style for a scientific memoir. Philosophy cannot become scientifically healthy without an immense technical vocabulary. We can hardly imagine our great-grandsons turning over the leaves of this dictionary without amusement over the paucity of words with which their grandsires attempted to handle metaphysics and logic. Long before that day, it will have become indispensably requisite, too, that each of these terms should be confined to a single meaning which, however broad, must be free from all vagueness. This will involve a revolution in terminology; for in its present condition a philosophical thought of any precision can seldom be expressed without lengthy explanations. Already, when philosophy is only just beginning to resemble science, the influx of new terms is getting to be considerable. One of the chief purposes of this dictionary seems to have been to fix the use of

them. Before long philosophers will find themselves confronted
with a Babel such as zoölogists and botanists have had to contend with; and scientific progress will be hampered until something like uniformity of usage has been attained. What is to
be done? Shall we go on, *laissant faire*, until we find our terminology in an inextricable snarl, and then call in an Alexander
to cut the knot with some Volapük system? Such would perhaps be the dictate of our glorious Anglo-Saxon genius, which
has endowed us, for example, with the word *bushel*, whose
meaning in any given State of the Union, for any given commodity, can be ascertained by simply consulting a table of
double-entry, and has given us that admirable word *inch*, which
cannot now be changed at a cost of less than a hundred million
dollars. Or shall [we] take time by the forelock, imitate the
French, with their metric system, their Academy, their Code
Napoleon, their Guyton de Morveau (with his chemical nomenclature, now universal, after modification), their minute
regulation of everything, and agree upon how the battle shall
be fought before we find ourselves actually engaged in it?
In the weightier matters of the law the French are none too
moral a people; but for the ethics of the mint and cummin, the
ought and ought not of manner and fashions, and other forms
of expression, they lead, and the rest of the world, after duly
prolonged demurs, generally ends by following them.

170. We must expect arduous labours yet to be performed
before philosophy can work its way out of the jungle and
emerge upon the high road of science. But the prospect is no
longer so desperately gloomy, if philosophers will only resign
themselves to the toilsome procedure of science, and recognize
that a single generation can make little headway, but yet may
faithfully clear away a few obstacles, and lying down to die,
resign the axe to their successors.

CHAPTER 10

LADY WELBY, *WHAT IS MEANING?* [1]

171.   Lady Victoria Welby's little volume is not what one would understand by a scientific book. It is not a treatise, and is free from the slightest shade of pedantry or pretension. Different people will estimate its value very differently. It is a feminine book, and a too masculine mind might think parts of it painfully weak. We should recommend the male reader to peruse chapters xxii. to xxv. before he reads the whole consecutively, for they will bear a second reading. The question dis-

[1] (Ed.) Paragraphs 171–175 are the review of Lady Victoria Welby's *What is Meaning?* (Macmillan, 1903, 321 pp.), *The Nation* 77(15 Oct 1903)308–309.

Paragraph 176 is from the Lowell Lectures of 1903 (from Lecture I, Vol. 2, following shortly after 1.611–615), Widener IB2–4, with an added quotation in 176n3.

Paragraphs 177–185 are from a long manuscript, undated, in Widener IB3a. The references in it indicate that this manuscript is part of a letter, but the extant part contains neither salutation nor signature. This manuscript required more editorial changes in punctuation, etc., than most of the manuscripts printed in the present volume.

Cf. the correspondence with Lady Welby in Book II of the present volume.

The review of Lady Welby's book in *The Nation* was combined with a brief mention of Bertrand Russell's *The Principles of Mathematics*, Vol. I (University Press, Cambridge; Macmillan, New York, 1903, 534 pp.). The combined review begins with the following paragraph: "Two really important works on logic are these; or, at any rate, they deserve to become so, if readers will only do their part towards it. Yet it is almost grotesque to name them together, so utterly disparate are their characters. This is not the place to speak of Mr. Russell's book, which can hardly be called literature. That he should continue these most severe and scholastic labors for so long, bespeaks a grit and industry, as well as a high intelligence, for which more than one of his ancestors have been famed. Whoever wishes a convenient introduction to the remarkable researches into the logic of mathematics that have been made during the last sixty years, and that have thrown an entirely new light both upon mathematics and upon logic, will do well to take up this book. But he will not find it easy reading. Indeed, the matter of the second volume will probably consist, at least nine-tenths of it, of rows of symbols." The remainder of the review is printed below.

cussed in these chapters is how primitive men ever came to believe in their absurd superstitions. This has generally been supposed to be the simplest of questions. Lady Victoria does not deign to mention La Fontaine's pretty fable (the sixth of the ninth book; the whole of it is worth rereading if you have forgotten it) of the sculptor and his statue of Jove:

> "L'artisan exprima si bien
> Le caractère de l'Idole,
> Qu'on trouva qu'il ne manquait rien
> A Jupiter que la parole.

> "Même l'on dit que l'ouvrier
> Eut à peine achevé l'image,
> Qu'on le vit frémir le premier,
> Et redouter son propre ouvrage.

> .   .   .   .   .   .

> "Il était enfant en ceci:
> Les enfants n'ont l'âme occupée
> Que du continuel souci
> Qu'on ne fâche point leur poupée.

> "Le coeur suit aisément l'esprit.
> De cette source est descendue
> L'erreur payenne qui se vit
> Chez tant de peuples répandue.

> .   .   .   .   .   .

> "Chacun tourne en réalités,
> Autant qu'il peut, ses propres songes.
> L'homme est de glace aux vérités;
> Il est de feu pour les mensonges."

172. La Fontaine's theory is somewhat complex, and allows more to the artistic impulse than modern ethnologists have done. They make mythology rather an attempt at a philosophical explanation of phenomena. But the authoress shows by a painstaking analysis that all such theories — La Fontaine's and the new current ones alike — are fatally irreconcilable with those traits of the primitive mind that have struck Tylor, Spencer, and ethnologists generally, as the deepest graven. In

place of them she offers a hypothesis of her own, and the reader is tempted to lose patience with her for regarding it only as provisional, so strongly does it recommend itself, until she presents quite another view which one must admit has its plausibility.

173.   The greatest service the book can render is that of bringing home the question which forms its title, a very fundamental question of logic, which has commonly received superficial, formalistic replies. Its vital and far-reaching significance has been even more ignored than usually happens with matters of universal and ubiquitous concern. To direct attention to the subject as one requiring study, both on its theoretical and on its practical side, is the essential purpose of the work. But in doing this the authoress has incidentally made a contribution towards the answer to the question, in pointing out three orders of signification. She has wisely abstained from any attempt at formal definitions of these three modes of signification. She tells us what she means only in the lowest of those three senses. To have gone further would have shunted her off upon a long and needless discussion.

174.   One can see, though she does not remark it, that her three·kinds of meaning correspond roughly to Hegel's three stages of thought. Her distinction, too, partly coincides with what was long ago said, that to understand a word or formula may, in the first place, consist in such familiarity with it as will enable one to apply it correctly; or secondly, may consist in an abstract analysis of the conception or understanding of its intellectual relations to other concepts; or, thirdly, may consist in a knowledge of the possible phenomenal and practical upshot of the assertion of the concept.[2] We might point out other interesting affiliations of her thought, sufficient to show that she must be on the right track.

175.   Lady Victoria, however, does not wish the matter to be agitated in the logician's study alone. She urges that people do not sufficiently take to heart the ethics of language. She thinks that modern conceptions call for a modern imagery of speech. But we fear that she does not realize how deep the knife would have to go into the body of speech to make it really scientific. We should have to form words like those the chemists use — if

[2] (Ed.) Cf. "How to Make Our Ideas Clear," 5.388–410.

they can be called words. In particular, she preaches making
logic — "significs," she calls it, but it would be logic — the
basis or core of education. All those ideals deserve to be pon-
dered. The book is very rich in illustrations drawn from contemporary writing.

176.   A little book by Lady Victoria Welby has lately appeared, entitled "What is Meaning." The book has sundry
merits, among them that of showing that there are three modes
of meaning. But the best feature of it is that it presses home
the question "What is Meaning." A word has meaning for us
in so far as we are able to make use of it in communicating our
knowledge to others and in getting at the knowledge that these
others seek to communicate to us. That is the lowest grade
of meaning. The *meaning* of a word is more fully the sum
total of all the conditional predictions which the person who
uses it *intends* to make himself responsible for or intends to
deny. That conscious or quasi-conscious *intention* in using the
word is the second grade of meaning. But besides the consequences to which the person who accepts a word knowingly
commits himself to, there is a vast ocean of unforeseen consequences which the acceptance of the word is destined to bring
about, not merely consequences of knowing but perhaps revolutions of society. One cannot tell what power there may be in
a word or a phrase to change the face of the world; and the
sum of these consequences makes up the third grade of meaning.[3]

177.   [My definition of a sign is:] A Sign is a Cognizable
that, on the one hand, is so determined (i.e., specialized,

[3] (Ed.) Cf. "How to Make Our Ideas Clear," 5.388–410.

In his application for a grant from the Carnegie Institution, 1902, Widener
VB5, Peirce describes his proposed thirty-second memoir, *On Definition and
the Clearness of Ideas,* as follows: "In January, 1878, I published a brief sketch
of this subject wherein I enunciated a certain maxim of 'Pragmatism,' which has
of late attracted some attention, as indeed, it had when it appeared in the *Journal
Philosophique.* I still adhere to that doctrine; but it needs more accurate definition in order to meet certain objections and to avoid certain misapplications.
Moreover, my paper of 1878 was imperfect in tacitly leaving it to appear that
the maxim of pragmatism led to the last stage of clearness. I wish now to show
that this is not the case and to find a series of Categories of clearness."

bestimmt,) by something *other than itself*, called its Object,[4] while, on the other hand, it so determines some actual or potential Mind, the determination whereof I term the Interpretant created by the Sign, that that Interpreting Mind is therein determined mediately by the Object.[5]

178. This involves regarding the matter in an unfamiliar way. It may be asked, for example, how a lying or erroneous Sign is determined by its Object, or how if, as not infrequently happens, the Object is brought into existence by the Sign. To be puzzled by this is an indication of the word determine being taken in too narrow a sense. A person who says Napoleon was a lethargic creature has evidently his mind determined by Napoleon. For otherwise he could not attend to him at all. But here is a paradoxical circumstance. The person who interprets that sentence (or any other Sign whatsoever) must be determined by the Object of it through collateral observation quite independently of the action of the Sign. Otherwise he will not be determined to thought of that object. If he never heard of Napoleon before, the sentence will mean no more to him than that some person or thing to which the name "Napoleon" has been attached was a lethargic creature. For Napoleon cannot determine his mind unless the word in the sentence calls his attention to the right man and that can only be if, independently, [a] habit has been established in him by which that word calls up a variety of attributes of Napoleon the man. Much the same thing is true in regard to any sign. In the sentence instanced Napoleon is not the only Object. Another Partial Object is Lethargy; and the sentence cannot convey its meaning unless collateral experience has taught its Interpreter what Lethargy is, or what that is that 'lethargy' means in this sentence. The Object of a Sign may be something to be created by the sign. For the Object of "Napoleon" is the Universe of Existence so far as it is determined by the fact of Napoleon being a Member of it. The Object of the sentence "Hamlet was insane" is the Universe of Shakespeare's Creation so far as

---

[4] (Ed.) The following occurs here in parentheses: "(or, in some cases, as if the Sign be the sentence 'Cain killed Abel,' in which Cain and Abel are equally Partial Objects, it may be more convenient to say that that which determines the Sign is the Complexus, or Totality, of Partial Objects. And in every case the Object is accurately the Universe of which the Special Object is member, or part)." [5] (Ed.) Cf. 2.228ff. for another discussion of signs.

it is determined by Hamlet being a part of it. The Object of the Command "Ground arms!" is the immediately subsequent action of the soldiers so far as it is affected by the molition [6] expressed in the command. It cannot be understood unless collateral observation shows the speaker's relation to the rank of soldiers. You may say, if you like, that the Object is in the Universe of things desired by the Commanding Captain at that moment. Or since the obedience is fully expected, it is in the Universe of his expectation. At any rate, it determines the Sign although it is to be created by the Sign by the circumstance that its Universe is relative to the momentary state of mind of the officer.

179. Now let us pass to the Interpretant. I am far from having fully explained what the Object of a Sign is; but I have reached the point where further explanation must suppose some understanding of what the Interpretant is. The Sign creates something in the Mind of the Interpreter, which something, in that it has been so created by the sign, has been, in a mediate and *relative* way, also created by the Object of the Sign, although the Object is essentially other than the Sign. And this creature of the sign is called the Interpretant. It is created by the Sign; but not by the Sign quâ member of whichever of the Universes it belongs to; but it has been created by the Sign in its capacity of bearing the determination by the Object. It is created in a Mind (how far this mind must be real we shall see). All that part of the understanding of the Sign which the Interpreting Mind has needed collateral observation for is outside the Interpretant. I do not mean by "collateral observation" acquaintance with the system of signs. What is so gathered is *not* COLLATERAL. It is on the contrary the prerequisite for getting any idea signified by the sign. But by collateral observation, I mean previous acquaintance with what the sign denotes. Thus if the Sign be the sentence "Hamlet was mad," to understand what this means one must know that men are sometimes in that strange state; one must have seen madmen or read about them; and it will be all the better if one specifically knows (and need not be driven to *presume*) what Shakespeare's notion of insanity was. All that is collateral observation and is no part of the Interpretant. But to put together

[6] (Ed.) Cf. 8.303.

the different subjects as the sign represents them as related —
that is the main [i.e., force] of the Interpretant-forming. Take
as an example of a Sign a *genre* painting. There is usually a
lot in such a picture which can only be understood by virtue of
acquaintance with customs. The style of the dresses for example, is no part of the *significance*, i.e. the deliverance, of the
painting. It only tells what the *subject* of it is. *Subject* and
Object are the same thing except for trifling distinctions. . . .
But that which the writer aimed to point out to you, presuming
you to have all the requisite collateral information, that is to
say just the quality of the sympathetic element of the situation,
generally a very familiar one — a something you probably
never did so clearly realize before — *that* is the Interpretant
of the Sign, — its "significance."

180.   Now all this is, so far, very muddled for the lack of
certain distinctions which I proceed to point out, though it
will be hard to make them fully comprehended.

181.   In the first place, it should be observed that so far
as the Sign denotes the Object, it calls for no particular *intelligence* or *Reason* on the part of its Interpreter. To read the
Sign at all, and distinguish one Sign from another, what is
requisite is delicate perceptions and acquaintance with what
the usual concomitants of such appearances are, and what the
conventions of the system of signs are. To know the Object,
what is requisite is previous experience of that Individual Object. The Object of every sign is an Individual, usually an
Individual Collection of Individuals. Its *Subjects*, i.e., the
Parts of the Sign that denote the *Partial Objects*, are either
directions for *finding the Objects* or are Cyrioids, i.e., signs of
single Objects. . . . Such for example are all *abstract* nouns,
which are names of single characters, the personal pronouns,
and the demonstrative and relative pronouns, etc. By directions for finding the Objects, for which I have as yet invented
no other word than "Selectives," I mean such as "Any" (i.e.,
any you please), "Some" (i.e., one properly selected), etc. To
know the Interpretant, which is what the sign itself expresses,
may require the highest power of reasoning.

182.   In the second place, to get more distinct notions of
what the Object of a Sign in general is, and what the Interpretant in general is, it is needful to distinguish two senses of "Ob-

137

ject" and three of "Interpretant." It would be better to carry the division further; but these two divisions are enough to occupy my remaining years. . . .

183.   As to the Object, that may mean the Object as cognized in the Sign and therefore an Idea, or it may be the Object as it is regardless of any particular aspect of it, the Object in such relations as unlimited and final study would show it to be. The former I call the *Immediate* Object, the latter the *Dynamical* Object. For the latter is the Object that Dynamical Science (or what at this day would be called "Objective" science,) can investigate. Take for example, the sentence "the Sun is blue." Its Objects are "the Sun" and "blueness." If by "blueness" be meant the Immediate Object, which is the quality of the sensation, it can only be known by Feeling. But if it means that "Real," existential condition, which causes the emitted light to have short mean wave-length, Langley has already proved that the proposition is true. So the "Sun" may mean the occasion of sundry sensations, and so is Immediate Object, or it may mean our usual interpretation of such sensations in terms of place, of mass, etc., when it is the Dynamical Object. It is true of both Immediate and Dynamical Object that acquaintance cannot be given by a Picture or a Description, nor by any other sign which has the Sun for its Object. If a person points to it and says, See there! *That* is what we call the "Sun," the Sun is *not* the Object of that sign. It is the *Sign* of the sun, the *word* "sun" that his declaration is about; and that *word* we must become acquainted with by collateral experience. Suppose a teacher of French says to an English-speaking pupil, who asks "comment appelle-t-on ça?" pointing to the Sun, . . . "C'est le soleil," he begins to furnish that collateral experience by speaking in French of the Sun itself. Suppose, on the other hand, he says "Notre mot est 'soleil' " then instead of expressing himself in language and *describing* the word he offers a pure *Icon* of it. Now the Object of an Icon is entirely indefinite, equivalent to "something." He virtually says "our word is like this:" and makes the sound. He informs the pupil that the word, (meaning, of course, a certain *habit*) has an effect which he *pictures* acoustically. But a pure picture without a legend only says "something is like this:". True he attaches what amounts to a legend. But that only makes his sentence

analogous to a portrait we will say of Leopardi with Leopardi written below it. It conveys its information to a person who knows who Leopardi was, and to anybody else it only says "something called Leopardi looked like this." The pupil is in the state of a person who was pretty sure there was a man Leopardi; for he is pretty sure there must be a word in French for the sun and thus is already acquainted with it, only he does not know how it sounds when spoken nor how it looks when written. I think by this time you must understand what I mean when I say that no sign can be understood — or at least that no *proposition* can be understood — unless the interpreter has "collateral acquaintance" with every Object of it. As for a mere *substantive*, it must be borne in mind that it is not an indispensable part of speech. The Semitic languages seem to be descendants of a language that had no "common nouns." Such a word is really nothing but a *blank form* of proposition and the Subject is the blank, and a blank can only mean "something" or something even more indefinite. So now I believe I can leave you to consider carefully whether my doctrine is correct or not.

184. As to the Interpretant, i.e., the "signification," or "interpretation" rather, of a sign, we must distinguish an Immediate and a Dynamical, as we must the Immediate and Dynamical Objects. But we must also note that there is certainly a third kind of Interpretant, which I call the Final Interpretant, because it is that which *would finally* be decided to be the true interpretation if consideration of the matter were carried so far that an ultimate opinion were reached. My friend Lady Welby has, she tells me, devoted her whole life to the study of *significs*, which is what I should describe as the study of the relation of signs to their interpretants; but it seems to me that she chiefly occupies herself with the study of words. She also reaches the conclusion that there are three senses in which words may be interpreted. She calls them *Sense, Meaning*, and *Significance*. Significance is the deepest and most lofty of these, and thus agrees with my *Final Interpretant*; and Significance seems to be an excellent name for it. *Sense* seems to be the logical analysis or definition, for which I should prefer to stick to the old term *Acception* or *Acceptation*. By *Meaning* she means the *intention* of the utterer.

185.   But it appears to me that all symptoms of disease, signs of weather, etc., have no utterer. For I do not think we can properly say that God *utters* any sign when He is the Creator of all things. But when [Lady Welby] says, as she does, that this is connected with Volition, I at once note that the volitional element of Interpretation is the *Dynamical Interpretant*. In the Second Part of my Essay on Pragmatism, in *The Popular Science Monthly* of 1877 Nov. and 1878 Jan., I made three grades of clearness of Interpretation.[7] The first was such familiarity as gave a person familiarity with a sign and readiness in using it or interpreting it. In his consciousness he seemed to himself to be quite *at home* with the Sign. In short, it is Interpretation *in Feeling*. The second was Logical Analysis = Lady Welby's *Sense*. The third, . . . Pragmatistic Analysis, would seem to be a Dynamical Analysis, but [is] identified with the Final Interpretant.[8]

[7] (Ed.) See [Bibliography] G–1877–5a and 5b, 5.358–387 and 5.388–410, respectively. The three kinds of clearness are discussed in the second of these two articles. The two articles did not form a unit in the original series, but in later years Peirce considered republishing them as two parts of a single essay (cf. [Bibliography] G–1909–1).

[8] (Ed.)   Cf. 5.476, 5.491.

CHAPTER 11

C. A. STRONG, *WHY THE MIND HAS A BODY* [1]

186.   Today, the animating endeavour of the younger philosophers is to bring their queen within the circle of the genuine sciences, — those careful and prudent sciences whose occasional leaps and strides are rendered achievable by their habitual training in picking their steps, slowly and laboriously, so as to make sure of each foothold. It is this commendable spirit, and this alone, that justifies high hopes for the future of philosophy; and the past twelvemonth has brought no worthier pattern of it than Prof. Strong's 'Why the Mind has a Body' — a remark that, to our knowledge, has fallen from more than one or two pairs of weighty lips. A cool and painstaking attempt is here made to set forth the contemporary issues of the question of the nature of the connection between mind and matter, to subject the different contentions to brief but penetrating criticism, and to develope by original studies the panpsychism of Clifford and Paulsen. A plainly marked stadium is thus set up whence for some years all discussions of this subject must set out. Not that any real solution of the problem has been reached. Let us hope that such may some day appear; but at present, no peering into the future descries its features nor yields us any confidence out of what quarter of the horizon it shall first loom. Meantime, the information that a thorough student of philosophy, highly intelligent, and exceptionally impartial, understands such and such to be the present state of the discussion will be a great help to sober inquirers. Doubtless Prof. Strong himself anticipates that not a few additions and corrections will be found needed in this first draught of his analysis. He will

---

[1] (Ed.)   Review of C. A. Strong's *Why The Mind Has A Body* (Macmillan, 1903, 355 pp.), Widener IV, dated c.1903 on the basis of the date of the book.

want, for example, to supply some proof that interactionism, automatism, and parallelism are really conflicting doctrines and not mere ways of apprehending the same facts. He will also desire to take some notice of the pragmatist position to which so many minds are flocking.[2] He has, to be sure, a section entitled 'Thoroughgoing Phenomenalism,' — a phrase that ought, we should think, to denote pragmatism; but the author does not seem to see that thorough-going phenomenalism must be phenomenalism *aufgehoben*; that it must involve the opinion that the reader of this page directly perceives the very page itself some ten inches from his eye, and that another person, looking over his shoulder, will see the very same object, although under a different angle, and although each sees the real object, not in its entirety, but only as it is related to his own view-point, literal and tropical. Not only must the pragmatist entertain this opinion, but he must hold that no other can be held by anybody, except in a sense in which a self-contradictory opinion is possible. For all men acknowledge that the statement that the reader sees the real page answers all human purposes, prompts the suitable conduct on each ocasion on which it gives any prompting. Now the pragmatist maintains that there is no other conception of reality to be by any means had than the conception of what must ultimately appear to answer human purposes, where '*human*' means belonging to the communion of mankind. He holds that one who thinks he believes that anything is real for something more than human purposes, in reality merely believes that it is true for human purposes that something is real for more than human purpose, — which may perhaps be quite true in the only sense it can have, namely, that for human purposes so it is. Pragmatism makes or ought to make no pretension to throwing positive light on any problem. It is merely a logical maxim for laying the dust of pseudoproblems, and thus enabling us to discern what pertinent facts the phenomena may present. But this is a good half of the task of philosophy.

187.   We must here content ourselves with a further remark or two which we trust may prove useful to a critical reader of the volume. Prof. Strong has much to say about the conservation of energy. The ordinary abstract statement of this doc-

[2] (Ed.) See [CP] V, *Pragmatism and Pragmaticism*.

trine is ill-adapted for philosophical discussion and is apt to be more or less misunderstood by metaphysicians. Better suited to their purposes is a recognized mathematical equivalent. Namely, the doctrine precisely amounts to this, that those motions of particles of which all physical events, considered as purely physical, are composed, undergo no "accelerations" (under which term are included all states of undergoing changes of motion) except such as are determined, according to fixed laws, *exclusively by the relative positions* of those particles at the very instants of those accelerations. The accelerations, which are the immediate effects, are absolutely simultaneous with the positions which are their causes. Yet Prof. Strong never fails to insist, in connection with the doctrine of energy, that causes precede their effects; — which is true of much causation, but is emphatically false of "conservative" forces.[3] It is, indeed, a mathematical consequence of the doctrine of conservation that if the velocities of all the particles were at any instant precisely reversed, all those particles would move back over their former paths with precisely the same, though reversed, velocities as before. Thus, the laws of motion do not favor any one determinate direction in an entire course of change, rather than the reverse direction. The physical universe is full of changes regularly taking place in determinate directions; — so full that this might almost be said to be the predominant character of nature. But with such features of phenomena the doctrine of the conservation of energy has as much and as little to do as has the Monroe doctrine. When light strikes upon a glass prism, *some* of the rays *usually* emerge more highly colored than they entered the prism, which is an effect of chance. So when a man is exposed to natural agencies, *some* of these *usually* emerge from his organism highly marked with a purposive character. We know not exactly how this comes about; but one thing we may be sure of: the conservation of energy has nothing to do with it. Another point to be noted about physical causation is that *acceleration*, the effect, and *relative position*, the cause, are of disparate natures, not to be measured in terms of the same units. Yet Prof. Strong holds it to be an argument against the interaction of body and soul that their natures are disparate. Had he said that every

[3] (Ed.) See [CP] VI, Chapter 3, "Causation and Force."

effect is disparate to its cause he would have been nearer the mark. There is still another important suggestion to be derived from dynamics. In treating any ordinary problem in analytic mechanics, — say, for example, that of two pendulums swinging from one yielding support, — we begin by expressing the state of facts by means of that form of the law of energy enunciated above.[4] This furnishes a differential equation which represents the interactions of the different parts of the system, (say the two pendulums). We now subject this equation to a mathematical transformation. It continues to express the same facts, or a portion of them; but from the new form of statement the conception of interaction has disappeared and each part of the system is represented as moving under a regularity of its own, independently of every other part. Each pendulum, to recur to our example, is now asserted to perform a regular harmonic motion consisting of two simple oscillations like one train of waves passing over another such train, while the other pendulum is ignored in the statement. This is a "parallelistic" form of stating the same facts that were at first stated "interactionistically." Hence we see that "interactionism" and "parallelism" may be merely two forms of expressing the same truth. Only the dynamist would hold that it is the original interactionist form that expresses the facts in their real relations to the general course of nature, while the parallelistic form is merely a partial expression [of the] facts which happens to be convenient for a particular purpose. However enigmatic the assertion may appear (and it is impossible here to defend it) it is certain that interactionism is in no logical conflict with the assumption that every transformation of motion is determined by physical conditions exclusively.[5]

[4] (Ed.)   See 6.272ff., 7.491.
[5] (Ed.)   Cf. 7.370, 8.274.

CHAPTER 12

JOHN DEWEY, *STUDIES IN LOGICAL THEORY* [1]

188.   The volume of which Professor Dewey is the father forms a part of the University of Chicago's exhibit of an impressive decade's work, and is a worthy part of it, being the monument of what he has done in his own department. Here are eleven essays, four by himself, defining his conception of the business of the logician, seven by the students whom he has helped to form and set upon their own intellectual legs. It affords conclusive proof of the service he has rendered to these accomplished thinkers and, no doubt, to others; and they in their turn will render to another generation services of the same nature. Whatever there was to be gained by contact with a sincere student of philosophy, as such, they have manifestly gained. Are there any further services that logic could be expected to perform? Are any logical questions now being agitated in the different sciences? Is there any such question as to the constitution of matter, the value of mechanical hypotheses, now open in physics? Are there any methods as to more or less statistical methods of philological and historical criticism? If there are such questions, has past experience gone to show that there was any help to be had from broader sweeps of study than specialists can make? Is it worth while to examine at all into the questions here asked; and if it be, is it best to carry to them vague impressions, or the exactest conceptions that studies specially directed to them have been able to evoke?

189.   There are specialists who are disposed to think any inquiries from the outside into their methods are impertinent. They say, with perfect justice, that they understand fully their

[1] (Ed.) Review of John Dewey's *Studies in Logical Theory* (The Decennial Publications, Second Series, Volume XI, University of Chicago Press, 1903, 378 pp.), *The Nation* 79(15 Sept 1904)219–220.

own business, and wish to be let alone. Unquestionably, they must be right. There is, however, another class of specialists whose aims are of such a nature that they can sometimes make good use of ideas which have grown up in other studies. Such specialists, when they have created, say, physical chemistry, the new astronomy, physiological psychology, stylometry, etc., have sometimes gained a certain measure of esteem even from those of straiter sects. It has often happened that general studies of logic have resulted in such applications of one science to another. Analytical geometry was first conferred upon the human race as an illustrative example of the 'Discours de la Méthode.' The group of writers whom, abandoning all attempt at finding a descriptive designation, we may roughly call the English school of logicians, meaning, for example, Boole, De Morgan, Whewell, J. S. Mill, Jevons, Venn, Pearson, Mac-Coll, etc., while pursuing studies often purely theoretical, are nevertheless taking a road which may be expected to lead to results of high value for the positive sciences. Those whom we may as roughly call the German school of logicians, meaning such writers as Christoph Sigwart, Wundt, Schuppe, Benno Erdmann, Julius Bergmann, Glogau, Husserl, etc., are engaged upon problems which must be acknowledged to underlie the others, but attack them in a manner which the exact logicians regard as entirely irrelevant, because they make *truth*, which is a matter of fact, to be a matter of a way of thinking or even of linguistic expression. The Chicago school or group are manifestly in radical opposition to the exact logicians, and are not making any studies which anybody in his senses can expect, directly or indirectly, in any considerable degree, to influence twentieth-century science.

190.   Prof. Dewey regards himself as radically opposed to the German school, and explains how he is so. We must confess that had he not put so much emphasis upon it, we should hardly have deemed the point of difference so important; but we suppose he must know what his own affiliations are and are not. He seems to regard what he calls "logic" as a natural history of thought.[2] If such a natural history can be worked out, it will undoubtedly form valuable knowledge; and with all our heart we wish the Chicago school godspeed in their enterprise

[2] (Ed.) See the correspondence to Dewey in the present volume, Book II.

of discovery. But their task will call for such extreme subtlety, precision, and definiteness of thought that we hope their new science will not disdain to take a lesson, if not from any of the older logicians of the country, nor from that American thinker who first essayed to use his great powers of observation to establish a natural history of mental products — we mean Dr. James Rush — at least from the well-established natural history of Nature, chemistry, botany, and zoology; the lesson, to wit, that a natural history can hope to begin a successful course of discovery only from the day when it abandons altogether the trivial language of practical life, and sets up a thoroughly new glossary of words exclusively its own, thereby not confusing our meagre philosophical vocabulary with the burden of added meanings to old words. If calling the new natural history by the name of "logic" (a suspicious beginning) is to be a way of prejudging the question of whether or not there be a logic which is more than a mere natural history, inasmuch as it would pronounce one proceeding of thought to be sound and valid and another to be otherwise, then we should regard this appropriation of that name to be itself fresh confirmation of our opinion of the urgent need of such a normative science at this day.[3]

[3] (Ed.) Logic as a normative science is discussed in [CP] I, Book IV, "The Normative Sciences."

CHAPTER 13

ON PRAGMATISM, FROM A REVIEW OF A BOOK ON COSMOLOGY [1]

191.   No criticism of such a book, no characterization of it, not even as slight a one as that here to be attempted, can have any meaning until the standpoint of the critic's observations be recognized.   Our standpoint will be pragmatism; [2] but this word has been so loosely used, that a partial explanation of its nature is needful, with some indications of the intricate process by which those who hold it become assured of its truth. If philosophy is ever to become a sound science, its students must submit themselves to that same ethics of terminology that students of chemistry and taxonomic biology observe; and when a word has been invented for the declared purpose of conveying a precisely defined meaning, they must give up their habit of using it for every other purpose that may happen to hit their fancy at the moment.   The word *pragmatism* was invented to express a certain maxim of logic, which, as was shown at its first enouncement, involves a whole system of philosophy.   The maxim is intended to furnish a method for the analysis of concepts.   A concept is something having the mode of being of a general type which is, or may be made, the rational part of the purport of a word.   A more precise or fuller definition cannot

[1] (Ed.) Paragraphs 191–193 are from a draft of a review of Herbert Nichols's *A Treatise on Cosmology*, Vol. I, *Introduction* (The University Press, Cambridge, Mass., 1904, 455 pp.), Widener IV, dated c.1904 from the date of the book.

Paragraphs 194-195 are from Section 2, "What Pragmatism is," of a manuscript entitled, "Nichols' Cosmology and Pragmaticism," Widener IB1–2, dated c.1904 from the date of the book. In this manuscript, however, Peirce deals only slightly with Nichols's book. Section 2 is similar in many respects to the published article of the same title, [Bibliography] G–1905–1a (5.411–437).

Cf. [Bibliography] G–1905–2.

[2] (Ed.) See [CP] V, *Pragmatism and Pragmaticism*.

here be attempted. The method prescribed in the maxim is
to trace out in the imagination the conceivable practical consequences, — that is, the consequences for deliberate, self-controlled conduct, — of the affirmation or denial of the concept;
and the assertion of the maxim is that herein lies the *whole* of
the purport of the word, the *entire* concept. The sedulous exclusion from this statement of all reference to sensation is specially to be remarked. Such a distinction as that between red
and blue is held to form no part of the concept. This maxim
is put forth neither as a handy tool to serve so far as it may be
found serviceable, nor as a self-evident truth, but as a far-
reaching theorem solidly grounded upon an elaborate study of
the nature of signs.[3] Every thought, or cognitive representation, is of the nature of a sign. "Representation" and "sign"
are synonyms. The whole purpose of a sign is that it shall be
interpreted in another sign; and its whole purport lies in the
special character which it imparts to that interpretation. When
a sign determines an interpretation of itself in another sign,
it produces an effect external to itself, a physical effect, though
the sign producing the effect may itself be not an existent object but merely a type. It produces this effect, not in this or
that metaphysical sense, but in an indisputable sense. As to
this, it is to be remarked that actions beyond the reach of self-
control are not subjects of blame. Thinking is a kind of action,
and reasoning is a kind of deliberate action; and to call an
argument illogical, or a proposition false, is a special kind of
moral judgment, and as such is inapplicable to what we cannot help. This does not deny that what cannot be conceived
today may be conceivable tomorrow. But just as long as we
cannot help adopting a mode of thought, so long it must be thoroughly accepted as true. Any doubt of it is idle make-believe
and irredeemable paper. Now we all do regard, and cannot help
regarding, signs as *affecting* their interpretant signs. It is by a
patient examination of the various modes (some of them quite
disparate) of interpretations of signs, and of the connections
between these (an exploration in which one ought, if possible,
to provide himself with a guide, or, if that cannot be, to prepare his courage to see one conception that will have to be mastered peering over the head of another, and soon another peer-

[3] (Ed.) See 2.227ff.

ing over that, and so on, until he shall begin to think there is
to be no end of it, or that life will not be long enough to complete the study) that the pragmatist has at length, to his great
astonishment, emerged from the disheartening labyrinth with
this simple maxim in his hand. In distrust of so surprising a
result he has searched for some flaw in its method, and for some
case in which it should break down, but after every deep-laid
plot for disproving it that long-working ingenuity could devise has recoiled upon his own head, and all doubts he could
start have been exhausted, he has been forced at last to acknowledge its truth. This maxim once accepted, — intelligently accepted, in the light of the evidence of its truth, —
speedily sweeps all metaphysical rubbish out of one's house.
Each abstraction is either pronounced to be gibberish or is provided with a plain, practical definition. The general leaning of
the results is toward what the idealists call the naïve, toward
common sense, toward anthropomorphism. Thus, for example,
the *real* becomes that which is such as it is regardless of what
you or I or any of our folks may think it to be.[4] The *external*
becomes that element which is such as it is regardless of what
somebody thinks, feels, or does, whether about that external
object or about anything else. Accordingly, the external is necessarily real, while the real may or may not be external; nor is
anything absolutely external nor absolutely devoid of externality. Every assertory proposition refers to something external, and even a dream withstands us sufficiently for one description to be true of it and another not. The *existent* is that which
reacts against other things. Consequently, the external world,
(that is, the world that is comparatively external) does not
consist of existent objects merely, nor merely of these and their
reactions; but on the contrary, its most important reals have
the mode of being of what the nominalist calls "mere" words,
that is, general types and would-bes. The nominalist is right
in saying that they are substantially of the nature of words;
but his "mere" reveals a complete misunderstanding of what
our everyday world consists of.

192. With this preface, let us examine a fair specimen of
Dr. Nichols's power of analytic thought, which is the first re-

---

[4] (Ed.) The notions of reality, externality, existence, law, etc., are discussed
in many places; see especially [CP] I, V, and VI.

quirement of a philosopher. This specimen shall consist of his
definition of scientific law, or, as he prefers to term it, of "lawfulness." We all know that John Mill banished the word 'law'
and substituted 'uniformity' for it, as more precisely expressing
what is meant. But pragmatism discovers a serious error here.
For while uniformity is a character which might be realized, in
all its fulness, in a short series of past events, law, on the other
hand, is essentially a character of an indefinite future; and
while uniformity involves a regularity exact and exceptionless,
law only requires an approach to uniformity in a decided majority of cases. This appears as follows: when the pragmatist
puts to himself his stereotyped question, How could law ever
reasonably affect human conduct, the answer that reflection
brings him is that law could affect such conduct only through
the knowledge of it creating and warranting anticipations of
future experience. Now this sort of influence upon reasonable
conduct requires no more than that those predictions should
ordinarily be fulfilled; nor does it in the least preclude their
being vague to almost any degree. But what the answer to the
pragmatist's self-question does require is that the law should
be a truth expressible as a conditional proposition whose antecedent and consequent express experiences *in a future tense*,
and further, that, as long as the law retains the character of a
law, there should be possible occasions in an indefinite future
when events of the kind described in the antecedent may come
to pass. Such, then, *ought* to be our conception of law, whether
it has been so or not. But upon examining the usage of physicists, we find there are not a few truths called laws by the most
careful terminologists which are not of an exact nature and
which present downright exceptions. Such is Dulong and Petit's
law, such is the periodic law of the chemical elements; and
everybody can name others, galore. But in all the range of
science there is no single proposition that goes by the name of
a law, from which conditional predictions as to future experiences may not be deduced.

193. Dr. Nichols devotes a chapter of thirteen of his large
pages to making out what "lawfulness" consists in, — full
double what any pragmatist would require for the most convincing elucidation. But Dr. Nichols wastes part of his space
on trifles, and occupies a good deal with old-fashioned declama-

tory rhetoric against "hypostatized entities." What was the use of this? Nobody will now-a-days dispute that the writers who are the target of all these philippics, those who used to talk so much about "causation" and "immediate causes" and the like, were at fault. Only, their real fault was of no other nature than precisely that of the eloquent declaimers against "entities" and "hypostatizing." Namely, in each case, it is not so much any positively erroneous doctrine, as it is that having before them ill-apprehended phenomena, instead of patiently sitting down to analyze the same, as they should have done, they content themselves with applying names of redoubtable sound but of little or no pragmatic purport.

194. A practical attitude of mind concerns itself primarily with the living future, and pays no regard to the dead past or even the present except so far as it may indicate what the future will be. Thus, the pragmaticist is obliged to hold that whatever means anything means that something will happen (provided certain conditions are fulfilled), and to hold that the future alone has primary reality. The fact that Napoleon did run his marvellous career *consists* in the fact that anybody who looks for them will find a thousand and one vestiges of that career. A questioner to whom pragmaticism comes as a novelty will naturally ask, "Do you mean to say that you do not believe there has been any past?" To which the pragmaticist will reply, — and note well his answer, because it is analogous to the answer he will give to a host of questions to which no further allusion will be made, — "Why, I believe in the reality of the past just as completely as you do, and just in the way that you do, except that either you or I perhaps do not describe correctly the intellectual side of [its] real meaning. To any memory [of] the past, there attaches a certain color, — a certain quality of feeling, — just as there does to the sight of a Jacqueminot rose.[5] Ontological metaphysicians usually say that 'secondary sensations,' such as colors, are delusive and false; but not so the Pragmaticist. He insists that the rose really *is* red; for *red* is, by the meaning of the word, an appearance; and to say that a Jacqueminot rose really is red means, and can mean,

[5] (Ed.) Cf. 5.458ff.

nothing but that if such a rose is put before a normal eye, in the daylight, it will look red. Just so, the feeling qualities attaching to memories are entirely true and real, though obviously relative, as pastness itself obviously is relative."

195. "But what say you to the myriad details of Napoleon's life of which no vestige remains, — his having winked, let us suppose, one night when he was in absolute darkness. Did those events not occur?" So the questioner: to which the Pragmaticist will reply, "You speak of a wink as if it were a small event. How many trillions of corpuscles are involved in the action, through how many million times their diameters they move, and during how many billions of their revolutions in their orbits the action endures, I will not undertake to calculate. But certainly you cannot yourself think that so vast an operation will have had no physical effects, or that they will cease for ages yet to come. Certainly, when you talk of an actual event leaving at a subsequent time absolutely no consequences whatever, I confess that I can attach no meaning at all to your words, and I believe that for you yourself it is simply a formula into which by some form of logic you have transformed a proposition that had a real meaning while overlooking the circumstance that the transformation has left no real meaning in it, unless one calls it a meaning that you continue vaguely to associate the memory-feeling with this empty form of words. At any rate, you will remark that in all important respects you and I think alike about time, and that it is only in regard to metaphysical statements of no earthly consequence to anybody that we differ, — you allowing them to confuse and litter up your mind, while I sweep them out of doors." "But why look upon past and future so differently?" "The intellectual meaning of a statement is precisely the same whether it refers to past or future time. To say that a piece of porcelain is soft before it is baked is equivalent to saying that if anybody during that period tries to scratch it with a knife he will succeed, and to say this is again equivalent to saying that every experiment which is logically necessitated, if this be true, to turn out in a certain way, will turn out in that way; and this last statement has a corresponding equivalent, and so on endlessly. But of this endless series of equivalent propositions there is one which my situation in time makes to be the prac-

tical one for me, and that one becomes for me the primary meaning. As long as the porcelain is not yet baked, I mean by calling it soft that if anyone tries to scratch it with a knife he will readily succeed. But after it has been baked, and nobody has taken occasion to try that experiment, it is a different experiment among the endless series of equivalents that now expresses my primary meaning. The nature of the fact does not change; but my relation to it and consequent mode of conceiving do change, although I all the time recognize the equivalence of the different meanings." "Then you maintain, do you, that when you directly act upon a thing in making an experiment, this direct action consists entirely in the fact that subsequent experimental investigators will ultimately be led to the conclusion that you did act upon it?" "Ah, that I have not said, but have carefully guarded against such an interpretation by saying that it is only of *conceptions*, that is, of the intellectual part of meaning that I was speaking. The pragmaticist need not deny that such ideas as those of action, of actual happening, of individuality, of existence, etc., involve something like a reminiscence of an exertion of brute force which is decidedly anti-intellectual, which is an all-important ingredient of the practical, although the pragmat[ic]istic interpretation leaves it out of account. Yet while he may admit that this idea of brute thereness, — or whatever best names it, — is quite distinct from any concept, yet he is bound to maintain that this does not suffice to make an idea of practical reality."

CHAPTER 14

WILHELM WUNDT, *PRINCIPLES OF PHYSIOLOGICAL PSYCHOLOGY* [1]

196. When, in 1862, two years after Fechner's 'Psychophysik,' Wundt emerged from the physiological laboratory with his 'Beiträge zur Theorie der Sinneswahrnehmung,' students in this country there were who saw in the little volume the harbinger of a new science of experimental psychology; and the next year their hopes seemed to be crowned in the same author's 'Vorlesungen über die Menschen- und Thierseele,' concerning which, by the way, it had better be noted that, like other of Wundt's books, it has lost most of its original flavor in a second, reconsidered edition, and that the English translation represents this later edition. Without this explanation, the sensation it first caused would be incomprehensible. Its readers heard in it the promise that the new science should keep pace with the other strictly experimental sciences, and should quickly outstrip all those sciences (more numerous then than now) in which experimentation had not become practicable. Alas, today we are forty years wiser, and a chilling shade settles on hearts of enthusiasts of the sixties who now compare the advance that psychology has achieved — indisputable, but how modest! — with the unheard-of leaps that every other science has performed, be it an experimental one or not. Since 1860 the foundations of pure mathematics have been reconstructed; exact logic has been developed; physics has gained an optico-electrical theory, and radically new conceptions of molecular

---

[1] (Ed.) Review of Wilhelm Wundt's *Principles of Physiological Psychology*, translated from the fifth German edition (1902) by Edward Bradford Titchener, Vol. I (Macmillan, 1904), *The Nation* 81(20 July 1905)56–57, with an added quotation in 201n3 from a draft in Widener IV, dated c.1905 on the basis of the dates of the book and the published review.

155

forces have been established; organic chemistry has followed
out the doctrine of the aromatic compounds, and has been
enriched by the doctrine of the unsymmetrical carbon atom;
in its inorganic division the classification of the elements has
been laid bare, the group of helium-argon elements has been
added, and Mme. Curie has pronounced her magical "Open,
sesame!" Besides all that, a new and more scientific kind of
chemistry has been opened up. Biology has been equally revolutionized; astronomy has its new astro-physics, and geognosy
has kept pace with the other sciences. Even on the psychical
wing, linguistics, ethnology, archaeology, the history of high
antiquity, have all found and matured new methods. In short,
there is not a science that has not left psychology lingering
in the rear; and the burning question of to-day is, why this
should be so? Who will diagnose the malady of psychology?

197.   It has been remarked that, at present, there is nothing
which for the psychical wing of science fulfils that function
which the science of dynamics fulfils on the physical side.
Everybody knows what that function is. Every attempt to
explain any phenomenon physically consists in first proposing
some hypothesis as to the existence of designated dynamical
conditions from which, according to the principles of dynamics,
phenomena such as have been observed would take place, and
then going on to put the hypothesis to the test of making it the
basis of predictions concerning untried experiments.

198.   Now it is a circumstance most significant for the logic
of science, that this science of dynamics, upon which all the
physical sciences repose, when defined in the strict way in
which its founders understood it, and not as embracing the law
of the conservation of energy, neither is nor ever was one of the
special sciences that aim at the discovery of novel phenomena,
but merely consists in the analysis of truths which universal
experience has compelled every man of us to acknowledge.
Thus, the proof by Archimedes of the principle of the lever,
upon which Lagrange substantially bases the whole statical
branch of the science, consists in showing that that principle is
virtually assumed in our ordinary conception of two bodies of
equal weight. Such universal experiences may not be true to
microscopical exactitude, but that they are true in the main is
assumed by everybody who devises an experiment, and is

therefore more certain than any result of a laboratory experiment.

199.   The sort of science that is founded upon the common experience of all men was recognized by Jeremy Bentham under the name of *cenoscopy*, in opposition to *idioscopy*, which discovers new phenomena. But long before Bentham's day the situation was sufficiently understood to set up a movement in the more enlightened countries to supply the psychical sciences with an analogous analytical foundation. The innumerable grades in the distinctness of thought prevent us from assigning dates, but one may say that the idea is struggling to the light in Locke's 'Essay' of 1689, and that its development was the best fruit of the eighteenth century. It moved in Italy, in France, and especially in Scotland. The analytical economics of Adam Smith and of Ricardo were examples of it. The whole doctrine in its totality is properly termed the Philosophy of Common Sense, of which analytical mechanics and analytical economics are branches. That Pragmatism of which so much has been said of late years is only an endeavor to give the philosophy of common sense a more exact development, especially by emphasizing the point that there is no intellectual value in mere feeling *per se*, but that the whole function of thinking consists in the regulation of conduct.[2] All this it is most needful to comprehend in order to assign to Wundt his proper rating in the history of philosophy.

200.   The 'Physiological Psychology' is Wundt's most imposing and monumental work, but no man of science will call it his *chef-d'oeuvre*. That rank can be accorded to one production alone, his 'Untersuchungen zur Mechanik der Nerven und Nervencentren,' of which the first part appeared in 1871; the second, which is less fundamental but perhaps not less important, having been delayed by accidental causes until 1876, after the first edition of the 'Physiological Psychology' had appeared. Four traits of the 'Mechanik der Nerven' command admiration. One of them is a natural gift; two are results of scientific training; and one is a moral virtue. The gift is an astonishing sagacity about nerve-physiology — a subterconscious susceptibility to the noeto-meteorological premonitions

---

[2] (Ed.) See "Pragmatism and Critical Common-Sensism," 5.497–501, and elsewhere in [CP] V.

of a hailstorm of evidence that, when it bursts, will be cold, hard, and cutting enough.

201.   Of the two scientific perfections the more striking is the mature prestudy of the methods that were or might have been pursued in the investigation. The other is the vigilant scrutiny of all details of the phenomena, especially of such as, being unlooked for, might easily have been overlooked. But the most admirable trait of all — that self-respecting quality of Wundt's which no foibles can obscure — is his genuine anxiety to correct the opinions which he at the time entertains, and to cast away his most brilliant theories the instant the dicta of experience seem to be against them — a quality in which he so contrasts with all the metaphysical charlatans and self-admirers and with every other quintessential extract of littleness.[3] Wundt's great service to man, aside from that special research described in the 'Mechanik der Nerven,' has consisted in teaching the students of cenoscopy the beauty of those virtues upon which the students of idioscopy, especially those on the physical wing, have always insisted — virtues that will necessarily result from any well-considered desire to know the truth. That such service has been Wundt's undoubtedly remains true, notwithstanding some lapses.

202.   But the work of which Professor Titchener is publishing his translation is not to be classed as a performance of idioscopy, and little given is idioscopy to expressing itself in big books. It is not work of heuretic science of any kind. It is a product of that useful industry of collecting, arranging, and digesting the deductions of mathematics, the analyses of cenoscopy, and the discoveries of idioscopy — a service of which the Germans have assumed the burden, and which, as being the "systematization of knowledge," they as well as the general

---

[3] (Ed.) "Endeavoring to sum up the results of this elaborate investigation so far as they concern psychology in such imperfect fashion as they can be reduced to one simple sentence, we may say that Wundt finds that the function of our thinking-organ lies in its regulation of motor reactions. Now this is neither more nor less than the substance of pragmatism in the dress of physiology. The original definition of pragmatism put it into this form of maxim: 'Consider what effects that might conceivably have practical bearings you conceive the object of your conception to have. Then, your conception of those effects is THE WHOLE of your conception of the object.' What is that than to say that the sole function of thought is to regulate motor reactions?" From a fragmentary draft (see 196n1).

public are too apt to mistake for the business of science. From the date of the publication of this work, Wundt has turned a corner in his career, and has pursued a course not determined by the intrinsic affinities of his previous work. His principal publications (aside from revisions and from papers in his periodical *Philosophische Studien*) have consisted in an extensive treatise on logic, another on ethics, and a 'System der Philosophie.' These are subjects to which the majority of their devotees have been led by a desire to settle their beliefs about God, freedom, and immortality. But students of science are a good deal given to thinking that high theory is more apt to lead men wrong than right about religion, while religion has never done theory more good than harm. The doubts which impelled the few men of science who have been led to any thorough study of philosophy have almost always been concerned with the limits of trustworthiness of scientific results. But Wundt has never entertained any such general doubts. He explicitly says that whatever is not based upon the results of the special sciences has no real basis at all. He makes no exception in favor of dynamics, on the truth of which all his own work reposes. But, for him, common sense is nothing but an imperfect kind of science; and it is remarkable that his physiology recognizes no very fundamental difference between the functions of the cerebral cortex and those of the organs at the base of the brain. To the question what could have been Wundt's motive in putting himself forward as a leader in philosophy, for which he had never displayed any genius, but rather the reverse, the answer to which the study of his writings must lead is that the results of experimental psychology, meagre though they be as compared with those of other sciences, so dazzled the imagination of Wundt as to make him think that that study alone must be set up as the queen of the sciences, and prompted him to try to prove that logic, ethics, and philosophy could be securely based on that special science.

203.   Wundt's philosophical publications have not met the acclamations that he undoubtedly at first expected; nor can it be said that the two scientific merits above mentioned are here one whit better exemplified than in the general run of second-rate philosophical treatises of the time. They rather fall below that average. In the matter of the deliberate pre-

159

selection of methods, for example, one will not often meet with
anything weaker than Wundt's admission that it seems self-
evident that metaphysics should not be made to depend on the
results of special science, while defending himself by saying
that, having come to philosophy from physical science by the
route of experimental psychology, it is natural that he should
be unable to pursue philosophical investigations by any other
method than that which his own sequence of study suggested
to him. ("Ship ahoy! — Where are you bound?" "For the
port of Philosophy." "Then why, in Heaven's name, are you
sailing on that course, Captain Wundt?" "Well, the truth is,
this is the way the vessel was heading at the time it occurred
to me to make that port.") Other equally gross departures from
the two scientific ideals could easily be pointed out. Whether
or not, if Wundt had possessed any analytical strength, it would
have been possible for him to imagine that he could base such
matters as dynamics, geometry, and arithmetic upon his physiological experiments, or whether in that case he could have failed
to perceive the value of the pragmatist analysis in binding together nerve-physiology and psychology, must remain matters
of opinion. But, unfortunately for his good fame, there exist
departments of logic upon which he has touched that no more
fall within the marches of opinion than does the principle of
the lever or the doctrine of limits; and here he simply places
himself where Hobbes placed himself by his attempts at reasoning on exact subjects; and those who, nevertheless, talk of
Hobbes as a "great logician" will be free to entertain the same
opinion of Wundt — and of Lord Timothy Dexter.

204. As for the 'Ethics' and the 'System of Philosophy,' we
shall simply say that no person of discrimination would prove
that quality by ranking them among works of the first order.
We say no more, because such deviations from a great career
are too unpleasant to contemplate. Of course, even in the
'Logic' there are brilliant chapters; it could not be otherwise,
their author having achieved such things as he had, though in
a distant field. As to the 'Physiological Psychology,' there will
probably be no break in the unanimity that it is the most important monument of the new experimental psychology. Professor Titchener's translation has been eagerly awaited for
long years. He explains the delay in his preface. It appears

that he has made three complete translations of the work which have twice been superseded by revisions of the original. He is himself of opinion that his third is the least good of the three, but one does not see how that could possibly be. His unusual skill in making agreeable English of a faithful rendering from disagreeable German had already been proved — a psychological accomplishment which Oxford training, the experience of the psychological laboratory, and practice in this very thing have perfected. It is not comprised in the verbal expression. Unerring judgment has been exercised in the editing both of the present volume and of others. The author's slips, if not too numerous, have to be corrected, with or without mention, according to circumstances. Whether the lettering of diagrams shall continue to represent German words or not, whether or not bad figures shall be replaced by better ones, etc., are questions about which the least talent for judging wrong would have betrayed itself if it had lurked in the translator. The present volume, the first of three, includes only the first and perhaps the most interesting of the six divisions of the original work. It relates to the subject in which Wundt's opinions have the greatest weight; and it is a subject whose practical corollaries will be obvious to every reader — "the bodily substrate of the mental life."

Book II

CORRESPONDENCE

CHAPTER 1

TO SIGNOR CALDERONI, ON PRAGMATICISM [1]

205. I have delayed thanking you, as I now very warmly do, for sending me the three numbers of *Leonardo*,[2] and for your too flattering references to my formulation. In the April number of the *Monist* [3] I proposed that the word "pragmatism" should hereafter be used somewhat loosely to signify affiliation with Schiller, James, Dewey, Royce, and the rest of us, while the particular doctrine which I invented the word to denote, which is your first kind of pragmatism, should be called "*pragmaticism*." The extra syllable will indicate the narrower meaning.

206. Pragmaticism is not a system of philosophy. It is only a method of thinking; and your correspondent, Juliano il Sofista,[4] is quite right in saying that it is not a new way of thinking. If it were so, that, to my mind, would be almost sufficient to condemn it. It is only the formulation of it which was new thirty years ago, unless your correspondent is prepared to cite the volume and page on which an equivalent formulation had already been given. From his tone, I infer that he is quite prepared to do this; and I shall thus congratulate myself on an unknown fellow-thinker. Of those who have used this way of thinking Berkeley is the clearest example, though

[1] (Ed.) From an unsigned letter with the salutation, "Dear Signor Calderoni," Widener VB2a. The internal bibliographical references indicate that the letter was written c.1905. Cf. 8.260.

The intended recipient was probably Mario Calderoni, an Italian pragmatist. Cf. Giovanni Papini, *Le démon m'a dit . . .* , Payot, Paris, 1923, "Mario Calderoni," pp. 181–189; M. Calderoni and G. Vailati, *Il Pragmatismo*, Lanciano, 1920.

[2] (Ed.) An Italian philosophical journal to which Mario Calderoni contributed.

[3] (Ed.) [Bibliography] G–1905–1a.

[4] (Ed.) Giuliano il Sofista was a frequent contributor to *Leonardo*.

Locke (especially in the fourth book of his Essay), Spinoza, and Kant may be claimed as adherents of it.

207. Although pragmaticism is not a philosophy, yet, as you rightly say, it best comports with the English philosophy, and more particularly with the Scotch doctrine of common sense.

208. In an article which should have appeared in the July *Monist*[5] but which seems to have been crowded out by matters of superior importance, magic squares and the like, I specify six errors which I find in the Scotch doctrine of common sense, of which the most important is that those philosophers failed to remark the extreme vagueness of our indubitable beliefs. For example, everybody's actions show that it is impossible to doubt that there is an element of order in the world; but the moment we attempt to define that orderliness we find room for doubt. There is, besides, another respect in which pragmaticism is at issue not only with English philosophy more particularly, but with all modern philosophy more or less, even with Hegel; and that is that it involves a complete rupture with nominalism. Even Duns Scotus is too nominalistic when he says that universals are contracted to the mode of individuality in singulars, meaning, as he does, by singulars, ordinary existing things. The pragmaticist cannot admit that. I myself went too far in the direction of nominalism when I said that it was a mere question of the convenience of speech whether we say that a diamond is hard when it is not pressed upon, or whether we say that it is soft until it is pressed upon.[6] I *now* say that experiment will prove that the diamond is hard, as a positive fact. That is, it is a real fact that it *would* resist pressure, which amounts to extreme scholastic realism. I deny that pragmaticism as originally defined by me made the intellectual purport of symbols to consist in our conduct. On the contrary, I was most careful to say that it consists in our *concept* of what our conduct *would* be upon *conceivable* occasions. For I had long before declared that absolute individuals were *entia rationis*, and not realities. A concept determinate in all respects is as fictitious as a concept definite in all respects. I do not think we can ever have a logical right to infer, even as probable,

[5] (Ed.) [Bibliography] G–1905–1b.
[6] (Ed.) At 5.403.

the existence of anything entirely contrary in its nature to all that we can experience or imagine. But a nominalist must do this. For he must say that all future events are the total of all that will have happened and therefore that the future is not endless; and therefore, that there will be an event not followed by any event. This *may* be, inconceivable as it is; but the nominalist must say that it *will* be, else he will make the future to be endless, that is, to have a mode of being consisting in the truth of a general law. For every future event will have been completed, but the endless future will not have been completed. There are many other turns that may be given to this argument; and the conclusion of it is that it is only the general which we can understand. What we commonly designate by pointing at it or otherwise indicating it we assume to be singular. But so far as we can comprehend it, it will be found not to be so. We can only *indicate* the real universe; if we are asked to describe it, we can only say that it includes whatever there may be that really is. This is a universal, not a singular.

209.   The truth of pragmaticism may be proved in various ways. I would conduct the argument somewhat as follows. In the first place, there are but three elementary kinds of reasoning. The first, which I call *abduction* (on the theory, the doubtful theory, I confess, that the meaning of the XXVth chapter of the second book of the Prior Analytics has been completely diverted from Aristotle's meaning by a single wrong word having been inserted by Apellicon where the original word was illegible) consists in examining a mass of facts and in allowing these facts to suggest a theory. In this way we gain new ideas; but there is no force in the reasoning. The second kind of reasoning is *deduction*, or necessary reasoning. It is applicable only to an ideal state of things, or to a state of things in so far as it may conform to an ideal. It merely gives a new aspect to the premises. It consists in constructing an image or diagram in accordance with a general precept, in observing in that image certain relations of parts not explicitly laid down in the precept, and in convincing oneself that the same relations will always occur when that precept is followed out. For example, having convinced ourselves of the truth of the *pons asinorum* with the aid of a diagram drawn with a common lead pencil, we are quite sure it would be the same with a diagram drawn in

167

red; and a form of syllogism which is certain in black is equally so in red. A phenomenon having been observed in a laboratory, though we may not know on what conditions it depends, yet we are quite sure that it would make no difference whether the number of degrees of the longitude of the planet Eros just one week previous were a prime or composite number. The third way of reasoning is *induction,* or experimental research. Its procedure is this. Abduction having suggested a theory, we employ *de*duction to deduce from that ideal theory a promiscuous variety of consequences to the effect that if we perform certain acts, we shall find ourselves confronted with certain experiences. We then proceed to try these experiments, and if the predictions of the theory are verified, we have a proportionate confidence that the experiments that remain to be tried will confirm the theory. I say that these three are the only elementary modes of reasoning there are. I am convinced of it both *a priori* and *a posteriori.* The *a priori* reasoning is contained in my paper in the Proceedings of the American Academy of Arts and Sciences for April 9, 1867.[7] I will not repeat it. But I will mention that it turns in part upon the fact that induction is, as Aristotle says, the inference of the truth of the major premiss of a syllogism of which the minor premiss is made to be true and the conclusion is found to be true, while abduction is the inference of the truth of the minor premiss of a syllogism of which the major premiss is selected as known already to be true while the conclusion is found to be true. Abduction furnishes all our ideas concerning real things, beyond what are given in perception, but is mere conjecture, without probative force. Deduction is certain but relates only to ideal objects. Induction gives us the only approach to certainty concerning the real that we can have. In forty years diligent study of arguments, I have never found one which did not consist of those elements. The successes of modern science ought to convince us that induction is the only capable *imperator* of truth-seeking. Now pragmaticism is simply the doctrine that the inductive method is the only essential to the ascertainment of the intellectual purport of any symbol.

210. This argument must be supplemented by examples of the wholesome effect of pragmatistic interpretations. Among

[7] (Ed.) [Bibliography] G–1867–1b.

the most signal of these is the explanation of probability. We begin by asking, what is the use of calculations of probabilities; and the answer is that the great business of insurance rests upon such calculations. The probability upon which this business proceeds consists in the practical certainty that for every ten thousand dollars paid in about a certain number of dollars will have to be paid out. In the rare, the very rare, case in which decidedly more must be paid out, there are not only reserves more than ample, but there is the knowledge that such large payments will cause a great increase in the amounts paid in. A probability, therefore, is the known ratio of frequency of a specific future event to a generic future event which includes it. That is what probability must mean in order to have any importance for business. What, then, does it mean to say that if a man sees a phenomenon occur on m successive days, the probability is $m + 1/m + 2$ that the same phenomenon will appear on the next following day? Does it mean that if we put a large number of universes in a bag, shake them up well, and draw out one at random this will be the average result? It plainly means nothing at all of any consequence.

211.   But all this neither proves, nor tends to prove, the whole proposition. It goes to show that the practical consequences are *much*, but not that they are *all* the meaning of a concept. A new argument must supplement the above. All the more active functions of animals are adaptive characters calculated to insure the continuance of the stock. Can there be the slightest hesitation in saying, then, that the human intellect is implanted in man, either by a creator or by a quasi-intentional effect of the struggle for existence, virtually in order, and solely in order, to insure the continuance of mankind? But how can it have such effect except by regulating human conduct? Shall we not conclude then that the conduct of men is the sole purpose and sense of thinking, and that if it be asked *why* should the human stock be continued, the only answer is that that is among the inscrutable purposes of God or the virtual purposes of nature which for the present remain secrets to us?

212.   So it would seem. But this conclusion is too vastly far-reaching to be admitted without further examination. Man seems to himself to have some glimmer of co-understanding with God, or with Nature. The fact that he has been able in

169

some degree to predict how Nature will act, to formulate general "laws" to which future events conform, seems to furnish inductive proof that man really penetrates in some measure the ideas that govern creation. Now man cannot believe that creation has not some ideal purpose. If so, it is not mere action, but the development of an idea which is the purpose of thought; and so a doubt is cast upon the ultra pragmatic notion that action is the *sole* end and purpose of thought.

213.   It was in the desperate endeavor to make a beginning of penetrating into that riddle that on May 14, 1867, after three years of almost insanely concentrated thought, hardly interrupted even by sleep, I produced my one contribution to philosophy in the "New List of Categories" in the Proceedings of the American Academy of Arts and Sciences, Vol. VII, pp. 287–298.[8] Tell your friend Julian that this is, if possible, even less original than my maxim of pragmatism; and that I take pride in the entire absence of originality in all that I have ever sought to bring to the attention of logicians and metaphysicians. My three categories are nothing but Hegel's three grades of thinking. I know very well that there are other categories, those which Hegel calls by that name. But I never succeeded in satisfying myself with any list of *them*. We may classify objects according to their matter; as wooden things, iron things, silver things, ivory things, etc. But classification according to structure is generally more important. And it is the same with ideas. Much as I would like to see Hegel's list of categories reformed, I hold that a classification of the elements of thought and consciousness according to their formal structure is more important. I believe in inventing new philosophical words in order to avoid the ambiguities of the familiar words. I use the word *phaneron* to mean all that is present to the mind in any sense or in any way whatsoever, regardless of whether it be fact or figment. I examine the phaneron and I endeavor to sort out its elements according to the complexity of their structure. I thus reach my three categories.[9]

---

[8] (Ed.) [Bibliography] G–1867–1c.

[9] (Ed.) Peirce then begins a long discussion of the categories and signs (cf. [CP] I, II).

CHAPTER 2

TO PAUL CARUS, ON "ILLUSTRATIONS OF THE LOGIC OF SCIENCE"[1]

214. Ever since I was paid that money by you and Mrs. Carus, I have been engaged with all my energy, allowing only for such as I had to expend upon my wife's health and upon getting this house habitable and in salable condition, in trying to write an article or articles for you upon the second grade of clearness, i.e., that which results from analytic definition, and upon corrections to the errors and other faults of the articles of mine that appeared in *The Popular Science Monthly* in 1877 and 1878,[2] to which I should be glad if you would add a reprint of the article of January, 1901,[3] which requires no correction.

215. I have written a great deal but am satisfied with but the smaller part of it . . . Since I got your letter I have . . .

[1] (Ed.) From an incomplete draft of a letter, bearing no date, to "My Dear Doctor Carus," Widener VB2a, with added quotations below in the present footnote and in 225n10. The similarity of this letter to 2.661–668 (1910) and to the letter described below in this footnote (19 July 1910) indicates that it was probably written c.1910. This draft was written when Peirce was in ill health, and it is in very rough form. Considerable editing has been done on it. The Carus papers at the Open Court Publishing Company, LaSalle, Illinois, contain what appears to be a typed copy of the letter of which this is a draft.

In a draft of a letter of July 19, 1910, to "My dear Doctor Carus," Widener VB2a, Peirce discusses the republication of [Bibliography] G–1877–5a and 5b, "The Fixation of Belief" and "How to Make Our Ideas Clear," as two parts of a single essay with the title, "Pragmatic Clearness of Thought." His main point is that "The error of the Essay lies in its *Nominalism*." He further states that 1873 "is the date of my formulating the opinion expressed in the two articles that are the two parts of that Essay on Pragmatistic Clearness . . ." Cf. [Bibliography] G–1909–1.

[2] (Ed.) [Bibliography] G–1877–5, "Illustrations of the Logic of Science," *The Popular Science Monthly*, 1877–1878.

[3] (Ed.) [Bibliography] G–1901–1, a review of Pearson's *The Grammar of Science*.

gradually been forced to the conclusion that since you are very reasonably impatient, my best course is simply to write a preface in which I state in general terms how what I then say ought to be altered, and I will here . . . try to indicate the points I should make.

216.   In regard to the first Essay consisting of the first two articles,[4] the principal positive error is its nominalism, especially illustrated by what I said about Gray's stanza, "Full many a gem" etc., . . .[5] I must show that the *will be's*, the actually *is's*, and the *have beens* are not the sum of the reals. They only cover actuality. There are besides *would be's* and *can be's* that are real. The distinction is that the *actual* is subject both to the principles of contradiction and of excluded middle; and in *one* way so are the *would be's* and *can be's*. In *that* way a *would be* is but the negation of a *can be* and conversely. But in another way a *would be* is not subject to the principle of excluded middle; both *would be X* and *would be not X* may be false. And in this latter way a *can be* may be defined as that which is not subject to the principle of contradiction. On the contrary, if of anything it is only true that it *can be X* [then] it *can be not X* as well.

217.   It certainly can be proved very clearly that the Universe does contain both *would be's* and *can be's*.

218.   Then in regard to the second article, I ought to say that my three grades of clearness are *not*, as I seemed then to think, such that either the first or the second are superseded by the third, although we may say that they are acquired, mostly, in the order of those numbers. I ought to describe, if only in a paragraph, how to train oneself and one's children in the first grade of clearness, so that, for example, one will recognize a millimetre length when one meets with it, and so with colors. I have done a great deal of work in training myself to this kind of clearness. It would if put together amount to two or three years of industry; and I should recommend systematic exercises of the sort to everybody.[6] Useful as that is, however, I don't hesitate to say that the second grade of clearness is far

---

[4] (Ed.) "The Fixation of Belief" and "How to Make Our Ideas Clear."

[5] (Ed.) 5.409. The stanza referred to is the fourteenth in "Elegy Written in a Country Church-yard," by Thomas Gray.

[6] (Ed.) Cf. [Bibliography] G–1898–1, Lecture 5, "Training in Reasoning."

more important, and all my writings of late years illustrate that. Still, I continue to admit that the third grade is the most important of all and a good example of it is William James who is so phenomenally weak in the second grade, yet ever so high above most men in the third. But there is no reason why all three should not be symmetrically developed.

219.   The bulk of these *Popular Science* articles, after the first two, are occupied with a criticism of the underlying principles of Laplace's *Théorie Analytique des Probabilités* and Mill's *System of Logic* — two writers of a high order which have had and still have a great and deplorable influence.

220.   Before the third article, on probability, I should like to insert a short and easy account of my existential graphs [7] because when that system is well in hand, it becomes so much easier to show great faults of Laplace and Mill; and that shorter account I could now easily write.

221.   It would also be well to show how all numbers involve *essentially* nothing but ideas of *succession*. Then I should like to point out how utterly Laplace fails to define what he means by *probabilité*, his account of it resting upon what he calls the *également possible*, which I maintain has none but the vaguest meaning. I ought on my side to define *probability*.[8] For that purpose, I should have to begin by distinguishing three ways — three quite different *directions* so to speak, as different as the X, Y, Z of a system of orthogonal co-ordinates — in which cognitions can fall short of absolute certainty, or rather of *mathematical* certainty, which is not absolute, because blunders may have been committed in reaching it.[9]

222.   The names which I would propose for general adoption for the three different kinds of acceptability of propositions are plausibility, verisimilitude, probability. . . .

223.   The last alone seems to be capable of a certain degree of exactitude or measurement. By plausibility, I mean the degree to which a theory ought to recommend itself to our belief independently of any kind of evidence other than our instinct urging us to regard it favorably. All the other races of animals certainly have such instincts; why refuse them to mankind?

[7] (Ed.)   Existential graphs are discussed in [CP] IV, Book II.
[8] (Ed.)   Peirce's theory of probability is discussed mainly in [CP] II.
[9] (Ed.)   Cf. 7.108ff.

Have not all men some notions of right and wrong as well as purely theoretical instincts? For example, if any man finds that an object of no great size in his chamber behaves in any surprising manner, he wonders what makes it do so; and his instinct suggests that the cause, most plausibly, is also in his chamber or in the neighbourhood. It is true that the alchemists used to think it might be some configuration of the planets, but in my opinion this was due to a special derangement of natural instinct. Physicists certainly today continue largely to be influenced by such plausibilities in selecting which of several hypotheses they will first put to the test.

224. By verisimilitude I mean that kind of recommendation of a proposition which consists in evidence which is insufficient because there is not enough of it, but which will amount to proof if that evidence which is not yet examined continues to be of the same virtue as that already examined, or if the evidence not at hand and that never will be complete, should be like that which is at hand. All determinations of probability ultimately rest on such verisimilitudes. I mean that if we throw a die 216 times in order to ascertain whether the probability of its turning up a six at any one throw differs decidedly from $\frac{1}{6}$ or not, our conclusion is an affair not of probability as Laplace would have it, by assuming that the antecedent probabilities of the different values of the probability are equal, but is a verisimilitude or as we say a "likelihood." That Laplace is wrong can be demonstrated, since his theory leads to contradictory results. But perhaps the easiest way to show it is wrong is to point out that there is no more reason for assuming that all the values of the probability are equally probable than for assuming that all the values of the *odds* are so; or that all the values of the logarithms of the odds are so, since this is our instinctive way of judging of probabilities, as is shown by our "balancing the probabilities."

225. Having thus defined plausibility and verisimilitude, I come to define probability. None of the books contain a definition of mathematical probability (which is what I mean by "probability" however measured) which will hold water. For the sake of simplicity, I will define it in a particular example. If, then, I say that the probability that if a certain die be thrown in the usual way it will turn up a number divisible by 3

174

(i.e., either 3 or 6) is ⅓, what do I mean?   I mean, of course, to state that that die has a certain habit or disposition of behaviour in its present state of wear.[10] It is a *would be* and does not consist in actualities or single events in any multitude finite or infinite. Nevertheless a habit does consist in what *would* happen under certain circumstances if it should remain unchanged throughout an endless series of actual occurrences. I must therefore define that habit of the die in question which we express by saying that there is a probability of ⅓ (or odds of 1 to 2) that if it be thrown it will turn up a number divisible by 3 by saying how it *would* behave if, while remaining with its shape, etc. just as they are now, it *were to be* thrown an endless succession of times. Now it is very true that it is quite impossible that it should be thrown an infinite succession of times. But this is no objection to my supposing it, since that impossibility is merely a physical, or if you please, a metaphysical one, and is not due to any logical impossibility to the occurrence in a finite time of an endless succession of events each occupying a finite time. For when Achilles overtook the tortoise he had to go through such an endless series (endless *in the series*, but not endless *in time*) and supposedly actually did so.

226.   Very well, I will further suppose that tallies are kept during the throwings, one tally of the throws turning up 6 or 3,

---

[10] (Ed.) "No sign can function as such except so far as it is interpreted in another sign (for example, in a "thought," whatever that may be). Consequently it is absolutely essential to a sign that it should *affect* another sign. In using this causal word, 'affect,' I do not refer to invariable accompaniment or sequence, merely, or necessarily. What I mean is that when there is a sign there *will be* an interpretation in another sign. The essence of the relation is in the conditional futurity; but it is not essential that there should be absolutely no exception. If, for example, in the 'long run' (that is, in an endless series of experiences taken in their experiential order) there WOULD BE as many cases of interpreted signs as of signs, I should say that this 'would be' constitutes a causal relation, even though there were, as there might be, an infinite number of exceptions. If the exceptions are, as they occur, as many or nearly as many as the cases of following the rule, the causality would be in my terminology 'very weak.' But if there is any WOULD BE at all, there is more or less causation; for that is all I mean by causation. I do not pretend that this is an accurate analysis of the ordinary conception, or a parlance to be recommended. It is simply what I mean in this connection. It leaves the whole question of what there may be of a *metaphysical* character quite open." From a sheet which is very probably part of an incomplete letter, dated July, 1904, Widener Vβ. Cf. 2.661ff.

but the other tally of the throws turning up 1, 2, 4, 5, and further I will suppose that after each throw the number that the latter tally has reached shall be divided by the number that the former tally has reached. I will use the expression that this quotient *changes its value* at every new throw, instead of saying that a new quotient differs from the last. When the quotient changes from being greater than 2 [or] being less than 2 . . . to being either just 2 or on the opposite side of 2 to what it was before, as for example if it passes from being 21:10 to being 21:11 or from 21:11 to 22:11 or from 25:12 to 25:13, etc., I shall say it touches 2 (meaning strictly that it either comes to 2 or passes across 2). Then after the first throw it will be either 0 or ∞ and there it may remain for any number of throws. But after it has once moved away it never will return to either of these values, but after it has finally recovered from the effects of the first throws it will oscillate in a very irregular way, and soon it will "touch" (or pass over) some other values *for the last time* although nobody can *know* that it is to prove to have been for the last time; and then values still nearer to 2 will be touched or traversed for the last time. And in its endless series there will be no value that it would not touch or traverse for the last time excepting only the value 2. And this "would be" is what constitutes the habit which we state in saying that the odds against its turning up a number divisible by 3 are 2:1 or that the probability of its turning up a 6 or a 3 is $\frac{1}{3}$. . . .

227. In order to get this matter straightened out, I think it would be well to change the place of the sixth paper and place it directly after the third.[11] Then I would append a *Correction* in which I would state that the division of the elementary kinds of reasoning into three heads was made by me in my first lectures and was published in 1869 in Harris's *Journal of Speculative Philosophy*.[12] I still consider that it had a sound basis. Only in almost everything I printed before the beginning of this century I more or less mixed up Hypothesis and Induction. . . .

228. The general body of logicians had also at all times come very near recognizing the trichotomy. They only failed

[11] (Ed.) Peirce is proposing to place "Deduction, Induction, and Hypothesis" between "The Doctrine of Chances" and "The Probability of Induction."

[12] (Ed.) [Bibliography] G–1868–2c.

to do so by having so narrow and formalistic a conception of inference (as necessarily having formulated judgments for its premises) that they did not recognize Hypothesis (or, as I now term it, *retroduction*) [13] as an *inference.* . . .

229.   When one contemplates a surprising or otherwise perplexing state of things (often so perplexing that he cannot definitely state what the perplexing character is) he may formulate it into a judgment or many apparently connected judgments; he will often finally strike out a hypothesis, or problematical judgment, as a mere possibility, from which he either fully perceives or more or less suspects that the perplexing phenomenon would be a necessary or quite probable consequence.

230.   That is a retroduction. Now three lines of reasoning are open to him. First, he may proceed by mathematical or syllogistic reasoning at once to demonstrate that consequence. That of course will be deduction.

231.   Or, second, he may proceed still further to study the phenomenon in order to find other features that the hypothesis will *explain* (i.e. in the English sense of explain, to deduce the facts from the hypothesis as its necessary or *probable* consequences). That will be to continue reasoning retroductively, i.e., by hypothesis.

232.   Or, what is usually the best way, he may turn to the consideration of the hypothesis, study it thoroughly and deduce miscellaneous observable consequences, and *then* return to the phenomena to find how nearly these consequences agree with the actual facts.

233.   This is not essentially different from induction. Only it is most usually an induction from instances which are not discrete and numerable. I now call it Qualitative Induction. It is this which I used to confound with the second line of procedure, or at least not to distinguish it sharply.

234.   A good account of Quantitative Induction is given in my paper in *Studies in Logic, By Members of the Johns Hopkins University*,[14] and its two rules are there well developed. But what I there call hypothesis is so far from being that, that it is rather Quantitative than Qualitative Induction. At any

[13] (Ed.) Peirce often calls this "abduction."
[14] (Ed.) [Bibliography] G–1883–7b.

177

rate, it is treated *mostly* as Quantitative. Hypothesis proper is in that paper only touched upon in the last section.

235.   There is a third kind of Induction. In order to show this, it is requisite to define Induction.

236.   Now the essential character of induction is that it infers a *would-be* from actual singulars. These singulars must, in general, be finite in multitude and then, as I show in my Johns Hopkins paper, the inductive conclusion can be (usually) but *indefinite*, and can never be *certain*. . . .

237.   But in ordinary cases an induction would become both *precise* and *certain*, — though even then it would not be apodictic certainty, if the instances were of denumeral (or simply endless) multitude. Therefore, defining induction as the sort of inference which produces verisimilitude or likelihood (that is, which regards an endless series of actualities as conclusive evidence of a *would-be* since it is the best evidence possible when we are not behind the scenes), . . . any plausible proposition that is supported by instances in every respect is justifiable so long as one keeps on the alert for the first exception. Of course, such an induction has the very minimum of likelihood, yet it has *some*; and we very often find ourselves driven to accept it. The world has always turned on its axis so far as we know about once every 24 hours and therefore we presume (vaguely) that it always will continue to do so. In every case that has been sufficiently inquired into, every human being has been born of a woman not a maiden. So almost everybody feels sure it always will be found so. People are far more confident of it than they have any right to be. All former generations of men have died off. Therefore, people say, they always will. In one sense I suppose this is certain. But that they always *would* even if there were no accidents, seems to me as weak an inference as any that I would not positively condemn as utterly worthless. I call this kind of thing crude induction. I must confess that although my explanation of the validity of induction seems to me to be far superior to any other, I am not altogether satisfied with it, or rather with its results. Quantitative Induction depends upon the possibility of making a truly representative sample. That is to say, the examples composing it must be chosen as possessing the conditional character, which is easy enough, but also so that the choice of them shall not

be influenced one way or the other, by whether or not they possess the consequent character. They must be such on the whole in that course of experience to which the induction is to be applied. That, to be sure, cannot but be the case, should the entire class sampled be alike in respect to the consequent character. But the further this ideal state of things is from being realized the more extremely difficult it becomes to get a truly representative sample, and the result, after every precaution has been taken, is that we cannot expect any great precision in inductive conclusions when the class is anywhere near being equally divided between individuals that do and that do not possess the consequent character. However, this is not owing to any falsity in my theory, but to the essential imperfection of induction itself when applied to these cases.

238.   As for the validity of the hypothesis, the retroduction, there seems at first to be no room at all for the question of what supports it, since from an actual fact it only infers a *may-be* (*may-be* and *may-be not*). But there is a decided leaning to the affirmative side and the frequency with which that turns out to be an actual fact is to me quite the most surprising of all the wonders of the universe.

CHAPTER 3

TO JOHN DEWEY, ON THE NATURE OF LOGIC [1]

239. I mean, if I can manage it, to get some notice of the book of your logical school into the *Nation*.[2] But the editor fights very shy of the subject as I write about it and it is necessary to dilute and decorate it so that the result has not much value for serious students. I will therefore write to express how your position appears as viewed from mine. I am struck with the literary tone of your men, a sort of maturity which bespeaks the advantage of studying under you and thoroughly applaud your efforts to set them on their own legs. All that is admirable and warms my heart. But I must say to you that your style of reasoning about reasoning has, to my mind, the usual fault that when men touch on this subject, they seem to think that no reasoning can be too loose, that indeed there is a merit in such slipshod arguments as they themselves would not dream of using in any other branch of science. You propose to substitute for the Normative Science which in my judgment is the greatest need of our age a "Natural History" of thought or of experience. Far be it from me to do anything to hinder a man's finding out whatever kind of truth he is on the way to finding out. But I do not think anything like a natural history can answer the terrible need that I see of checking the awful waste of thought, of time, of energy, going on, in consequence of men's

---

[1] (Ed.) Paragraphs 239–242 are a letter dated "1904 June 9"; paragraphs 243–244 are from an incomplete letter, bearing no date, but from the evidence given in 243n4 it was written c.1905. Both letters are in Widener VB2a, and both have the salutation, "My dear Prof. Dewey."

[2] (Ed.) [Bibliography] N–1904–16, reprinted in Book I of the present volume.

Dewey had written from the University of Chicago, saying that he was sending Peirce a copy of the book and expressing his general indebtedness to Peirce. The letter, dated 11 January 1904, is in Widener VB2a.

not understanding the theory of inference. Though you use the expression "Natural History," yet of the two branches of Natural History, physiology and anatomy, which are as sharply sundered today as ever they were, you seem to be alluding only to the latter, since you speak of its being revolutionized by conceptions of evolution. Now the doctrine of evolution has not affected physiology either much or little, unless by lending a competing interest to anatomy [3] and thus *weakening* physiology. It has certainly neither directly, nor indirectly, strengthened it. So, using the word anatomy without reference to its etymological suggestions, but simply as a designation of the sort of business that Comparative Anatomists are engaged in, you seem to conceive your occupation to be the studying out of the Anatomy of Thought. Thereupon, I remark that the "thought" of which you speak cannot be the "thought" of normative logic. For it is one of the characteristics of all normative science that it does not concern itself in the least with what actually takes place in the universe, barring always its assumption that what is before the mind always has those characteristics that are found there and which Phänomenologie is assumed to have made out. But as to particular and variable facts, no normative science has any concern with them, further than to remark that they form a constant constituent of the phenomenon. Now nothing like the study the Comparative Anatomists are occupied with can be made of *mere possibilities*. It absolutely requires a rich experimental field. If it were not so, one could have an anatomy of Higher Plane Curves; and upon a superficial examination it might seem as if that were possible. But more thorough study will show that such a thing would be entirely artificial. There is no anatomy of possibilities because one can say in advance how pure possibilities vary and diverge from one another. Namely, they do so in every possible way. What renders a Comparative Anatomy possible is that certain conceivable forms do not occur. Only a minute proportion of them occur. Thus we have a comparative anatomy of the chemical elements, because though Mendeléef's Table *roughly* describes what elements there are *in part*, yet

[3] (Ed.) A marginal note on the first page of this letter reads: "The idea that two such elements as Evolution and Function can in the same sense depend upon one another seems to me *absurd*."

each element has peculiarities which that table does not account for and besides there are no elements except Manganese in one column and the rare earths do not differ from one another in any such way as the table predicts and besides the table sets no limits to the atomic weights; but we find that elements of very high atomic weights are radioactive in every column of the table and beyond these we find no elements at all. Thus there is in the list of chemical elements just that experiential diversity and absence of most possible forms that renders the kind of study called anatomical possible. If then you have a "Natural History" (i.e. a comparative anatomy) of thought, — it is not the merely *possible* thought that Normative Science studies, but thought as it presents itself in an *apparently* inexplicable and irrational experience.

240.   The effect of teaching that such a Natural History can take the place of a normative science of thought must be to render the rules of reasoning lax; and in fact I find you and your students greatly given over to what to me seems like a debauch of loose reasoning. Chicago hasn't the reputation of being a moral place; but I should think that the effect of living there upon a man like you would be to make you feel all the more the necessity for Dyadic distinctions, — Right and Wrong, Truth and Falsity. These are only to be kept up by self control. Now just as Moral Conduct is Self-controlled conduct so Logical Thought is Moral, or Self-controlled, thought. The Germans have always been in favor of giving thought the rein. What is taught in German Universities bespeaks only the fashion of the day. No doubt a slow evolutionary process will gradually bring them round to the truth. But that is the Wild Oats doctrine applied to thought. It involves unspeakable waste.

241.   Although I am strongly in favor of your Pragmatistic views, I find the whole volume penetrated with this spirit of intellectual licentiousness, that does not see that anything is so very false. Of course you will understand that I should not write in such underscored terms to any man with whom I did not feel a very deep respect and sympathy. I am simply *projecting upon the horizon*, where distance gets magnified indefinitely, the *direction* of your standpoint as viewed from mine.

242.   There are three sciences according to me to which Logic ought to appeal for principles, because they do not de-

pend upon Logic. They are Mathematics, Phenomenology, and Ethics. There are several sciences to which logicians often make appeal by arguments which would be circular if they rose to the degree of correctness necessary to that kind of fallacy. They are Metaphysical Philosophy, Psychology, Linguistics (of which they barely know that of the Aryan Languages, — and not Gaelic which does not ordinarily give a sentence a subject nominative), History, etc.

---

243.   Your letter about my April Monist article [4] gave me keen pleasure, — all the more so because I was somewhat surprised to learn you found so much good in what I said. For your Studies in Logical Theory certainly forbids all such researches as those which I have been absorbed in for the last eighteen years. That is what I liked least in those four papers. First, because it is contrary to a maxim I never infringe "Never permanently bar the road of any true inquiry," and my studies are so real that they compel me to say that certain highly esteemed and "genetical" methods are leading to false conclusions, certain others that are despised are most precious. Secondly, because your mode of arguing that every inquiry ought to be conducted genetically is a wretched method, considering the extreme importance of the conclusion. Thirdly, because some of your premises are entirely contrary to the convictions which half a dozen years of careful historical studies and my personal experience force upon me. For according to my studies there are some sciences which can be and ought to be studied genetically, while others cannot be so studied without rendering them perfectly futile. Such, for example, is pure mathematics; such are dynamics and general physics; such is chemistry; such is physiology proper. Again, you take as premiss of a confirmatory argument that any non-genetic logic will reach no conclusions that have any meaning in their real applications. But all my studies are conducted in full view of actual scientific memoirs and other records of scientific inquiry, in which they lead to denials of conclusions to which bad logic

[4] (Ed.) [Bibliography] G–1905–1a. Dewey had written from Columbia University, praising this article. The letter, dated 11 April 1905, is in Widener VB2a. The date of the article and the date of Dewey's letter establish the date of Peirce's letter as c.1905 (see 239n1).

has led their authors; and some of my non-genetical studies have led directly to discoveries in mathematics and others to instituting experimental researches about the reality, if not the solidity, of which there can be no question; and in short I should like to know what genetic logician ever came to have such close quarters with actual science as I have done.

244. If it were not for this uncalled for intolerance of your logical theory, I should have no serious objection to it; and there are parts of it that seem to me admirable and of great value. I regretted your making everything turn on Lotze, as if he were a Hume. He was in his day a very careful, serious inquirer. But he was never a thinker of great subtilty, and he is now so entirely left behind, that I thought you might have left his doctrine to be disposed of by Jones and men of that calibre; and that he was rather small game for you. Whenever I come across a dilemma, I look out for the fallacy, my experience having shown me there almost always was one. Your reasoning generally is that either Lotze or you must be right, now Lotze isn't, etc. But you in no case, or in *one* at most, convince me at all that these are the only alternatives. In short, I think you could have made a stronger argument if you had let Lotze alone. That would not have been *genetic*, perhaps! But if instead of this argumentation which I can but believe to be artificial, you had just narrated how as historic fact you arrived at your opinion, that would have been genetic, and I venture to think that it would have seemed to me a conclusive proof, not of precisely all your propositions but of your main contention; and the errors would easily have been separated as merely the exaggerations of over-precision. The fallacy of over-precision which consists not in taking an ell when one has a right to an inch, but in stretching a warrant for a percentage of a micro-micron to more than the sum of all macro-kilometres, may be called the Philosopher's Fallacy. The first maxim of my "Synechism" runs: "Let us not precide our conclusions beyond what our premises definitely warrant." What you had a right to say was that for certain logical problems the entire development of cognition and along with it that of its object become pertinent, and therefore should be taken into account. What you do say is that no inquiry for which this development is not pertinent should be permitted.

CHAPTER 4

TO WILLIAM T. HARRIS, ON MIND [1]

245. I send to you today two proof-sheets.[2] I should have sent the first one on some days ago but was ill when it came.

246. I suppose you saw that I struck out the paragraph referring to Hegelians. I intended no *slur* on them, or any appeal to the ignorant against them. What I meant was to protest respectfully but energetically *to* them against a certain tendency in their philosophy. In fact with all the disposition of this school to find every philosophical doctrine true for its time and stage of development, yet if their categories should happen not to be true it is plain that to classify men according to them may be one of the most unfair things in the world.

247. I have considered your remark that you do not see the drift of my making man entirely ignorant of his own states of mind. I suppose I have not written very clearly for one thing, — and that I have tried to correct in the proof. But the real difficulty is that the article is truncated. I had intended to wind up with a long discussion about the metaphysics — the ontology of the soul. I left this off on account of the length of the article. But now I find by your criticism that it is wanted, and I have endeavored to put it into the briefest and most meagre form and send it to you, in hopes you will be able to tack it on to the end of the article.

248. I do not say that we are ignorant of our states of mind. What I say is that the mind is virtual, not in a series of moments, not capable of existing except in a space of time — nothing so far as it is at any one moment.[3]

---

[1] (Ed.) A letter to "Wm. T. Harris Esq.," dated "1868 Nov. 30," in the Hoose Library at the University of Southern California. Harris was the editor of the *Journal of Speculative Philosophy*.

[2] (Ed.) For one of the articles, probably the second, of the series on intuitive knowledge in the *Journal of Speculative Philosophy*, 1868–1869; [Bibliography] G–1868–2.

[3] (Ed.) Cf. 5.289, 5.313.

CHAPTER 5

TO WILLIAM JAMES[1]

§1. PRAGMATISM

249.   [March 13, 1897] Your letter and the dedication and the book gave me more delight than you would be apt to believe.[2] The note came day before yesterday. I got the book last night. I have read the first essay which is of great value, and I don't see that it is so very "elementary" as you say, unless you mean that it is very easy to read and comprehend, and it is a masterpiece in that respect.

250.   That everything is to be tested by its practical results was the great text of my early papers;[3] so, as far as I get your general aim in so much of the book as I have looked at, I am quite with you in the main. In my later papers,[4] I have seen more thoroughly than I used to do that it is not mere action as brute exercise of strength that is the purpose of all, but say generalization, such action as tends toward regularization, and the actualization of the thought which without action remains unthought. . . .

---

[1] (Ed.) From a series of letters from Peirce to James in the William James Collection in Houghton Library. The date of each letter is given in brackets at the beginning of the first paragraph. Peirce's salutation is "My dear William," with but one exception (the letter of November 10, 1900) when he uses "My dear Willie." No letter is printed in full.

There is considerable overlap between the contents of this chapter and [Perry] II, but each contains Peirce-James correspondence not to be found in the other.

[2] (Ed.) James, *The Will to Believe*, 1897, was dedicated "To My Old Friend, CHARLES SANDERS PEIRCE, to whose philosophic comradeship in old times and to whose writings in more recent years I owe more incitement and help than I can express or repay."

[3] (Ed.) [Bibliography] G–1877–5.

[4] (Ed.) Cf. [Bibliography] G–1891–1.

186

251. As to "belief" and "making up one's mind," if they mean anything more than this, that we have a plan of procedure, and that according to that plan we will try a given description of behaviour, I am inclined to think they do more harm than good. "Faith," in the sense that one will adhere consistently to a given line of conduct, is highly necessary in affairs.[5] But if it means you are not going to be alert for indications that the moment has come to change your tactics, I think it ruinous in practice. If an opportunity occurs to do business with a man, and the success of it depends on his integrity, then if I decide to go into the transaction, I must go on the hypothesis he is an honest man, and there is no sense at all in halting between two lines of conduct. But that won't prevent my collecting further evidence with haste and energy, because it may show me it is time to change my plan. That is the sort of "faith" that seems useful. The hypothesis to be taken up is not necessarily a probable one. The cuneiform inscriptions could never have been deciphered if very unlikely hypotheses had not been tried. You must have a consistent plan of procedure, and the hypothesis you try is the one which comes next in turn to be tried according to that plan.[6] This justifies giving nominalism a fair trial before you go on to realism; because it is a simple theory which if it doesn't work will have afforded indications of what kind of realism ought to be tried first. I do not say probability ought not to be considered. It will be a prominent factor in a well considered plan of research. Probability is simply absurd and nonsensical in reference to a matter of "supreme interest," and any decision of such a question on probable grounds is illogical. But wherein does the illogicality lie? Simply in considering any interest as supreme. No man can be logical who reckons his personal well-being as a matter of overwhelming moment. . . .

252. I am much encouraged at your thinking well of "tychism." [7] But tychism is only a part and corollary of the general principle of Synechism. That is what I have been studying these last fifteen years, and I become more and more encouraged and delighted with the way it seems to fit all the wards of your

---

[5] (Ed.) Cf. 1.616ff.
[6] (Ed.) Cf. [CP] VII, Book II, "Scientific Method."
[7] (Ed.) Cf. 6.102.

lock. It was a truly sweet thing, my dear William, to dedicate
your book to me.

————◆————

253. [November 10, 1900] Now, however, I have a particular occasion to write. Baldwin, arrived at J in his dictionary, suddenly calls on me to do the rest of the logic, in the
utmost haste, and various questions of terminology come up.

Who originated the term *pragmatism*, I or you? Where did
it first appear in print? What do you understand by it? [8]

————◆————

254. [November 25, 1902] You feel, as I do, that the importance of pragmatism is not confined to philosophy. The
country is at this moment in imminent danger on which I
need not expatiate. In philosophy those who think themselves
pragmatists, like Mr. Schiller, miss the very point of it, that
one simply can't form any conception that is other than pragmatistic.

255. But I seem to myself to be the sole depositary at
present of the completely developed system, which all hangs
together and cannot receive any proper presentation in fragments. My own view in 1877 was crude. Even when I gave
my Cambridge lectures [9] I had not really got to the bottom of
it or seen the unity of the whole thing. It was not until after
that that I obtained the proof that logic must be founded on
ethics,[10] of which it is a higher development. Even then, I was
for some time so stupid as not to see that ethics rests in the
same manner on a foundation of esthetics, — by which, it is
needless to say, I don't mean milk and water and sugar.

256. These three normative sciences correspond to my three
categories, which in their psychological aspect, appear as Feeling, Reaction, Thought.[11] I have advanced my understanding
of these categories much since Cambridge days; and can now

[8] (Ed.) On a post card dated November 26, 1900, Widener VB2a, James
replies: "You invented 'pragmatism' for which I gave you full credit in a lecture
entitled 'Philosophical conceptions and practical results' of which I sent you 2
(unacknowledged) copies a couple of years ago."

[9] (Ed.) [Bibliography] G–1898-1.

[10] (Ed.) Cf. 1.573ff.

[11] (Ed.) See Chapter 4, "Consciousness," [CP] VII, Book III.

put them in a much clearer light and more convincingly. The
true nature of pragmatism cannot be understood without them.
It does not, as I seem to have thought at first, take Reaction as
the be-all, but it takes the end-all as the be-all, and the End
is something that gives its sanction to action. It is of the third
category. Only one must not take a nominalistic view of
Thought as if it were something that a man had in his consciousness. Consciousness may mean any one of the three categories. But if it is to mean Thought it is more without us than
within. It is we that are in it, rather than it in any of us. Of
course I can't explain myself in a few words; but I think it
would do the psychologists a great service to explain to them
my conception of the nature of thought.

257.   This then leads to synechism,[12] which is the keystone
of the arch.

---

258.   [March 7, 1904] [13] I want to thank you for your kind
reference to me in your piece about Schiller's *Humanism*.[14] . . .
The humanistic element of pragmatism is very true and important and impressive; but I do not think that the doctrine can
be *proved* in that way. The present generation likes to skip
proofs. I am tempted to write a little book of 150 pages about
pragmatism, just outlining my views of the matter, and append-
ing to it some of my old pieces with critical notes.[15] You and
Schiller carry pragmatism too far for me. I don't want to ex-
aggerate it but keep it within the bounds to which the evidences
of it are limited. The most important consequence of it, by
far, on which I have always insisted, as for example in my
notice of Fraser's Berkeley in the *North American Review* of
October, 1871,[16] is that under that conception of reality we
must abandon nominalism. That in my opinion is the great need

---

[12] (Ed.) Cf. 6.102ff.
[13] (Ed.) The letter bears dates of March 1 and 7, 1904, but the passage
quoted comes under the latter date.
[14] (Ed.) "Quite recently the word 'pragmatism,' first used thirty years ago
by our American philosopher, C. S. Peirce, has become fashionable as the designation of a novel way of looking at the mind's relations to reality." From
p. 175 of James's review of F. C. S. Schiller's *Humanism*, in *The Nation* 78(3
March 1904) 175–176. (This is identified as James's by [Haskell].)
[15] (Ed.) Cf. [Bibliography] G–1909–1.
[16] (Ed.) 8.7–38.

of philosophy. Notwithstanding what Royce says, Hegel appears to me to be on the whole a nominalist with patches of realism rather than a real realist.

259. I also want to say that after all pragmatism solves no real problem. It only shows that supposed problems are not real problems. But when one comes to such questions as immortality, the nature of the connection of mind and matter (further than that mind acts on matter not like a *cause* but like a *law*) we are left completely in the dark. The effect of pragmatism here is simply to open our minds to receiving any evidence, not to furnish evidence.

———————

260. [July 23, 1905] [17] To begin with I want to emphasize my particular gratitude for your papers, as well as for the copies of Leonardo and a paper from Prof. Vailati no doubt sent at your prompting.[18] . . . I read the French paper [19] first of this batch you have last sent. I found it entirely clear as well as beautifully written. When you write English (it is better to say the disagreeable thing) I can seldom at all satisfy myself that I know what you are driving at. Your writing would, I can see, be immensely forcible if one knew what you meant; but one (No. 1) doesn't. Now, for example, when you talk about doubting whether "consciousness" exists, you drive me at once to consulting a lot of books (in that particular case just 23 without counting the dictionaries of Baldwin, Eisler, etc.) to see what you could mean; and they left me as much in the dark as ever.[20] But now that you are tied down to the rules of French rhetoric, you are perfectly perspicuous; and I wish, and I am sure lots of others do, that you would consider yourself so tied down habitually. Because one sees that it only aids your force of style. Of course, you can smile at my undertaking to advise you about anything whatever. The fact that you can do so, if you like, emboldens me to say what I say.

261. I also agree to every word you say in this French article to the full, with one exception. That is that I am quite sure

[17] (Ed.) Some of the paragraphing in this letter is the editor's.
[18] (Ed.) Cf. 8.205.
[19] (Ed.) "La Notion de Conscience," *Archives de Psychologie* 5(June 1905) 1–12.
[20] (Ed.) See 270–305.

the doctrine is not at all so novel as you say. Of course it is all the better for not being novel. My recent delvings in the psychologies showed me that. Besides, it is nothing in the world but the well-known doctrine of immediate perception (followed out, of course, into other fields). This same thing, therefore, was held by our old friend Sir Wm. Hamilton, who had the same unfounded idea of its novelty. Not only Reid, but Kant, in his refutation of Berkeley, explicitly accepts it. As for the scholastics, no doubt so far as they were influenced by St. Augustine they were medium-ists, if I may coin the word for the purpose. But insofar as they followed Aristotle, I do not believe they were. I could easily mention several moderns who agree with you, and I have myself preached immediate perception as you know; — and you can't find a place where I distinguish the objective and subjective sides of things. I think I will mail you a paper of mine that was printed Jan., 1901, in the *Popular Science Monthly* [21] where you will see this, — not developed in the beautiful way you do, but plainly enough stated, I think. I refer you particularly to p. 301 et seq. I will quote a few phrases, though of course it is the continuous text that talks: "He tells us that each of us is like the operator at a central telephone office. . . Not at all! . . . When we first wake up to the fact that we are thinking beings . . . we have to set out upon our intellectual travels from the home where we already find ourselves. Now this home is the parish of Percepts. It is not inside our skulls but out in the open. It is the external world that we directly observe. . . . The inkstand is a *real* thing. Of course, in being real and external, it does not in the least cease to be a purely psychical product, a generalized percept." [22] If I had had the least idea that I was uttering anything newer than the doctrine of immediate perception, I should have argued the matter more closely. Of course, this doctrine of immediate perception is a *corollary from the corollary* of pragmaticism that the object perceived is the immediate object of the destined ultimate opinion, — not of course, identical as a psychological phenomenon, for there never will be a necessarily ultimate opinion as a psychological phenomenon, but identical logically and metaphysically. I am

[21] (Ed.)   8.132ff.
[22] (Ed.)   From 8.144; Peirce's deletions.

quite sure that lots of others have held the same view, some of them pragmatists and some not. (I hope the word "pragmatism" may be accepted, as I suggest, as the term expressive of these things, — perhaps we cannot be sure just what they are — in which the group of us are in agreement, as to the interpretation of thought.)

262. As for humanism, it appears to me to be an allied doctrine, in perfect harmony with pragmatism, but not relating exactly to the same question. Indeed, since Schiller identifies it with the old humanism, I prefer the word "anthropomorphism" as expressive of *the scientific opinion*. For the old humanism was not a scientific opinion but an aim; and whether in harmony with scientific aims or not, quite exterior to the scientific aim. To Schiller's anthropomorphism I subscribe in the main. And in particular if it implies *theism*, I am an anthropomorphist. But the God of my theism is not finite. That won't do at all. For to begin with, existence is reaction, and therefore no existent can be *clear supreme*. On the contrary, a finite being, without much doubt, and at any rate *by presumption*, is one of a genus; so that it would, to my mind, involve polytheism. In the next place, anthropomorphism for me implies above all that the true Ideal is a living power, which is a variation of the ontological proof due, I believe, to Moncure Conway's predecessor, William Johnson (*not* James) Fox. That is, the esthetic ideal, that which we *all* love and adore, the altogether admirable, has, *as ideal*, necessarily a mode of being to be called living. Because our ideas of the infinite are necessarily extremely vague and become contradictory the moment we attempt to make them precise. But still they are not utterly unmeaning, though they can only be interpreted in our religious adoration and the consequent effects upon conduct. This I think is good sound solid strong pragmatism. Now the Ideal is not a finite existent. Moreover, the human mind and the human heart have a filiation to God. That to me is the most comfortable doctrine. At least I find it most wonderfully so every day in contemplating all my misdeeds and shortcomings. Pluralism, on the other hand, does not satisfy either my head or my heart. I am as sure as I am of anything that the logical doctrines connected with it, — Achilles and the Tortoise etc., — are utterly false.

263. As for the "problem of evil," and the like, I see in them only blasphemous attempts to define the purposes of the Most High, — or rather that is what I think of such disturbances of religious consciousness generally; but that particular problem has received the most beautiful and satisfactory solution in *Substance and Shadow*. We had a tramp working for us for a few days not long ago. One day he started the problem of evil. In twenty words I put before him the *Substance and Shadow* solution. He saw it, at once, did my tramp; and after a few moments' reflexion he looked up and said to me, "Yes, I guess that is just it." There is, however, nothing more wholesome for us than to find problems that quite transcend our powers, and I must say, too, that it imparts a delicious sense of being cradled in the waters of the deep, — a feeling I always have at sea. It is, for example, entirely inscrutable to me why my three categories have been made so luminous to me without my being given the power to make them understood by those who alone are in a condition to see their meaning, — i.e. my fellow-pragmatists. It seems to me that you all must have a strange blind spot on your mental retina not to see what others see and what pragmatism ought to make so much plainer; . . .

§2. CATEGORIES

264. [June 8, 1903] It rather annoys me to be told that there is anything novel in my three categories; [23] for if they have not, however confusedly, been recognized by men since men began to think, that condemns them at once. To make them as distinct as it is in their nature to be is, however, no small task. I do not suppose they are so in my own mind; and evidently, it is not in their nature to be sharp as ordinary concepts. But I am going to try to make here a brief statement that, I think, will do something for them.

265. By the *phenomenon* I mean whatever is before our minds in any sense. The three categories are supposed to be the three kinds of elements that attentive perception can make out in the phenomenon.

266. The practical exigencies of life render Secondness the

[23] (Ed.) Cf. 7.524ff. and [CP] I, Book III, "Phenomenology."

most prominent of the three. This is not a conception, nor is it a peculiar quality. It is an experience. It comes out most fully in the shock of reaction between ego and non-ego. It is there the double consciousness of effort and resistance. That is something which cannot properly be conceived. For to conceive it is to generalize it; and to generalize it is to miss altogether the *here*ness and *now*ness which is its essence. According to me, the idea of a reaction is not the idea of two *plus* forcefulness. On the contrary to think of two dots as two is to have a little experience of reaction and then to tell ourselves that that is to be taken only in a Pickwickian sense, as a mere reaction within the world of ideas, the experience of reaction itself at once leading us to think of a world of seconds or existences and a world of mere tame ideas; the one resistant, the other subject to our wills. We also find ourselves thinking of the things without us, as acting on one another, as really connected. Now it is your business as a psychologist to say how that comes about, not mine. I merely look at the phenomenon, and say that all idea of real relation, or connection, has in it that same element of irrational reaction. All the *actual* character of consciousness is merely the sense of the shock of the non-ego upon us. Just as a calm sea sleeps except where its rollers dash upon the land.

267.   If we imagine that feeling retains its positive character but absolutely loses all relation, (and thereby all *vividness*, which is only the sense of shock), it no longer is exactly what we call feeling. It is a mere sense of quality. It is the sort of element that makes *red* to be such as it is, whatever anything else may be. I do not see how that can be described except as being such as it is, positively, of itself, while secondness is such as it is relatively to something else. Anything familiar gains a peculiar positive quality of feeling of its own; and that I think is the connection between Firstness and Hegel's first stage of thought. The second stage agrees better with Secondness.

268.   The third stage is very close indeed to Thirdness, which is substantially Hegel's *Begriff*. Hegel, of course, blunders monstrously, as we shall all be seen to do; but to my mind the one fatal disease of his philosophy is that, seeing that the Begriff in a sense implies Secondness and Firstness, he failed to see that nevertheless they are elements of the phenomenon not to be *aufgehoben*, but as real and able to stand their ground

as the Begriff itself. The third element of the phenomenon is that we perceive it to be intelligible, that is, to be subject to law, or capable of being represented by a general sign or Symbol. But I say the same element is in all signs. The essential thing is that it is capable of being represented. Whatever is capable of being represented is itself of a representative nature. The idea of representation involves infinity, since a representation is not really such unless it be interpreted in another representation. But infinity is nothing but a peculiar twist given to generality.[24] There is not anything truly general that does not actually make irrational existences conform to itself. That is the very heart of the idea.

269. That is a very bald statement. An immense number of items might be added. But I endeavor so to draw it up that these ideas may appear less of the nature of will-o'-the-wisps to you, — as steady lights. The more you reflect upon them the steadier they will become; — at least, such is my experience.

§3. CONSCIOUSNESS

270. [June 12, 1902] There is a point of psychology which has been interesting me. I should like to know from you whether there is any book which can give me aid about it. My own notion, which I dare say is crude, is this: The question is what passes in consciousness, especially what emotional and irritational states of feeling, in the course of forming a new belief. The man has some belief at the outset. This belief is, as to its principal constituent, a habit of expectation. Some experience which this habit leads him to expect turns out differently; and the emotion of *surprise* suddenly appears. Under the influence of *fatigue* (is this right?) this emotion passes into an irritational feeling, which, for want of a better name, I may call *curiosity*. I should define it as a feeling causing a reaction which is directed toward the invention of some *possible* account, or *possible* information, that might take away the astonishing and fragmentary character of the experience by rounding it out. (Of course, we want later to get a *real* explanation; but at first it seems to me that we merely say, "What *can* it

[24] (Ed.) Cf. 7.535.

be?") When such possible explanation is suggested, the idea of it instantly sets up a second peculiar emotion of "Gad! I shouldn't wonder!" Fatigue (?) again transforms this into a second irrational feeling which might perhaps be called *suspicion*. I should define it as a feeling causing a reaction directed toward unearthing the fault by which the original belief that encountered the surprise became erroneous in the respect in which it is now suspected to be erroneous. When this weak point in the process is discovered, it at once and suddenly causes an emotion of "Bah!" Fatigue (?) transforms this into the irrational feeling called *doubt*, i.e. a feeling producing a reaction tending to the establishment of a new habit of expectation. This object attained, there is a new sudden emotion of "Eureka" passing on fatigue into a desire to find an occasion to try it.

271. I had got to that point, when the expressman came in bringing me the copy of your new book.[25] I have spent five minutes turning over the leaves. I can see what the general feature of your position is, sufficiently to say that I am heartily in accord with you.

272. I say to people, — imaginary interlocutors, for I have nobody to talk to, — you think that the proposition that truth and justice are the greatest powers in this world, is metaphorical. Well, I, for my part, hold it to be *true*. No doubt Truth has to have defenders to uphold it. But truth creates its defenders and gives them strength. The mode in which the idea of truth influences the world is essentially the same as that in which my desire to have the fire poked causes me to get up and poke it. There is efficient causation and there is final, or ideal, causation. If either of them is to be set down as a metaphor, it is rather the former. Pragmatism is correct doctrine only in so far as it is recognized that material action is the mere husk of ideas. The brute element exists and must not be explained away as Hegel seeks to do. But the end of thought is action only in so far as the end of action is another thought. Far better abandon the word thought and talk of representation and then *define* what kind of a representation it is that constitutes consciousness.

273. But I want to tell you that you should study the new ideas about multitude and continuity (I alone as yet understand

[25] (Ed.) *The Varieties of Religious Experience*, 1902.

196

continuity, and have published nothing since I mastered it).
Ah, my logic will give a tremendous boost to spiritual views!
I hope it will get finished, although *personally* it makes mighty
little odds to me.

274.   Consider the plane spiral curve whose equation in
polar co-ordinates is [26]

$$\frac{r^2 - 4r + 3}{r - 2} = C\theta.$$

That curve will start at r = 1 and coil outwards toward r = 2
making an endless series of revolutions before it reaches r = 2.
Then it will keep right on and perform an endless series of revolutions before *r* becomes 2 + e, no matter how small a distance
e may be. Finally, when *r* becomes 3 the curve will come to an
abrupt stop. This shows that although it be true that Being
immediately acts only on Being and Representation immediately acts only on Representation, still there may be two endless series, whereby Being and Representation act on one another without any *tertium quid*.

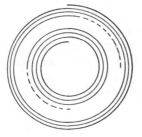

275.   If atoms are vortices in an ether, which ether is composed of atoms themselves, vortices in another ether, and so on
ad infinitum, as may possibly be the case (and we care only for
possibilities, since we are only refuting a supposed necessity),
then it is very likely that the sound waves of my voice should
be converted into heat, and this heat into the *ether's* heat, and
so on, and that the whole infinite series should be traversed in
a fraction of a second, after which they will be in the form of
thoughts in your mind and so you will come to understand the

[26] (Ed.) In the manuscript "θ" is an exponent on the constant "C." Cf.
7.370.

meaning of those sounds. My logic will open up a world for investigation and show how to set about it.

276. With your notions of spiritual influence, why don't you join the Church? Surely you won't allow metaphysical formulae, dead as the dust of the catacombs, to deprive you of your RIGHT to the influences of Church.

277. I have been studying Royce's book.[27] The ideas are very beautiful. The logic is most execrable. I don't think it very good taste to stuff it so full of the name of God. The Absolute is strictly speaking only God, in a Pickwickian sense, that is, in a sense that has no effect.

278. Forgive the garrulity that comes of my eremitical life and God bless you!

---

279. [September 28, 1904] Your article about consciousness [28] comes to me very *a propos* as I am writing about consciousness and have been reading up about it as well as my library (!) permits. But your paper floors me at the very opening and I wish you would do me the favor (I suppose it to be a simple matter) of explaining what you mean by saying that consciousness is often regarded as an "entity." I do not think you capable of setting up a man of straw and have no doubt you can tell me just how any given writer regards consciousness as an "entity." But this word, in modern philosophy, has never conveyed to my mind any idea except that it is a sign the writer is setting up some man of straw whom he imagines to entertain opinions too absurd for definite statement. Now I do not think anybody has any such opinions.

Therefore much as I am concerned to read your article, it is barred to me until I can find out what it is that you are opposing.

280. It appears to me that many writers think, or have influential vestiges of having formerly thought, that we have before us at each moment something far more detailed and determinate than any picture, and also think that all we are in any sense aware of is somehow in that image.

[27] (Ed.) *The World and the Individual.* Cf. 8.117ff.
[28] (Ed.) "Does 'Consciousness' Exist?", *The Journal of Philosophy, Psychology, and Scientific Methods* 1(1 Sept 1904)477–491.

281.   For my part,[29] I think first that feelings, — say red, — are present when they are present in a peculiar positive self-contained way; so that although contrast makes us attend to them, contrast in no way constitutes their peculiarities; and feelings are thus present to us wholly, — wholly within consciousness in such a way that one might if one chose very well limit the meaning of consciousness to the feeling of an instant, — though then it would be something that we only know by analysis.

282.   In the next place there is a two-sided consciousness, in which we separate the element under control from the element we cannot help, — *although in this mode of consciousness* there is no inseparable reflection that this is done. We separate the past and the present. The past is the inner world, the present the outer world. Now, this joined with feeling (which it involves or requires) might be called consciousness and would be the world, were it not for the phenomena of *error* and *ignorance*, which force us to reflect that there were two worlds in that two-sided consciousness. This consciousness furnishes all our facts. It is this that makes them facts.

283.   Then we have in our minds as the main body of its contents, what never can be in consciousness in either of these senses and never can be in existence or be distinctly supposed to exist. This is the whole world of triadic relations, thought. We are aware of it, and thus it might be included in consciousness.

284.   Second, I think there are writers who limit consciousness to what we know of the *past* which they mistake for the *present* and who thus think it to be a question whether we are to say the external world alone is *real* and the internal world *fiction* or whether we shall say that the internal world is the real and the external world a fiction. While the true idealism, the pragmatistic idealism, is that reality consists in the *future*. By mellonization (Gr. μέλλων the being about to do, to be, or to suffer) I mean that operation of logic by which what is conceived as having been (which I call conceived as *parelelythose*) is conceived as repeated or extended indefinitely into what always will be (or what will some day be, that is, its absence will *not* always be, which equally involves mellonization, which

²⁹ (Ed.) Cf. Chapter 4, "Consciousness," [CP] VII, Book III.

does not *assert* anything but is merely a mode of *conceiving*).[30] The conception of the *real* is derived by a mellonization of the constraint-side of double-sided consciousness. Therefore to say that it is the world of thought that is real is, when properly understood, to assert emphatically the reality of the public world of the indefinite future as against our past opinions of what it was to be.

285.   This long and vaporous letter is all intended to ask the simple question what you mean when you say that some people regard consciousness as an *entity*.[31]

———

286.   [October 3, 1904] Now I will speak first of my meaning of which you "don't understand a word" and then of what you say.

287.   It is very vexatious to be told at every turn that I am utterly incomprehensible, notwithstanding my careful study of language. When I say it is vexatious, I don't mean that I don't wish to be told so. On the contrary, I am aware that my modes of thought and of expression are peculiar and gauche, and that twenty years of a recluse life have made them more so, and am grateful to people who help me by correcting me. But when, as in the present case, I am able to show that the accusation is a mere auto-suggestion due to your having told yourself that everything that Peirce says is unintelligible, and really having commanded yourself not to understand, it gives me a certain glee to feel authorized to yield to my natural vexation. You will be gratified, with your truly kind nature, to have afforded me so much innocent pleasure. Questions being usually answered at cross-purposes, in asking you what you meant by saying you did not believe that consciousness was an entity, I set down, — I mean I "sot" down, — one of the commonplaces

---

[30] (Ed.) Cf. 8.330.

[31] (Ed.)   James replied in a letter dated September 30 [1904] (James Collection, Houghton Library) as follows:

"I have to confess that I don't understand a word of your letter, . . .

"As for what entity may mean in general I know not, except it be some imperceptible kind of being. In my article it meant a *constituent principle* of all experience, as contrasted with a certain *function or relation* between particular parts of experience. The distinction seems to me plain enough.

"I will shortly send you a couple more articles which build out that one farther."

of psychology, not that I thought you could have lost sight of it, but that I thought it very likely you might think that I had done so. It was that "consciousness," — the word, — is used by different psychologists in three senses, and that connected therewith are three doctrines about the thing or things. Well, you "don't understand a word" of it. Listen, then, and see how the same things precisely, only less explicitly stated, will sound when scratched from other pens.

288. 1ˢᵗ. *Consciousness means feeling.*

"Whenever there is any kind of feeling, there consciousness exists. . . . It is needless to point out that, from the very nature of an infinite series, it cannot be a present modification of consciousness. We may, I think, confidently assert [32] that the object of thought is never a content of our finite consciousness." ([George F.] Stout, *Analytic Psychology*, I, [1896], pp. 1 and 45.)

"To feel an idea and to be conscious of that feeling are not two things; the feeling and the consciousness are but two names for the same thing." (James Mill, *Analysis*, New Ed., I, 225.) [33]

"Perhaps as good a definition as can be given of consciousness would be: a knowledge of a feeling." (Lester F. Ward, *The Psychic Factors of Civilization*, [1893], p. 298.)

289. These people are all sensationalists. They analyze psychic phenomena into their smallest portions, just as a physicist does physical phenomena, — and just as the latter, if you ask him what composes the physical universe, will say "matter and motion," so these sensationalists find nothing present to the mind but feelings. If you say to the physicist "What! Nothing but matter and motion? Are there no signs?" he will reply, "Undoubtedly, but they are psychical phenomena." Just so if you say to a sensationalist "What! Nothing but feeling? Are there no signs?" he will say, "Undoubtedly, but they are cerebral connections, — purely physical phenomena."

290. 2ⁿᵈ. *Consciousness is a dual affair* (therefore *not* feeling which has no duality) *and just how makes little odds. Some say because all is relative in consciousness: some say because*

[32] (Ed.) In the text quoted this word is "affirm."

[33] (Ed.) *Analysis of the Phenomena of the Human Mind by James Mill* with notes illustrative and critical by Alexander Bain, Andrew Findlater, and George Grote, 2 vols., second edition, London, 1878.

of the distinction of subject and object that is always present.

"Consciousness is the widest word in our vocabulary. By common consent it embraces everything that 'mind' embraces. . . . We speak of the object-consciousness as our attitude in being cognisant of the extended universe; while our attitude under feeling and thought we call subject-consciousness or mind." (Bain, Note to Mill's *Analysis*, I, 226.) [34]

"Consciousness without contrast is impossible." ([William DeWitt] Hyde, *Practical Idealism*, p. 18.)

Hamilton's hammering on the *ego* and *non-ego*, we'll take for granted.

"Are the sensationalists right in asserting that sensational and affective elements of consciousness are the only ones? The writer [of this book] is convinced that the introspective analysis of sensationalists is inexact. . . . What James calls the feelings of 'and' and of 'but' — that is, the consciousness of connection and of oppositon," etc. (Mary W. Calkins, *An Introduction to Psychology*, [1901], pp. 130, 131.) [35]

291. 3rd. *More or less explicitly, some writers, namely the Thomists, the Hegelians, and other Intellectualists, together with some scientific thinkers not too much sophisticated by reading philosophy, recognize with me (until I shall have studied your views, which I don't believe will carry me entirely away from this anchorage) three modes of consciousness, that of feeling, that of* EXPERIENCE *(experience meaning precisely that which the history of my life has* FORCED *me to think; so that the idea of a struggle, of not mere twoness but active oppugnancy is in it), and thirdly the consciousness of the future (whether veridical or not is aside from the question) in expectation, which enters into all general ideas according to my variety of pragmatism.*[36]

"In its widest sense, consciousness, as opposed to unconsciousness, denotes all modes of mental life. It comprises all

---

[34] (Ed.) Note 74 by Alexander Bain in *Analysis of the Phenomena of the Human Mind by James Mill* with notes illustrative and critical by Alexander Bain, Andrew Findlater, and George Grote, 2 vols., second edition, London, 1878.

[35] (Ed.) The words in brackets appear in the quoted text, but were omitted without notice by Peirce. In the quoted text the last word of the second sentence is "inadequate" where Peirce has "inexact." The first words of the quotation appear on p. 129 of the work.

[36] (Ed.) Cf. 7.539ff.

cognitive, emotional, and appetitive states which are capable of being apprehended; it is, in fact, synonymous with the sumtotal of our psychical existence. In its second sense, it signifies the mind's direct, intuitive, or immediate knowledge either of its own operations, or of something other than itself acting upon it. . . . In its third meaning the word is limited," etc. etc. ([Michael] Maher, *Psychology, Empirical and Rational,* 4th Ed., [1900], p. 26.)

"In truth the field of science is much more consciousness than an external world." (Karl Pearson, *The Grammar of Science,* 1st Ed., [1892], p. 63; 2nd Ed., [1900], p. 52.)

"If one listens to any simple rhythm, such as the ticking of a watch, one can note how the succession of separate ticks is viewed by our consciousness in such a way that the successive beats do not stand as merely separate facts, but are always elements in the whole experienced rhythm to which they seem to belong, while the successive presentations of the rhythm form a sort of stream of events, each one of which gradually dies out of mind as the new event occurs.[37] In consciousness there is no such thing as an indivisible present moment." ([Josiah] Royce, *Outlines of Psychology,* [1903], p. 83.)

292.   I submit that this is all as clear as your New Hampshire air of October, and as familiar "comme votre poche," and that I said it plainly enough; only it had to be unintelligible because I said it.

293.   Now as to what you say, of course it is perfectly clear (or seems to be) NOW. But see how far from clear it is in your article. You note that the sentence "I deny that the word stands for an entity" was put forward *as an explanation*; — as clearly explaining how your view differs from the usual one, so that it implies that most persons, or most students of philosophy are in the habit of saying "Consciousness is an entity." So you still say, since you say that *you* don't know what "entity" means, and presumably don't believe it means anything clearly; so that it must be the other fellows' statement. I take your word for it, as your reading is immense, that they do say so. Yet I declare I do not remember to have met the expression, and am very much surprised to learn that "entity" can be commonly used to mean "a constituent principle of all experience."

[37] (Ed.) In the quoted text this word is "enters."

My difficulty lay in this terrible word "entity," and I cannot
help thinking that it was not a perspicuous way of expressing
the opinion you combat. . . .

294.   I shall probably have very different notions after having studied your articles from those I entertain now. Hitherto
I have been with the other fellows as to all three kinds of consciousness. I don't believe much that we shouldn't hear the
music of spheres if there were any. I have been inclined to
think that there is a certain tinge or tone of feeling connected
with living and being awake, though we cannot *attend* to it, for
want of a background. That would answer your description of
a "constituent principle of all experience," would it not? I ask
to make sure of my understanding of the opinion. In the second
place, *experience*, from the very essence of the word, consists of
our belief about a universe, — "the truth," — over against our
opinions and beliefs, which are thought of as fallible and ignorant. Consequently, I do not see how you can possibly deny
that consciousness in the second sense is a "constituent principle of experience." In the third place we carry about a sort
of a bass counterpoint melody of beliefs in all our living. Now
as I understand pragmatism it is of the very essence of it that
belief is expectation of the future in all cases. Consequently
it seems to me that the third kind of consciousness is also a
"constituent principle of all" our life, and *a fortiori* of all experience.

295.   As I understand you, then, the proposition which you
are arguing is a proposition in what I have called *phenomenology*, that is, just the analysis of what kind of constituents there
are in our thoughts and lives, (whether these be valid or invalid
being quite aside from the question). It is a branch of philosophy I am most deeply interested in and which I have worked
upon almost as much as I have upon logic.[38] It has nothing to
do with psychology.

296.   Your mind and mine are as little adapted to understanding one another as two minds could be, and therefore I
always feel that I have more to learn from you than from anybody. At the same time, it gives great weight in my mind to
our numerous agreements of opinion.

[38] (Ed.) Cf. [CP] I, Book III, "Phenomenology," and [CP] VII, Book III,
"Philosophy of Mind."

297.   Perhaps the most important aspect of the series of papers of which the one you send me is the first, will prove to be that it shows so clearly that phenomenology is one science and psychology a very different one. I know that you are not inclined to see much value in distinguishing between one science and another. But my opinion is that it is absolutely necessary to any progress. The standards of certainty must be different in different sciences, the principles to which one science appeals altogether different from those of the other. From the point of view of logic and methodical development the distinctions are of the greatest concern. Phenomenology has no right to appeal to logic, except to deductive logic. On the contrary, logic must be founded on phenomenology. Psychology, you may say, observes the same facts as phenomenology does. No. It does not *observe* the same facts. It looks upon the same world; — the same world that the astronomer looks at. But what it *observes* in that world is different. Psychology of all sciences stands most in need of the discoveries of the logician, which he makes by the aid of the phenomenologist.

298.   I am not sure that it will do to call this science *phenomenology* owing to Hegel's *Phänomenologie* being somewhat different. But I am not sure that Hegel ought not to have it named after his attempt.

299.   At the top of p. 483 you speak of various worlds. But the number is not so great. F. E. Abbot, one of the strongest thinkers I ever encountered, first showed me that there were just three; the outer, the inner, and the logical world. The others are not distinct worlds.

300.   On the same page, a little below, you mention as a difficulty people will have in understanding this doctrine, that they are so accustomed to think of percepts as the only realities. "To think of realities as similar to percepts," I should amend this. That is the chief reason why people do not understand me, or I them without a special effort. For I am thoroughly accustomed to think of percepts or rather of perceptual judgments as the data of all knowledge, and as such having a certain imperfect reality. They *exist*, — the percepts themselves do. But developed reality only belongs to signs of a certain description. Percepts are signs for psychology; but they are not so for phenomenology.

301. What you call "pure experience" is not experience at all and certainly ought to have a name. It is downright bad morals so to misuse words, for it prevents philosophy from becoming a science. One of the things I urge in my forthcoming *Monist* paper [39] is that it is an indispensable requisite of science that it should have a recognized technical vocabulary composed of words so unattractive that loose thinkers are not tempted to use them, and a recognized and legitimated way of making up new words freely when a new conception is introduced, and that it is vital for science that he who introduces a new conception should be held to have a *duty* imposed upon him to invent a sufficiently disagreeable series of words to express it. I wish you would reflect seriously upon the moral aspect of terminology. My "phenomenon" for which I must invent a new word is very near your "pure experience" but not quite since I do not exclude time and also speak of only *one* "phenomenon."

---

302. [December 17, 1909] [40] I was and had been long working as hard as I could upon my "System of Logic, from the point of view of Semiotic," when Juliette was enabled to start up the repairs which may enable me to finish that book, by keeping us alive. Then Carus having written me already offering me $200 or $250 (I forget which) for the copyright of my 6 articles in the *Popular Science Monthly* [41] for 1877 and '78, I agreed for $250 to allow him to print *one edition*, with a revision that I would furnish together with an Article for the *Monist* on my method of performing logical analyses. Owing to a lot of interruptions, . . . I either forgot, or never comprehended that Carus particularly cared to have that Article a *separate* one, and I had been working on it as a chapter of my first essay,[42] consisting of the two articles with which I began in the *Popular Science Monthly* called, — "The Settlement of Opinion" and "How to make our Ideas clear." Of course Definition, which is the end of Logical Analysis, is the first step, (after general familiarity in use,) toward making Ideas clear. However, he has lately written, remonstrating on

[39] (Ed.) 5.413.
[40] (Ed.) Some of the paragraphing is the editor's.
[41] (Ed.) [Bibliography] G–1877–5.
[42] (Ed.) Cf. [Bibliography] G–1909–1.

my delay, and in consequence I am going immediately to write that article, which I think will be a really helpful one to many people.

303.   I mean to begin by drawing a distinction between what I call "Psychology Proper," meaning an account of how the mind functions, developes, and decays, together with the explanation of all this by motions and changes of the brain, or, in default of this kind of explanation, by generalizations of psychical phenomena, so as to account for all the workings of the soul in the sense of reducing them to combinations of a few typical workings, — in short a sort of physiology of the mind, on the one hand, — and what I call "Phaneroscopy" on the other, or a description of what is before the mind or in consciousness, as it *appears*, in the different kinds of consciousness,[43] which I rank under . . . three headings. . . . *First*, "Qualisense," which means that element of Feeling which consists in consciousness of the Quality of the Feeling, but omitting the element of Vividness, which does not alter the Quality (thus a faint memory of a highly luminous, and chromatic vermillion does not appear less luminous or less high colored, for all its dimness) and omitting all other concomitants of present feeling that are absent from a correct recollection of the same Quality. *Second Heading*: what I call *Molition*, which is volition minus all desire and purpose, the mere consciousness of *exertion* of any kind. *Third Heading*: the recognition of Habit of any kind in consciousness.

304.   Then as preliminary to an argument tending to show that there are conscious elements that do not come under one of these three heads, I shall go on to show reason for thinking, first, that these three kinds of consciousness are entirely unlike; second, that they are connected with the ideas of *one*, *two*, *three* which are the three elementary forms with which logical analysis has to deal. *One* being the form of a simple idea, *two* that of an ordinary relative idea, and *three* the only *simple* form of combination of a direct union of more than two ideas, but being incapable itself of reduction to a pair of pairs but involving the idea expressed by "and" which always unites a triad or higher collection. Qualisense is the sort of consciousness of any whole regardless of anything else, and therefore

[43] (Ed.) Cf. 7.539ff.

regardless of the parts of that whole. Molition is a double consciousness of exertion and resistance. Consciousness of habit is a consciousness at once of the substance of the habit, the special case of application, and the union of the two.

305. Now third, I argue that there seem to be no other modes of consciousness by taking up some of the most difficult and analyzing them, which will at the same time illustrate my method of analysis. I shall show that a Concept is a Sign and shall define a Sign and show its triadic form. I shall define the Modality of a Sign and show that in this respect every Object is either a Can-be, an Actual, or a Would-be.[44] I shall show (as generally recognized,) that an Actual cannot be defined and that the Can-be's and Would-be's when accurately discriminated are only definable in different senses. There is no use of going through these headings, however, because they are unintelligible until they are defined at length. I don't pretend that my argument that there are only three kinds of consciousness does more than raise a presumption by the precision with which I succeed in defining a great variety of terms without calling in any fourth element. It will remain for those who question the conclusion to find a term I cannot define with this apparatus. After all this I shall undertake to show (still somewhat imperfectly) that concepts are capable of such phaneroscopic analysis, or in common parlance "logical analysis"; but there are only a few cases in which I pretend as yet to carry the analysis so far as to resolve the concept into its ultimate *elements*. After a few more such questions have been discussed, I show how to go to work to perform the analysis; and then I proceed to show that a definition constructed according to my method at once clears up various puzzles relating to the concept.

§4. FREE WILL

306. [March 18, 1897] I have been much struck with the *Dilemma of Determinism*.[45] I do not mean that there was any new thought to me in it, because this matter has been the subject of a very serious analysis on my part, a work much more

[44] (Ed.) Cf. 8.216.

[45] (Ed.) James had recently sent Peirce a copy of *The Will to Believe*, which contains this essay; cf. 249.

elaborate than anybody would suppose from anything I have printed. But I was surprised to see how far you had penetrated into the logical analysis so long ago as 1884.

307.   Two points particularly struck me. One was your resolving the matter altogether into a question of plurality, which is another name for my "variety" of nature. About that I need say no more, because I have developed the idea in print.

308.   The other was your remark that the question is, is possibility a mode of being. Good. Precisely so. As I remarked in the last *Monist*,[46] my old definition of the possible as that which we do not know not to be true (in some state of information real or feigned) is an anacoluthon. The possible is a positive universe, and the two negations happen to fit it, but that is all. Of course, there *is* a general logical possible that is no more than I defined it. But there is also a possible which [is] something else. I reached this truth by studying the question of possible grades of multitude, where I found myself arrested until I could form a whole logic of possibility, — a very difficult and laborious task. You would not have reached it that way. You must have some short cut, which I am curious to know more about.

309.   Very well. You have said the whole question of determinism is the question of ultimate plurality; and you have also said the same question is the question of positive possibility. But you have not said anything to show that you perceive how these two statements agree.

310.   I have never read the *Logique* of Charles Renouvier. Do you possess a copy of it; and if so could you spare it long enough for me to read it?

311.   There are some things in your *Dilemma of Determinism* that I cannot assent to. I cannot admit the *will* is free in any appreciable measure, for reasons that may be found in my *Man's Glassy Essence*.[47] Namely, chance can only amount to much in a state of things closely approximating to unstable equilibrium. Now in the act of willing there is no such state of things. The freedom lies in the *choice* which long antecedes the will. *There* a state of nearly unstable equilibrium is found. But this makes a great difference in your doctrine.

[46] (Ed.) 3.527.
[47] (Ed.) 6.238–271.

312.   As for the note about God being out of time, it seems to me probable that it was hastily penned. For it appears plain that (as has been often said, — by Kant for instance) if God is out of time the difficulty is removed. And in my opinion the scholastics were right in holding that, putting God into time, there is no contradiction between Foreknowledge and Free Will.

I forget what your father said about it, but I remember being much struck with it. Your father saw a long way in a certain direction.

§5. SIGNS

313.   [January 22, 1905] [48] Now an assertion belongs to the class of phenomena like going before a notary and making an affidavit, executing a deed, signing a note, of which the essence is that one voluntarily puts oneself into a situation in which penalties will be incurred unless some proposition is true. One may maintain that every proposition involves an assertion. Very likely that may be true as a psychological truth; but if so the element of assertion is frequently altogether or in great degree inhibited and disavowed. I have nothing further to say about assertion. What I want to come to is the question what a proposition consists in, when the element of assertion is, as far as possible, removed from it. It is of course a kind of sign. . . . What kind of a sign is a proposition? A symptom is not a proposition although it justifies a proposition. The reason is that it lacks what is most essential to propositions and to various other kinds of signs, that of *professing* something, making a *pretension*, representing itself to be such and such. It professes to be a certain kind of sign, namely that kind that is a sign by virtue of being *really* connected with its object, which means that it has that kind of relation to its object which subsists in those two correlates regardless of all else. So, then, according to me, reality is a conception that every man has because it is involved in every proposition; and since every man makes assertions he deals with propositions. (Of course, I have not fully defined a proposition, because I have not discriminated the proposition from the individual sign which is the

[48] (Ed.) This letter is unsigned and has some scratch work on the last page.

embodiment of the proposition. By a proposition, as something which can be repeated over and over again, translated into another language, embodied in a logical graph or algebraical formula, and still be one and the same proposition, we do not mean any existing individual object but a type, a general, which does not exist but governs existents, to which individuals conform.)

314. [March 14, 1909] We must distinguish between the Immediate Object, — i.e. the Object as represented in the sign, — and the Real (no, because perhaps the Object is altogether fictive, I must choose a different term, therefore), say rather the Dynamical Object, which, from the nature of things, the Sign *cannot* express, which it can only *indicate* and leave the interpreter to find out by *collateral experience*. For instance, I point my finger to what I mean, but I can't make my companion know what I mean, if he can't see it, or if seeing it, it does not, to his mind, separate itself from the surrounding objects in the field of vision. It is useless to attempt to discuss the genuineness and possession of a personality beneath the histrionic presentation of Theodore Roosevelt with a person who recently has come from Mars and never heard of Theodore before. A similar distinction must be made as to the Interpretant. But in respect to *that* Interpretant, the dichotomy is not enough by any means. For instance, suppose I awake in the morning before my wife, and that afterwards she wakes up and inquires, "What sort of a day is it?" *This* is a sign, whose Object, as expressed, is the weather at that time, but whose Dynamical Object is the *impression which I have presumably derived from peeping between the window-curtains*. Whose Interpretant, as expressed, is the quality of the weather, but whose Dynamical Interpretant, is *my answering her question*. But beyond that, there is a third Interpretant. The *Immediate Interpretant* is what the Question expresses, *all* that it immediately expresses, which I have imperfectly restated above. The *Dynamical Interpretant* is the actual effect that it has upon me, its interpreter. But the Significance of it, the *Ultimate*, or *Final*, *Interpretant* is her *purpose* in asking it, what effect its answer will have as to her plans for the ensuing day. I reply, let us

suppose: "It is a stormy day." Here is another sign. Its *Immediate Object* is the notion of the present weather so far as this is common to her mind and mine — not the *character* of it, but the *identity* of it. The *Dynamical Object* is the *identity* of the actual or Real meteorological conditions at the moment. The *Immediate Interpretant* is the *schema* in her imagination, i.e. the vague Image or what there is in common to the different Images of a stormy day. The *Dynamical Interpretant* is the disappointment or whatever actual effect it at once has upon her. The *Final Interpretant* is the sum of the *Lessons* of the reply, Moral, Scientific, etc. Now it is easy to see that my attempt to draw this three-way, "trivialis" distinction, relates to a real and important three-way distinction, and yet that it is quite hazy and needs a vast deal of study before it is rendered perfect. Lady Welby has got hold of the same real distinction in her "Sense, Meaning, Significance," but conceives it as imperfectly as I do, but imperfectly in other ways. Her *Sense* is the *Impression* made or normally to be made. Her *meaning* is what is intended, its purpose. Her Significance is the real upshot.[49]

315. [April 1, 1909] . . . let me give a *little* fuller explanation of my distinction between the Immediate, the Dynamical, and the Final Interpretants . . . The Dynamical Interpretant is whatever interpretation any mind actually makes of a sign. This Interpretant derives its character from the Dyadic category, the category of Action. This has two aspects, the Active and the Passive, which are not merely opposite aspects but make relative contrasts between different influences of this Category as More Active and More Passive. In psychology this category marks Molition [50] in its active aspect of a force and its passive aspect as a resistance. When an imagination, a day-dream fires a young man's ambition or any other active passion, that is a more Active variety of his Dynamical Interpretation of the dream. When a novelty excites his surprise, — and the scepticism that goes along with surprise, — this is a more Passive variety of Dynamical Interpretant. I

[49] (Ed.) Cf. 8.171ff. and 8.342ff.
[50] (Ed.) Cf. 303.

am not speaking of the *feelings* of passion or of surprise as *qualities*. For those *qualities* are no part of the dynamic Interpretant. But the *agitations* of passion and of surprise are the actual dynamic Interpretants. So surprise again has its Active and its Passive variety; — the former when what one perceives positively *conflicts* with expectation, the latter when having no positive expectation but only the absence of any suspicion of anything out of the common something quite unexpected occurs, — such as a total eclipse of the sun which one had not anticipated. Any surprise involves a resistance to accepting the fact. One rubs one's eyes, as Shaler used to do, determined not to admit the observation until it is plain one will be compelled to do so. Thus every actual interpretation is dyadic. . . . [As] pragmaticism says . . . (one part of pragmaticism, for Pragmaticism is not exclusively an opinion about the Dynamic Interpretant), . . . it says, for one thing, that the meaning of any sign for anybody consists in the way he reacts to the sign. When the captain of infantry gives the word "Ground arms!" the dynamic Interpretant is in the thump of the muskets on the ground, or rather it is the Act of their Minds. In its $\left\{\begin{array}{c}\text{Active}\\\text{Passive}\end{array}\right\}$ forms, the Dynamical Interpretant indefinitely approaches the character of the $\left\{\begin{array}{c}\text{Final}\\\text{Immediate}\end{array}\right\}$ Interpretant; and yet the distinction is absolute. The Final Interpretant does not consist in the way in which any mind does act but in the way in which every mind would act. That is, it consists in a truth which might be expressed in a conditional proposition of this type: "If so and so were to happen to any mind this sign would determine that mind to such and such *conduct*." By "conduct" I mean *action* under an intention of self-control. No event that occurs to any mind, no action of any mind can constitute the truth of that conditional proposition. The Immediate Interpretant consists in the *Quality* of the Impression that a sign is fit to produce, not to any actual reaction. Thus the Immediate and Final Interpretants seem to me absolutely distinct from the Dynamical Interpretant and from each other. And if there be any fourth kind of Interpretant on the same footing as those three, there must be a dreadful rupture of my mental retina, for I can't see it at all.

213

CHAPTER 6

TO CHRISTINE LADD-FRANKLIN, ON COSMOLOGY [1]

316. My work in philosophy has consisted in an accurate analysis of concepts, showing what is and what is not essential to the subject of analysis. Particularly, in logic, my motive for studying the algebra of the subject, has been the desire to find out with accuracy what are the essential ingredients of reasoning in general and of its principal kinds. To make a powerful calculus has not been my care.

317. I may mention that my chief avocation in the last ten years has been to develop my cosmology.[2] This theory is that the evolution of the world is *hyperbolic*, that is, proceeds from one state of things in the infinite past, to a different state of things in the infinite future. The state of things in the infinite past is chaos, tohu bohu, the nothingness of which consists in the total absence of regularity. The state of things in the infinite future is death, the nothingness of which consists in the complete triumph of law and absence of all spontaneity.[3] Between these, we have on *our* side a state of things in which there is some absolute spontaneity counter to all law, and some degree of conformity to law, which is constantly on the increase owing to the growth of *habit*. The tendency to form habits or tendency to generalize, is something which grows by its own action, by the habit of taking habits itself growing. Its first germs arose from pure chance. There were slight tendencies to obey rules that had been followed, and these tendencies were rules which were more and more obeyed by their own action. There were also slight tendencies to do otherwise than previously, and these destroyed themselves. To be sure, they would sometimes be strengthened by the opposite tendency, but the

---

[1] (Ed.) From an incomplete letter to "My dear Mrs. Franklin," dated "1891 Aug 29," Widener VB2a.

[2] (Ed.) See *The Monist* series of 1891–1893, [Bibliography] G–1891–1.

[3] (Ed.) Cf. 6.33.

stronger they became the more they would tend to destroy themselves. As to the part of time on the further side of eternity which leads back from the infinite future to the infinite past, it evidently proceeds by contraries.

318. I believe the law of habit to be purely psychical. But then I suppose matter is merely mind deadened by the development of habit. While every physical process can be reversed without violation of the law of mechanics, the law of habit forbids such reversal. Accordingly, time may have been evolved by the action of habit. At first sight, it seems absurd or mysterious to speak of time being evolved, for evolution presupposes time. But after all, this is no serious objection, and nothing can be simpler. Time consists in a regularity in the relations of interacting feelings. The first chaos consisted in an infinite multitude of unrelated feelings. As there was no continuity about them, it was, as it were, a powder of feelings. It was worse than that, for of particles of powder some are nearer together, others farther apart, while these feelings had no relations, for relations are general. Now you must not ask me what happened first. This would be as absurd as to ask what is the smallest finite number. But springing away from the infinitely distant past to a very very distant past, we find already evolution had been going on for an infinitely long time. But this "time" is only our way of saying that something had been going on. There was no real time so far as there was no regularity, but there is no more falsity in using the language of time than in saying that a quantity is zero. In this chaos of feelings, bits of similitude had appeared, been swallowed up again. Had reappeared by chance. A slight tendency to generalization had here and there lighted up and been quenched. Had reappeared, had strengthened itself. Like had begun to produce like. Then even pairs of unlike feelings had begun to have similars, and then these had begun to generalize. And thus relations of contiguity, that is connections other than similarities, had sprung up. All this went on in ways I cannot now detail till the feelings were so bound together that a passable approximation to a real time was established. It is not to be supposed that the ideally perfect time has even yet been realized. There are no doubt occasional lacunae and derailments.[4]

[4] (Ed.) The letter breaks off here without a period.

CHAPTER 7

TO F. C. S. SCHILLER, ON PRAGMATISM [1]

319. . . . I think the very first application that should be made of pragmatism of any stripe is to define words. Renouvier (in his 'Essais de Critique Philosophique' or elsewhere) has well said that as regards definitions in philosophy there are two classes of words. The one class consists [of] technical terms which ought to be defined before they are used and which ought to be supplanted by *new terms* and not by new definitions of old terms; the other class consists of the words of the vernacular, representing the vague ideas of common sense, which it is a part of the business of philosophy *to discover* the definitions of. You consider "real" to belong to the latter class. I hold that it ought to be kept in the former class where it was put by Duns Scotus who brought the word into common use, Albertus Magnus having only occasionally employed it, borrowing it from the law phrase 'real property.' As to the plasticity of the real, I am, on one side, entirely with you, having in 1892 and 1893 [argued] . . . that it is presumable that the laws of nature are not absolutely rigid.[2] And whether they be so or not, it is to *my* mind quite certain that there are general signs, — namely, laws of nature, — which influence, or determine, actual events, and equally certain there are also other general signs which, having been shaped in human reasoning, further influence, or determine, muscular contractions, and through these, other actual events . . .

320. I do not know whether or not you will approve of

---

[1] (Ed.) Paragraphs 319–320 (originally one paragraph) are from an undated letter; paragraphs 321–326 are from a letter dated Sept. 10, 1906. Both letters are in Widener VB2a and bear the salutation, "My dear Mr. Schiller." Neither is signed.

[2] (Ed.) In [Bibliography] G–1891–1.

my particular way of denying Necessitarianism. But as it is certain that the proposition that every physical event is directly determined by dynamical non-telic conditions and laws alone while every mental representation is directly determined by logical and, as such, telic conditions and laws alone, does not conflict with the proposition that physical events are determined by mental representations and mental representations by physical events [3] (as every student of G. Cantor will perceive); so on the other hand the propositions that the laws of nature are not absolute and that important physical events are due to human reasoning are far from proving that human action is (in any important degree) free, except in the sense that a man is a machine with automatic controls, one over another, for five or six grades, at least. I, for my part, am very dubious as to man's having more freedom than that, nor do I see what pragmatic meaning there is in saying that he has more. The power of self-control is certainly not a power over what one is doing at the very instant the operation of self-control is commenced. It consists (to mention only the leading constituents) first, in comparing one's past deeds with standards, second, in rational deliberation concerning how one will act in the future, in itself a highly complicated operation, third, in the formation of a resolve, fourth, in the creation, on the basis of the resolve, of a strong determination, or modification of habit. This operation of self-control is a process in which logical sequence is converted into mechanical sequence or something of the sort. How this happens, we are in my opinion as yet entirely ignorant. There is a class of signs in which the logical sequence *is* at the same time a mechanical sequence and very likely this fact enters into the explanation.

---

321. Let me thank you very particularly for sending me a copy of your last article [4] which I have read with profit and entertainment, as I do all of your articles that I am so fortunate as to see.

[3] (Ed.) Cf. 7.370.

[4] (Ed.) "Pragmatism and Pseudo-Pragmatism," *Mind* n.s. 15(July 1906) 375–390. This is the last paper in a controversy between F. C. S. Schiller and A. E. Taylor in *Mind*, n.s. vols. 14 and 15.

322. Of course I agree entirely to most of what you say, —
as well as I can understand it without having seen any writing
of Taylor. For example, I agree that of the two implications
of pragmatism that concepts are purposive, and that their meaning lies in their conceivable practical bearings, the former is the
more fundamental. I think, however, that the doctrine would
be quite *estropiée* without the latter point. By "practical" I
mean apt to affect conduct; and by conduct, voluntary action
that is self-controlled, i.e. controlled by adequate deliberation.
But the neater definition you put into a footnote is worth fully
all you claim for it.[5]

323. However, it would be idle to write merely to note
points of agreement. They are too many. Let me rather note
that some of the ends which you mention as going to the meanings of concepts seem to me to form no part of those meanings.
What the hundredth decimal figure of π means consists to my
mind in just what any other figure means. For it is quite *conceivable* that it should be an important practical quantity. It
is one of the beauties of pragmatism that it gives some symbols
much more meaning than others, and the hundredth figure of π
certainly has precious little. A much better question is, What
on pragmatist principles is the difference between a rational
and an irrational quantity or what it means to say that the diagonal of a square is incommensurable with its side? It is interpreted in the conduct of the arithmetician as such. . .

324. As for Cantor's cardinal transfinites, though called
numbers by him, they are not properly so called but are *multitudes*, or many-nesses of infinite collections. The first is the
multitude of the objects of an endless series of objects. I call
it the *denumeral* multitude. The next is the multitude of all
collections of objects involved in an endless series (by collection I mean simply a plural). The rest are each the multitude
of all collections involved in a collection of the next preceding
multitude. I call these the *abnumerable* multitudes. . .

325. These abnumerable multitudes are describable intelligibly and exactly, but only in general terms. No precise idea
can be formed of the simplest of them; and they increase in
difficulty at a frightful rate (that is in the characters that *would*

---

[5] (Ed.) Schiller defines "the practical as *'whatever tends to the control of
events'* " in *Mind* n.s. 15(July 1906)386.

make difficulty if it were surmountable at all). If anything violates the principle of pragmatism it is these. But I have no doubt whatever of the validity of the concepts. They are interpretable in the conduct of the logician or logico-mathematician in dealing with them. If they were not exact, so as [to] lay definite logical obligations upon him they would be meaningless, or without definite meaning.

326. When you say that Logical consequences cannot be separated from psychological effects, etc. in my opinion you are merely adopting a mode of expression highly inconvenient which cannot help, but can only confuse, any sound argumentation. It is a part of nominalism which is utterly antipragmatistic, as I think, and mere refusal to make use of valuable forms of thought.

CHAPTER 8

TO LADY WELBY

§1. ON SIGNS AND THE CATEGORIES [1]

327. But I wanted to write to you about signs, which in your opinion and mine are matters of so much concern. More in mine, I think, than in yours. For in mine, the highest grade of reality is only reached by signs; that is by such ideas as those of Truth and Right and the rest. It sounds paradoxical; but when I have devolved to you my whole theory of signs, it will seem less so. I think that I will today explain the outlines of my classification of signs.

328. You know that I particularly approve of inventing new words for new ideas. I do not know that the study I call *Ideoscopy* can be called a new idea, but the word *phenomenology* is used in a different sense.[2] *Ideoscopy* consists in describing and classifying the ideas that belong to ordinary experience or that naturally arise in connection with ordinary life, without regard to their being valid or invalid or to their psychology. In pursuing this study I was long ago (1867) led, after only three or four years' study, to throw all ideas into the three classes of Firstness, of Secondness, and of Thirdness.[3] This sort of notion

---

[1] (Ed.) From a letter dated "1904 Oct 12" to "My dear Lady Welby." A photostat copy of the original letter is in the Yale University Library. The complete letter is also in [Bibliography] M–20a, pp. 7–14, published by Whitlock's, Inc., New Haven, Conn., with whose permission the parts given here and the quotations in 330n4 and 330n6 are reprinted.

Lady Victoria Welby was an English semanticist, at one time Maid of Honour to Queen Victoria. For Peirce's review of her *What is Meaning?* see Book I of the present volume. For additional correspondence see [Bibliography] M–20.

[2] (Ed.) Peirce's phenomenology and categories are discussed at various places in [CP], especially in [CP] I, Book III. See also 7.524–538.

[3] (Ed.) In [Bibliography] G–1867–1c, 1.545–559.

is as distasteful to me as to anybody; and for years, I endeavored to pooh-pooh and refute it; but it long ago conquered me completely. Disagreeable as it is to attribute such meaning to numbers, and to a triad above all, it is as true as it is disagreeable. The ideas of Firstness, Secondness, and Thirdness are simple enough. Giving to being the broadest possible sense, to include ideas as well as things, and ideas that we fancy we have just as much as ideas we do have, I should define Firstness, Secondness, and Thirdness thus:

Firstness is the mode of being of that which is such as it is, positively and without reference to anything else.

Secondness is the mode of being of that which is such as it is, with respect to a second but regardless of any third.

Thirdness is the mode of being of that which is such as it is, in bringing a second and third into relation to each other.

I call these three ideas the cenopythagorean categories.

329. The typical ideas of firstness are qualities of feeling, or mere appearances. The scarlet of your royal liveries, the quality itself, independently of its being perceived or remembered, is an example, by which I do not mean that you are to imagine that you *do not* perceive or remember it, but that you are to drop out of account that which may be attached to it in perceiving or in remembering, but which does not belong to the quality. For example, when you remember it, your idea is said to be *dim* and when it is before your eyes, it is *vivid*. But dimness or vividness do not belong to your idea of the quality. They *might* no doubt, if considered simply as a feeling; but when you think of vividness you do not consider it from that point of view. You think of it as a degree of disturbance of your consciousness. The quality of red is not thought of as belonging to you, or as attached to liveries. It is simply a peculiar positive possibility regardless of anything else. If you ask a mineralogist what hardness is, he will say that it is what one predicates of a body that one cannot scratch with a knife. But a simple person will think of hardness as a simple positive possibility the *realization* of which causes a body to be like a flint. That idea of hardness is an idea of Firstness. The unanalyzed

total impression made by any manifold not thought of as actual fact, but simply as a quality, as simple positive possibility of appearance, is an idea of Firstness. Notice the *naïveté* of Firstness. The cenopythagorean categories are doubtless another attempt to characterize what Hegel sought to characterize as his three stages of thought. They also correspond to the three categories of each of the four triads of Kant's table. But the fact that these different attempts were independent of one another (the resemblance of these Categories to Hegel's stages was not remarked for many years after the list had been under study, owing to my antipathy to Hegel) only goes to show that there really are three such elements. The idea of the present instant, which, whether it exists or not, is naturally thought as a point of time in which no thought can take place or any detail be separated, is an idea of Firstness.

330. The type of an idea of Secondness is the experience of effort, prescinded from the idea of a purpose. It may be said that there is no such experience, that a purpose is always in view as long as the effort is cognized. This may be open to doubt; for in sustained effort we soon let the purpose drop out of view. However, I abstain from psychology which has nothing to do with ideoscopy. The existence of the word *effort* is sufficient proof that people think they have such an idea; and that is enough. The experience of effort cannot exist without the experience of resistance. Effort only is effort by virtue of its being opposed; and no third element enters. Note that I speak of the *experience*, not of the *feeling*, of effort. Imagine yourself to be seated alone at night in the basket of a balloon, far above earth, calmly enjoying the absolute calm and stillness. Suddenly the piercing shriek of a steam-whistle breaks upon you, and continues for a good while. The impression of stillness was an idea of Firstness, a quality of feeling. The piercing whistle does not allow you to think or do anything but suffer. So that too is absolutely simple. Another Firstness. But the breaking of the silence by the noise was an experience. The person in his inertness identifies himself with the precedent state of feeling, and the new feeling which comes in spite of him is the non-ego. He has a two-sided consciousness of an ego and a non-ego. That consciousness of the action of a new feeling in destroying the old feeling is what I call an *experience*. Experi-

ence generally is what the course of life has *compelled* me to think. Secondness is either *genuine* or *degenerate*. There are many degrees of genuineness. Generally speaking genuine secondness consists in one thing acting upon another, — brute action. I say brute, because so far as the idea of any *law* or *reason* comes in, Thirdness comes in. When a stone falls to the ground, the law of gravitation does not act to make it fall. The law of gravitation is the judge upon the bench who may pronounce the law till doomsday, but unless the strong arm of the law, the brutal sheriff, gives effect to the law, it amounts to nothing. True, the judge can create a sheriff if need be; but he must have one. The stone's actually falling is purely the affair of the stone and the earth at the time. This is a case of *reaction.* So is *existence* which is the mode of being of that which reacts with other things. But there is also action without reaction. *Such is the action of the previous upon the subsequent.*[4] It is a difficult question whether the idea of this one-sided determination is a pure idea of secondness or whether it involves thirdness. At present, the former view seems to me correct. I suppose that when Kant made Time a form of the internal sense alone, he was influenced by some such considerations as the following. The relation between the previous and the subsequent consists in the previous being determinate and fixed for the subsequent, and the subsequent being indeterminate for the previous. But indeterminacy belongs only to ideas; the existent is determinate in every respect; and this is just what the law of causation consists in. Accordingly, the relation of time concerns only ideas. It may also be argued that, according to the law of the conservation of energy, there is nothing in the physical universe corresponding to our idea that the previous determines the subsequent in any way in which the subsequent does not determine the previous. For, according to that law, all that happens in the physical universe consists in the exchange of just so much *vis viva* $\frac{1}{2}m\left(\frac{ds}{dt}\right)^2$ for so much displacement. Now the square of a negative quantity being positive, it follows that if all the velocities were reversed at any instant, everything would go on just the same, only time going back-

---

[4] (Ed.) "The italicized sentence is, in manuscript, underlined in pencil. Perhaps it was underlined by Lady Welby, yet it was not her habit to annotate Peirce's letters." From [Bibliography] M–20a, p. 9.

ward as it were. Everything that had happened would happen again in reversed order. These seem to me to be strong arguments to prove that temporal causation (a very different thing from physical dynamic action) is an action upon ideas and not upon existents.[5] But since our idea of the past is precisely the idea of that which is absolutely determinate, fixed, *fait accompli*, and dead, as against the future which is living, plastic, and determinable, it appears to me that the idea of one-sided action, in so far as it concerns the being of the determinate, is a pure idea of Secondness; and I think that great errors of metaphysics are due to looking at the future as something that will have been past. I cannot admit that the idea of the future can be so translated into the Secundal ideas of the past. To say that a given kind of event never will happen is to deny that there is any date at which its happening will be past; but it is not equivalent to any affirmation about a past relative to any assignable date. When we pass from the idea of an event to saying that it never will happen, or will happen in endless repetition, or introduce in any way the idea of endless repetition, I will say the idea is *mellonized* ($\mu\acute{\epsilon}\lambda\lambda\omega\nu$, about to be, do, or suffer). When I conceive a fact as acting but not capable of being acted upon, I will say that it is *parelelythose* ($\pi\alpha\rho\epsilon\lambda\eta$-$\lambda\upsilon\theta\acute{\omega}s$, past) and the mode of being which consists in such action I will call *parelelythosine* (-ine = $\epsilon\hat{\imath}\nu\alpha\iota$, being); I regard the former as an idea of Thirdness, the latter as an idea of Secondness. I consider the idea of any dyadic relation not involving any third as an idea of Secondness; and I should not call any completely degenerate except the relation of identity. But similarity which is the only possible identity of Firsts is very near to that. Dyadic relations have been classified by me in a great variety of ways; but the most important are, first, with regard to the nature of the Second in itself and, second, with regard to the nature of its First. The Second, or *Relate*,[6] is, in itself, either a *Referate*, if it is intrinsically a possibility, such as a quality, or it is a *Revelate* if it is of its own nature an Existent. In respect to its First, the Second is divisible either

---

[5] (Ed.) Reversible and irreversible actions are discussed further in Chapter 3, "Habit," [CP] VII, Book III.

[6] (Ed.) " 'Relate', in manuscript, is underlined in pencil." From [Bibliography] M–20a, p. 10.

in regard to the dynamic first or to the immediate first. In regard to its dynamic first, a Second is determined either by virtue of its own intrinsic nature, or by virtue of a real relation to that second (an action). Its immediate second is either a Quality or an Existent.

331. I now come to Thirdness. To me, who have for forty years considered the matter from every point of view that I could discover, the inadequacy of Secondness to cover all that is in our minds is so evident that I scarce know how to begin to persuade any person of it who is not already convinced of it. Yet I see a great many thinkers who are trying to construct a system without putting any thirdness into it. Among them are some of my best friends who acknowledge themselves indebted to me for ideas but have never learned the principal lesson. Very well. It is highly proper that Secondness should be searched to its very bottom. Thus only can the indispensableness and irreducibility of thirdness be made out, although for him who has the mind to grasp it, it is sufficient to say that no branching of a line can result from putting one line on the end of another.[7] My friend Schröder fell in love with my algebra of dyadic relations. The few pages I gave to it in my Note B in the 'Studies in Logic by Members of the Johns Hopkins University' were proportionate to its importance.[8] His book is profound,[9] but its profundity only makes it more clear that Secondness cannot compass Thirdness. (He is careful to avoid ever saying that it can, but he does go so far as to say that Secondness is the more important. So it is, considering that Thirdness cannot be understood without Secondness. But as to its application, it is so inferior to Thirdness as to be in that aspect quite in a different world.) Even in the most degenerate form of Thirdness, and thirdness has two grades of degeneracy, something may be detected which is not mere secondness. If you take any ordinary triadic relation, you will always find a *mental* element in it. Brute action is secondness, any mentality involves thirdness. Analyze for instance the relation involved in 'A gives B to C.' Now what is giving? It does not consist [in] A's putting B away from him and C's subsequently taking

[7] (Ed.) Cf. 1.347, 3.421.
[8] (Ed.) [Bibliography] G–1883–7d, 3.328–358.
[9] (Ed.) Cf. [Bibliography] G–1896–6.

B up. It is not necessary that any material transfer should take place. It consists in A's making C the possessor according to *Law*. There must be some kind of law before there can be any kind of giving, — be it but the law of the strongest. But now suppose that giving *did* consist merely in A's laying down the B which C subsequently picks up. That would be a degenerate form of Thirdness in which the thirdness is externally appended. In A's putting away B, there is no thirdness. In C's taking B, there is no thirdness. But if you say that these two acts constitute a single operation by virtue of the identity of the B, you transcend the mere brute fact, you introduce a mental element. . . . The criticism which I make on [my] algebra of dyadic relations, with which I am by no means in love, though I think it is a pretty thing, is that the very triadic relations which it does not recognize, it does itself employ. For every combination of relatives to make a new relative is a triadic relation irreducible to dyadic relations. Its *inadequacy* is shown in other ways, but in this way it is in a conflict with itself *if it be regarded*, as I never did regard it, *as sufficient for the expression of all relations*. My universal algebra of relations, with the subjacent indices and Σ and Π, is susceptible of being enlarged so as to comprise everything; and so, still better, though not to ideal perfection, is the system of *existential graphs*.[10]

332. I have not sufficiently applied myself to the study of the degenerate forms of Thirdness, though I think I see that it has two distinct grades of degeneracy. In its genuine form, Thirdness is the triadic relation existing between a sign, its object, and the interpreting thought, itself a sign, considered as constituting the mode of being of a sign.[11] A sign mediates between the *interpretant* sign and its object. Taking sign in its broadest sense, its interpretant is not necessarily a sign. Any concept is a sign, of course. Ockham, Hobbes, and Leibniz have sufficiently said that. But we may take a sign in so broad a sense that the interpretant of it is not a thought, but an action or experience, or we may even so enlarge the meaning of sign that its interpretant is a mere quality of feeling. A *Third* is

---

[10] (Ed.) This is treated at length in [CP] IV, Book II.
[11] (Ed.) Signs are discussed at various places in [CP]. See 8.313ff., 2.227ff., and the letter following the present one. See also [Bibliography] M–20a.

something which brings a First into relation to a Second. A sign is a sort of Third. How shall we characterize it? Shall we say that a Sign brings a Second, its Object, into *cognitive* relation to a Third? That a Sign brings a Second into the same relation to a first in which it stands itself to that First? If we insist on *consciousness*, we must say what we mean by consciousness of an object. Shall we say we mean Feeling? Shall we say we mean association, or Habit? These are, on the face of them, psychological distinctions, which I am particular to avoid. What is the essential difference between a sign that is communicated to a mind, and one that is not so communicated? If the question were simply what we *do* mean by a sign, it might soon be resolved. But that is not the point. We are in the situation of a zoölogist who wants to know what ought to be the meaning of "fish" in order to make fishes one of the great classes of vertebrates. It appears to me that the essential function of a sign is to render inefficient relations efficient, — not to set them into action, but to establish a habit or general rule whereby they will act on occasion. According to the physical doctrine, nothing ever happens but the continued rectilinear velocities with the accelerations that accompany different relative positions of the particles. All other relations, of which we know so many, are inefficient. Knowledge in some way renders them efficient; and a sign is something by knowing which we know something more. With the exception of knowledge, in the present instant, of the contents of consciousness in that instant (the existence of which knowledge is open to doubt) all our thought and knowledge is by signs. A sign therefore is an object which is in relation to its object on the one hand and to an interpretant on the other, in such a way as to bring the interpretant into a relation to the object, corresponding to its own relation to the object. I might say 'similar to its own' for a correspondence consists in a similarity; but perhaps correspondence is narrower.

333. I am now prepared to give my division of signs, as soon as I have pointed out that a sign has two objects, its object as it is represented and its object in itself. It has also three interpretants, its interpretant as represented or meant to be understood, its interpretant as it is produced, and its interpretant in itself. Now signs may be divided as to their own ma-

terial nature, as to their relations to their objects, and as to their relations to their interpretants.

334.   As it is in itself, a sign is either of the nature of an appearance, when I call it a *qualisign*; or secondly, it is an individual object or event, when I call it a *sinsign* (the syllable *sin* being the first syllable of *sem*el, *sim*ul, *sin*gular, etc.); or thirdly, it is of the nature of a general type, when I call it a *legisign*. As we use the term 'word' in most cases, saying that 'the' is one 'word' and 'an' is a second 'word,' a 'word' is a legisign. But when we say of a page in a book, that it has 250 'words' upon it, of which twenty are 'the's, the 'word' is a sinsign. A sinsign so embodying a legisign, I term a 'replica' of the legisign. The difference between a legisign and a qualisign, neither of which is an individual thing, is that a legisign has a definite identity, though usually admitting a great variety of appearances. Thus, &, *and*, and the sound are all one word. The qualisign, on the other hand, has no identity. It is the mere quality of an appearance and is not exactly the same throughout a second. Instead of identity, it has *great similarity*, and cannot differ much without being called quite another qualisign.

335.   In respect to their relations to their dynamic objects, I divide signs into Icons, Indices, and Symbols (a division I gave in 1867).[12] I define an Icon as a sign which is determined by its dynamic object by virtue of its own internal nature. Such is any qualisign, like a vision, — or the sentiment excited by a piece of music considered as representing what the composer intended. Such may be a sinsign, like an individual diagram; say a curve of the distribution of errors. I define an Index as a sign determined by its dynamic object by virtue of being in a real relation to it. Such is a Proper Name (a legisign); such is the occurrence of a symptom of a disease. (The symptom itself is a legisign, a general type of a definite character. The occurrence in a particular case is a sinsign.) I define a Symbol as a sign which is determined by its dynamic object only in the sense that it will be so interpreted. It thus depends either upon a convention, a habit, or a natural disposition of its interpretant or of the field of its interpretant (that of which the interpretant is

_____

[12] (Ed.) 1.558 ([Bibliography] G–1867–1c).

a determination). Every symbol is necessarily a legisign; for it is inaccurate to call a replica of a legisign a symbol.

336. In respect to its immediate object a sign may either be a sign of a quality, of an existent, or of a law.

337. In regard to its relation to its signified interpretant, a sign is either a Rheme, a Dicent, or an Argument. This corresponds to the old division, Term, Proposition, and Argument, modified so as to be applicable to signs generally. A *Term* is simply a class-name or proper-name. I do not regard the common noun as an essentially necessary part of speech. Indeed, it is only fully developed as a separate part of speech in the Aryan languages and the Basque, — possibly in some other out of the way tongues. In the Shemitic languages it is generally in form a verbal affair, and usually is so in substance, too. As well as I can make out, such it is in most languages. In my universal algebra of logic there is no common noun. A rheme is any sign that is not true nor false, like almost any single word except 'yes' and 'no,' which are almost peculiar to modern languages. A *proposition* as I use that term, is a dicent symbol. A dicent is not an assertion, but is a sign *capable* of being asserted. But an assertion is a dicent. According to my present view (I may see more light in future) the act of assertion is not a pure act of signification. It is an exhibition of the fact that one subjects oneself to the penalties visited on a liar if the proposition asserted is not true. An act of judgment is the self-recognition of a belief; and a belief consists in the deliberate acceptance of a proposition as a basis of conduct. But I think this position is open to doubt. It is simply a question of which view gives the simplest view of the nature of the proposition. Holding, then, that a Dicent does not assert, I naturally hold that an Argument need not actually be submitted or urged. I therefore define an argument as a sign which is represented in its signified interpretant not as a Sign of that interpretant (the conclusion) [for that would be to urge or submit it] [13] but *as if* it were a Sign of the Interpretant or perhaps as if it were a Sign of the state of the universe to which it refers, in which the premisses are taken for granted. I define a dicent as a sign represented in its signified interpretant *as if it were* in a Real Relation to its Object. (Or as being so, if it is asserted.) A

[13] (Ed.) The brackets are Peirce's.

rheme is defined as a sign which is represented in its signified interpretant as *if it were* a character or mark (or as being so).

338. According to my present view, a sign may appeal to its dynamic interpretant in three ways:

1st, an argument only may be *submitted* to its interpretant, as something the reasonableness of which will be acknowledged.

2nd, an argument or dicent may be *urged* upon the interpretant by an act of insistence.

3rd, argument or dicent may be, and a rheme can only be, presented to the interpretant for *contemplation*.

339. Finally, in its relation to its immediate interpretant, I would divide signs into three classes as follows:

1st, those which are interpretable in thoughts or other signs of the same kind in infinite series,

2nd, those which are interpretable in actual experiences,

3rd, those which are interpretable in qualities of feelings or appearances.

340. Now if you think on the whole (as I do) that there is much valuable truth in all this, I should be gratified if you cared to append it to the next edition of your book, after editing it and of course cutting out personalities of a disagreeable kind, ESPECIALLY IF [IT WERE] ACCOMPANIED BY ONE OR MORE (running or other) CLOSE CRITICISMS; for I haven't a doubt there is more or less error involved. . . .

341. P. S. On the whole, then, I should say there were ten principal classes of signs

　　1. Qualisigns

　　2. Iconic Sinsigns

　　3. Iconic Legisigns

　　4. *Vestiges*, or Rhematic Indexical Sinsigns

　　5. *Proper Names*, or Rhematic Indexical Legisigns

　　6. Rhematic Symbols

　　7. Dicent Sinsigns (as a portrait with a legend)

8. Dicent Indexical Legisigns
9. *Propositions*, or Dicent Symbols
10. Arguments.[14]

§2. ON THE CLASSIFICATION OF SIGNS [15]

342. The publishers of the Britannica have given an unequivocal earnest of their determination to make every edition
of their encyclopaedia maintain its supereminence in employ-
ing editors who would enlist you for an epitome of your exploration of "significs." [16] It greatly encourages me in my endeavours, since, as well as I can make out, what you call "significs" is equivalent to the study that I entitle logic. In my
paper of 1867 May 14 (Proc. Am. Acad. of Arts & Sci., Vol.
VII, p. 295) I said, "We come to this, that logic treats of the
reference of symbols in general to their objects. In this view
it is one of a trivium of conceivable sciences. The first would
treat of the formal conditions of symbols having meaning, that
is of the reference of symbols in general to their grounds, or
imputed characters; and this might be called Formal Grammar
[the *grammatica speculativa* of Duns]. The second, logic,
would treat of the formal conditions of the truth of symbols.
The third would treat of the formal conditions of the force
of symbols, or their power of appealing to a mind, that is, of
their reference in general to interpretants, and this might be

---

[14] (Ed.) Cf. 2.254 and [Bibliography] M–20a, Appendix B.

[15] (Ed.) From a partial draft of a letter to Lady Welby, bearing dates of
24, 25, and 28 December 1908, Widener IB3a, with an added quotation in
368n23. The editor has made more than the usual number of alterations in
punctuation, capitalization, etc., in both this and the previous letter, and in the
present letter he has made several changes in format.

In a letter to Lady Welby, with dates 31 January, 24 February, and 14
March 1909, Peirce says: "I find in my portfolio some part of a letter, if not
the whole, dated December 28. I suppose I sent you that" [Bibliography]
M–20a, p. 35. It is probable that in this passage Peirce is referring to the letter
printed here. This letter never reached Lady Welby; cf. *Other Dimensions: A
Selection from the Later Correspondence of Victoria Lady Welby*, p. 309n1
(listed with [Bibliography] M–20a).

The letter printed here resembles, but is distinct from, a letter with dates of
14 and 23 December 1908, printed in [Bibliography] M–20a, pp. 22–32, q.v.

[16] (Ed.) Lady Welby wrote "Significs" for the 11th edition of *The Encyclo-
pedia Brittanica*, 1910–11.

called formal rhetoric." [17] I should still opine that in the future there probably will be three such sciences. But I have learned that the only natural lines of demarcation between nearly related sciences are the divisions between the social groups of devotees of those sciences; and for the present the cenoscopic studies (i.e., those studies which do not depend upon new special observations) of all signs remain one undivided science, — a conclusion I had come to before I made your acquaintance, but which the warm interest that you and I have in each other's researches in spite of the difference in their lines, decidedly confirms.

343. It seems to me that one of the first useful steps toward a science of *semeiotic* (σημειωτική), or the cenoscopic science of signs, must be the accurate definition, or logical analysis, of the concepts of the science.[18] I define a *Sign* as anything which on the one hand is so determined by an Object and on the other hand so determines an idea in a person's mind, that this latter determination, which I term the *Interpretant* of the sign, is thereby mediately determined by that Object. A sign, therefore, has a triadic relation to its Object and to its Interpretant. But it is necessary to distinguish the *Immediate Object*, or the Object as the Sign represents it, from the *Dynamical Object*, or really efficient but not immediately present Object. It is likewise requisite to distinguish the *Immediate Interpretant*, i.e. the Interpretant represented or signified in the Sign, from the *Dynamic Interpretant*, or effect actually produced on the mind by the Sign; and both of these from the *Normal Interpretant*, or effect that would be produced on the mind by the Sign after sufficient development of thought. On these considerations I base a recognition of ten respects in which Signs may be divided. I do not say that these divisions are enough. But since every one of them turns out to be a trichotomy, it follows that in order to decide what classes of signs result from them, I have 3^{10}, or 59049, difficult questions to carefully consider; and therefore I will not undertake to carry my systematical division of signs any further, but will leave that for future explorers.

[17] (Ed.) 1.559 ([Bibliography] G–1867–1c). The brackets are in the manuscript.

[18] (Ed.) For references to other discussions of signs, see 332n11.

344.   The ten respects according to which the chief divisions of signs are determined are as follows:

1st, According to the Mode of Apprehension of the Sign itself,

2nd, According to the Mode of Presentation of the Immediate Object,

3rd, According to the Mode of Being of the Dynamical Object,

4th, According to the Relation of the Sign to its Dynamical Object,

5th, According to the Mode of Presentation of the Immediate Interpretant,

6th, According to the Mode of Being of the Dynamical Interpretant,

7th, According to the Relation of the Sign to the Dynamical Interpretant,

8th, According to the Nature of the Normal Interpretant,

9th, According to the Relation of the Sign to the Normal Interpretant,

10th, According to the Triadic Relation of the Sign to its Dynamical Object and to its Normal Interpretant.

345.   The ten divisions appear to me to be all Trichotomies; but it is possible that some of them are not properly so. Of these Ten Trichotomies, I have a clear apprehension of some, (which I mark δ for δῆλος), an unsatisfactory and doubtful notion of others (which I mark a for ἄδηλος), and a tolerable but not thoroughly tried conception of others (which I mark μ for μέτριος, σ for σχεδόν, almost clear, χ for χαλεπῶς hardly better than a).

The Ten Main Trichotomies of Signs
(as they are apprehended by me 1908 Dec. 24)

346.   I. A Sign is necessarily in itself present to the Mind of its Interpreter. Now there are three entirely different ways in which Objects are present to minds: [19]

First, in themselves as they are in themselves. Namely, Feelings are so present. At the first instant of waking from pro-

---

[19] (Ed.) For references to discussions of Peirce's categories, see 328n2.

233

found sleep when thought, or even distinct perception, is not yet awake, if one has gone to bed more asleep than awake in a large, strange room with one dim candle. At the instant of waking the *tout ensemble* is felt as a unit. The feeling of the skylark's song in the morning, of one's first hearing of the English nightingale.

Secondly, the sense of something opposing one's Effort, something preventing one from opening a door slightly ajar; which is known in its individuality by the actual shock, the Surprising element, in any Experience which makes it *sui generis*.

Thirdly, that which is stored away in one's Memory; Familiar, and as such, General.

347. Consequently, Signs, in respect to their Modes of possible Presentation, are divisible (σ) into

A. *Potisigns*, or Objects which are signs so far as they are merely possible, but felt to be positively possible; as, for example, the seventh ray that passes through the three intersections of opposite sides of Pascal's hexagram.

B. *Actisigns*, or Objects which are Signs as Experienced *hic et nunc*; such as any single word in a single place in a single sentence of a single paragraph of a single page of a single copy of a book. There may be repetition of the whole paragraph, this word included, in another place. But that other occurrence is not *this* word. The book may be printed in an edition of ten thousand; but THIS word is only in my copy.

C. *Famisigns*, familiar signs, which must be General, as General signs must be familiar or composed of Familiar signs. (I speak of signs which are "general," not in the sense of *signifying* Generals, but as being *themselves* general; just as Charlemagne is general, in that it occurs many times with one and the same denotation.)

348. I think I might as well have marked this division δ instead of σ, except that perhaps the question may arise whether I ought not to have recognized a division according as the sign is a *natural sign*, which has no party to the dialogue as its author, or whether it be an *uttered sign*, and in the latter case, is the very sign that is getting uttered or another. But it seems to me that this division turns upon the question of whether or not the sign uttered is a sign of a sign as its Object. For must not every sign, in order to become a sign, get uttered?

349.   II. . . . Objects may be presented in three ways, thus:

1st, As mere Ideas, or what might be if things were not as they are; such as a geometrical surface, or an absolutely definite or distinct notion.

2nd, As brutely compelling attention.

3rd, As Rationally recommending themselves, or as Habitudes to which one is already reconciled.

350.   Adopting this enumeration as a basis of a division of Signs, I obtain

A. *Descriptives*, which determine their Objects by stating the characters of the latter.

B. *Designatives* (or *Denotatives*), or Indicatives, *Denominatives*, which like a Demonstrative pronoun, or a pointing finger, brutely direct the mental eyeballs of the interpreter to the object in question, which in this case cannot be given by independent reasoning.

C. *Copulants*, which neither describe nor denote their Objects, but merely express the logical relations of these latter to something otherwise referred to.[20] Such, among linguistic signs, as "If — then — ," " — is — ," "— causes — ," " — would be —," "— is relative to — for —," "Whatever" etc.

351.   Shall I appoint this famous distinction (as I have stated it, or modified [it]) to the governance of my Second way of dividing Signs, or shall I yield this place to a distinction prominent in every language on earth, that between the three 'persons,' *amo, amas, amat*? If *I* and *thou* are the Objects, we say *We*; if *thou* and *he* are the Objects, we say *Ye*. But if *I* and *We* are the Objects to the exclusion of *Thee*, I know no other linguistic form than the French expression "*Nous autres.*" *I, Thou*, and *He* can be expressed by the Tri-al and *Quadral* numbers of Polynesian languages. In English we can only say "*We all of us.*" Thus there ought, logically one would say, to be *seven* grammatical persons, if any at all. But none at all are needed, if we have the Designative pronouns *I, Thou, He*. But hold! When I say there are only 7 persons I forget the differences between Thou and I are Anglo-Saxon. Thou and I are correspondents. Thou and I are endurer and endured.

---

[20] (Ed.) Peirce had revised the manuscript here, but since his revision is unintelligible, we give the text as it was originally.

Thou and I are admired and admirer. Thou, he, and I are accuser to and of, accuser of and to, accused by and to, accused to and by, informed of by, informed by of. In short this distinction does not require any special form of sign, nor could any form be adequate without numerous variations.

352.   On the other hand [is] the distinction of *Designatives* such as concrete subjects of signs or essentially nominative signs, [and] *Descriptives* such as Predicates and Predicative Signs (such as a portrait with a legend designating the person represented), [with] Abstract nouns to be reckoned among Descriptives. The copulants are likewise indispensable and have the property of being *Continuant*. What I mean is that the sign 'A is red' can be decomposed so as to separate 'is red' into a Copulative and a Descriptive, thus: 'A possesses the character of redness.' But if we attempt to analyze 'possesses the character' in like manner, we get 'A possesses the character of the possession of the character of Redness'; and so on *ad infinitum*. So it is, with 'A implies B,' 'A implies its implication of B,' etc. So with 'It rains and hails,' 'It rains concurrently with hailing,' 'It rains concurrently with the concurrence of hailing,' and so forth. I call all such sign Continuants. They are all Copulants and are the only *pure* copulants. These signs *cannot be explicated*: they must convey Familiar universal elementary relations of logic. We do not derive these notions from observation, nor by any sense of being opposed, but from our own reason. This trichotomy, then, sustains criticism and must be marked (μ) at least. I would mark it (δ) if I were satisfied with the distinction between Descriptives and Denominatives.

353.   Before proceeding to the third trichotomy, let [us] inquire what relations, if any, are found between the two that have been brought to light. What I mean precisely by *between these relations* is whether or not the three members of the first trichotomy, which we may for the moment denote as 11, 12, 13, are or are not independent of the three members of the second, which we may denote by 21, 22, 23; so that they form nine classes, which, if we use a dot to mean "which is," will be denoted by

$$11 \cdot 21 \qquad 11 \cdot 22 \qquad 11 \cdot 23$$
$$12 \cdot 21 \qquad 12 \cdot 22 \qquad 12 \cdot 23$$
$$13 \cdot 21 \qquad 13 \cdot 22 \qquad 13 \cdot 23$$

354.   The inquiry ought, one would expect, to be an easy one, since both trichotomies depend on there being three Modes of Presence to the mind, which we may term

The Immediate, — The Direct, — The Familiar
Mode of Presence.

The difference between the two trichotomies is that the one refers to the Presence to the Mind of the Sign and the other to that of the Immediate Object. The Sign may have any Modality of Being, i.e., may belong to any one of the three Universes; its Immediate Object must be in some sense, in which the Sign need not be, Internal.

355.   To begin, then, it is evident that an Actisign, or one that belongs to the Universe of Experience, which Brutely acts on the person, can also be a Denominative, that is, that its Immediate Object is represented as belonging to the same Universe; so that $12 \cdot 22$, the central class of our block of nine, is possible. Indeed, a pointing finger is a familiar example of a Sign of that class. Let us next ask whether all the four corner classes of the block are possible. We fully expect to find that a Potisign can be Descriptive and that a Famisign can be Copulant. But we may well doubt whether a Potisign can be Copulant or a Famisign can be Descriptive. Let us see.

356.   Before taking up the cases, let me notice a source of possible confusion. By a "General Sign," or a "General Term," we do not, in the ordinary language of Logic, mean, as might be supposed, a Famisign. For we do not mean that the Sign *itself* is General: we only mean that its Object is so.

357.   The Northern United States are full of I know not how many thousand "villages," as they are called in the State of New York, "towns" as they are called in New England, which are governed in a simple way by "town meetings" or otherwise; and in Pennsylvania "boroughs," whose head is a "chief burgess"; and there are also countless little places somewhat larger (especially in the West) called "cities." In the middle of any one of these where one might wander he would find a small green of an acre or two and in the middle of this will be a stone statue, often of granite, representing a common soldier standing in his regulation overcoat and resting on his grounded musket. Nothing imaginable could be more devoid of imagination, less idealized, less artistically beautiful. They are eye-sores to all

cultivated people; but not to me. For I know that that means
that almost every family in that place . . . had in the war of
the southern rebellion sent its flower, who had no military instinct whatever, much less any hatred for southern people, to
the war, bitterly contrary to all his instincts but simply from
a sense of duty; and only a fraction of them came back. The
very fact of their vulgarity, which the statue proclaims above
all else, makes this universal self-sacrifice on the altar of the
abstraction which we call the "general government" pathet-
ically sublime. To each such family, that very realistic statue
represents the mourned one who fell in the war. That statue
is one piece of granite, and not a Famisign. Yet it is what we
call a "General" sign, meaning that it is *applicable* to many
singulars. It is not *itself* General; it is its Object which is
taken to be General. And yet this Object is not truly Universal,
in the sense of implying a truth of the kind of 'Any S is P'; it
only expresses 'Some S is P.' This makes it *not* a *Copulant*
(Copulative) but only a *Descriptive*. This needs to be borne in
mind. And this warning having been noticed, we can proceed
to inquire about the corners of our block of supposed classes,
which I will designate according to the usual map that has N
above, S below, E to the right, W to the left.

358.   As to the NW corner, a Geometrical diagram is always
capable of being *imagined*, seldom or never of *existing*; since
the limits of solid bodies are the loci at which forces of cohe-
sion are neither very great nor very small, which being vague,
has not the character of a geometrical surface. The diagram is
therefore a *Potisign*. It is clearly Descriptive; and therefore
$11 \cdot 21$ is possible.

359.   The verbal expression "If — , then — " is a Famisign,
as all words are (in the sense in which two that are just alike
are the very same "word"). It is also a Copulative since it expresses a universal sequence, 'If A, then C,' meaning that in
every state of things whatever, either not-A or is-C is true.
So that the SE corner $13 \cdot 23$ is possible.

360.   "Given any 4 rays in space; then either there can be
only 2 rays, at most, that cut them all, or there can be any number." True or not, this is a Copulant; and any single expression
of it is an Actisign. It is also expressible in Existential Graphs

238

in the form of a geometrical diagram, which is a Potisign. Therefore, the NE corner 11·23 is possible.

361.   But can a Famisign be Descriptive? Everybody will make haste to cry, "Of course, it can: of course, a description can be expressed in words, when even a universal can." Yet, while I am more than usually sensible of the danger of my being mistaken, I venture, for the present, the opinion that it is not so. The proper way to pursue the inquiry is to start from the definition already given of the triadic relation of Sign-Object-Interpretant. We thus learn that the Object determines (i.e. renders definitely to be such as it will be,) the Sign in a particular manner. Now it is of the essence of the Sign to determine certain Ideas, i.e. certain Possibles; and it is the essence of any Tendency to determine Occurrences. Therefore, an Actisign or a Potisign may be a Copulative. But no Occurrence or collection of occurrences can logically determine a Habit or other Tendency. Thus, if wishing to test a *die* to see whether it is loaded (whether intentionally or not) I throw it say 900 times. If the different faces come up with as equal frequency as they could be expected to do, what can I infer? Only that *as long as the habit or tendency of the die remains what it is*, it will probably not bring the different faces up so unequally as to show decisively in 900 throws. That is, I base my inference on the assumption that *there is some habit*. Or take a simpler case. If I positively knew (what I cannot *know*) that a certain shilling had a habit when pitched to turn up *heads* and *tails* with equal frequency, then I should positively know that if it were pitched often enough, it would *sometime* turn up "heads." For if it *always* would turn up tails, that would constitute a habit contrary to the habit supposed to be known.[21] That known habit may be defined thus: Let a tally be kept of the heads as they occur and another of the tails; and after each throw let the exact quotient of the number of heads divided by the number of tails be calculated. Then, given any positive number (not zero therefore) there will *certainly* come a time after which none of the quotients will differ by as much as that number from 1. The value 1 being the only one about which the values of the quotients will never cease to oscillate. Thus the tendency consists entirely in what *will be*; and what

[21] (Ed.)   See 8.225ff.

has been has nothing to do with it. But what *will be* is not an Actual Occurrence. It is true that physiological and some other habits are determined by what has been done; but not by those occurrences *of themselves*, but only because there is a *special Tendency* by virtue of which what has been done *will be* done oftener than what has not been done. In general, it is of the essence of a Real Tendency that no Actual Occurrence can of itself determine it in any way. Whence a Denominative cannot be a Famisign. Whence the middle of the S side of the block 13·22 is impossible. But an Actual Occurrence always determines the Possibility of its character; whence no Descriptive can be a Famisign; or [i.e.] the SW corner of the block 13·21 is impossible. As an example of this, no number of Descriptive propositions of the type "Some S is P" can ever determine the truth of a Copulative Proposition "Any S is P." It is, if possible, still more obvious that Possibility can never determine Actuality and therefore a Descriptive cannot be an Actisign, or [i.e.] the middle of the W side of the block 12·21 is impossible. The remaining six classes are possible, i.e.,

Copulative Potisigns
Denominative Potisigns   Copulative Actisigns
Descriptive Potisigns   Denominative Actisigns   Copulative Famisigns

362. There are four objections that would probably be raised against my doctrine; but I will not lengthen this letter with the refutations of them. I have carefully considered them, and have found them to be unsound.

363. From the summer of 1905 to the same time in 1906, I devoted much study to my ten trichotomies of signs. It is time I reverted to the subject, as I know I could now make it much clearer. But I dare say some of my former names are better than those I now use. I formerly called a Potisign a Tinge or Tone, an Actisign a Token, a Famisign a Type; — a Descriptive an Indefinite (but this was bad), a Denominative a Designation, a Copulative (which is bad) a Distributive (which is much better).

364. I think Potisign, Actisign, [and] Famisign might be called Mark, Token, [and] Type(?) [22] [respectively], while

---

[22] (Ed.) It is clear from the format of the manuscript that the question mark applies only to the term "type."

Descriptive, Denominative, [and] Copulative might be called Descriptive, Denominative, [and] Distributive, [respectively].

365.   I have now given as much time to this letter as I can afford and I cannot now re-examine the remaining trichotomies, although I must do so as soon as possible. So I just give them as they stood two years and more ago. In particular, the relations I assumed between the different classes were the wildest guesses, and cannot be altogether right I think.

366.   III. In respect to the Nature of their Dynamical Objects, Signs I found to be either

1. Signs of Possibles. That is *Abstractives* such as Color, Mass, Whiteness, etc.

2. Signs of Occurrences. That is *Concretives* such as Man, Charlemagne.

3. Signs of Collections. That is *Collectives* such as Mankind, the Human Race, etc.

By *Abstractives* I meant signs of *immediate* abstractions; but was in some doubt what to do with abstractions resulting from experiment. I thought it would be requisite to study subdivisions of these classes but never went into that research.

367.   I was of the opinion that if the Dynamical Object be a mere Possible the Immediate Object could only be of the same nature, while if the Immediate Object were a Tendency or Habit then the Dynamical Object must be of the same nature. Consequently an Abstractive must be a Mark, while a Type must be a Collective, which shows how I conceived Abstractives and Collectives.

368.   IV. The fourth Trichotomy is the one which I most frequently use: Icon, Index,[23] Symbol.

[23] (Ed.) "An *index* represents an object by virtue of its connection with it. It makes no difference whether the connection is natural, or artificial, or merely mental. There is, however, an important distinction between two classes of indices. Namely, some merely stand for things or individual quasi-things with which the interpreting mind is already acquainted, while others may be used to ascertain facts. Of the former class, which may be termed *designations*, personal, demonstrative, and relative pronouns, proper names, the letters attached to a geometrical figure, and the ordinary letters of algebra are examples. They act to force the attention to the thing intended. Designations are absolutely indispensable both to communication and to thought. No assertion has any meaning unless there is some designation to show whether the universe of reality or what universe of fiction is referred to. The other class of indices may be

All the remaining six trichotomies have to do with the Inter-pretants, which you have, I imagine, studied much more thoroughly than I have done.

369.   V. As to the nature of the Immediate (or Felt?) Interpretant, a sign may be: Ejaculative, or merely giving utterance to feeling; Imperative, including, of course, Interrogatives; Significative.

But later I made this the 7th Trichotomy and for the fifth substituted — with great hesitation — : Hypothetic, Categorical, Relative.

370.   VI. As to the Nature of the Dynamical Interpretant: Sympathetic, or Congruentive; Shocking, or Percussive; Usual.

371.   VII. As to the Manner of Appeal to the Dynamic Interpretant: Suggestive, Imperative, Indicative.

372.   VIII. According to the Purpose of the Eventual Interpretant: Gratific; To produce action; To produce self-control.

373.   IX. As to the Nature of the Influence of the Sign: Seme, like a simple sign; Pheme, with antecedent and consequent; Delome, with antecedent, consequent, and principle of sequence.

374.   X. As to the Nature of the Assurance of the Utterance: assurance of Instinct; assurance of Experience; assurance of Form.

375.   I don't know whether these trichotomies will suggest anything to you or not. No doubt you have studied relations to Interpretants in some directions much further than I. . . .

376.   P. S. 1908 Dec 28. Well, dear Lady Welby, you deserve this infliction, for having spoken of my having "al-

---

called *reagents*. Thus water placed in a vessel with a shaving of camphor thrown upon it will show whether the vessel is clean or not. If I say that I live two and a half miles from Milford, I mean that a rigid bar that would just reach from one line to another upon a certain bar in Westminster, might be successively laid down on the road from my house to Milford, 13200 times, and so laid down on my reader's road would give him a knowledge of the distance between my house and Milford. Thus, the expression "two miles and a half" is, not exactly a reagent, but a description of a reagent. A scream for help is not only intended to force upon the mind the knowledge that help is wanted, but also to force the will to accord it. It is, therefore, a reagent used rhetorically. Just as a designation can denote nothing unless the interpreting mind is already acquainted with the thing it denotes, so a reagent can indicate nothing unless the mind is already acquainted with its connection with the phenomenon it indicates." From "Notes on Topical Geometry," undated, Widener IA–2.

ways been kindly [! ! !] interested in the work to which my life is devoted," [24] when I have myself been entirely absorbed in the very same subject since 1863, without meeting, before I made your acquaintance, a single mind to whom it did not seem very like bosh. I add some scraps.

Signs divided into Ten Classes [25]

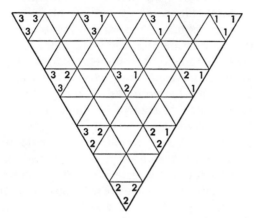

The number above to the left describes the Object of the Sign. That above to the right describes its Interpretant. That below describes the Sign itself. 1 signifies the Possible Modality, that of an Idea. 2 signifies the Actual Modality, that of an Occurrence. 3 signifies the Necessary Modality, that of a Habit. . . .

377.   I have often thought that if it were not that it would sound too German (and I have an utter contempt for German logic) I would entitle my logic-book (which is now coming on) "Logic considered as Semeiotic" (or probably *Semeotic* without the *i*;) but everybody would think I was translating *als Semeiotik betrachtet*, which I couldn't stand.

378.   The fact that I have entertained this idea shows how near together you and I are. "Significs" sounds to me narrower than Semeotic, since *signification* is only *one* of the *two* chief functions of signs; as the elegant and correct John of Salisbury notices, in referring to "quod fere in omnium ore celebre est, aliud scilicet esse quod appellatiua significant, et

[24] (Ed.) The brackets are Peirce's.
[25] (Ed.) Cf. [Bibliography] M–20a, Appendix B.

aliud esse quod nominant. Nominantur singularia, sed uni-uersalia significantur." (*Metalogicus* II. xx. I copy from the ed. of 1620.) [26] So *significs* appears to be limited to the study of the relations of Signs to their Interpretants; and I presume you do so limit it. On the other hand Logic is more interested in the *Truth* of Signs, i.e. in their relation to their Objects. But I am satisfied that in the present state of the subject, there is but one General science of the nature of Signs. If we were to separate it into two, — then, according to my idea that a "science," as scientific men use the word, implies a social group of devotees, we should be in imminent danger of erecting two groups of one member each! Whereas, if you and I stick to-gether, we are, at least, two of us. I remember in my college days that the Statutes of Harvard defined a "group" as *three* persons or more convening together. We shall have to try to seduce one of the linguists to our more fundamental study. Max Müller was, in a feeble way, perhaps one of our group. I hope in your Britannica article you will adhere to the stern method of treatment proper to an Encyclopaedia, and show the reader that distinct positive discovery is what we are laboring upon. I remember one day, when I was in the twenties, on my way to the post-office I fell in with the novelist Wm. D. Howells, who began criticizing one of my articles from the point of view of rhetorical elegance. I said to him, "Mr. Howells, it is no part of the purpose of my writings to give readers pleasure." Such an idea was quite out of his horizon; and I heard of his repeating it as very amusing. People do not consult an encyclopaedia to be amused, but to receive definite instruction as condensed as clearness permits. I hope your article will cause readers to appreciate Significs as a study of grave importance not merely from the point of view of Morals, but also from that of Truth. But I am absolutely sure your article will be a valuable one however far it may depart from what I should wish the article to be. It must be so, simply because you have been a devoted student of the subject. It is your own message that you are to deliver and nobody else's.

379.   It is a remarkable thing that no other people but the Greeks ever so felt the desire to avoid errors as to strike out a

[26] (Ed.)   See Clemens C. I. Webb, *Ioannis Saresberiensis Episcopi Carnotensis Metalogicon*, Oxford University Press, 1929, Liber II, Cap. 20, p. 104.

logic for themselves. All other logic down to the invention of the Doctrine of Chances was made on the Greek model. The Greeks so strongly felt that need that they erected no less than 5 independent systems! Namely, 1st, though Prantl's "Megaric logic" is poppy-cock, there are unmistakable indications of early strivings for a logical system; 2nd, came the logic of Socrates, who had a much clearer idea of what logic should be than such writers as Wundt, Chr. Sigwart, Jerusalem, Bradley, Bosanquet, Dewey, etc. etc., — not to notice the Joseph's and such quasi-minds, — have today; 3rd, passing by Plato, there was Aristotle; 4th, the Epicurean logic, very closely allied to Mill's system, yet distinctly different, as shown by the Herculaneum Papyrus of the περὶ σημείων καὶ σημειώσεων of Philodemus; 5th, there was the logic illustrated by the strict methods of the mathematicians, — which was not merely a *practice* of reasoning, but was a definite theory of logic greatly superior to Aristotle's, as far as deductive reasoning is concerned. Here are my 5 without including either Zeno of ῞Ηλις [27] nor Chrisippus, both original logicians.

[27] (Ed.) In early Greek this word was written with an initial symbol called digamma followed by ᾶλις. In the manuscript Peirce wrote a digamma followed by ῆλις. We have substituted the conventional spelling since the digamma is no longer used.

CHAPTER 9

TO F. A. WOODS, ON "WOULD BE" [1]

380.   I have duly received the copy of your new work,[2] and have already read pp. iii–xiii, 1–46, and 196–417, and have found it perfectly convincing; so that my only criticism relates to Chap. XVIII,[3] which, though convincing to me, might, I think, be improved by introducing, in some form, some considerations like the following: A conditional proposition, — say "If A, then B" is equivalent to saying that *"Any* state of things in which A should be true, *would* (within limits) *be* a state of things in which B is true."[4] It is therefore essentially an assertion of a *general* nature, the statement of a *"would-be."* But when the antecedent supposes an *existential* fact to be different from what it actually is or was, the conditional proposition does not accurately state anything; and if it conveys any meaning, i.e. if it is calculated to produce any state of mind, in a person who trusts in it, it must be that it establishes a *habit* in that mind, using the word "habit" in the original sense, as meaning only that the person or thing that has the habit, *would* behave

<hr/>

[1] (Ed.) From a long letter to "My dear Dr. Woods," written over a period between 14 October 1913 and 19 November 1913, with an added quotation in 380n4. The letter was sent to Woods, but it is now in Widener VB2a.

Frederick Adams Woods, M.D., was a lecturer in biology at the Massachusetts Institute of Technology.

[2] (Ed.) *The Influence of Monarchs, Steps in a New Science of History*, The Macmillan Co., New York, 1913, xiii + 422 pp.

[3] (Ed.) This chapter is titled, "Causation in History."

[4] (Ed.) "An ordinary *hypothetical proposition*, as propositions containing an antecedent condition and a consequent result are called, relates to what *would* occur in states of things not all coincident with the existing state of things. Suppose I say 'If I were to upset the inkstand the table cloth would be injured.' This means that of all the different courses of events that might occur, the disposition of things in the room being what it is, every one is one in which either the inkstand is not upset or the tablecloth is spoiled." From an undated fragment, Widener IA–8. Cf. 5.453, 6.327, and 8.216.

(or usually behave) in a certain way *whenever* a certain occasion should arise. But if this occasion did in actuality *not* arise, such habit of thought as the conditional proposition might produce would be a nullity pragmatistically and practically. A historian simply talks nonsense when he says "If Napoleon had not done as he did before the battle of Leipzig (specifying in what respect his behaviour is supposed different from what it was) he would have won that battle." Such historian may have meant something; but he utterly fails to express any meaning.

381.   To this it might be objected, that when a man deliberates as to what line of conduct he shall pursue, he will very advantageously consider conditional propositions whose antecedents are of the form "If I should do so and so." To this conceivable objection I should reply that the case of the deliberating mind and that of the futile historian's are essentially different in that the former reasons at some stage of his deliberations as follows (that is, he will unless he decides to verify the antecedent in question by adopting the contemplated line of conduct):

If I should do so and so, I should bring about such and such a result,

Now I will not bring about that result,

Ergo, I shall not do "so and so."

He thus comes to a profitable conclusion, provided he had not already fully made up his mind not to "do so and so," in which case he would be pursuing an idle dream, and a bad dream at that.

382.   But the supposed historian knows well already that the supposition of the antecedent is false; and therefore he has no occasion to seek a proof that it is so; and there is no intelligent purpose to which he or anybody can put his conditional proposition, unless he can find enough similar instances about other persons belonging to the same class as Napoleon so that he will be able to make an *induction* serving as a *maxim* by which other men may profitably regulate their conduct. For instance, if Napoleon before the battle slept with his head close to a red hot stove, and was "not himself," as we say, during the battle, a historian may be excused for putting the two facts together. But unless there is some *general* antecedent to be

247

gained in a reasonable manner, a conditional proposition with a singular antecedent known to be false, is worse than a puerility. It is downright nonsense, a series of words without meaning. . . .

383.   . . . logicians generally almost always confine what they have to say about reasoning to its "correctness," by which they mean its leaving an absolute inability to doubt the truth of a conclusion so long as the premises are assumed to be true. But that amounts to confining their study to deduction. When one thinks as long about certainty as I have done, one does not very often find oneself in this state of inability to doubt. . . .

384.   I think logicians should have two principal aims: 1st, to bring out the amount and kind of *security* (approach to certainty) of each kind of reasoning, and 2nd, to bring out the possible and esperable uberty, or value in productiveness, of each kind.

385.   I have always, since early in the sixties, recognized three different types of reasoning, viz: 1st, *Deduction* which depends on our confidence in our ability to analyze the meanings of the signs in or by which we think; 2nd, *Induction*, which depends upon our confidence that a run of one kind of experience will not be changed or cease without some indication before it ceases; and 3rd, *Retroduction*, or Hypothetic Inference, which depends on our hope, sooner or later, to guess at the conditions under which a given kind of phenomenon will present itself.[5]

386.   Each of these three types occurs in different forms requiring special studies.

387.   From the 1st type to the 3rd the security decreases greatly, while the uberty as greatly increases. . . .

388.   I don't think the adoption of a hypothesis on probation can properly be called induction; and yet it is *reasoning* and though its *security* is low, its *uberty* is high.

[5] (Ed.) These types of reasoning are discussed in more detail in [CP] VII, Book II, Chapter 3, "The Logic of Drawing History from Ancient Documents."

BIBLIOGRAPHY OF THE WORKS
OF
CHARLES SANDERS PEIRCE

INTRODUCTION

This bibliography has three main sections: (I) General, (II) Items from *The Nation*, and (III) Miscellaneous. The first section includes all Peirce's works which have been published from manuscripts in the eight volumes of *Collected Papers of Charles Sanders Peirce* and all his known works which were presented as addresses or were printed in publications other than *The Nation* during his lifetime. The second section consists of all the works published in *The Nation* that have been identified as Peirce's contributions. The third section consists of correspondence by Peirce, and also works by other authors which quote or describe manuscripts by Peirce that are not published in *Collected Papers*, volumes I–VIII.

Sections I and II are arranged primarily in chronological order. The date under which an item appears is the year of its first public appearance, either in print or as an address, except for manuscripts not published during Peirce's life. For these latter cases the item appears under the date when the manuscript was written, where this was known or could be inferred from the available evidence; the dates of subsequent "revisions," including corrections and marginal notes, are given in the same entry. Undated manuscripts are listed at the end of Section I. Various public presentations which there is reason to believe are the same material are listed together if the dates of the public appearances fall within the same calendar year (see, for example, the first item of 1879 in Section I); otherwise they are listed separately with appropriate back references (for example, the sixth item of 1878 in Section I). Functionally related series of articles, lectures, and associated items are grouped together and listed by the *year of the first*. The third section of the bibliography is arranged alphabetically according to the name of the recipient of the correspondence or the name of the author or editor of the work cited; these names are numbered.

References and cross-references to items of the bibliography are made as follows: to an item in the General section, [Bibliography]G–year–item number, e.g., [Bibliography]G–c.1901–3b; to an item in *The Nation* section, [Bibliography]N–year–item number, e.g., [Bibliography]N–1892–1; and to an item in the Miscellaneous section, [Bibliography]M–name number, e.g., [Bibliography]M–6. A list of the abbreviations for publication titles precedes the bibliography proper.

An item that has been reprinted in *Collected Papers* is followed by the designation "[CP]" and the volume and paragraph numbers. For example, in [Bibliography] G–1908–1a the reference [CP] 4.585–593 indicates that the article described in this item ("Some Amazing Mazes") is reprinted at paragraphs 585–593 of Volume 4 of *Collected Papers*. It should be noted that the [CP] reference may follow explanatory material concerning the item, as in this example.

A cross-reference index from the paragraphs in *Collected Papers* to the entries of the bibliography is given at the end of the bibliography. The reader's attention is also invited to the list of errata for *Collected Papers*, volumes I–VI, which concludes this introduction.

Sources for the Bibliography. The bibliographies by Cohen and the one by Fisch and Haskell, the information in *Collected Papers*, volumes I–VI, and personal communications from Max Fisch constituted the original basis for the present bibliography. In connection with the process of going through Peirce's published works and the unpublished manuscripts at Harvard University and elsewhere, considerable effort was devoted to finding new items and acquiring more information about known items. There are undoubtedly Peirce publications not discovered in this search, especially unsigned contributions, but in the editor's opinion it is not likely that any of these are of great importance.

Much, though not all, of the information derived from the sources mentioned above was checked before it was incorporated. Every item published while Peirce was alive, with the exception of articles in the *New York Evening Post* (access to which is difficult) and an unlocated item, has been examined and the information given in the present bibliography confirmed. With regard to manuscripts or parts of manuscripts not published during Peirce's lifetime, but included in *Collected Papers*, volumes I–VI, the information in the published volumes was accepted as given; in particular, the present editor has not attempted to re-date the manuscripts printed there. In the course of going through the Harvard manuscripts, however, a considerable amount of this information has been checked and the necessary corrections have been incorporated in the present bibliography.

Knight McMahon, in connection with his preparation of a catalogue of the Widener manuscripts, was able in some instances to unite manuscripts that were in separate pieces when *Collected Papers*, volumes I–VI, were edited; and the present editor has also succeeded in recombining some fragments. In cases where different dates have been assigned to the respective parts of a work, the work as a whole is listed under one of the dates, and the respective parts, with the date appropriate to each, are listed under this heading. Concerning the problem of dating Peirce's work, it is worth noting that, especially after he moved to Milford (1887), Peirce was constantly reworking drafts of articles and books, with the result that many of the manuscripts are confused jumbles of various drafts, some of them written at quite different times.

Many of Peirce's published works are unsigned — this is true of most of the items published in *The Nation* — and in a few cases they bear signatures other than Peirce's, though there is conclusive evidence in the Harvard manuscripts and correspondence that these are by him. In many such instances the present editor has accepted the authority of other bibliographies concerning the identity of the items, after examining each one (with the exception, as before, of articles in the *New York Evening Post* and one unlocated item) for internal evidence that it was written by Peirce. Unless otherwise indicated, the items from *The Nation* were unsigned and the identification has been taken from Haskell's *Index to the Nation*, which is based on the records of *The Nation*.

The present editor has sometimes made identifications on the basis of correspondence, manuscript drafts, a list in Widener VA² of some of Peirce's reviews in volumes 50 through 57 of *The Nation*, and proof sheets. Rather strict criteria of identification were used. Except for two or three items where there seemed good independent reason to believe the publication was by Peirce, the mere presence of proof sheets alone among the manuscripts was not accepted as sufficient evidence of authorship; however, in some cases identification was based on scraps of manuscript. It would be possible to establish Peirce's authorship, with varying degrees of probability, of a number of additional reviews by the use of proof sheets, inconclusive references in correspondence, and internal evidence; but in every such instance that came to this editor's attention, the review was of such little significance that it seemed better to confine the bibliography to items where the evidence was more conclusive. Even so, the reader should be aware of the nature of the evidence on which the identifications were based. He should further understand that many of Peirce's reviews in *The Nation* were modified by the editor of that journal. (See [CP] 8.117n10 and [Fisch-Haskell]377.) Where the identification is the work of the present editor on the basis of Harvard manuscripts, the expression, "Identification based on Harvard mss.," is used.

Peirce Manuscript Sources. The most important collection of Peirce manuscripts, the source of almost all of the previously unpublished papers in *Collected Papers*, is in the Archives of Widener Library at Harvard University. It consists of sixty-one boxes and bundles, listed under the call number HUG 1680.402. A catalogue for this collection, prepared by Knight W. McMahon, *Catalogue of C. S. Peirce Manuscripts*, December, 1941, typed, 99 pp., is available at the Archives. While this catalogue is not complete, it gives a list of the contents of most of the boxes, and it is extremely useful. The collection is divided according to Peirce's classification of sciences as follows, with the number of boxes and bundles listed after each division:

I.	Science of Discovery	
	A. Mathematics	8
	B. Philosophy	
	1. Pragmatism and the Categories	2
	2. Normative Sciences (Logic)	12
	3. Metaphysics	2
	C. Idioscopy	8
II.	Science of Review: Classification of the Sciences	1
III.	Practical Science and Miscellaneous	3
IV.	Book Reviews	2

BIBLIOGRAPHY

These manuscripts are identified in the present volume by designations, such as "Widener IB2–7," "Widener VA²," etc., following the above classification.

There is also a large collection of Peirce manuscripts in Houghton Library at Harvard University. This consists of about twenty-one boxes and bundles of material, mainly fragments and items of minor importance, which are unclassified and uncatalogued.

Considerable effort was made to locate other Peirce materials, and many sources were uncovered. In each case the source was inspected by the editor or by someone known to him to insure that all manuscripts of general importance were included in the series. A complete list of all known sources of Peirce manuscripts is given below. It is evident from this list and from the description given above of the Harvard materials that the total quantity of unpublished Peirce manuscripts is tremendous. It may be of interest to Peirce scholars to have a general estimate of the value of the manuscripts not included in *Collected Papers*. In the present editor's opinion, *Collected Papers*, volumes I–VIII, include all manuscripts that would be of interest to the general philosophic reader; they also include sufficient material for the Peirce specialist to trace the development of Peirce's thought in some detail. There still remains among the unpublished manuscripts much material of value for a personal biography of Peirce and for very detailed studies of Peirce's intellectual development.

Sources of Peirce Manuscripts

1. Archives, Widener Library, Harvard University.

(a) The main Peirce collection in the Archives, referred to above.

(b) The class book of 1859 (Call No. HUD 259.714F) and the photographs of the class of 1859 (Call No. HUD 259.704F).

(c) Peirce mss. and related materials: HUG 1680.402.10, HUG 1680.402.12.

(d) Correspondence in the papers of Josiah Royce and F. E. Abbot.

2. Houghton Library, Harvard University.

(a) The material referred to above.

(b) Letters between Peirce and James in the William James Collection.

(c) Peirce's interleaved and annotated copy of the *Century Dictionary*; cf. [Bibliography] G–1889–3.

254

BIBLIOGRAPHY

(d) Approximately six additional items listed in the catalogues of Widener and Houghton.

(e) A letter from Peirce in the C. E. Norton papers.

3. Other Harvard University sources.

(a) There are some of Peirce's copies of his own reprints in Widener Library. There are many of Peirce's books in Widener Library and at least one in the Philosophy Library, but these are not identified as Peirce's in the card catalogue and no record of them has been found. A record of Peirce's class, *Harvard College Records of the Class of 1859*, Edward W. Wheeler, Cambridge, 1896 (Call No. HUD 259.775), is in Widener Library.

(b) The records of the Harvard College Observatory during the period Peirce was associated with it are stored in the Harvard University Deposit Library. Volumes N11 through N19, and perhaps others, contain records of Peirce's observations. There are also eight volumes of Peirce's "Photometric Observations" and a volume of his "Experiments with Photometer."

4. National Archives, Washington, D. C. Letters and papers in the records of the United States Coast and Geodetic Survey.

5. Library of Congress, Washington, D. C., Manuscript Division. Peirce's side of a correspondence with Simon Newcomb; Newcomb's letters to Peirce are at Harvard. Cf. [Bibliography] M–6c.

6. Johns Hopkins University Library, Baltimore.

(a) Letters and papers in the Daniel C. Gilman Collection.

(b) Letters and papers in the records of the *American Journal of Mathematics*.

(c) Books and reprints that belonged to Peirce. Peirce sold several hundred books to this library; a list of these is in the Accession Book of the Hopkins Library for February 7–9, 1881. Cf. [Fisch-Cope] 292ff.

7. Smithsonian Institution, Washington, D. C. Manuscripts and correspondence published by Wiener; cf. [Bibliography] G–1901–2. In addition there are other manuscripts and about twenty-five letters; cf. [Bibliography] M–6b.

8. Yale University Library, New Haven.

(a) Photostat copies of the correspondence with Lady Welby; cf. [Bibliography] M–20a, p. 34, ftn. 79.

(b) Rare Book Room, Sterling Library. A letter from Peirce to Josiah Gibbs. (Also a letter from Melusina Fay Peirce, Peirce's wife, to George Eliot and letters from Benjamin and James Mills Peirce to people at Yale.)

9. Hoose Library of Philosophy, University of Southern California, Los Angeles. About eighteen letters from Peirce to William T. Harris.

10. Columbia University, New York City.

(a) Some Peirce reprints; cf. [Bibliography] M–15b, p. 718.

(b) A few items in the Plimpton Collection and in the David Eugene Smith Library; cf. [Bibliography] M–6a.

11. Private possession of Mrs. D. P. Abbot. A letter; cf. [Bibliography] M–21b, p. 252.

12. St. John's College, Cambridge University, Cambridge, England. About eight letters from Peirce to J. J. Sylvester regarding nonions. Cf. [Bibliography] G–1883–1.

BIBLIOGRAPHY

13. Private possession of André Lalande. A letter from Peirce to Lalande. (There is a typed copy in Widener VB2.)

14. Open Court Publishing Company, La Salle, Illinois. At least ten letters from Peirce to Paul Carus and numerous carbon copies of Carus's letters to Peirce.

15. Private possession of Sylvia Wright. Some minor biographical items. (There is a description in Widener VA².)

ERRATA IN *COLLECTED PAPERS* I–VI

VOLUME I

[CP] I, p. 366: Index s.n. Spencer, add 174, delete 533.

VOLUME II

2.147: In line three replace "stimulation" by "simulation."
2.367: First sentence, replace "not" by "now."
2.391n2, p. 238: Not in the original; a later addition, probably 1893.
[CP] II, p. 526: Index s.v. Hemilogical, delete 567; add this entry in [CP] I.

VOLUMES II–VI

[CP] II–VI: In references to Baldwin's *Dictionary of Philosophy and Psychology* some errata occur in the assignment of authorship of dictionary entries. Some entries and portions of entries are listed as of joint authorship which were actually by Peirce alone: Imaging (in logic), Knowledge (in logic), Logic, Middle term (and Middle), Negation, Observation, Particular, Petitio Principii, Symbolic Logic or Algebra of Logic, Universal (and Universality), Universe, and Validity. A portion of an entry and an entry are ascribed to him which he did not write though they were accepted by him: Signification (and Application, in logic), Transposition. Authorship is assigned to Peirce, Baldwin, and Stout for a portion of an entry of which Stout was not a co-author: Whole (and Parts). Cf. [Bibliography] G–1901–6.

VOLUME III

3.181n1: In line 2 replace "vol. 4" with "vol. 10."
3.200n*, p. 128: Replace "vol. 3" by "vol. 3 of the American Journal of Mathematics."
[CP] III, p. 417: Index s.n. Ladd-Franklin, "210n" should be "201n"; s.n. Keynes, "J. M." should be "J. N."
[CP] III: For a list of errata, see Willard V. Quine, "Review: Collected Papers of Charles Sanders Peirce (Vol. III)," *Isis* 22 (Dec 1934) 296–297.

256

BIBLIOGRAPHY

VOLUME IV

4.1n*: Change "6–10" to "6–11."

4.96: In line 2 replace "intransitive" by "transitive."

4.214: Change "2^{2^n}" in line 3 to "n." In line 8 the second occurrence of "denumerable" should be "primipostnumeral," although the manuscript has "denumerable."

4.264n‖: Place a bar over "x" at its second occurrence.

[CP] IV, p. 581: Index s.n. Abbott, replace "150" by "50" and "Abbott" by "Abbot."

    p. 582: Index s.n. Keynes, replace "J. M." by "J. N."; s.n. Sylvester, replace "304" by "305."

    p. 597: Index s.v. Reasoning, corollarial, replace "616" by "613."

VOLUME V

5.7n§: The reference is to 3.491.

5.22n1: Delete the subscript "2" on "n."

5.71n1: This note is concluded at the bottom of p. 50.

5.300n1: "Intuition *vs.* Contemplation," *The Journal of Speculative Philosophy* 2(1868)191–192, is referred to as "anonymous." But in the index to *ibid.*, "Editor" [William T. Harris] is listed in the author column.

5.318: This article was published in 1869, not 1868.

5.363: In the original the fourth sentence reads, "Lavoisier's method was not to read and pray, not . . ." rather than ". . . pray, but . . ." It is clear that "not" (rather than "but") is correct, for the process of dreaming outside of the laboratory, working in the laboratory without direction, and publishing the last dream is surely characteristic of the alchemists rather than of Lavoisier. Also, the French translation agrees with this interpretation.

5.428n*: There is a printed erratum sheet in Widener IA–8, making the correction suggested here.

5.494n†: "(1906)" should be "(1907)."

5.533n*: "1.616 ff." should be "1.611 ff."

5.604n*: This should read "In 1892–1893."

5.611, p. 428: In line 19 replace "definite" by "definitive."

[CP] V, p. 432: Index s.n. Stewart, delete 611; add the entry: Stewart, J. A., 611.

    p. 454: Index s.v. Truth, replace "25" by "26."

VOLUME VI

6.390n*: "pp. 281–282" should read "pp. 373–374."

6.395: Move superscript "E" from chapter title, "The Order of Nature" (1878), to section title, "The Significance of Order."

6.606: In line 6, replace "world" by "word."

[CP] VI, p. 448: Index s.v. Autobiographical, replace "334n" by "335n."

    p. 453: Index s.v. Idealism, objective, replace "603" by "605."

BIBLIOGRAPHY

LIST OF ABBREVIATIONS AND SYMBOLS

* As a guide to the general reader of philosophical literature, those items which, in the editor's opinion, are Peirce's main contributions to philosophy (exclusive of symbolic logic) are marked with an asterisk.

† Of the items which have been published but are not included in *Collected Papers*, those most interesting to specialists in Peirce's philosophy have been marked with a dagger.

[AJM] *American Journal of Mathematics.*

[BPSW] *Bulletin of the Philosophical Society of Washington.*

[Cohen] Morris R. Cohen, "Charles S. Peirce and a Tentative Bibliography of his Published Writings," *The Journal of Philosophy, Psychology, and Scientific Methods* 13(21 Dec 1916)726–737; "Bibliography," pp. 733–737. Additions were published in *ibid.*, 15(10 Oct 1918)578–584. Both were reprinted with modifications in "Bibliography of Peirce's Published Writing," *Chance, Love, and Logic* (edited by Morris R. Cohen), Harcourt, Brace, and Company, 1923, and Peter Smith, 1949, pp. 309–318. The abbreviation designates all these publications collectively.

[CP] *Collected Papers of Charles Sanders Peirce*, 8 vols. *Collected Papers* I–VI were edited by Charles Hartshorne and Paul Weiss, Harvard University Press, Cambridge, 1931–1935: Vol. I, *Principles of Philosophy*; Vol. II, *Elements of Logic*; Vol. III, *Exact Logic*; Vol. IV, *The Simplest Mathematics*; Vol. V, *Pragmatism and Pragmaticism*; Vol. VI, *Scientific Metaphysics*. Vol. VII, *Science and Philosophy*, and the present volume, Vol. VIII, *Reviews, Correspondence, and Bibliography*, were edited by Arthur W. Burks, Harvard University Press, Cambridge, 1958. References to paragraphs employ the decimal notation used in *Collected Papers*, I–VI, e.g., "[CP] 5.431" refers to [CP], Vol. V, paragraph 431. Page references are given by the designation [CP] and the volume and page number, e.g., [CP] IV, 291.

[CS ——]. . . . *Report of the Superintendent of the United States Coast Survey Showing the Progress of the Work for the Fiscal Year Ending with June, ——*. Wash.: Gov. Printing Office, ... (Title pages for some years are unimportant variations of this.) Items from these reports are dated by year of publication and not by the fiscal year of the report.

[Fisch] Max H. Fisch, "Alexander Bain and the Genealogy of Pragmatism," *Journal of the History of Ideas* 15(June 1954)413–444.

[Fisch-Cope] Max H. Fisch and Jackson I. Cope, "Peirce at the Johns Hopkins," *Studies in the Philosophy of Charles Sanders Peirce* (edited by Philip P. Wiener and Frederick H. Young), Harvard University Press, 1952, pp. 277–311, 355–360, 363–374.

[Fisch-Haskell] Max H. Fisch and Daniel C. Haskell, "Some Additions to Morris R. Cohen's Bibliography of Peirce's Published Writings," *ibid.*, pp. 375–381. ("During the time when the *Nation* was in effect a weekly edition of the *Post*, it will probably be found that most of Peirce's reviews in the *Nation* had already appeared in the *Post*." We have included the *Post* references given here, but have made no further search.)

BIBLIOGRAPHY

[Harvard ——] *A Catalogue of the Officers and Students of Harvard University for the Academical Year* ——, Cambridge.

[Haskell] Daniel C. Haskell, *Index to the Nation* (Volumes 1–105, 1865–1917), The New York Public Library, New York: Volume 1, *Index of Titles*, 1951; Volume 2, *Index of Contributors*, 1953.

[International Geodetic Comm., ——, ——]. . . . Proceedings of the meeting of the Permanent Commission of the International Geodetic Association held at —— in the year ——, published in the year . . . . For example, '[International Geodetic Comm., Hamburg, 1878]1879' abbreviates: *Comptes-Rendus des Séances de la Commission Permanente de l'Association Géodésique Internationale pour la Mesure des Degrés en Europe Réunie à Hambourg du 4 au 8 Septembre 1878*, rédiges par les secrétaires C. Bruhns and A. Hirsch, George Reimer, Berlin, 1879. These volumes are listed on Library of Congress cards under the heading: Internationale erdmessung, Permanente commission.

[International Geodetic Conference, ——, ——]. . . . Proceedings of the International Geodetic Conference which met at —— in the year ——, published in the year . . . . For example, '[International Geodetic Conference, Stuttgart, 1877]1878' abbreviates: *Comptes-Rendus des Séances de la Cinquième Conférence Géodésique Internationale pour la Mesure des Degrés en Europe Réunie à Stuttgart du 27 Septembre au 2 Octobre 1877*, rédiges par les secrétaires C. Bruhns and A. Hirsch, Georg Reimer, Berlin, 1878. These volumes are listed on Library of Congress cards under the heading: Internationale erdmessung, Allgemaine Conferenz.

[JHUC] *Johns Hopkins University Circulars.*

[JHUR ——]. . . . *Annual Report of Johns Hopkins University for the year* ——, published in the year. . . . (Title pages for some years are unimportant variations of this.)

[PAAAS] *Proceedings of the American Academy of Arts and Sciences.*

[Perry] Ralph Barton Perry, *The Thought and Character of William James*, 2 vols., Little, Brown and Company, Boston, 1935.

[RNA ——] *Report of the National Academy of Sciences*, for the year ——.

BIBLIOGRAPHY

I. GENERAL

1860

1. Reference to Peirce's azimuth and magnetic observations. [CS 1859] 1860, p. 36.

1861

1. Reference to Peirce's work on triangulation. [CS 1860] 1861, p. 86.

1862

1. Reference to Peirce's having checked computations of Benjamin Peirce on occultations of the Pleiades. [CS 1861] 1862, p. 220. Cf. pp. 196–221.

1863

† 1. "The Chemical Theory of Interpenetration," dated "Dec. 1862," *The American Journal of Science and Arts* 2nd series 35(Jan 1863)78–82.

2. Extracts from "The Place of Our Age in the History of Civilization," presented at the reunion of the Cambridge High School Association 12 Nov 1863, *Cambridge Chronicle* (a Cambridge, Mass., weekly newspaper) Vol. 18, No. 47, 21 Nov 1863, p. 1, columns 1–5.

1864

1. "Shakespearian Pronunciation," (with J. B. Noyes) unsigned, *The North American Review* 98(April 1864)342–369. A note in a bound volume of Peirce's reprints at Johns Hopkins University (*Papers on Logic*, Call No. BC10.P2) states that this paper "was written in collaboration with John Buttrick Noyes."

2. Reference to Peirce's having made computations for Benjamin Peirce on occultations of the Pleiades. [CS 1863] 1864, pp. 146–154.

3. Reference to a series of University Lectures, "On the Logic of Science," given by Peirce at Harvard during 1864–65. [Harvard 1865–66] 104; cf. [CP] 7.579n34. In a letter to F. E. Abbot dated March 17, 1865 (F. E. Abbot papers, Widener Archives), Peirce says "My lectures fell through for want of an audience."

1866

1. Reference to Peirce's work on computations for longitude from occultations of the Pleiades. [CS 1864] 1866, p. 114.

2. (a) Reference to twelve lectures on "The Logic of Science and Induction," given by Peirce at the Lowell Institute during the winter of 1866–67. Harriette Knight Smith, *The History of the Lowell Institute,*

1898, p. 63. Cf. [CP] 2.641n1. [CP] 7.131–138 (c.1866) and 7.579–596 (c.1867), Widener IB2–10, are probably parts of Lectures IV and XI, respectively; cf. [CP] 7.579n34.

(b) *Memoranda Concerning the Aristotelian Syllogism*, privately printed and distributed at the Lowell Institute, Nov 1866, perhaps in connection with the above lectures. [CP] 2.792–807.

1867

1. [PAAAS] series on logic. [CP] 4.2–4 contain comments on this series.

(a) "On an improvement in Boole's Calculus of Logic," 7(presented 12 March 1867)250–261. [CP] 3.1–19 with revisions of 1870.

* (b) "On the Natural Classification of Arguments," 7(presented 9 April 1867)261–287. Part II is in large part a restatement of [Bibliography] G–1866–2b. [CP] 2.461–516 with revisions of 1893.

* (c) "On a New List of Categories," 7(presented 14 May 1867)287–298. [CP] 1.545–559 except 549n1.

(d) "Upon the Logic of Mathematics," 7(presented 10 Sept 1867) 402–412. [CP] 3.20–44.

* (e) "Upon Logical Comprehension and Extension," 7(presented 13 Nov 1867)416–432. [Bibliography]G–1893–7 is a supplement to it. [CP] 2.391–426 with revisions of c.1870 and 1893.

* 2. Review of John Venn's *The Logic of Chance*, unsigned, *The North American Review* 105(July 1867)317–321. Identified in [Cohen]. Peirce refers to it in [CP] 3.19n1. [CP] 8.1–6.

1868

1. (a) "Nominalism *versus* Realism," an unsigned letter, *The Journal of Speculative Philosophy* 2(1868)57–61. Actually this is a portion of a letter from Peirce to William T. Harris, dated 24 Jan 1868, the original of which is in the Hoose Library of Philosophy, University of Southern California. This portion criticizes Harris' article, *ibid.*, 1(1867)250–256, and is interspersed with Harris' reply. [CP] 6.619–624, preceded by an introductory comment by Harris but without his reply.

(b) "What is Meant by 'Determined'?" an unsigned letter, *The Journal of Speculative Philosophy* 2(1868)190–191. This letter gives Peirce's rebuttal to Harris' reply to "Nominalism *versus* Realism" and contains Harris' rejoinder in footnotes. [CP] 6.625–630 without Harris' rejoinder.

* 2. *Journal of Speculative Philosophy* 1868–69 series on intuitive knowledge.

(a) "Questions Concerning Certain Faculties Claimed for Man," 2(1868) 103–114. [CP] 5.213–263.

(b) "Some Consequences of Four Incapacities," 2(1868)140–157. [CP] 5.264–317.

(c) "Grounds of Validity of the Laws of Logic: Further Consequences of Four Incapacities," 2(1869)193–208. [CP] 5.318–357 with revisions of 1893.

c.1868

1. "A Philosopher's Political Diagnosis" (on proportional representation), *New York: A Symphonic Study*, by Melusina Fay Peirce, The Neale Publishing Co., New York, 1918, pp. 100–104. This comment is quoted from Peirce (p. 99) and was made between 1865 and 1870.

1869

1. Reference to Peirce's latitude observations. [CS 1867] 1869, pp. 19–20.

2. References to a series of nine lectures on "British Logicians," given by Peirce at Harvard during 1869–70. [Harvard 1869–70]102; [Perry]I, 321. [CP] 1.28–34 is from Lecture I, "Early Nominalism and Realism."

1870

1. "Description of a Notation for the Logic of Relatives, resulting from an Amplification of the Conceptions of Boole's Calculus of Logic," *Memoirs of the American Academy of Arts and Sciences* ns 9(presented 26 Jan 1870) 317–378. Reprinted separately by Welch, Bigelow and Company, Cambridge, Mass., 1870, 62 pp. [CP] 3.45–149, except 45n*, with revisions from Peirce's own copy.

† 2. Review of Henry James's *The Secret of Swedenborg: being an Elucidation of his Doctrine of the Divine Natural Humanity*, unsigned, *The North American Review* 110 (April 1870)463–468. Identified by [Perry] I, 533, and in a personal communication from Max Fisch.

1871

* 1. Review of *The Works of* GEORGE BERKELEY, D.D., *formerly Bishop of Cloyne: including many of his writings hitherto unpublished* (edited by Alexander Campbell Fraser), signed "C.S.P.," *The North American Review* 113 (Oct 1871) 449–472. [CP] 8.7–38.

2. Reference to a series of thirty-five University Lectures on "Logic," given by Peirce at Harvard during the second term of 1870–71. [Harvard 1870–71]109.

3. Reference to "On the Appearance of Encke's Comet as Seen at Harvard College Observatory," presented 16 Dec 1871. [BPSW]1(1874)35.

1872

1. Items in [CS 1869]1872.
(a) References to Peirce's spectroscopic eclipse observations, pp. 39, 126, 187.

(b) Letter concerning the above, dated 20 Aug 1869, pp. 126–127.

(c) "Report on the Results of the Reduction of the Measures of the Photographs of the Partial Phases of the Eclipse of August 7, 1869 . . . ," pp. 181–185.

2. Reference to Peirce's presenting a paper on the photometric measurements of the stars and exhibiting an instrument for this purpose devised by Zöllner. [PAAAS]8 (12 March 1872)412.

Reference to "On Stellar Photometry," presented 19 Oct 1872. [BPSW] 1(1874)63.

3. Abstract of paper, "On the Coincidence of the Geographical Distribution of Rainfall and of Illiteracy, as shown by the Statistical Maps of the Ninth Census Reports," presented 21 Dec 1872, [BPSW]1(1874)68. Cf. [CP] 2.752.

1873

1. Reference to "On Logical Algebra," presented 17 May 1873. [BPSW]1(1874)88; cf. p. 87. Cf. [Bibliography]G–1870–1.

2. Items in [CS 1870]1873.

(a) Letter to Benjamin Peirce (Superintendent, Coast Survey) reporting Peirce's observations of the total solar eclipse of 22 Dec 1870 (made at Catania, Sicily), p. 125.

This is followed by a letter from Mrs. Charles S. Peirce, reporting on her observations of the eclipse, pp. 125–127, with a sketch near the end of the volume.

Cf. also references to Peirce on pp. 137, 230, 231.

(b) Appendix No. 21, "On the Theory of Errors of Observations," pp. 200–224 (with errata on a slip inserted after p. 200) and Diagram No. 27.

c.1873

* 1. "Logic," Widener IB2–8. [CP] 7.313–361, except 313n1, are from it. Cf. [CP] 7.313n1.

1874

1. Reference to "On Quaternions, as Developed from the General Theory of the Logic of Relatives," presented 3 Jan 1874. [BPSW]1 (1874)94.

2. Reference to "On Various Hypotheses in Reference to Space," presented 14 March 1874. [BPSW]1(1874)97.

3. References to the work of Peirce and his wife in connection with the solar eclipse of 22 Dec 1870. [CS 1871] 1874, pp. 10, 11, 182. (Pages 10 and 11 are the same as [CS 1870]1873, pp. 230, 231.)

1875

1. Reference to "Photometric Measurements of the Stars." [PAAAS]ns 2, ws 10(9 March 1875)473. Cf. [Bibliography]G–1872–2.

2. "On the Application of Logical Analysis to Multiple Algebra," [PAAAS]ns 2, ws 10(presented 11 May 1875)392–394. [CP] 3.150–151. See [CP] 3.648 for a possible reference to this paper.

3. "A Plan and an Illustration" (on proportional representation), *The Democratic Party; A Political Study*, by a Political Zero (Melusina Fay Peirce), John Wilson and Son, Cambridge, 1875, pp. 36–37. Both the whole work and Peirce's contribution are anonymous, but these are identified in [Fisch-Haskell].

4. Items in [CS 1873]1875. See p. 60 and also [CS 1872] 1875, p. 50, for biographical remarks.
(a) Reference to Peirce's pendulum experiments, p. 14.
(b) Appendix No. 14, "A List of Stars for Observations of Latitude," prepared under Peirce's direction, pp. 138–174.
(c) Appendix No. 15, "Errata in the Heis Catalogue of Stars," prepared under Peirce's direction, pp. 175–180.

5. References to Peirce's participation in the meetings of the Permanent Committee of the International Geodetic Association, 1885. [International Geodetic Comm., Paris, 1875]1875, pp. 13, 16, 19–23, 32, 51, 54, 58–61, 71. Cf. [CS 1876]1879, pp. 8–9 and [CS 1881]1883, p. 360. See also [International Geodetic Comm., Brussels, 1876] 1877, pp. 12, 18, 19, 41–42, 47–49, for references to Peirce's work. Cf. [CS 1881]1883, p. 360.

c.1875

1. "Third," a fragment. [CP] 1.337.

1876

1. "Logical Contraposition and Conversion," *Mind* 1(July 1876)424–425. This is a comment on a statement by the Editor (George Croom Robertson), *ibid.*, (Jan 1876)148; the Editor's reply is at *ibid.*, 1(July 1876)425. [CP] 2.550.

2. Reference to "On a new edition of Ptolemy's Catalogue of Stars." [PAAAS]ns 4, ws 12(11 Oct 1876)283.

1877

1. "Note on the Sensation of Color," *The American Journal of Science and Arts* 3rd series 13(April 1877)247–251. Reprinted with slight omissions in *Philosophical Magazine and Journal of Science* 5th series 3(1877) 543–547.

2. The unsigned obituary of Nicholas St. John Green in [PAAAS]ns 4, ws 12(9 May 1877)289–291, contains a quotation (pp. 290–291) from a

letter from "one who was familiar with his modes of thought" (p. 290) about Green. Max Fisch suggests this letter was written by Peirce.

3. "De l'Influence de la Flexibilité du Trépied sur l'Oscillation du Pendule à Réversion," [International Geodetic Conference, Stuttgart, 1877] 1878, pp. 171–187, with a letter of introduction by E. Plantamour (pp. 171–172). See pp. 188–190 of the proceedings for comments by Th. von Oppolzer on Peirce's paper. See pp. 4, 20, 23, 100–101, 118, 139, for references to Peirce's attendance and remarks at the conference. E. Plantamour, *Recherches Expérimentales sur le Mouvement Simultané d'un Pendule et de ses Supports* is an appendix. See pp. 3–5 for references to Peirce. A translation by Peirce is printed at [CS 1881]1883, pp. 427–436, with revisions and notes of 1882; [Bibliography]G–1883–5b.

4. "Note on Grassmann's Calculus of Extension," [PAAAS] ns 5, ws 13(presented 10 Oct 1877)115–116. [CP] 3.152–153 with revisions.

*5. "Illustrations of the Logic of Science," *The Popular Science Monthly*, 1877–1878.

(a) "The Fixation of Belief," 12(Nov 1877)1–15. [CP] 5.358–387, except 358n*, with revisions and notes of 1893, 1903, and c.1910.

(b) "How to Make Our Ideas Clear," 12(Jan 1878) 286–302. [CP] 5.388–410, except 402n3, with revisions and notes of 1893 and 1903.

(c) "The Doctrine of Chances," 12(March 1878) 604–615. [CP] 2.645–660 with revisions of 1893 and a note of 1910.

(d) "The Probability of Induction," 12(April 1878) 705–718. [CP] 2.669–693.

(e) "The Order of Nature," 13(June 1878)203–217. [CP] 6.395–427.

(f) "Deduction, Induction, and Hypothesis," 13(Aug 1878)470–482. [CP] 2.619–644.

6. Reference to Peirce's pendulum observations. [CS 1874]1877, p. 18.

1878

1. "On the Influence of Internal Friction upon the Correction of the Length of the Second's Pendulum for the Flexibility of the Support," [PAAAS]ns 5, ws 13 (presented 13 March 1878)396–401; cf. p. 433. Reprinted at [CS 1881]1883, pp. 437–441; [Bibliography] G–1883–5b.

2. Review of Annibale Ferrero's *Esposizione del Metodo dei Minimi Quadrati*, [AJM]1(1878)59–63.

3. Reference to "On the acceleration of gravity at initial stations," presented 5–8 Nov 1878. [RNA 1883]49.

4. A brief statement of Peirce's experimental pendulum work during 1878, [International Geodetic Comm., Hamburg, 1878]1879, pp. 116–120. "The details of all this work will be given in my forthcoming memoir upon the comparison of the European and American pendulum work" (p. 120). Cf. [Bibliography]G–1879–5d. See also [International Geodetic Comm., Geneva, 1879] 1880, pp. 9, 19–20, for references to Peirce's work.

5. Items in [CS 1875]1878.

(a) Reference to Peirce's pendulum observations, p. 19.

(b) Appendix No. 15, "Description of an Apparatus for Recording the Mean of the Times of a Set of Observations," pp. 249–253, with a plate facing p. 250.

6. *Photometric Researches*, Vol. 9 of *Annals of the Astronomical Observatory of Harvard College*, Leipzig, 1878, vi + 181 pp. + errata sheet + five diagrams. Cf. [Bibliography]G–1872–2 and G–1875–1.

"The chief end of observations of the magnitudes of stars is to determine the form of the cluster in which our sun is situated. . . . I shall . . . [endeavor] to show the general forms of the surfaces of equal star density throughout the cluster" *Photometric Researches*, p. 174.

Solon I. Bailey (in *The History and Work of Harvard Observatory, 1839–1927*, Harvard Observatory Monograph No. 4, McGraw-Hill, New York, 1931) says of the work reported in *Photometric Researches*: "The first attempt at the Harvard Observatory to determine the form of the Milky Way, or the galactic system, was made by Charles S. Peirce. . . . The investigation was of a pioneer nature, founded on scant data" (pp. 198–199). Cf. pp. 52, 53, 86, 95, 110, 124, 125, 196, 240, 260, 274, for further references to Peirce.

7. "La Logique de la Science," *Revue Philosophique*, 1878–1879.

(a) "Comment se fixe la croyance," 6(Dec 1878)553–569. This is a republication with some changes of [Bibliography]G–1877–5a. The last paragraph is omitted, and "or to a reformed Catholic . . . Bible" is deleted from the penultimate paragraph.

(b) "Comment rendre nos idées claires," 7(Jan 1879) 39–57. This is a republication with some changes of [Bibliography]G–1877–5b. Everything is deleted after "I will not trouble the reader with any more Ontology at this moment" which occurs in the penultimate paragraph of the English version. Erratum: delete "ne . . . pas" from line 22 of page 56. See [Fisch-Cope] ftn. 35 for Peirce's comment on the two articles of this series.

1879

1. "Note on the Progress of Experiments for comparing a Wave-length with a Meter," *The American Journal of Science and Arts* 3rd series 18(July 1879)51.

Reference to "Comparisons of the meter with wave lengths," presented 15–18 April 1879. [RNA 1883]50.

Reference to "On the Reference of the Unit of Length to the Wave-Lengths of Light." [PAAAS]ns 7, ws 15 (presented 11 June 1879)370.

2. "On a method of Swinging Pendulums for the Determination of Gravity, proposed by M. Faye," *The American Journal of Science and Arts* 3rd series 18, ws 118(Aug 1879)112–119.

Reference to "On the errors of pendulum experiments, and on the method of swinging pendulums proposed by M. Faye," presented 17 April 1879. [RNA 1883]50.

3. "On the Ghosts in Rutherfurd's Diffraction-Spectra," [AJM]2 (1879)330–347.

Reference to "Ghosts in the diffraction spectra," presented 15–18 April 1879. [RNA 1883]50.

4. "A Quincuncial Projection of the Sphere," [AJM]2(1879) 394–396 with one plate. Erratum, *ibid.*, 3(1880)v.

Reference to "On the projections of the sphere which preserve the angles," presented 15–18 April 1879. [RNA 1883]50.

5. Items in [CS 1876]1879.

(a) Reference to Peirce's pendulum observations at European stations, pp. 6–9.

(b) The list of stars given in Appendix No. 7, "A Catalogue of Stars for Observations of Latitude," pp. 83–129, was selected under the direction of Peirce. The data from Ptolemy's catalogue "is based on Mr. Peirce's transcript of the Paris manuscript, an account of which he has presented to the American Academy of Arts and Sciences" (p. 84). Cf. [Bibliography]G–1876–2. Reprinted with the additional heading, "Methods and Results," Washington, 1879.

* (c) Appendix No. 14, "Note on the Theory of the Economy of Research," pp. 197–201. [CP] 7.139–157 with some corrections from a ms. version in Widener IC2a.

(d) Appendix No. 15, "Measurements of Gravity at Initial Stations in America and Europe," dated 13 Dec 1878, pp. 202–337, with fifteen plates, and pp. 410–416. Cf. [Bibliography]G–1878–3. See [CS 1883]1884, p. 476 (ftn.) for a correction. See *The American Journal of Science* 3rd series 20(Oct 1880)327 for an erratum. Reprinted with the additional heading, "Methods and Results," Washington, 1879.

6. Reference to "Geographical Problem of the Four Colors," presented to the Scientific Association, 5 Nov and 3 Dec 1879. [JHUC]1(Jan 1880) 16.

7. Abstract of a paper, "Questions concerning certain Faculties claimed for Man," presented to the Metaphysical Club, 11 Nov 1879, [JHUC]1 (Jan 1880)18. Cf. [Bibliography]G–1868–2a.

1880

1. References to Peirce's courses at Johns Hopkins University for 1879–80. [JHUC]1(Dec 1879)6, 7; 1(Jan 1880)12; 1(Feb 1880)25; 1(May 1880)62; 1(Aug 1880)71; [JHUR 1880] 1880, p. 50.

2. Reference to Peirce's comments on Alan Marquand's talk on a treatise of Philodemus at the Metaphysical Club, 13 Jan 1880. [JHUC]1 (Feb. 1880)34.

3. Reference to Peirce's discussion of Stringham's "A Generalization, for *n*-fold Space, of Euler's Equation for Polyhedra," at the Mathematical Seminary, 21 Jan 1880. [JHUC]1(Feb 1880)35.

4. Abstract of a comment on Jevons and Schroeder made at the Metaphysical Club, 9 March 1880, [JHUC]1(April 1880)49.

5. Abstract of "On Kant's 'Critic of the Pure Reason' in the light of Modern Logic," presented to the Metaphysical Club, 9 March 1880, [JHUC]1(April 1880)49.

6. "Results of Pendulum Experiments," *The American Journal of Science* 3rd series 20, ws 120(Oct 1880)327. This note gives the main results of [Bibliography]G–1879–5d. Reprinted in *Philosophical Magazine and Journal of Science* 5th series 10(Nov 1880)387.

7. References to Peirce's courses at Johns Hopkins University for 1880–81. [JHUC]1(Dec 1880)76, 77; 1(April 1881)124, 125; [JHUR 1881]1882, p. 16; Ellery W. Davis, "Charles Peirce at Johns Hopkins," *The Mid-West Quarterly* 2(Oct 1914)48–56.

8. "On the Algebra of Logic," [AJM]3(1880)15–57. The original ends with "to be continued"; cf. same title [Bibliography]G–1885–3. [CP] 3.154–251, except 154n1 and 200n* (p. 128), with revisions of 1880 and c.1882 and undated revisions.

9. "Sur la valeur de la pesanteur à Paris," *Comptes Rendus des Séances de l'Académie des Sciences* 90 (14 June 1880)1401–1403. See comments by M. Faye, *ibid.*, (21 June 1880)1443, 1463–1466. A translation by Peirce is printed at [CS 1881]1883, pp. 461–462; [Bibliography] G–1883–5e.

10. Reference to "On the ellipticity of the earth as deduced from the pendulum experiments," presented 16–19 Nov 1880. [RNA 1883]53.

11. Items in [CS 1877]1880.
(a) Reference to Peirce's pendulum experiments, pp. 17–18.
(b) Appendix No. 15, "A Quincuncial Projection of the Sphere," pp. 191–192, and sketch 25. The same as [Bibliography]G–1879–4 ([AJM]). Reprinted in Thomas Craig, *A Treatise on Projections*, Govt. Printing Office, Washington, 1882, pp. 132, 247.

12. Letter to M. Faye concerning Peirce's gravity work, [International Geodetic Conference, Munich, 1880]1881, pp. 30–32; repeated on pp. 84–86. See pp. 43, 96, and Appendix IIa, pp. 5–8, for references to Peirce. See also the following references to Peirce's work: [International Geodetic Conference, Rome, 1883]1884, pp. 41, 44–45, 50–52, 59–60, of Appendix VIb; [International Geodetic Comm., Nice, 1887]1888, pp. 1, 2, 15–16, Table IV of Appendix IIa and pp. 1, 3, 15–17, Table IV of Appendix IIf; [International Geodetic Conference, Paris, 1900]1901, Vol. 2, pp. 330–335 of Appendix IX.

c.1880

1. On a Boolean algebra with one constant. [CP] 4.12–20.

2. "One, Two, Three." [CP] 1.353 is from it.

1881

1. Abstract of "A New Computation of the Compression of the Earth, from Pendulum Experiments," presented to the Scientific Association, Feb 1881, [JHUC]1(April 1881)128.

2. Reference to Peirce's comments on O. H. Mitchell's "On Binomial Congruences" at the Mathematical Seminary, March 1881. [JHUC]1 (April 1881)132.

3. Reference to "On the progress of pendulum work," presented 19–22 April 1881. [RNA 1883]53. Cf. [Bibliography]G–1880–6.

4. Reference to "On Relations between Sensations," presented to the Metaphysical Club, April 1881. [JHUC]1 (July 1881)150.

5. "Width of Mr. Rutherfurd's Rulings," *Nature* 24(21 July 1881)262.
"There is a solar spectral line, well suited for precise observation . . . I would propose that this line be adopted as a standard of reference by such observers of wave-lengths as desire to escape the arduous operation of measuring the mean width of their rulings . . ."

6. References to Peirce's courses at Johns Hopkins University for 1881–82. [JHUC]1(July 1881)139, 142; 1(Dec 1881) 157, 159, 160, 161; 1(March 1882)195, 196; 1(July 1882)218, 233, 234; [JHUR 1882]1882, pp. 17, 47, 61.

7. "On the Logic of Number," [AJM]4(1881)85–95. [CP] 3.252–288 with undated revisions.
Reference to "On the logic of number," presented 15–17 Nov 1881. [RNA 1883]54.

8. References to "A Fallacy of Induction," presented to the Scientific Association, Nov 1881. [JHUC]1(Feb 1882)172; Ellery W. Davis, "Charles Peirce at Johns Hopkins," *The Mid-West Quarterly* 2(Oct 1914) 52–53.

9. Reference to Peirce's comments on B. I. Gilman's "Theories of Induction," at the Metaphysical Club, Nov 1881. [JHUC]1(Feb 1882)177.

10. Notes and two addenda to Benjamin Peirce's "Linear Associative Algebra," [AJM]4(1881)97–229. Errata for the notes, *ibid.*, p. iv. The two addenda are: Addendum II, "On the Relative Forms of the Algebras," pp. 221–225; Addendum III, "On the Algebras in which Division is Unambiguous," pp. 225–229. [CP] 3.289–305 contain the two addenda. *Linear Associative Algebra*, including Peirce's notes, was reprinted by van Nostrand, New York, 1882.
"Proof that there are only Three Linear Associative Algebras in which Division is an Unambiguous Process," presented to the Mathematical Seminary, Jan 1881. [JHUC]1(April 1881) 131.

11. Reference to Peirce's pendulum experiments and work on meter. [CS 1878]1881, p. 18. "The records of the various experiments mentioned in this abstract are contained in twenty-six volumes."

12. Report on Peirce's researches on pendula, using light as a standard of length, and projections, with quotations from Peirce, [CS 1879]1881, pp. 27–29.

1882

1. *A Brief Description of the Algebra of Relatives*, Baltimore, 7 Jan 1882, 6 pp., with a postscript of 16 Jan 1882. A privately printed brochure; cf. [CP] 3.294, 3.306. [CP] 3.306–322.
Reference to "On the logic of relatives," read 14–17 Nov 1882. [RNA 1883]55.

2. Reference to "J. S. Mill's Logic," presented to the Metaphysical Club, Jan 1882. [JHUC]1(Feb 1882)178.

3. Abstract of "On the Relative Forms of Quaternions," presented to the Mathematical Seminary, Jan 1882, [JHUC]1(Feb 1882)179. [CP] 3.323.

4. Reference to "On a fallacy in induction," presented 18–21 April 1882. [RNA 1883]54. Cf. [Bibliography]G–1881–8.

5. Abstract of remarks on B. I. Gilman's "On Propositions and the Syllogism," both presented to the Metaphysical Club, April 1882; both published in [JHUC]1(Aug 1882)240.

6. References to Peirce's course at Johns Hopkins University for 1882–83. [JHUC]1(July 1882)234; 2(Nov 1882) 18; 2(Dec 1882)39; 2(April 1883)93; [JHUR 1883]1883, p. 35.
* An abstract of one lecture of the course, "Introductory Lecture on the Study of Logic," presented Sept 1882, [JHUC]2(Nov 1882)11–12. [CP] 7.59–76 are from it.

7. "On Irregularities in the Amplitude of Oscillation of Pendulums," *The American Journal of Science* 3rd series 24(Oct 1882)254–255.

8. Abstract of "On a Class of Multiple Algebras," presented to the University Mathematical Society, 18 Oct 1882, with a note of 30 Oct, [JHUC]2(Nov 1882)3–4. [CP] 3.324–327.

9. Brief summary of opening remarks on the object of the Metaphysical Club, presented 14 Nov 1882, [JHUC]2(Dec 1882)38.

10. Reference to "On the determination of the figure of the earth by the variations of gravity," presented 14–17 Nov 1882. [RNA 1883]55. Cf. [Bibliography]G–1880–10.

11. Reference to "On Ptolemy's catalogue of stars," presented 14–17 Nov 1882. [RNA 1883]55. Cf. [Bibliography]G–1879–5b.

12. Reference to Peirce's pendulum observations and comparison of the meter with a wave length of light. [CS 1880]1882, pp. 19–20.

13. References to Peirce's telescopic observations made during 1866–1872. Joseph Winlock and Edward C. Pickering, *Micrometric Measurements*, Part I of Vol. 13 of *Annals of the Astronomical Observatory of Harvard College*, Cambridge, 1882, pp. iv, 19ff., 28ff., 63ff., 86ff., 172ff., 184ff.

270

14. Reference to "Report on the spectrum meter (U. S. Superintendent of Weights and Measures, Report, in press)." [JHUR 1882]1882, p. 112. The publication date is given as 1882 in *Bibliographia Hopkinsiensis*, 1876–1893, Part IV, Physics, p. 18 (volume page 120). The editor has been unable to find such a publication and questions that the report was published.

1883

1. "A Communication from Mr. Peirce," [JHUC]2(April 1883) 86–88. This is Peirce's answer to J. J. Sylvester's "Erratum," *ibid.*, (Feb 1883)46. Sylvester's rebuttal is at *ibid.*, (April 1883)86. See in this connection the footnote reference to Sylvester's comment of *ibid.*, 1(May 1882)203 supplied by Peirce, and Sylvester's comment on Peirce, *ibid.*, 1(Feb 1882) 180. [CP] 3.646–648.

2. References to Peirce's courses at Johns Hopkins University for 1883–84. [JHUC]2(June 1883)119, 136; 3(Nov 1883)27, 28; 3(March 1884)69; 3(June 1884)101, 119; [JHUR 1884]1884, p. 38; [Fisch-Cope] 290–291.

3. Reference to "Reply to Professor Morris on 'Life'," presented to the Metaphysical Club, 13 Nov 1883. [JHUC] 3(Jan 1884)46.

4. "A New Rule for Division in Arithmetic," *Science* 2 (21 Dec 1883) 788–789.

5. Items in [CS 1881]1883.

(a) Reference to Peirce's pendulum observations, p. 26.

(b) Appendix No. 14, "On the Flexure of Pendulum Supports," pp. 359–441. Pages 427–436 contain a translation by Peirce of [Bibliography]G–1877–3 with revisions and notes of 1882. Pages 437–441 contain a reprint of [Bibliography]G–1878–1. Erratum, p. 463. [CP] 7.1–12 are from pp. 359–361.

(c) Appendix No. 15, "On the Deductions of the Ellipticity of the Earth from Pendulum Experiments," pp. 442–456. Cf. [Bibliography]G–1880–10 and G–1882–10.

(d) Appendix No. 16, "On a Method of Observing the Coincidence of Vibration of Two Pendulums," dated 2 Aug 1878 with a note dated 20 Feb 1883, pp. 457–460.

(e) Appendix No. 17, "On the Value of Gravity at Paris," pp. 461–463. Pages 461–462 contain a translation of [Bibliography]G–1880–9.

6. Items in [CS 1882]1883.

(a) References to Peirce's pendulum work, pp. 4, 19, 32–33, 557.

(b) Appendix No. 22, "Report of a Conference on Gravity Determinations, Held at Washington, in May, 1882," pp. 503–516. Contributions by Peirce at pp. 506–508 ("Six Reasons for the Prosecution of Pendulum Experiments"), 508, 509, 512–516, with errata in the quarter sheet between pp. 502–503. Reprinted with some changes and with the additional heading, "Methods and Results," Washington, 1883. [CP] 7.13–20,

"Six Reasons for the Prosecution of Pendulum Experiments," as corrected from a reprint in Widener IC2c.

7. *Studies in Logic, By Members of the Johns Hopkins University* (edited by Peirce), Little, Brown and Company, Boston, 1883, vi + 203 pp.; also published by University Press, John Wilson and Son, Cambridge (copyright 1883 by C. S. Peirce). The following are by Peirce.

(a) "Preface," pp. iii–vi. Reprinted in [JHUC]2(Dec 1882)34 with slight differences.

* (b) "A Theory of Probable Inference," pp. 126–181; two maps between pp. 178–179. [CP] 2.694–754 with the omission of maps and the addition of changes from Peirce's own copy. Cf. [CP] 2.752 with [Bibliography]G–1872–3.

(c) Note A: "Extension of the Aristotelian Syllogistic," pp. 182–186. [CP] 2.517–531, as rewritten in 1893 for *Grand Logic*.

(d) Note B: "The Logic of Relatives," pp. 187–203. Cf. [Bibliography] G–1882–1. [CP] 3.328–358 with a marginal note and indications of the revisions of 1893 for *Grand Logic*.

8. References to two lectures, "The Observational Element in Mathematics," and "The *a priori* Element in Physics," presented in a pedagogical series given 1883–84. [JHUC]3(Jan 1884)32 and 3(June 1884)119.

1884

1. References to "On the Mode of Representing Negative Quantity in the Logic of Relatives," presented to the Mathematical Society 16 Jan 1884. [JHUC]3(March 1884)70 and 3(June 1884)102.

2. Reference to "Design and Chance," presented to the Metaphysical Club, 17 Jan 1884. [JHUC]3(March 1884)70.

3. Reference to "The Logic of Religion," presented to the Metaphysical Club, 13 May 1884. [JHUC]3(July 1884)138.

4. Reference to "On Gravitation Survey," presented 14–17 Oct 1884. [RNA 1884]12.

5. Reference to "On the Algebra of Logic," presented 14–17 Oct 1884. [RNA 1884]13.

6. "The numerical measure of the success of predictions," a letter to the Editor, *Science* 4(14 Nov 1884) 453–454.

7. Reference to "On 'The Magnet' a fourteenth century manuscript of Petrus Peregrinus," presented to the Metaphysical Club, 18 Nov 1884. [JHUC]4(Dec 1884)28. Cf. [Bibliography]G–c.1893–4.

8. "The 'Old Stone Mill' at Newport," *Science* 4(5 Dec 1884) 512–514.

9. Items in [CS 1883]1884.

(a) References to Peirce's pendulum work, and determination of longitude, pp. 27, 36–37, 41–42, 42. Cf. p. 97.

(b) Appendix No. 19, "Determinations of Gravity at Allegheny, Ebensburgh, and York, Pa., in 1879 and 1880," pp. 473–487. Apparently this is the paper promised under the title, "Experimental Researches on the

Force of Gravity," [Bibliography]G–1883–6a, p. 557. Reprinted with the heading, *Methods and Results, Determinations of Gravity at Stations in Pennsylvania*, Govt. Printing Office, Washington, 1884, 58 pp. Pages 1–15 are identical with pp. 473–487 of the appendix (except for a number omitted on p. 3); pp. 16–58 contain tables of data not included in the main report.

10. Reference to "On Minimum Differences of Sensibility," (with J. Jastrow), presented 14–17 Oct 1884. [RNA 1884]12. Published under title, "On Small Differences of Sensation," (with J. Jastrow), *Memoirs of the National Academy of Sciences* 3, Part I(1884)73–83. Cf. [CP] 7.21n1 for references to statements by Jastrow about this article. [CP] 7.21–35 with corrections from a reprint in Widener IC1a.

11. Reference to a paper on pendulum experiments, presented to the American Metrological Society, 30 Dec 1884. *Proceedings of the American Metrological Society* 5(Dec 1884) 46. See also pp. 47–48. See further [CS 1885]1886, p. 38.

1885

1. Peirce's testimony concerning the office of weights and measures, presented 24 Jan 1885, *Testimony before the Joint Commission to Consider the Present Organizations of the Signal Service, Geological Survey, Coast and Geodetic Survey, . . .* 49th Congress, 1st Session, Mis. Doc. No. 82, Govt. Printing Office, Washington, 1886, pp. 370–378. See pp. 839 and 852 for references to Peirce's expenditures.

2. (a) "The Coast Survey Investigation," *New York Evening Post* (14 Aug 1885)3:3. Cf. next item.

(b) A signed note concerning Peirce's work for the Coast Survey, *Science* 6(21 Aug 1885)158.

3. "On the Algebra of Logic: A Contribution to the Philosophy of Notation," [AJM]7(1885)180–202. Cf. [Bibliography]G–1880–8 of which this item may have been intended as a continuation. Cf. [Bibliography] G–1884–5. [CP] 3.359–403, except 396n† (p. 230), with an undated marginal note, 384n1. [CP] 3.403A–403M (c.1885) are a note on the article.

4. Items in [CS 1884]1885.

(a) References to Peirce's pendulum work and comparisons of standards in Europe and in the United States, pp. 40, 80, 81, 89, 93; cf. p. 2. Page 81 contains a quotation from Peirce on the ratio of the meter to the yard.

(b) A letter and a statement by Peirce concerning corrections to the thermometers of the Kater pendulum apparatus, Appendix No. 14, pp. 442–443.

(c) Appendix No. 15, "On the Use of the Noddy for Measuring the Amplitude of Swaying in a Pendulum Support," pp. 475–482, with corrections on a half-sheet inserted between pp. 474 and 475.

(d) Appendix No. 16, "Note on the Effect of the Flexure of a Pendulum upon its Period of Oscillation," pp. 483–485, with corrections on a half-sheet inserted between pp. 474 and 475. Printed separately with the title, *Methods and Results, Gravity Research, Effect of the Flexure . . .* , Govt. Printing Office, Washington, 1885.

c.1885

1. "One, Two, Three: Fundamental Categories of Thought and of Nature." [CP] 1.369–372, 1.376–378 are from it.

2. An unpublished, uncompleted review of T. K. Abbott's translation of Kant's *Introduction to Logic*, 1885. [CP] 1.35.

3. An unpublished, incomplete manuscript of a review of Josiah Royce's *The Religious Aspect of Philosophy* (1885), Houghton Library. [CP] 8.39–54.

1886

1. Reference to "Review of Paper on Color Contrast," presented 20–23 April 1886. *Proceedings of the National Academy of Sciences*, Vol. 1, Part 3(1895)269.

2. Items in [CS 1885]1886.

(a) References to Peirce's gravity work and experimental researches, pp. 37–38, 46, 83, 84; cf. p. 99.

(b) Appendix No. 15, "Note on a Device for Abbreviating Time Reductions," pp. 503–508.

(c) Appendix No. 16, "On the Influence of a Noddy on the Period of a Pendulum," pp. 509–510.

(d) Appendix No. 17, "On the Effect of Unequal Temperature upon a Reversible Pendulum," pp. 511–512.

1887

1. "Science and Immortality," *The Christian Register* 66 (7 April 1887) 214. The journal, *ibid.*, p. 210, had solicited "the opinions of some of the most prominent scientific men in this country. . ." The above was Peirce's contribution. Reprinted in *Science and Immortality* (The Christian Register Symposium, Revised and Enlarged, edited by S. J. Barrows), George H. Ellis, Boston, 1887, with revisions. [CP] 6.548–556, as in *Science and Immortality*.

† 2. "Logical Machines," *The American Journal of Psychology* 1(Nov 1887)165–170.

† 3. "Criticism on 'Phantasms of the Living,' An Examination of an Argument of Messrs. Gurney, Myers, and Podmore," *Proceedings of the American Society for Psychical Research* 1(Dec 1887)150–157. "Mr. Peirce's Rejoinder," *ibid.*, pp. 180–215. Replies by the authors are (1) Edmund Gurney, "Remarks on Professor Peirce's Paper," *ibid.*, pp. 157–179; (2) Edmund Gurney, "Remarks on Mr. Peirce's Rejoinder," *ibid.*,

(March 1889)286–300; (3) Frederic W. H. Myers, "Postscript to Mr. Gurney's Reply to Professor Peirce," *ibid.*, pp. 300–301. Cf. [Bibliography]N–1894–14 and N–1897–2; also see [CP] 6.549, 7.597n3.

4. References to Peirce's pendulum experiments. [CS 1886]1887, pp. 41, 49, 85, 86, 99, 100, 103. (On pp. 135 and 137 are references to records and books turned in to the office by Peirce.)

1888

1. Items in Adolphus W. Greely, *Report on the Proceedings of the United States Expedition to Lady Franklin Bay, Grinnell Land*, 2 vols., Govt. Printing Office, Washington, 1888. Cf. pp. 14–15, 50, 61, 104, 107 of Vol. 1 and pp. 716–729 and chart opposite p. 724 of Vol. 2. (See further Adolphus W. Greely, *Three Years of Arctic Service*, 2 vols., Charles Scribners Sons, New York, 1886; pp. xii, 130–132, 180 of Vol. 1; pp. 67–68, 135–136 of Vol. 2.)

(a) "Pendulum Observations," Vol. 2, pp. 701–714.

(b) An explanatory note, half-sheet opposite p. 714 of Vol. 2, replying to Greely's comments on (a) above, Vol. 2, p. 715.

c.1888

1. *Proceedings of the Assay Commisison of 1888; also, Laws of the United States Relating to the Annual Assay, and Rules for the Organization and Government of the Board of Assay Commissioners*, Treasury Department, Document No. 1089, Director of the Mint, 25 pp. (There are copies in Houghton Library.) Peirce was designated by Grover Cleveland to be one of several "Commissioners to test and examine the weight and fineness of the coins reserved at the several mints during the year 1887" (p. 3). "Report of the Committee on Weighing," pp. 8–12, "Report of the Committee on Counting," pp. 12–13, and the general report, signed at p. 16, are signed by Peirce and others.

1889

1. Reference to "On Sensations of Color," presented 16–19 April 1889. [RNA 1889]6.

2. Reference to "On Determinations of Gravity," presented 16–19 April 1889. [RNA 1889]6.

3. Contributions to *The Century Dictionary and Cyclopedia*; first edition, 6 vols., The Century Co., New York, 1889–1891. Peirce is listed in front as a contributor, but the entries are unsigned. Information concerning his contributions is given in the dictionary, and further information is given at [CP] 1.106, 1.209, 1.559n, 3.416, 3.427 (cf. [Bibliography]N–1902–2, p. 179), 6.38n, 6.51n, 6.164n*, 6.211n, 6.592, 6.618, *The Monist* 3:80, [Fisch] ftn.64, [Fisch-Cope] 278, and Peirce's personal interleaved copy of the dictionary (in 24 parts) in Houghton Library, with indications by him of what definitions he wrote.

The following published contributions are reprinted in *Collected Papers*: Continuous, 6.164 (cf. below); Method or doctrine of limits, 4.118n1; Solid (1890–91), 6.241n1; Syntheme (1891), 3.396n†.

The following notes from Peirce's personal copy are reprinted in *Collected Papers*: on pragmatism (c.1902), 5.13n1; on the continuum, 6.165–168. (6.164n* assigns a date of 1903 to 6.165–167 and does not identify 6.168. The dating in Peirce's copy is not clear, but it seems to the editor that "Sept. 18, 1903" applies only to 6.168 and not to 6.165–167.)

In *The Century Dictionary Supplement*, 2 vols., 1909 (republished with revisions and additions in the 1911 edition of the complete dictionary), the definition of "phenoscopy" is signed by Peirce. Cf. "firstness," "secondness," "thirdness," "phenomenology (Caenopythagorean phenomenology)," "phaneron," and "pragmaticism" in the supplement.

4. Reference to Peirce's pendulum experiments. [CS 1887] 1889, pp. 116–117; cf. p. 88.

1890

1. References to Peirce's work. [CS 1889]1890, pp. 100 and 179.

c.1890

*1. *A Guess at the Riddle.* [CP] 1.354–368, 1.373–375, 1.379–416. [CP] 1.1–2 are from an alternative version of Sec. 1 (c.1898); see [CP] 1.355n†. According to [CP] I, this uncompleted work was to have nine sections: Sec. 2, 8, 9 were unwritten; Sec. 3 only partly written; pages of Sec. 4 are missing.

2. "Notes on the Question of the Existence of an External World." [CP] 1.37–38. [CP] 1.36 and 1.39 are from fragmentary alternative mss. of the same date. Cf. [CP] 1.35n*.

1891

* 1. *The Monist* series of 1891–1893 on metaphysics with a reply to a criticism. See [CP] 5.436 for a reference to an additional article on "the principle of continuity" planned for this series; cf. [CP] 6.239 and 6.242.

(a) "The Architecture of Theories," 1(Jan 1891) 161–176. [CP] 6.7–34.

(b) "The Doctrine of Necessity Examined," 2(April 1892)321–337. [CP] 6.35–65 with two minor corrections ([CP] 6.63) from "Reply to the Necessitarians," (f) below.

(c) "The Law of Mind," 2(July 1892)533–559. [CP] 6.102–163.

(d) "Man's Glassy Essence," 3(Oct 1892)1–22. [CP] 6.238–271, except 241n1.

(e) "Evolutionary Love," 3(Jan 1893)176–200. [CP] 6.287–317.

(f) "Reply to the Necessitarians. Rejoinder to Dr. Carus," 3(July 1893)526–570. [CP] 6.588–618. This is a reply to the following two articles by Paul Carus, which criticize mainly (b) above: (1) "Mr.

Charles S. Peirce's Onslaught on the Doctrine of Necessity," 2(July 1892)560–582; (2) "The Idea of Necessity, Its Basis and its Scope," 3(Oct 1892)68–96. Carus replied to Peirce in "The Founder of Tychism, His Methods, Philosophy, and Criticisms, In Reply to Mr. Charles S. Peirce," 3(July 1893) 571–622. This contains a quotation from a letter from Peirce, p. 571. Cf. the following two items by Carus: (1) "The Criterion of Truth," 1(Jan 1891)229–244; (2) "Mr. Charles S. Peirce on Necessity," 2(April 1892)442.

2. Reference to "Astronomical Methods of Determining the Curvature of Space," presented 10–12 Nov 1891. [RNA 1891] 16.

3. Reference to Peirce's gravity research. [CS 1890]1891, p. 104.

c.1891

1. "Questions on William James's Principles of Psychology," Widener IC1a. [CP] 8.72–90 are from it. Cf. [Perry] II, 105–108, where this manuscript is quoted in part.

1892

1. *The Open Court* series of 1892 on the methods of reasoning. See the announcement and the advertisement at 6(1 Sept 1892)3374.
 (a) "Pythagorics," 6(8 Sept 1892)3375–3377.
 (b) "The Critic of Arguments." "I. Exact Thinking," 6(22 Sept 1892) 3391–3394. [CP] 3.404–414. "II. The Reader is Introduced to Relatives," 6(13 Oct 1892)3415–3418. [CP] 3.415–424. Only two papers were published, but more were planned; see [CP] 3.422. [CP] 4.187n1 is from "The Critic of Arguments," III (1892). It seems likely that this is from a third paper in this series.

2. "Dmesis," *The Open Court* 6(29 Sept 1892)3399–3402.

3. Reference to Peirce's gravity research. [CS 1891] 1892, Part I, p. 97.

4. Reference to twelve lectures delivered by Peirce on "The History of Science," at the Lowell Institute, 1892–1893. Harriette Knight Smith, *The History of the Lowell Institute*, 1898, p. 88. [CP] 7.267–275, except 267n8, are the concluding remarks (1893) and one quotation in [CP] 7.267n8 is from Lecture V (c.1892), both in Widener IC1b, of a series which very probably is this Lowell Institute series. See [CP] 7.267n7.

c.1892

1. Two passages on Hegel from separate fragments.
 (a) [CP] 1.40.
 (b) [CP] 1.41–42.

2. "Immortality in the Light of Synechism," Widener IB3. [CP] 7.565–578.

1893

1. "The Marriage of Religion and Science," *The Open Court* 7(16 Feb 1893)3559–3560. [CP] 6.428–434.

2. "Cogito Ergo Sum," a letter to the Editor, *The Open Court* 7(15 June 1893)3702.

3. "What is Christian Faith?" *The Open Court* 7(27 July 1893)3743–3745. [CP] 6.435–448.

4. Review of Arthur Lévy's *Napoléon Intime*, unsigned, *The Independent* 45(21 Dec 1893)1725–1726 and (28 Dec 1893)1760. Identification based on Harvard mss.

* 5. *Grand Logic*, or, an alternative title, *How to Reason: A Critick of Arguments*, a completed but unpublished book. The quotations below are from two drafts of an advertisement written by Peirce, c.1893, Widener IB2–1. The organization of the book given further below is a reconstruction from data found in a table of contents (c.1893) and ms. at Widener IB2–1 (where the material printed in [CP] VII is located) and from data in *Collected Papers* I–VI.

"This work is distinguished from other logics, 1st, by the way it makes the nature of inquiry into real facts illuminate that of demonstration from fixed assumptions, and *vice versa*; 2nd, by drawing, not from any 'cannot-help-thinking,' but from an accurate analysis of inference, as its unavoidable consequences, rules that resolve the most obstinate logical doubts; and 3rd, by accepting (here is the upshot of the whole discussion) the principle of continuity for *lucerna pedibus* in all the dark paths of scientific and philosophical exploration." [There follows a description of the contents; cf. the table of contents below.]

"But if, however, the field of possibility is not continuous, absolutely exact conclusions may be warranted. For this reason (among others), it is proper to consider the evidences for the reality of continuity. That we have a perfectly consistent *conception* of continuity has been shown. But what evidence is there that it is real? The author maintains that it is given in direct presentation. In this he is sustained by the psychological studies of Professor James; and he adds sundry arguments of his own. Besides, even if continuity is not given intuitively, its reality answers the logical conditions of a good theory.

"The reality of continuity once admitted, the next question is what are we to regard as continuous and what as discontinuous? It is shown that to say that anything is continuous is to leave possibilities open which are closed by asserting that it is discontinuous. Accordingly a regulative principle of logic requires us to hold anything as continuous until it is proved discontinuous. But absolute discontinuity cannot be proved to be real, nor can any good reason for believing it real be alleged. We thus reach the conclusion that as a regulative principle, at least, ultimate continuity ought to be presumed everywhere.

"The reality of continuity appears most clearly in reference to mental phenomena; and it is shown that every general concept is, in reference to its individuals, strictly a continuum. This (though asserted by Kant and others) did not appear quite evident as long as the doctrine of generals was restricted to non-relative terms. But in the light of the logic of relatives, the general is seen to be precisely the continuous. Therefore, the doctrine of the reality of continuity is simply that doctrine the scholastics called realism; and though as they held it, it was a crude notion enough, yet as Dr. F. E. Abbot has proved, in another dress it is the doctrine of all modern science.

"This point reached, a massive foundation has been laid for a philosophy which shall not take for its first axiom a principle utterly irreconcilable with all spiritual truth, and with some lighter matters the volume is brought to a close."

The contents included the following chapters of which some had been published earlier, and some were revised in 1893. Cf. [CP] 4.88n* and 6.278n1.

Book I, Of Reasoning in General. Introduction, The Association of Ideas; [CP] 7.388–450 (c.1893), except 392n7, are from it.

Division I, Reasoning Formally Studied. Chapter I, The Categories; [CP] 1.545–559, except 549n1; [Bibliography] G–1867–1c. Chapter II, Signs. (A manuscript in Widener IB2–1, with a heading, "The Art of Reasoning," and a title, "Ch. 2. What is a Sign?" is probably chapter two of a draft of the *Grand Logic*. [CP] 2.281, 2.285, 2.297–302 are from this manuscript, c.1895.)

Division II, Transcendental Logic. Chapter III, The Materialistic Aspect of Reasoning; [CP] 6.278–286. Chapter IV, What is the Use of Consciousness?; [CP] 7.559–564 (c.1893). Chapter V, The Fixation of Belief; [CP] 5.358–387; [Bibliography]G–1877–5a.

Division III, Reasoning Substantially Studied. Chapter VI, The Essence of Reasoning; [CP] 4.21–52 and 7.463–467 are from one draft, in that order; [CP] 4.53–79 are from an alternative draft with deletions.

Book II, Demonstrative Reasoning. Introduction, Chapter VII, Analysis of Propositions.

Division I, Stecheology. Part 1, Non Relative. Chapter VIII, The Algebra of the Copula. Chapter IX, The Aristotelian Syllogistic; [CP] 2.445–460 with deletions. Chapter X, Extension of the Aristotelian Syllogistic; [CP] 2.532–535 with deletions. Chapter XI, The Boolian Calculus. Part 2, Relative. Chapter XII, The Logic of Relatives. Chapter XIII, Simplification for Dual Relatives. (According to [CP] 2.517n* and 3.345n† this chapter contained rewritten versions of [Bibliography] G–1883–7c and 7d, [CP] 2.517–531 and 3.328–358, respectively.) Chapter XIV, Second Intentional Logic; [CP] 4.80–84.

Division II, Methodology. Chapter XV, Breadth and Depth; [CP] 2.391–426; [Bibliography]G–1867–1e. ("Terminology," [CP] 2.427–430, [Bibliography]G–1893–7, is a supplement to it.) Chapter XVI, Clearness of Ideas; [CP] 5.388–410; [Bibliography]G–1877–5b.

Book III, Quantitative Logic. Chapter XVII, Logic of Quantity; [CP] 4.85–152 with deletions and a marginal note. Chapter XVIII, The Doctrine of Chances; [CP] 2.645–660; [Bibliography]G–1877–5c. Chapter XIX, Induction etc.

Appendix I, Recreations and Exercises. Glossarial Index.

*6. *Search for a Method*, an unpublished book. The contents included the following "Essays," all of which had been published earlier and some of which have revisions of 1893.

I. On the Natural Classification of Arguments. [CP] 2.461–516; [Bibliography]G–1867–1b.

II. On a New List of Categories. [CP] 1.545–559, except 549n1; [Bibliography]G–1867–1c.

III. Upon Logical Comprehension and Extension. [CP]2.391–426; [Bibliography]G–1867–1e. ("Terminology," [CP] 2.427–430, [Bibliography]G–1893–7, is a supplement to it.)

Essays IV, V, and VI consisted of the series on intuitive knowledge in the original order: [CP] 5.213–263, 5.264–317, 5.318–357; [Bibliography]G–1868–2a, 2b, 2c.

Essays VII and IX through XIII consisted of the series on the logic of science in the original order: [CP] 5.358–387, 5.388–410, 2.645–660, 2.669–693, 6.395–427, 2.619–644; [Bibliography] G–1877–5a through 5f. (This identification of Essay XII is suggested by Manley Thompson, *The Pragmatic Philosophy of C. S. Peirce*, p. 279; it is not made in [CP].)

XIV. A Theory of Probable Inference. [CP] 2.694–754; [Bibliography]G–1883–7b.

7. "Terminology," a supplement to [Bibliography]G–1867–1e. [CP] 2.427–430.

c.1893

1. A fragment on axioms. [CP] 1.130–132.

2. "The Connection between Mind and Matter." [CP] 6.272–277.

3. Chapter I, "Of Reasoning in general," from "Short Logic," Widener IB2–10. No further chapters have been found. [CP] 2.282, 2.286–291, 2.295–296 (with 2.295 continuing 2.291), 2.435–443, 7.555–558 (with 7.555 continuing 2.443), and 2.444 are from it in that order; cf. [CP] 7.553n17.

4. Prospectus of *The Treatise of Petrus Peregrinus on the Lodestone*, 16 pp. There is a copy in Widener, catalogued under Phys. 5.1. Cf. [Bibliography]N–1894–1 and N–1894–4. The prospectus is dated c.1893 on the basis of the items in *The Nation* and of information in Harvard mss. Peirce's edition of Peregrinus was never published as far as can be discovered. [CP] 7.392n7 contains a footnote from p. 16. A quotation from pp. 1–6 of the prospectus is given below because it well illustrates Peirce's aim in studying the history of science, to gain an understanding of the nature of scientific method.

"The brief treatise on the lodestone by Petrus Peregrinus, dated 1269, occupies a unique position in the history of the human mind, being without exception the earliest work of experimental science that has come down to us. Nor can we learn that anything of this sort had been written earlier. No doubt experiments had been made earlier. The medical papyrus contains a prescription said to have been given for the mother of King Thoth; and something had been accomplished in optics. But no ancient experiments can be considered as scientific, for several reasons. First, they were not made for the simple purpose of learning the truth, but with a *parti pris*, except where they were merely accidental. In the second place, in no single case was a piece of apparatus devised by any person before Peregrinus — at least there is no evidence of such a thing — for the purpose of obtaining an experimental answer to a question. Now, with instruments already existing we may make casual observations; but unless they are much more complicated than those of the ancients were, we can hardly make with them genuine experiments. At any rate, the total absence of experiments made with apparatus devised for the purpose, betrays a complete absence of the spirit of experimental inquiry. The quintessence of science, however, consists precisely in, and its success depends upon, the spirit with which it is prosecuted. In the third place, no law or general proposition of ancient science was consciously based upon experiment. In the fourth place, no ancient experiments were ever conducted in one connected series, each one after the first based on the truth the previous one had established. The work of Petrus is absolutely the first that fulfils a single one of the conditions here indicated; and it fulfils them all. The sole direct purpose of his experiments was evidently the analysis of the properties of the lodestone and the ascertainment of their laws. His experiments are made with several distinct pieces of apparatus constructed and devised for no other end. Upon his experiments he bases a general theory of the lodestone, which, though in part not correct, yet remains in error only because, as he virtually confesses, he had not sufficient mechanical skill to construct an apparatus described by him and proposed for the purpose of making the crucial experiment which, had it been made, would have corrected his error. His experiments all do follow in sequence, each reposing on the result of the one that went before. Not only does Peregrinus in practice follow these four conditions, but he is fully alive to the importance of each one of them. Thus, on the whole, this little book must be considered as one of the most important monuments of human progress. The experimentation of Gilbert, who has often been considered as the founder of magnetical science, is in large part downright plagiarism upon Peregrinus; and though his real merits are far from inconsiderable, yet he is not at all upon the plane of importance of the earlier writer, even without making allowance for the more advanced state of civilization of his century.

"Time was when educated people could imagine that the idea of inductive science could spring full grown from the brain of Francis Bacon; but in our days we have learned better the natural course of development of ideas. Thoughts of that comprehensive kind do not start up in the mushroom-beds of individual brains. They require the broader fields of societies; and generations must pass by before they can acquire any maturity of strength. There is plenty of testimony both of Peregrinus

281

and of his pupil, Roger Bacon, from which we may securely infer that they were acquainted with older physicists, although those elders may perhaps not have committed their experiments to writing. But whether it will be possible ever to make out with any plausibility the earlier history of experimental science, previous and prelusive to the work of Peregrinus, time alone can show. Certain it is that the early school of physicists, of which Peregrinus and Roger Bacon remain for us the only representatives, was shortly overwhelmed by the rising tide of theology, between which on the one side and popular superstition on the other, no place was left for it. Was the flame of scientific inquiry, then, utterly quenched, or did a spark remain alive from which, in historical fact, the sacred fire was rekindled in the sixteenth century? To the solution of this problem the introduction of this volume will offer some contributions.

"The text of the treatise here presented is substantially that of a contemporary MS. in the Paris Library.* [Footnote: "*MSS. latins 7378."] All deviations from that authority are noted. Three other important texts have, however, been carefully collated, together with several that are incomplete. The work, though much written about, has, it is believed, never been printed, except at Augsburg in 1558, and that edition is of the extremest rarity. True, Libri, in his valuable work on the history of the mathematical sciences in Italy, did attempt a transcription of the very MS. here used; but, owing to its extreme illegibility, though he invoked the aid of the most expert paleographers, he has hardly been able to make perfect sense out of a single sentence, not to speak of places where his text suggests a wrong meaning, nor of innumerable lesser errors."

5. *The Principles of Philosophy*: or, *Logic, Physics, and Psychics, considered as a unity, in the Light of the Nineteenth Century*, a planned and partly executed work of twelve volumes. [CP] 1.176–179 (c.1896) is apparently a foreword.

The following is almost all of a printed prospectus in Widener VA². Cf. [Bibliography]N–1894–1 on the basis of which this is dated c.1893.

"This philosophy, the elaboration of which has been the chief labor of the author for thirty years, is of the nature of a Working Hypothesis for use in all branches of experiential inquiry. Unmistakable consequences can be deduced from it, whose truth is not yet known but can be ascertained by observation, so as to put the theory to the test. It is thus at once a philosophy and a scientific explanation of observed facts.

"The actual comparison of its consequences with observation can by Mr. Peirce himself only be commenced. He will, however, carry the operation far enough to convince the most skeptical of its entire feasibility.

"Both logically and dynamically the whole doctrine develops out of the *desire to know*, or philosophia, which carries with it the confession that we do not know already. In those branches of knowledge that are the most perfect no self-respecting man puts forth a statement without affixing to it his estimate of its *probable error*, while in branches where arbitrary opinion is uncurbed authors are unwilling to confess that the smallest doubt hangs over their conclusions. Nothing can be more com-

pletely contrary to a philosophy the fruit of a scientific life than infallibilism, whether arrayed in its old ecclesiastical trappings, or under its recent
'scientistic' disguise. Mr. Peirce will, therefore, not be understood himself
to make any such pretensions. He hopes some power of truth is in his
theory, because it has been conceived in a spirit of utter surrender to the
force majeure of Experience, or the Course of Life; and it is through
such self-abnegation that all Power comes. But how far this hope is fulfilled must be determined by the success or failure of such *predictions*
as are deducible from the theory.

"The principles supported by Mr. Peirce bear a close affinity with
those of Hegel; perhaps are what Hegel's might have been had he been
educated in a physical laboratory instead of in a theological seminary.
Thus, Mr. Peirce acknowledges an objective logic (though its movement differs from the Hegelian dialectic), and like Hegel endeavors
to assimilate truth got from many a looted system.

"The entelechy and soul of the work, from which every part of its
contents manifestly flows, is the *principle of continuity*, which has been
the guiding star of exact science from the beginning, but of which novel
and unexpected applications are now made. The logical ground of this
principle is examined and its precise formula established.

"The principle of continuity leads directly to Evolutionism, and naturally to a hearty acceptance of many of the conclusions of Spencer,
Fiske, and others. Only, Matter, Space, and Energy will not be assumed
eternal, since their properties are mathematically explicable as products
of an evolution from a primeval (and infinitely long past) chaos of un-
personalized feeling. This modified doctrine, so much in harmony with
the general spirit of evolutionism, quite knocks the ground from under
both materialism and necessitarianism.

"In religion, the new philosophy would teach us to await and expect
definite and tangible facts of experience, actually undergone. While details of dogma are beyond its province, it would favor rather old-fashioned
Christianity, than any attempt to make a christianoidal metaphysics serve
in lieu of religion. Still less could it accept a theology of phrases which
should label an abstraction 'God' and influence with posterity 'A future
life.' It distinctly upholds a *Christian Sentimentalism*, as contra-dis-
tinguished from a gospel of salvation through intelligent greed."

The following is all but the title of a printed prospectus in Widener,
catalogued under Phys. 5.1.

"Vol. I. (Nearly ready.) *Review of the Leading Ideas of the Nineteenth Century*. Defines the essential ideas involved in and sentiments
fostered by political economy, machinery and modern inventions, labor
unions, socialism, scientific associations, centennials, nationalism, emi-
gration, various forms of idealism, Hegel's objective logic, the historical
method, modern mathematics and its imaginaries, the theory of heat and
conservation of energy, statistical methods of research, the kinetical theory
of gases, Darwinism, etc. It is believed that these analyses will be found
valuable, apart from the conclusions drawn from them. Next, a definite
affinity is traced between all these ideas, and is shown to lie in the prin-

283

ciple of *continuity*. The idea of continuity traced through the history of the Human Mind, and shown to be the great idea which has been working itself out. (The author's papers in the *North American Review* are here used.) Modern science due to it exclusively. A great part, if not all, of evolution in all departments, and at all times, probably to be ascribed to the action of this principle. The urgent needs of our time may, we have strong reason to hope, be met by the further application of it. Sketch of a thoroughgoing philosophy of continuity. The great opponent of this philosophy has been in history, and is in logic, infallibilism, whether in its milder ecclesiastical form, or in its more dire scientist and materialistic apparitions.

"Vol. II. (Substantially ready.) *Theory of Demonstrative Reasoning.* The first part of this volume contains a plain, elementary account of formal logic, ordinary and relative. It has been very carefully adapted to the use of young persons of mediocre capacities, and has been subjected to experimental tests with success. This is followed by more intricate developments for persons having a turn for such matters, and others may skip this part. (The author's papers in the *Memoirs of the American Academy* and in the *Journal of Mathematics* are here made use of.) Deductive reasoning having thus been accurately described and the working of it taught, the third part of the volume makes a careful analysis of it, and shows what the natures of its different ingredients are. The principle of continuity is shown to be the crown of the logic of relatives.

"Vol. III. *The Philosophy of Probability.* After an analysis of the nature of probability, the principles of the calculus are set forth. The doctrine of inverse probabilities refuted. The theory of inductive and hypothetic inference set forth nearly as in the Johns Hopkins 'Studies in Logic,' but the position there taken is reinforced with powerful new arguments. Mr. Peirce's rules for inductive reasoning are the strictest that have been advocated. New illustrations are given to show the absurdly bad reasoning into which those fall who follow looser rules. A few inferences admitted by Mr. Peirce as valid are disallowed by some writers. Their inconsistency in this shown, and that those writers simply maintain an unreasonable skepticism concerning some questions which they do not extend to others quite analogous.

"Vol. IV. *Plato's World: An Elucidation of the Ideas of Modern Mathematics.* A lucid analysis of the logic and conceptions of the calculus, imaginaries, the theory of functions, and the non-Euclidean geometry. The conceptions of infinity and continuity are now accurately analyzed. The notion that we cannot reason mathematically about infinity refuted. The doctrine of limits as stated by some authors inadequate to its purpose; as stated by others, really involves reasoning about infinity. It is imposible to assign any reason for the dogma that we cannot reason mathematically about infinity; one might as well say we cannot reason mathematically about imaginaries.

"Vol V. *Scientific Metaphysics.* Begins with the theory of cognition. The nature of reality discussed as in the author's papers in the *Popular Science Monthly*; but the position taken is now set forth more clearly, fully, and in psychological detail. The reality of the external world. Primary and secondary qualities. The evidence of the real existence of continuity. The question of nominalism and realism from the point of view of continuity. Continuity and evolution. Necessitarianism refuted. Further corollaries from the principle of continuity.

"Vol. VI. *Soul and Body*. Begins with an analysis of the law of association, which is somewhat generalized. The question of fatigue and its law. Review of psychological phenomena. The apparent discontinuity of sense-qualities considered. Definition of the soul, following out ideas put forth by the author in the *Journal of Speculative Philosophy*. The 'unity of consciousness' admits of degrees, and is probably in many cases very low. Phenomena of anæsthesia considered. The author's theory of universal evolution, which supposes matter and its laws to be the result of evolution, is now set forth more systematically and argumentatively. Still, it is to be regarded for the present as no more than a working hypothesis. Explanation of the method of reasoning by which a multitude of unmistakable consequences can be rigidly deduced from the hypothesis. A considerable number of these are shown to be true, while none are known to be false. One prediction of a fact hitherto unknown is shown to be supported by observation. Others remain to be tested by future experience, and the theory will have to stand or fall by the result.

"Vol. VII. *Evolutionary Chemistry*. The working out of the consequences of the theory of universal evolution into chemistry. Mendeléeff's law.

"Vol. VIII. *Continuity in the Psychological and Moral Sciences*. Mathematical economics. Precisely similar considerations supposed by utilitarians to determine individual action. But, this being granted, Marshall and Walras's theorem leads to a mathematical demonstration of free will. Refutation of the theory of motives. The true psychology of action expounded.

"Vol. IX. *Studies in Comparative Biography*. The application of mathematical principles in a new way to this study.

"Vol. X. *The Regeneration of the Church*. The philosophy of continuity is peculiar in leading unequivocally to Christian sentiments. But there it stops. This metaphysics is only an appendix to physics; it has nothing positive to say in regard to religion. It does, however, lead to this, that religion can rest only on positive observed facts, and that such facts may prove a sufficient support for it. As it must rest upon positive facts, so it must itself have a positive content. A series of plays upon words will not answer for a religion. This philosophy shows that there is no philosophical objection to the positive dogmas of Christianity; but the question as to their truth lies out of its province.

"Vol. XI. *A Philosophical Encyclopædia*. The philosophy of continuity leads to an objective logic, similar to that of Hegel, and to triadic categories. But the movement seems not to accord with Hegel's dialectic, and consequently the form of the scheme of categories is essentially different. Systematic perfection seems to be for the present neither requisite nor attainable; but something like Hegel's Encyclopædia is proposed.

"Vol. XII. *Index raisonné* of ideas and words.

"Mr. Peirce does not hold himself pledged to follow precisely the above syllabus, which, on the contrary, he expects to modify as the work progresses. He will only promise that he will not depart from this programme except to improve upon it. The work is to be published by subscription at $2.50 per volume. Address: Mr. C. S. Peirce, 'Arisbe,' Milford, Pa."

1894

1. Reference to Peirce at the 7 April 1894 meeting where he exhibited a 1424 arithmetic by Rollandus, and in the discussion of a certain paper proposed the term "galileo" for the c.g.s. unit of acceleration. *Bulletin of the New York Mathematical Society* 3(May 1894)199–200. See *New York Times* 43(8 April 1894)8, column 1, for a report on the first item.

2. Reference to "Rough Notes on geometry, Constitution of real space," presented 24 Nov 1894. *Bulletin of the American Mathematical Society* 1(Dec 1894)77. Cf. [Bibliography]M–1b.

c.1894

1. "The List of Categories: A Second Essay." [CP] 1.300–301, 1.293, 1.303, 1.326–329 are from it in this order. "The List of Categories: A Second Essay, X." [CP] 1.302 is from it.

c.1895

1. "That Categorical and Hypothetical Propositions are one in essence, with some connected matters." [CP] 2.332–339, 2.278–280, 1.564–567 (c.1899), 2.340–356 are from it in this order.

2. "Religion and Politics," apparently a proposed letter to a newspaper. [CP] 6.449–451 are from it.

3. "Thirdness," a fragment. [CP] 1.340–342 are from it.

4. A fragment on telepathy, Houghton Library. [CP] 7.597n3 is from it.

1896

1. Reference to "On the Logic of Quantity," presented 21–24 April 1896. [RNA 1896]9.

† 2. Review of Andrew Dickson White's *A History of the Warfare of Science with Theology in Christendom*, unsigned, *The American Historical Review* 2(Oct 1896)107–113. Identification based on Harvard mss.

3 Reference to "A Graphical Method of Logic," presented 17–18 Nov 1896. [RNA 1896]11.

4. Reference to "Mathematical Infinity," presented 17–18 Nov 1896. [RNA 1896]11.

5. Translation of William Hirsch's *Genius and Degeneration*, D. Appleton and Co., New York, 1896. No translator is given. Identification based on Harvard mss.

* 6. Review in *The Monist*, 1896–1897, of Ernst Schroeder's *Algebra und Logik der Relative*, Part I, Vol. 3, *Vorlesungen über die Algebra der Logik (exakte Logik)*. Cf. [Bibliography]N–1896–3.
 (a) "The Regenerated Logic," 7(Oct 1896)19–40. [CP] 3.425–455.
 (b) "The Logic of Relatives," 7(Jan 1897)161–217. [CP] 3.456–552 with revisions of 1908.

7. Reference to a lecture, "Number: A Study of the Methods of Exact Philosophical Thought," given before the Mathematics Department, Bryn Mawr College, during the year 1896–97. *Annual Report of the President of Bryn Mawr College, 1896–97*, p. 35.

c.1896

1. A fragment on knowledge of God. [CP] 6.492–493 are from it.

* 2. "The Logic of Mathematics; An Attempt to Develop My Categories from Within." First four pages of ms. missing. [CP] 1.417–520.

3. "Lessons of the History of Science." [CP] 1.43–125 are from it.

1897

1. "Multitude and Number," apparently a lecture ([CP] 4.217). [CP] 4.170–226, except 187n1, with deletions.

c.1897

1. A fragment of biographical comments. [CP] 1.3–7.

2. A fragment on Peirce's philosophy. [CP] 1.8–14 are from it.

3. A fragment on semiotics. [CP] 2.227–229, 2.444n1 are from it.

4. "Recreations in Reasoning." [CP] 4.153–169, "A Theory about Quantity," with deletions, are from it.

5. An untitled ms. (or mss.) apparently intended as part of a lecture ([CP] 1.141n, 1.155n). [CP] 1.141–175, on fallibilism, continuity, and evolution, are from it.

1898

* 1. Cambridge lectures. A number of different sets of lectures were prepared. Cf. [Perry]II, 418–421. There are mss. at Widener IB2–10 and IB3.
 The following is from a printed announcement at Widener VB3b. "CAMBRIDGE CONFERENCES, Revised Announcement: Mr. CHARLES SANDERS PEIRCE of Milford, Pennsylvania will give a course of Eight Class Lectures on REASONING AND THE LOGIC OF THINGS, at the rooms of the Cambridge Conferences, Studio House, 168

Brattle Street, on Monday and Thursday Evenings in February and March, 1898, at eight o'clock. The special topics and dates will be as follows:

February 10. Philosophy and the Conduct of Life.
February 14. Types of Reasoning.
February 17. The Logic of Relatives.
February 21. The First Rule of Logic.
February 24. Training in Reasoning.
February 28. Causation and Force.
March 3. Habit.
March 7. The Logic of Continuity.

The course herein outlined will be of unusual interest and value to students and teachers of Philosophy. It is hoped that many will avail themselves of the privilege of attending. . . ."

Selections from a set of eight lectures, originally written for the occasion on which the above lectures were given ([CP] 1.622, 6.212n*), are printed in *Collected Papers*, Volume VI as follows: Lecture 8, "Logic of Events," 6.1–5, 6.214–221 (with 6.214 continuing 6.5), with minor deletions; "Notes for Eight Lectures," 6.222–237 with deletion, cf. 6.222n*; "The Logic of Continuity," an alternative draft of Lecture 8 (6.1n*), 6.185–213 with deletions (cf. 7.514n14).

The following lectures are also associated with this occasion. It is implied at [CP] 6.212n* and elsewhere in [CP] I–VI that they were delivered under the title "Detached Ideas on Vitally Important Topics." Lecture 1. Philosophy and the Conduct of Life. [CP] 1.616–648 are from it. [CP] 1.649–677 are from an alternative version, "On Detached Ideas in general and on Vitally Important Topics as such," with deletions. Lecture 2. Detached Ideas. [CP] 4.1–5 are from it. Cf. [Bibliography] G–c.1898–1. Lecture 3. The First Rule of Logic. [CP] 5.574–589. Cf. [Bibliography] G–c.1899–1. Lecture 4. Causation and Force. [CP] 6.66–81, 7.518–523, 6.82–87 in that order are all but the first paragraph. Cf. [CP] 7.518n16.

The following very probably belong to this series. Lecture 2(?). "Detached Ideas; Induction, Deduction, and Hypothesis." [CP] 7.494n9 (c.1898) is from it. There is also a ms. in Widener IB2–10 entitled "Types of Reasoning," which may be a version of the second lecture. † Lecture 5. Training in Reasoning. A ms. at Widener IB2–10 bears this title, and there is good evidence that it is a draft of the fifth lecture, c.1898. This ms. was published, with deletions and pages missing, under the title, "Training in Reasoning," *The Hound and Horn* 2 (July–Sept 1929) 398–416. Lecture 7. Habit. A ms. at Widener IB3 bears this title, and there is good evidence that it is a draft of this lecture, c.1898. [CP] 7.468–517 are this manuscript.

2. "The Logic of Mathematics in Relation to Education," *Educational Review* 15(March 1898)209–216. (This ends with "to be continued," but no further articles were published in *ibid*.) [CP] 3.553–562. [CP] 3.562A–562I are taken from paginated page proofs of the original article,

apparently not published for lack of space. The proof sheet ends with the note "to be continued," but no further ms. has been found ([CP] 3.562In).

3. Review of *The "Opus Majus" of Roger Bacon* (edited by John Henry Bridges), unsigned, *The American Historical Review* 3(April 1898)526–528. Identification based on Harvard mss.

†4. "Note on the Age of Basil Valentine," *Science* ns 8 (12 Aug 1898)169–176.

c.1898

1. Comments on "On a New List of Categories," from a fragment of a proposed "DI" lecture. [CP] 1.563. Cf. "DI" with the title of [Bibliography]G–1898–1. Cf. [Bibliography]G–1867–1c.

1899

1. Reference to "The map-coloring problem," presented 15 Nov 1899. [RNA 1899]13.

2. "Professor Bunsen," unsigned, *Progressive Age; Gas-Electricity-Water* 17(1 Sept 1899)393–394. Reprinted from the *New York Evening Post*. Probably by Peirce; identification based on Harvard mss.

c.1899

1. "F.R.L." [CP] 1.135–140 are from it. Both the ms. from which [CP] 1.135–140 are taken and the ms. from which 5.574–589 ([Bibliography]G–1898–1, Lecture 3) are taken have "F.R.L." written in the corner of each sheet and there are other similarities.

1900

1. "Infinitesimals," a letter to the Editor, *Science* ns 11 (16 March 1900)430–433. [CP] 3.563–570.

2. Review of *Clark University, 1889–1899, Decennial Celebration, Science* ns 11(20 April 1900)620–622.

3. Review of George A. Coe's *The Spiritual Life* and Frank Thilly's *Introduction to Ethics*, signed "Jordan Brown," *The Bookman* 11(July 1900)491–492. Identification based on Harvard mss. Cf. [Bibliography] G–c.1900–1.

c.1900

1. Review of Frank Thilly's *Introduction to Ethics*, an alternative draft of the review in *The Nation* ([Bibliography]N–1900–20). [CP] 1.589–590 (c.1903).

2. Unpublished review of Josiah Royce's *The World and the Individual*, Vol. 1, Widener IV. [CP] 8.108–116. It is not known whether

or not this draft was intended for *The Nation*; cf. [CP] 8.100–107, [Bibliography]N–1900–15, for a published review. See [Bibliography]N–1902–10 for a review of Vol. 2.

1901

1. "Pearson's Grammar of Science," *The Popular Science Monthly* 58(Jan 1901)296–306. [CP] 8.132–152, except 136n3 and 138n4. [CP] 8.153–156 and 8.136n3 are from a partial draft of this review, c.1900, in Widener IV.

2. Three manuscripts written for Samuel P. Langley on Hume and miracles. See Philip P. Wiener, "The Peirce-Langley Correspondence and Peirce's Manuscript on Hume and the Laws of Nature," *Proceedings of the American Philosophical Society* 91(5 April 1947)201–228.

(a) "The Idea of a Law of Nature among the contemporaries of David Hume and among advanced thinkers of the present day." [CP] 1.133–134 are from it.

(b) "Hume on Miracles." [CP] 6.522–547.

† (c) "Hume on Miracles and Laws of Nature." Langley suggested changes and Peirce finished a revised version under the title, "The Laws of Nature and Hume's Argument Against Miracles." Wiener, *op. cit.*, pp. 212–228, gives the final draft together with deviations from the first draft and Langley's suggestions; see also letters between Peirce and Langley, 1 April 1901 to 6 May 1902, *ibid.*, pp. 205–211, 214.

3. "Campanus," *Science* ns 13(24 May 1901)809–811.

4. Reference to "On the Logic of Research into Ancient History," presented 12–14 Nov 1901. [RNA 1901]16. Cf. [Bibliography]N–1901–16.

* "On the Logic of drawing History from Ancient Documents especially from Testimonies," c.1901, Widener IB2–12. [CP] 7.164–255, except 182n7, are from it. Cf. [CP] 7.164n2.

5. Studies of great men. Cf. the references in [CP] 7.256n1.

† (a) "The Century's Great Men in Science," *Annual Report . . . of the Smithsonian Institution . . . for the Year Ending June 30, 1900*, Govt. Printing Office, Washington, 1901, pp. 693–699. Reprinted from *New York Evening Post* (12 Jan 1901) Sec. IV, "Review of the Nineteenth Century."

(b) On the productiveness of the nineteenth century in great men, c.1900, Widener IC1b. [CP] 7.256–261 are from one ms.; 7.262–266 are from an alternative draft.

* 6. Contributions to *Dictionary of Philosophy and Psychology* (edited by James Mark Baldwin), 3 vols., The Macmillan Co., New York. Vol. I, 1901; Vol. II, 1902; a new edition, with corrections, of Vols. I and II, 1911. The new edition apparently differs from the original only with regard to minor corrections; the introductions, pagination, etc., are the same.

The following information comes from the Editor's Preface, pp. xi–xii. The contributors are not responsible for the recommendations as to foreign equivalents. Joint authorship is indicated by connecting the two sets of initials by a hyphen. A comma between two signatures "as in '(A.B.C., X.Y.Z.)' indicates that the article was writen by A.B.C. and accepted without alteration by X.Y.Z., who thus adds the weight of his authority to it" (p. xii). The following contributions were written by Christine Ladd-Franklin, not by Peirce, though they were accepted by him: Signification (and Application, in logic), in part (see below for a contribution to this article that is by Peirce), Vol. II, p. 528, reprinted at [CP] 2.431–433; and Transposition, Vol. II, p. 713, reprinted at 3.644–645.

Peirce's contributions to the articles constitute in many cases only parts of articles, and sometimes these are not consecutive parts of an article. The references below to his works are given as follows. The term defined is given first, followed by the pagination of Peirce's contribution in the dictionary; if the contribution is joint, this is indicated in parentheses following the page reference. If the contribution is reprinted in *Collected Papers*, the paragraph reference follows a semicolon; if Peirce's contribution was not reprinted in its entirety, this is indicated.

Volume I: Economy (logical principle of), 309. Empirical Logic, 318 (with R. Adamson). Equipollence or -cy, 338. Genus (in logic), 411. Given, 414. Imaging (in logic), 518–519; [CP] 3.609–610. Implicit (in logic), 525–526; [CP] 2.603–604. Inconsistency, 529; [CP] 2.609–611. Independence, 530. Index (in exact logic), 531–532; [CP] 2.305–306. Individual (in logic), 537–538; [CP] 3.611–613. Inference, 542–543. Insolubilia, 554; [CP] 2.618. Intention, 561; [CP] 2.548. Involution, 574; [CP] 3.614–615. Kind, 600–601; [CP] 6.384. Knowledge (in logic), 603; [CP] 5.605–606. Laws of Thought, 641–643, 644; [CP] 2.593–600 (641–643 only).

Volume II: Leading of Proof, 1. Leading Principle, 1–2; [CP] 2.588–589. Lemma, 3. Light of Nature, 6. Limitative, 6–7; [CP] 2.381 (deletion). Logic, 20–23; [CP] 2.203–218 (deletion). Logic (exact), 23–27; [CP] 3.616–625 (deletions). Logical, 27–28; [CP] 2.537-543 (deletions). Logical Diagram (or Graph), 28; [CP] 4.347–349. Logomachy, 30. Major and Minor (in logic), 37. Mark, 43. Material Fallacy, 44; [CP] 2.617. Material Logic, 44–45; [CP] 2.549. Mathematical Logic, 47. Matter and Form, 50–55; [CP] 6.353–363. Maxim (in logic), 55. Method and Methodology, or Methodeutic, 75. Middle term (and Middle), 77; [CP] 2.581. Mixed, 87. Mnemonic Verses and Words (in logic), 87–89; [CP] 2.584. Modality, 89–93; [CP] 2.382–390. Modulus, 94. Modus ponens and Modus tollens, 94. Multitude (in mathematics), 117–118; [CP] 3.626–631. Name (in logic), 127–128. Necessary (in logic), 143. Necessity, 145–146. Negation, 146–147; [CP] 2.378–380 (deletion). Negative, 148; [CP] 2.580 is from it. Nominal, 179. Nomology, 180. Non-A (in logic), 180. Non-contradiction, 181. Non-sequitur, 181; [CP] 2.613. Norm (and Normality), 182. Nota notae, 183; [CP] 2.590–592. Numerical, 190. Observation, 198; [CP] 2.605–606. Obversion, 199; [CP] 2.551. Opposition, 206; [CP] 2.608. Organon, 219; [CP] 2.547 (deletion). P (in logic), 253. Paradox, 258. Paralogism, 259. Parity, 263. Parsimony (law of), 264; [CP] 7.92–93. Partial, 265. Particular, 265–266; [CP] 2.372–373. Particulate, 266. Parva Logicalia,

266. Per accidens, 276. Perseity and Per se, 281–282; [CP] 6.385. Perspicuity, 287. Pertinent, 287; [CP] 2.602. Petitio Principii, 287–288; [CP] 2.614. Philosopheme, 290; [CP] 2.615. Plurality of Causes, 306–307. Poly-, 309. Port Royal Logic, 310. Positive, 311–312. Possibility, Impossibility, and Possible, 313–315; [CP] 6.364–371. Post-predicament, 315. Postulate, 315–316; [CP] 3.632–634. Pragmatic and Pragmatism, 321–322; [CP] 5.1–4. (The contribution to this article by James Mark Baldwin contains on p. 322: "In the words of Peirce (comment on this article): 'Nominalism, up to that of Hegel, looks at reality retrospectively. What all modern philosophy does is to deny that there is any *esse in futuro.*' ") Precise, 323. Precision, 323–324; [CP] 1.549n1 (deletion). Predesignate, 324–325; [CP] 2.788–790. Predicable, 325. Predicament, 325. Predicate, 325–326; [CP] 2.358. Predication, 326–329; [CP] 2.359–361 (deletions). Predicative Proposition, 329. Premise (and Premiss), 330–331; [CP] 2.582–583. Presumption, 337; [CP] 2.791. Presupposition, 338; [CP] 3.635. Prime, 341. Primum cognitum, 341. Principal, 341. Priority (with Prior and Prius), 342–343; [CP] 6.386–389. Privation, 343. Probable Inference, 353–355; [CP] 2.783–787. Problem, 355. Problematic, 355–356. Progressive, 358. Proof, 359; [CP] 2.782. Proposition, 361–362 (with J. M. Baldwin). Protasis, 371. Provisional, 373. Proximate, 373–374; [CP] 6.390–392. Pure (in philosophy), 401–402; [CP] 2.544–546 (deletions). Quality (in grammar and logic), 408–409; [CP] 2.374–377. Quantity (in logic and mathematics), 410–412; [CP] 2.362–366. Ratio, 415. Ratiocination, 415. Rational, 415. Reasoning, 426–428; [CP] 2.773–778. Reductio ad absurdum, 434; [CP] 2.612. Reduction, 435; [CP] 2.585–587. Regular, 439; [CP] 2.601 is from it. Relatives (logic of), 447–450; [CP] 3.636–643 (deletion). Remote, 463. Represent, 464; [CP] 2.273. Representationism, 464–465; [CP] 5.607. Repugnance, 466. Residues (method of), 467–468. Rule, 481 (part with J. M. Baldwin). S (in logic), 483. Saltus, 484; [CP] 2.616 is from it. Scientific Method, 500–503; [CP] 7.79–88. Scope, 503. Secundum quid, 504. Series, 521. Sign, 527–528; [CP] 2.303–304 (deletion). Signification (and Application, in logic), 528–529; [CP] 2.434. Similar (with Similarity, Similitude), 530. Simple, 531–532 (parts with J. M. Baldwin). Singular, 533. Solution, 554. Some (in logic), 555. Sophism, 556. Sorites, 557. Species (and Specific Marks, in logic), 567 (with J. M. Baldwin). Spurious Proposition, 588; [CP] 2.607. State (and condition), 593. Subalternation, 606. Subcontrary, 607. Subject (in logic), 609–610; [CP] 2.357. Sublation, 611. Substitution (in logic), 614–615. Subsumption, 615. Sufficient Reason, 616–617; [CP] 6.393–394 (deletion). Summum Genus, 621. Supposition, 624–625. Syllogism, 628–629, 633–639; [CP] 2.552–554, 2.555–579 (deletions). Symbol, 640; [CP] 2.307 (deletion). Symbolic Logic or Algebra of Logic, 645–650; [CP] 4.372–393. Symbolical, 651. Synechism, 657; [CP] 6.169–173. Synthetic (-al), 658–659. Tautology, 663. Term, 676–677. Testimony, 686 (with J. M. Baldwin). Thema, 691–692; [CP] 2.308. Theorem, 693. Theory, 693–694; [CP] 7.94–96 are from it. Thesis, 695. Tree of Porphyry, 714. Trilemma, 715. Trivium, 716. Truth and Falsity and Error, 718–720; [CP] 5.565–

573. Ultimate, 723–724; [CP] 5.608–609. Uniformity, 727–731; [CP] 6.98–101. Unity (and Plurality), 734–736; [CP] 6.373–380. Universal (and Universality), 737–741; [CP] 2.367–371 (deletions). Universe, 742; [CP] 2.536 (deletions). Vague (in logic), 748. Validity, 748–749; [CP] 2.779–781. Verification, 761–762; [CP] 7.89–91. Virtual, 763–764; [CP) 6.372 (deletion). Whole (and Parts), 814 (with J. M. Baldwin), 814–815; [CP] 6.381, 6.382–383.

7. A draft of a report of the meeting of the National Academy of Sciences in Nov 1901, Widener IV. [CP] 7.162–163 are from it. See [Bibliography]N–1901–16 for the published report of the meeting.

8. A draft of a review of Sidney E. Mezes' *Ethics: Descriptive and Explanatory*, Widener IV. [CP] 8.158n3 is from it. See [CP] 8.157–163, [Bibliography]N–1901–15, for the published review.

9. Review of Henry Stevens's *Thomas Hariot, the Mathematician, the Philosopher, and the Scholar*, *The American Historical Review* 6(April 1901)557–561.

1902

1. Reference to "The Classification of the Sciences," presented 15–17 April 1902. [RNA 1902]13.

2. Reference to "The Postulates of Geometry," presented 15–17 April 1902. [RNA 1902]13.

3. Reference to "The Color System," presented 15–17 April 1902. [RNA 1902]13. Cf. [Bibliography]N–1902–5.

4. A section revised and rewritten by Peirce (pp. 280–286 in the chapter on units and measures) of Thomas J. McCormack's translation of Ernst Mach's *The Science of Mechanics*, Open Court, Chicago, 1902.

5. Translation of J. Marey's "The History of Chronophotography," *Annual Report . . . of the Smithsonian Institution . . . for the Year Ending June 30, 1901*, Govt. Printing Office, Washington, 1902, pp. 317–340. Pages 337–340 may not have been translated by Peirce.

6. Application for a grant from the Carnegie Institution, Widener VB5. [CP] 7.158–161 and 8.176n3 are from it. [CP] 7.158n5 contains a quotation from an alternative draft.

c.1902

1. A fragment on induction. [CP] 2.757n1 is from it.

* 2. *Minute Logic*, an uncompleted book. Ch. 1–3 and part of Ch. 4 were finished, and further chapters were planned ([CP] 1.274, 1.277, 1.283n‡, 1.584n*; [CP]II, iii; [CP] 2.197, 4.227, 4.242, 4.244, 4.274, 4.323, 6.349n†).

Chapter 1. Intended Characters of this Treatise. [CP] 2.1–118 (1902) with deletions. (See [Perry]II, 422 concerning an earlier version of [CP] 2.9.)

Chapter 2. Prelogical Notions. Section 1. Classification of the Sciences. Widener IB2–2, 1902. [CP] 1.203–283, 7.374n10, 7.279, and 7.362–387, except 381n19, are from it in that order; cf. 7.362n1, 7.363n5. Section 2. Why Study Logic. [CP] 2.119–202.

Chapter 3. The Simplest Mathematics. [CP] 4.227–323 (1902) with deletions.

Chapter 4. Ethics. [CP] 1.575–584 and 6.349–352 (both dated 1902–1903) are from it.

3. "Reason's Rules." [CP] 5.538–545 are from it.

4. Various partial drafts of a review of Josiah Royce's *The World and the Individual*, Vol. 2, Widener IV. [CP] 8.117 (in part), 8.118–119, 8.120 (in part), 8.121–125 (except 122n19) and 8.131 are from them. See [Bibliography]N–1902–10 for the published review, parts of which are reprinted with the above. See [Bibliography]N–1900–15 for a review of Vol. 1.

5. "Of the Classification of the Sciences. Second Paper. Of the Practical Sciences." Widener II. [CP] 7.53–57, 7.381n19, and 7.58 are from it in that order.

1903

* 1. A series of lectures on pragmatism, delivered at Harvard University, March–May, 1903.

Lecture I. On pragmatism and the normative sciences. [CP] 5.14–40.

Lecture II. Draft 1, "On Phenomenology"; [CP] 1.322–323 (c.1903) are from it. Draft 2, "On Phenomenology"; [CP] 5.41–56 (cf. 5.41n*) are from it. Draft 3, "On Phenomenology, or the Categories"; [CP] 5.59–65.

Lecture III. On the categories. (Cf. [CP] 5.66n*, 5.82n*.) Version "a," "The Categories continued"; [CP] 5.71n1 and 5.82–87 are from it. Version "b," "The Categories Defended"; [CP] 5.66–81 (except 5.71n1, 5.77n1) and 5.88–92 are from it

Lecture IV. "The Seven Systems of Metaphysics." [CP] 5.77n1, from the beginning; 5.93–119, following shortly after 5.77n1; 5.57–58, part of a digression at the end (5.57n*); 1.314–316, an apparently undelivered passage (1.314n*, 5.118n*).

Lecture V. On three kinds of goodness. [CP] 5.120–150, from the third and final draft.

Lecture VI. On three types of reasoning. [CP] 5.151–179 with a deletion.

Lecture VII. On pragmatism and abduction. [CP] 5.180–212. It is not certain that this lecture was given. According to the Peirce-James correspondence ([Perry]II, 426–427) and [CP] 5.180n*, only six lectures were planned. [CP] 5.180–212 are taken from a notebook which is marked "Pragmatism — Lecture VII" and which seems to belong to the set of notebooks from which the other lectures of this series printed in *Collected Papers* are taken. At the beginning of this notebook Peirce says this is an extra lecture.

In Lecture VII ([CP] 5.201) Peirce refers to "tomorrow evening's lecture on multitude and continuity." There is in Houghton Library a notebook labeled "Multitude and Continuity. A lecture to be delivered . . . in Harvard University, 1903 May 15." It should be noted in this connection that while [CP]V (n* preceding 5.14) gives March 26 to May 17, 1903, as the dates of the lectures, [Perry]II, 426, gives March 26 to May 14, 1903. The editor knows of no evidence other than that offered by the notebook that this eighth lecture was given.

* 2. Lowell lectures of 1903 and supplementary materials.

(a) The eight lectures were given the general title, "Some Topics of Logic Bearing on Questions Now Vexed." This title and the titles and dates for the individual lectures were taken from a ticket in Widener VA^2; the material printed in [CP] VII is in Widener IB2–4. Cf. [Perry]II, 426.

Lecture I. What Makes a Reasoning Sound? Nov. 23. The following are from it: [CP] 1.591–610 from Vol. 1, draft 3; 1.611–615 and 8.176 (except 176n3), following shortly after 1.611–615, from Vol. 2, draft 2, a continuation of Vol. 1, draft 3.

Lecture II. A System of Diagrams for Studying Logical Relations. Exposition of it begun. Nov. 27.

Lecture III. The Three Universal Categories and their Utility. Nov. 30. The following are from it: [CP] 1.15–26 from Lecture IIIa; 1.324 from Lecture III, Vol. 1, draft 3; 1.343–349 from Lecture III, Vol. 1, draft 3; 1.521–544 from Lecture III, Vol. 2, draft 3, following 1.349.

Lecture IV. Exposition of the System of Diagrams Completed. Dec. 3. [CP] 4.510–529 with deletions; 4.529n* contains material found on a separate sheet, apparently for use in a similar lecture.

Lecture V. The Doctrine of Multitude, Infinity and Continuity. Dec. 7. Cf. reference at [CP] 5.201n*.

Lecture VI. What is Chance? Dec. 10. [CP] 6.88–97 are from it.

Lecture VII. Induction as Doing, not mere Cogitation. Dec. 14. [CP] 7.110–130 are from Vol. 1.

Lecture VIII. How to Theorize. Dec. 17. [CP] 5.590–604 and 7.182n7, following shortly after 5.604, are from it.

Two quotations from these lectures are given at [CP] 3.45n* and 3.154n1.

(b) *A Syllabus of Certain Topics of Logic*, Alfred Mudge & Son, Boston, 1903. Cf. Peirce's notice of it, [Bibliography]N–1905–9. Reprinted in part as follows: "Preface," [CP] 1.180n*, "This syllabus has for its object to supplement a course of eight lectures to be delivered at the Lowell Institute . . ."; pp. 5–9, "An Outline Classification of the Sciences," [CP] 1.180–202; pp. 10–14, "The Ethics of Terminology," [CP] 2.219–226, continuing 1.202; pp. 15–23, "Existential Graphs," [CP] 4.394–417, continuing 2.226, with a revision of c.1910.

(c) A partly printed work in two parts:

"Nomenclature and Divisions of Dyadic Relations," printed separately in eight pages (c.1903). [CP] 3.571–587. [CP] 3.588–608 are from the ms. (c.1903).

"Nomenclature and Divisions of Triadic Relations, as far as they are determined." [CP] 2.233–272, from the ms. (c.1903), continuing 3.608.

This two-part work was apparently intended as the second part of the previous item. See references: [CP] 3.571n*, 3.587n‡, 3.598n* (p. 383), 3.608n‡, 2.233n*.

(d) "Syllabus" (c.1902). [CP] 2.274–277, 2.283–284, 2.292–294, 2.309–331 (with 2.309 continuing 2.294) are from it. There is a ms. in Widener IB2–4 which contains both this and most of the printed syllabus, (b) above. In the ms., as contrasted to the printed syllabus, this material comes between that of [CP] 2.219–226 and 4.394–417, but it is not adjacent to either.

3. Translation of Victor Schumann's *On the Absorption and Emission of Air and its Ingredients for Light of Wave-Lengths from 250 $\mu\mu$ to 100 $\mu\mu$*, Smithsonian Institution, Washington, 1903, iv + 30 pp. + 4 plates.

4. Comment by Peirce on his work on logic. [CP]II, xii.

5. "Telepathy," Widener IC1–a,b. [CP] 7.597–688, except 597n3, with deletions.

c.1903

1. A fragment on the classification of ends. [CP] 1.585–588 are from it.

* 2. "Logical Tracts, No. 2." [CP] 4.418–509, "On Existential Graphs, Euler's Diagrams, and Logical Algebra," are from it. For a statement about "Logical Tracts, No. 1," see [CP] 4.418n.

Peirce referred to his system of existential graphs as "My Chef d'Oeuvre." [CP]IV, 291 (undated).

3. "Graphs." [CP] 4.350–371 are from it.

4. A fragment on metaphysics. [CP] 6.6 is from it.

5. A draft of a review of James Mark Baldwin's *Dictionary of Philosophy and Psychology*, Widener IV. [CP] 8.167 (in part) and 168–170 are from it. See [Bibliography]N–1903–10 for the published review, reprinted in part at [CP] 8.164–166 and 167 (in part).

6. Unpublished review of C. A. Strong's *Why the Mind Has a Body* (Macmillan, 1903, 355 pp.), Widener IV. [CP] 8.186–187.

1904

1. "French Academy of Science," *New York Evening Post*, 5 March 1904.

2. Reference to "Note on the Simplest Possible Branch of Mathematics," presented 19–21 April 1904. [RNA 1904]14.

3. Reference to "On Topical Geometry," presented 15–16 Nov 1904. [RNA 1904]16. This paper was described in [Bibliography]N–1904–20. Cf. [Cohen]737.

4. An untitled manuscript, Widener Vβ. [CP] 8.225n10 is from it.

c.1904

1. "Notes on the List of Postulates of Dr. Huntington's Section 2." [CP] 4.324–330.

2. "Logic viewed as Semeiotics, Introduction Number 2, Phaneroscopy." [CP] 1.285–287, 1.304 (continuing 1.287) are from it.

3. A draft of a review of Herbert Nichols' *A Treatise on Cosmology*, Vol. 1, *Introduction*, Widener IV. [CP] 8.191–193 are from it. Cf. [Bibliography]G–1905–2.

"Nichols' Cosmology and Pragmaticism," Widener IB1–2. [CP] 8.194–195 are from it. Cf. [CP] 8.191n1.

1905

* 1. *The Monist* 1905–1906 series on pragmaticism, plus drafts (items (d) through (h) below) of an unpublished paper intended as a fourth article to appear Jan 1907. See [CP] 1.305n*, 1.306n*, 4.540, 4.540n*, 4.541, 4.572, 5.440, 8.191n1.

(a) "What Pragmatism Is," 15(April 1905)161–181. [CP] 5.411–437.

(b) "Issues of Pragmaticism," 15(Oct 1905)481–499. [CP] 5.438–463, except 448n1. [CP] 5.402n3 (1906) is from a ms., "Issues of Pragmaticism" (not "Consequences of Pragmaticism"), Widener IB1–1, which is similar to the printed article.

(c) "Prolegomena to an Apology for Pragmaticism," 16(Oct 1906) 492–546. Errata, 17(Jan 1907)160. [CP] 4.530–572 with the published corrections and with material from (e), (f), and (h) below in footnotes. [CP] 1.288–292 are from draft $\pi\lambda$ of the ms. (c.1908).

In a letter to F. A. Woods, [Bibliography]M–22, Peirce says that the material in [CP] 4.569, from "For the sake of illustrating this . . ." up to the statement of the Fourth Permission, is wrong. He says: "Instead of scribing

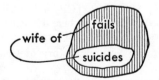

as I did, I should have scribed

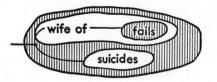

". . . [This fallacy] cost me the trouble of my nonsensical 'tinctures' and heraldry.

"I am also sceptical as to the universal validity of my '4th permission.' "

(d) "Basis of Pragmaticism." Portions dated 1906 published at: [CP] 1.573–574; 5.549–554, continuing 1.574; 5.448n1, following somewhat after 5.554.

(e) "The Bedrock beneath Pragmaticism." Portions dated c.1906 published at: [CP] 4.553n2; 4.561n1; 6.174–176.

(f) "Copy T." [CP] 4.564n1 (c.1906) is from it.

(g) "An Apology for Pragmaticism." [CP] 1.305 is from it.

(h) "Phaneroscopy $\phi\alpha\nu$." Portions dated c.1906 published at: [CP] 1.306–311, 4.6–11, 4.534n1, 4.553n1 (p. 441).

2. Review of Herbert Nichols' *A Treatise on Cosmology*, Vol. 1, signed "Cusp.," *The Monist* 15(Jan 1905)157–158. Identification based on Harvard mss.

3. "Substitution in Logic," *The Monist* 15(April 1905)294–295. This article was signed by "Francis C. Russell," but, judging by correspondence in Widener, it was written by Peirce though it was approved and perhaps modified by Russell.

4. Reference to "The Relation of Betweenness and Royce's 0–Collections," presented 14–15 Nov 1905. [RNA 1905] 15.

5. "Adirondack Lectures, 1905." [CP] 1.284 is from it.

6. "Analysis of Some Demonstrations Concerning Definite Positive Integers." [CP] 4.341–346.

c.1905

1. Ms. G of "A Neglected Argument for the Reality of God." [CP] 2.755–772 (on induction), except 757n1, are from it. Cf. [Bibliography] G–1908–2, especially [CP] 6.473.

2. "Logic and Spiritualism," intended for *The Forum*. [CP] 6.557–587.

3. On ordinals. [CP] 4.331–340. [CP] 4.331–334 are from a proposed lecture to the American Academy of Arts and Sciences; 4.335–340 are from "Topics," a revised version of the latter part of the lecture.

4. "Phaneroscopy or the Natural History of Concepts." [CP] 1.332–336 are from it.

5. "The Basis of Pragmatism." [CP] 1.294–299, 1.313n1 are from Notebook I. [CP] 1.313, 1.350–352 (undated) are from Notebook II.

6. "Sketch of Some Proposed Chapters on the Sect of Philosophy Called Pragmatism," a notebook. [CP] 1.126–129 are from "Introduction showing the point of view from which Philosophy appears to the author to be an interesting subject to a man of common-sense."

7. "The Basis of Pragmaticism." [CP] 5.497–501 with deletions.

* 8. "Pragmaticism, Prag. [4]." The first page of the ms. is missing. [CP] 5.502–537 with a deletion.

9. A draft of a review of Wilhelm Wundt's *Principles of Physiological Psychology*, Widener IV. [CP] 8.201n3 is from it. See [CP] 8.196–204, [Bibliography]N–1905–19, for the published review.

1906

1. "Mr. Peterson's Proposed Discussion," *The Monist* 16(Jan 1906) 147–151. Erratum, *ibid.*, 16(April 1906)20. This is a discussion of James B. Peterson's "Some Philosophical Terms," *ibid.*, 15(Oct 1905)629–633. [CP] 5.610–614.

2. Reference to "Recent Developments of Existential Graphs and their Consequences for Logic," presented 16–18 April 1906. [RNA 1906]15. This paper is described in [Bibliography]N–1906–4. [CP] 4.573–584 are from it.

3. Reference to "Phaneroscopy, or Natural History of Signs, Relations, Categories, etc.: A method of investigating this subject expounded and illustrated," presented 20–22 Nov 1906. [RNA 1906]18.

c.1906

1. "Reflexions upon Pluralistic Pragmatism and upon Cenopythagorean Pragmaticism." [CP] 5.555–564.

2. "Answers to Questions Concerning My Belief in God." [CP] 6.494–521.

1907

1. References to Peirce's two lectures on scientific method at the Philosophy Club at Harvard, June 1907. [Perry]II, 436; Paul Weiss, "Charles Sanders Peirce," *Dictionary of American Biography*, Vol. 14, New York, 1937, p. 402.

c.1907

* 1. An unpublished letter-article to the Editor of *The Nation* on pragmatism. The following are grouped together since there is considerable evidence that the manuscripts from which they come are different attempts at the same article. This is dated c.1907 since F.C.S. Schiller's *Studies in Humanism*, apparently referred to at [CP] 5.494 (see (c) below), was published in 1907 ([Fisch]413). Cf. [Bibliography] M–21b, pp. 20–21; see also [Fisch] 443–444.

   (a) "Pragmatism (Prag. [J])," comments on "On a New List of Categories," [Bibliography]G–1867–1c. [CP] 1.560–562 (c.1905).

   (b) "Pragmatism [1]." [CP] 5.5–10 (c.1905) are from it.

   (c) "Pragmatism (Editor [3])." [CP] 5.11–13, except 5.13n1, and 5.464–496, with 5.464 continuing 5.13, (both dated c.1906) are from it. [CP] 5.11–13 were previously printed in *The Hound and Horn* 2(April–June 1929)282–285, under the title, "The Founding of Pragmatism."

2. "Guessing," Widener IB2–12. [CP] 7.36–48, except 36n13, are from it. The ms. is published in *The Hound and Horn* 2(April–June 1929) 267–282. [CP] 7.36n13 is from an alternative fragmentary ms. in Widener IB2–12.

1908

1. *The Monist* 1908–1909 series on mazes, plus unpublished mss.

(a) "Some Amazing Mazes," 18(April 1908)227–241. Cf. Francis C. Russell, "Hints for the Elucidation of Mr. Peirce's Logical Work," *The Monist* 18(July 1908)406–415. In a letter to Russell, dated 6 July 1908 (Widener VB2a), Peirce says of this, "I must thank you for your very ingenious defense of me." [CP] 4.585–593.

(b) "Some Amazing Mazes, [Conclusion], Explanation of Curiosity the First," 18(July 1908)416–464. [CP] 4.594–642. *"Supplement*. 1908 May 24," Widener IA-3. [CP] 7.535n6 is from it.

(c) "Some Amazing Mazes, A Second Curiosity," 19(Jan 1909)36–45. [CP] 4.643–646.

(d) Reference to "The Third Curiosity" at [CP] 4.647n*.

(e) "Some Amazing Mazes, Fourth Curiosity," (c.1909). The following are from it: [CP] 6.318–348, on various topics in metaphysics; 4.647–681, on classes and numbers, with 4.647 following shortly after 6.348.

* 2. "A Neglected Argument for the Reality of God," *The Hibbert Journal* 7(Oct 1908)90–112. [CP] 6.452–485.

c.1908

1. A fragment on assertion. [CP] 5.546–548 are from it.

1909

1. A set of manuscripts with various titles, but all having "Meaning" and the date written in the upper left-hand corner of each page, Widener IB2–11. [CP] 1.27 and 7.313n1 are from these. The quote from Peirce in [CP] 5.358n* is, except for minor editorial changes, identical with a passage in one of these mss., "Studies in Meaning; The Import of Thought: An Essay in Two Chapters." Cf. [CP] 8.214ff., 8.302ff.

1910

1. "Definition." [CP] 1.312 is from it.

* 2. A comment on "The Doctrine of Chances," [Bibliography]G–1877–5c. [CP] 2.661–668.

3. "Meaning." [CP] 2.230–232 are from it.

4. On trichotomies. [CP] 1.568–572. See [CP] 1.568n† for a reference to a book of which this may have been a part. Several more pages of the ms. have been found since [CP] 1.572n* was written.

c.1910

1. "Additament," comments on "A Neglected Argument for the Reality of God," [Bibliography]G–1908–2. [CP] 6.486–490. [CP] 6.491 is from an alternative draft.

2. "Pragmatism," Fragment 2. [CP] 1.317–321 are from it.

3. "Notes for my Logical Criticism of Articles of the Christian Creed," Widener IB3. [CP] 7.97–109.

1911

1. Reference to "A method of computation," presented 21–22 Nov 1911. [RNA 1911]24.

2. Reference to "The reasons of reasoning, or grounds of inferring," presented 21–22 Nov 1911. [RNA 1911]24.

c.1911

1. "A Sketch of Logical Critic." [CP] 6.177–184 are from it.

Undated

1. On secondness. [CP] 1.325.

2. On secondness. [CP] 1.330–331 are from it.

3. On thirdness. [CP] 1.338–339 are from it.

4. "Of the Nature of Measurement," Widener IA–4. [CP] 7.280–312 are from it.

5. Quotation from the "Introduction" to a planned history of science, Widener IC1b. [CP] 7.267n8.

6. A fragment on non-Euclidean geometry, Widener IA7. [CP] 8.93n2.

7. "The Non Euclidean Geometry made Easy," Widener IA2. [CP] 8.97–99 are from it.

8. A manuscript on signs, Widener IB3a. This is part of a letter. [CP] 8.177–185 are from it.

9. An untitled ms. on primisense, altersense, and medisense, Widener IB1–2. [CP] 7.539–552, with 540n8 and 541n9 from an alternate draft at Widener IC1–a,b; cf. 7.539n7.

10. An incomplete ms., Widener IB2–10. [CP] 7.276–278 are Section 13, "Varieties of Medisense." This ms., has some resemblance to [Bibliography]G–Undated–9, and may have been written at about the same time.

11. *Qualitative Logic*, a partially completed book, Widener IB2–9. [CP] 7.451–462 are from it. Cf. [CP] 7.451n25 and 7.462n28.

12. "On Topical Geometry, in General," Widener IA–2. [CP] 7.524–538, except 534n4 and 535n6, are from it.

13. Mss. L and N, Widener IB2–9. [CP] 7.49–52 and 7.77–78, respectively, are from them. Cf. [CP] 7.59n4.

14. Two fragmentary drafts on consciousness, Widener IC1–a,b. [CP] 7.553 is one of these; 7.554 is from the other.

15. A fragment on matter, Widener IA–8. [CP] 7.534n4 is from it.

16. "Notes on Topical Geometry," Widener IA–2. [CP] 8.368n23 is from it.

17. On "would be," Widener IA–8. [CP] 8.380n4 is from it.

BIBLIOGRAPHY

II. ITEMS FROM *THE NATION*

1869

† 1. Review of Noah Porter's *The Human Intellect*, 8(18 March 1869) 211–213.

2. Review of Henry E. Roscoe's *Spectrum Analysis*, 9(22 July 1869) 73–74.

• † 3. "The English Doctrine of Ideas," a review of James Mill's *Analysis of the Phenomena of the Human Mind* (edited by John Stuart Mill), 2 vols., 9(25 Nov 1869)461–462.

1871

1. "Mr. Peirce and the Realists," a signed letter, 13(14 Dec 1871)386. This is a reply to editorial comments in *The Nation* 13(2 Nov 1871)294 and 13(30 Nov 1871)355–356, the latter by Chauncey Wright, on [Bibliography]G–1871–1.

1873

1. Review of H. M. Lazelle's *One Law in Nature*, 17(10 July 1873) 28–29.

1878

1. Review of Simon Newcomb's *Popular Astronomy*, 27(1 Aug 1878)74.

1879

1. Review of Carveth Read's *The Theory of Logic*, 28(3 April 1879) 234–235.

2. Review of Ogden N. Rood's *Modern Chromatics*, 29(16 Oct 1879) 260. All but the last two paragraphs are by Peirce.

3. Notes on the *American Journal of Mathematics*, 29(25 Dec 1879) 440.

1881

† 1. Review of W. Stanley Jevons' *Studies in Deductive Logic*, 32(31 March 1881)227.

1884

1. "The Reciprocity Treaty with Spain," a signed letter, 39(18 Dec 1884) 521.

1885

1. "The Spanish Treaty Once More," a signed letter, 40(1 Jan 1885)12.

1889

1. "The Century Dictionary," a signed letter, 48(20 June 1889)504–505. This is a reply to a letter from S. Newcomb, *The Nation* 48(13 June 1889)488. Newcomb's rejoinder is at *ibid.*, (27 June 1889)524.

1890

1. Review of E. Noel's *The Science of Metrology*, 50(27 Feb 1890)184. Identification based on Harvard mss.

2. Review of F. Howard Collins' *Epitome of the Synthetic Philosophy*, 50(27 March 1890)265. Identification based on Harvard mss.

† 3. Review of Th. Ribot's *The Psychology of Attention*, 50(19 June 1890)492–493.

† 4. Review of W. Stanley Jevons' *Pure Logic, and Other Minor Works*, 51(3 July 1890)16. Identification based on Harvard mss.

† 5. Review of Paul Carus' *Fundamental Problems*, 51(7 Aug 1890) 118–119. Identification based on Harvard mss.

6. Review of Thomas Muir's *The Theory of Determinants in the Historical Order of its Development*, Part I, 51(28 Aug 1890)177. Identification based on Harvard mss.

7. Review of Alexander Campbell Fraser's *Locke*, 51(25 Sept 1890) 254–255.

8. Review of R. O. Williams' *Our Dictionaries, and Other English-Language Topics*, 51(30 Oct 1890)349. Identification based on Harvard mss.

1891

1. Review of William James's *The Principles of Psychology*, 2 vols., 53(2 July 1891)15 and 53(9 July 1891)32–33. [CP] 8.55–71. Cf. [CP] 8.72–90, [Bibliography] G–c.1891–1, for some questions on this book.

2. "Abbot against Royce," a signed letter, 53(12 Nov 1891) 372.

† 3. Review of Herbert Spencer's *Essays, Scientific, Political, and Speculative*, 53(8 Oct 1891)283. Identification based on Harvard mss.

4. Review of J. Howard Gore's *Geodesy*, 53(15 Oct 1891)302. Identification based on Harvard mss.

5. Review of George F. Chambers' *Pictorial Astronomy for General Readers*, 53(26 Nov 1891)415. Identification based on Harvard mss.

6. Review of Dascom Greene's *An Introduction to Spherical and Practical Astronomy*, 53(17 Dec 1891)474. Identification based on Harvard mss.

1892

† 1. Review of *The New Calendar of Great Men* (biographies of 558 men in the Positivist Calendar of Auguste Comte), 54(21 Jan 1892) 54–55.

2. Review of Nicholaus Lobatchewsky's *Geometrical Researches on the Theory of Parallels*, 54(11 Feb 1892)116. [CP] 8.91–96, except 93n2. Cf. [Bibliography]G–undated–6 and 7.

3. Review of Cesare Lombroso's *The Man of Genius*, 54(25 Feb 1892) 151–153.

† 4. Notice of William James's *Psychology (Briefer Course)*, 54(17 March 1892)214.

5. Review of William J. McClelland's *A Treatise on the Geometry of the Circle*, 54(24 March 1892)237.

6. Notices of Netto's *Theory of Substitutions* and Joseph Edwards' *Elementary Treatise on the Differential Calculus*, 54(12 May 1892)358. Identification based on Harvard mss.

7. Review of W. W. Rouse Ball's *Mathematical Recreations*, 54(12 May 1892)366.

† 8. Review of Arabella B. Buckley's *Moral Teachings of Science*, 54(2 June 1892)417.

9. Review of William Ridgeway's *The Origin of Metallic Currency and Weight Standards*, 54(23 June 1892)472–473. Identification based on Harvard mss.

10. Review of Karl Pearson's *The Grammar of Science*, first ed., 55(7 July 1892)15. Identification based on Harvard mss.

11. Review of S. S. Curry's *The Province of Expression*, 55(14 July 1892)35. Identification based on Harvard mss.

12. Review of A. M. Worthington's *Dynamics of Rotation*, 55(11 Aug 1892)114–115. Identification based on Harvard mss.

† 13. Review of George Stuart Fullerton's *The Philosophy of Spinoza*, 55(25 Aug 1892)152. Identification based on Harvard mss.

† 14. Review of Edward Stanton's *Dreams of the Dead*, 55(8 Sept 1892) 190–191. Identification based on Harvard mss.

15. "The Boston Public Library," a signed letter, 55(6 Oct 1892)260.

† 16. Review of Alfred Sidgwick's *Distinction and the Criticism of Belief*, 55(27 Oct 1892)324–325. Identification based on Harvard mss.

17. Review of William J. Hussey's *Logarithmic and Other Mathematical Tables*, 55(10 Nov 1892)359–360. Identification based on Harvard mss.

1893

† 1. Review of A. E. H. Love's *A Treatise on the Mathematical Theory of Elasticity*, Vol. 1, 56(2 Feb 1893)90. Identification based on Harvard mss.

2. Notice of Part 2, Vol. 19, *Annals of the Harvard College Observatory*, 57(27 July 1893)65. Identification based on Harvard mss.

† 3. Review of George M. Gould's *The Meaning and the Method of Life*, 57(3 Aug 1893)88–89. Identification based on Harvard mss.

4. Review of Edward Everett Hale's *A New England Boyhood*, 57(17 Aug 1893)123–124.

5. Review of John Wellesley Russell's *An Elementary Treatise on Pure Geometry*, R. Lachlan's *An Elementary Treatise on Modern Pure Geometry*, and Paul H. Hanus' *Geometry in the Grammar School*, 57(24 Aug 1893)143. Identification based on Harvard mss.

† 6. Review of Ernst Mach's *The Science of Mechanics*, 57(5 Oct 1893)251–252.

† 7. Review of David G. Ritchie's *Darwin and Hegel*, 57(23 Nov 1893) 393–394.

8. Review of Charles Godfrey Leland's *Memoirs*, 57(30 Nov 1893) 414–415.

1894

1. Untitled announcement of Peirce's *The Principles of Philosophy*, 12 vols., and of Peirce's translation of Peter Peregrinus' *On the Lodestone*, 58(11 Jan 1894)30. Identified in [Fisch-Haskell]. Cf. advertisement, 58(15 Feb 1894)v. Cf. also [Bibliography]G–c.1893–5 for quotations from the prospectus for the first work, and [Bibliography]G–c.1893–4 for quotations from the prospectus for the latter.

† 2. Review of Thomas H. Huxley's *Method and Results*, 58(11 Jan 1894)34–35.

3. Review of *Familiar Letters of Sir Walter Scott*, 2 vols., 58(8 Feb 1894)105–107.

† 4. Review of William Gilbert's *On the Load-stone and Magnetic Bodies and on the Great Magnet, the Earth*, 58(15 Feb 1894)124–125 and 58(22 Feb 1894)141–142.

5. Review of *A Standard Dictionary* (edited by Isaac K. Funk), Vol. 1, 58(8 March 1894)180–181.

† 6. Review of A. R. Forsyth's *Theory of Functions of a Complex Variable*, James Harkness and Frank Morley's *A Treatise on the Theory of Functions*, and E. Picard's *Traité d'Analyse*, 58(15 March 1894)197–199.

7. Review of J. Norman Lockyer's *The Dawn of Astronomy*, 58(29 March 1894)234–236.

8. Review of David Gorton's *The Monism of Man* and David Hill's *Genetic Philosophy*, 58(12 April 1894)278. Probably by Peirce; identification based on Harvard mss.

9. Review of Florian Cajori's *A History of Mathematics*, 58(26 April 1894)316–317. Probably by Peirce; identification based on Harvard mss.

10. Review of Albert Ross Parsons' *New Light from the Great Pyramid*, 58(31 May 1894)415–416. Identification based on Harvard mss.

† 11. "Hemholtz," an article, 59(13 Sept 1894)191–193.

12. Review of W. Windelband's *A History of Philosophy*, Richard

Falkenberg's *History of Modern Philosophy*, John Bascom's *An Historical Interpretation of Philosophy*, and B. C. Burt's *A History of Modern Philosophy*, 59(27 Sept 1894)237–238 and 59(4 Oct 1894)251–252.

† 13. Review of Benedict de Spinoza's *Ethic*, 59(8 Nov 1894) 344–345.

14. "Hallucinations," a signed letter, 59(22 Nov 1894)381. This is a comment on a note in *The Nation* 59(8 Nov 1894) 343. Cf. [Bibliography]G–1887–3.

15. "Descartes and His Works," an article, 59(27 Dec 1894) 476–477.

1895

† 1. Review of John Watson's *Comte, Mill, and Spencer*, 60(11 April 1895)284–285.

2. Review of Henry Jones's *A Critical Account of the Philosophy of Lotze*, V. Eberhard's *Die Grundbegriffe der ebenen Geometrie*, Vol. 1, Felix Klein's *Riemann and his Significance for the Development of Modern Mathematics*, and Noah K. Davis' *Elements of Inductive Logic*, 61(4 July 1895)14–16.

1896

1. Review of Park Benjamin's *The Intellectual Rise in Electricity*, 62(2 Jan 1896)16–18.

2. Review of George John Romanes' *Mind and Matter, and Monism*, 62(26 March 1896)261–262. Probably by Peirce; identification based on Harvard mss.

3. Review of Ernst Schroeder's *Algebra und Logik der Relative*, Part I, Vol. 3, *Vorlesungen über die Algebra der Logik*, 62(23 April 1896)330–331. Probably by Peirce; identification based on Harvard mss. Cf. [Bibliography]G–1896–6.

4. Review of Levi Leonard Conant's *The Number Concept*, 62(21 May 1896)404.

5. Review of H. Durége's *Elements of the Theory of Functions of a Complex Variable*, 63(3 Sept 1896)181–182. Identification based on Harvard mss.

1897

1. Untitled note on James Joseph Sylvester, 64(25 March 1897)227. This is an abridgment of an article in the *New York Evening Post* (16 March 1897)7:3f. George Bruce Halsted, "Sylvester," *Science* ns 5(16 April 1897)597–604, criticizes Peirce for an error concerning Sylvester (p. 604).

2. Review of Frank Podmore's *Studies in Psychical Research*, 65(4 Nov 1897)362–363.

3. Review of D. Mendeléeff's *The Principles of Chemistry*, 65(25 Nov 1897)424.

4. Notice of *The Consolation of Philosophy of Boethius*, 65(9 Dec 1897)458–459. Identification based on Harvard mss.

1898

1. Review of Ignatius Singer and Lewis H. Berens' *Some Unrecognized Laws of Nature*, 66(3 Feb 1898)96.

2. Review of F. W. Edridge-Green's *Memory and its Cultivation*, 66(21 April 1898)311.

3. Notice of Reye's *Geometrie der Lage*, Part 1, 67(14 July 1898)31.

4. Review of Boris Sidis' *The Psychology of Suggestion* (with an introduction by William James), 67(25 Aug 1898) 154–155.

5. Review of Alfred Russel Wallace's *The Wonderful Century*, 67(22 Sept 1898)228–229.

6. Notice of Richard Kerr's *Wireless Telegraphy*, 67(29 Sept 1898)242.

† 7. Review of James Mark Baldwin's *The Story of the Mind*, 67(13 Oct 1898)281–282.

† 8. Review of Carveth Read's *Logic, Deductive and Inductive*, 67(20 Oct 1898)300–301.

9. Notice of P. A. Lambert's *Differential and Integral Calculus for Technical Schools and Colleges*, 67(24 Nov 1898)390.

10. Review of Noah Brooks' *The Story of Marco Polo*, 67(24 Nov 1898)397.

11. Review of H. H. Francis Hyndman's *Radiation*, 67(1 Dec 1898) 417–418.

† 12. Review of George Howard Darwin's *The Tides and Kindred Phenomena in the Solar System*, 67(22 Dec 1898)469–470.

1899

† 1. Review of Silas W. Holman's *Matter, Energy, Force, and Work*, 68(2 Feb 1899)95–96.

† 2. Review of *Leibniz: The Monadology and Other Philosophical Writings*, 68(16 March 1899)210.

3. Notice of Kepler's *Somnium*, 68(20 April 1899)296.

† 4. Review of Florian Cajori's *A History of Physics in its Elementary Branches*, 68(27 April 1899)316–317.

5. Review of John Beattie Crozier's *My Inner Life*, 68(4 May 1899) 338.

6. Review of Rouge et Noir's *The Gambling World* and John Ashton's *The History of Gambling in England*, 68(25 May 1899)403.

7. Review of Frank Hall Thorp's *Outlines of Industrial Chemistry*, 68(25 May 1899)405. Cf. [Bibliography]N–1900–7.

8. Review of David P. Todd's *Stars and Telescopes*, 68(22 June 1899) 482–483.

9. Review of Henry Rutgers Marshall's *Instinct and Reason*, 68(29 June 1899)499–500.

10. Review of F. J. Britten's *Old Clocks and Watches and their Makers*, 69(27 July 1899)77–78.

† 11. Review of Ch. Renouvier and L. Prat's *La Nouvelle Monadologie*, 69(3 Aug 1899)97–98.

† 12. Review of Robert Mackintosh's *From Comte to Benjamin Kidd* and J. Howard Moore's *Better-World Philosophy*, 69(7 Sept 1899)192–193.

13. Review of Hermann Schubert's *Mathematical Essays and Recreations* and Augustus de Morgan's *The Study and Difficulties of Mathematics*, 69(21 Sept 1899)231.

14. Review of Ray Stannard Baker's *The Boy's Book of Inventions*, 69(19 Oct 1899)303–304.

15. Review of Paul Leicester Ford's *The Many-Sided Franklin*, 69(9 Nov 1899)355–356.

† 16. Review of Daniel C. Gilman's *The Life of James Dwight Dana*, 69(14 Dec 1899)455.

1900

1. Notice of W. J. Lewis' *Treatise on Crystallography*, 70(4 Jan 1900)11.

2. Notice of Edward Pick's *Lectures on Memory Culture*, 70(4 Jan 1900)12–13.

† 3. Review of John Fiske's *A Century of Science*, 70(4 Jan 1900)18.

4. Review of J. J. Fahie's *A History of Wireless Telegraphy*, 70(25 Jan 1900)78.

5. Review of Vicomte G. d'Avenel's *Le Mécanisme de la vie moderne*, Vol. 3, 70(1 Feb 1900)97–98.

6. Review of Wemyss Reid's *Memoirs and Correspondence of Lyon Playfair*, 70(8 Feb 1900)114–115.

7. Notice of Frank Hall Thorp's *Outlines of Industrial Chemistry*, revised edition, 70(15 Feb 1900)128.

8. Notice of William Ripper's *Steam-Engine Theory and Practice*, 70(15 Feb 1900)128.

9. Notice of Philip Atkinson's *Power Transmitted by Electricity*, 70(15 Feb 1900)128.

10. Notice of Albert Gay and C. H. Yeaman's *An Introduction to the Study of Central-Station Electricity Supply*, 70(15 Feb 1900)128.

11. Notice of W. Watson's *A Text-Book of Physics*, 70(1 March 1900) 163.

12. Notice of Karl Pearson's *The Grammar of Science*, second edition, 70(15 March 1900)203–204. Cf. [Bibliography]G–1901–1.

13. Notice of Heinrich Hertz' *The Principles of Mechanics Presented in a New Form*, 70(15 March 1900)204.

14. Review of David Eugene Smith's *The Teaching of Elementary Mathematics*, 70(22 March 1900)230.

15. Review of Josiah Royce's *The World and the Individual*, Vol. 1, 70(5 April 1900)267. [CP] 8.100–107. Cf. [CP] 8.108–116, [Bibliography]G–c.1900–2, for a draft of a review of this book. See [Bibliography]N–1902–10 for the review of Vol. 2.

16. Review of Francis Seymour Stevenson's *Robert Grosseteste*, 70(19 April 1900)302–303.

† 17. Review of Sir Norman Lockyer's *Inorganic Evolution as Studied by Spectrum Analysis*, 70(10 May 1900)366.

18. Review of W. Windelband's *History of Ancient Philosophy*, 70(17 May 1900)384–385. Identification based on Harvard mss.

19. Notice of S. R. Bottone's *Wireless Telegraphy and Hertzian Waves*, 70(31 May 1900)417.

20. Review of Frank Thilly's *Introduction to Ethics*, 70(21 June 1900) 480–481. Identification based on Harvard mss. See [CP] 1.589–590, [Bibliography]G–c.1900–1, for an alternative draft.

21. Review of Paul T. Lafleur's *Illustrations of Logic*, 70(28 June 1900)502–503.

22. Notice of Boethius' *De Consolatione Philosophiae*, 71(5 July 1900) 14.

23. Review of Andrew Russell Forsyth's *Theory of Differential Equations*, 3 vols., 71(19 July 1900)59.

24. Review of Harold Höffding's *A History of Modern Philosophy*, 2 vols., 71(26 July 1900)78–79.

† 25. Review of Oskar Emil Myer's *The Kinetic Theory of Gases*, 71(26 July 1900)79.

26. Review of Harry C. Jones's *The Theory of Electrolytic Dissociation*, 71(30 Aug 1900)178.

27. Review of Édouard Feret's *Bordeaux and its Wines, Classed by Order of Merit*, 71(20 Sept 1900)235–236.

28. Review of Vivian B. Lewes' *Acetylene*, 71(27 Sept 1900) 257.

† 29. Review of Ferris Greenslet's *Joseph Glanvill*, 71(11 Oct 1900) 295–296.

30. Review of Karl Fink's *A Brief History of Mathematics*, 71(18 Oct 1900)314–315.

31. Review of Nathaniel Southgate Shaler's *The Individual*, 71(22 Nov 1900)410–411.

32. Review of Edward W. Byrn's *The Progress of Invention in the Nineteenth Century*, 71(6 Dec 1900)449–450.

† 33. Review of Henry Smith Williams' *The Story of Nineteenth Century Science,* 71(27 Dec 1900)515–516.

1901

1. Review of Alfred Russel Wallace's *Studies, Scientific and Social,* 72(10 Jan 1901)36–37.

2. Review of James Sime's *William Herschel and His Work,* 72(24 Jan 1901)72–73.

3. Review of Webster's *International Dictionary of the English Language* (edited by Noah Porter and W. T. Harris), 72(24 Jan 1901)76.

4. Review of *The Life, Unpublished Letters, and Philosophical Regimen of Anthony Earl of Shaftesbury* and Anthony Earl of Shaftesbury's *Characteristics,* 72(31 Jan 1901)96–97.

5. Notice of Arthur L. Bowley's *Elements of Statistics,* 72(28 March 1901)254.

6. Review of John M. Bacon's *By Land and Sea,* 72(28 March 1901)258–259.

7. Review of William Leighton Jordan's *Essays in Illustration of the Action of Astral Gravitation in Natural Phenomena,* 72(13 June 1901) 479–480.

8. Review of Edmond Goblot's *Le Vocabulaire Philosophique,* 72(20 June 1901)497–498.

9. Notice of Frederick Storrs Turner's *Knowledge, Belief, and Certitude,* 73(25 July 1901)70.

† 10. Review of *The Works of George Berkeley, D.D.* (edited by Alexander Campbell Fraser), 73(1 Aug 1901)95–96. Cf. [CP] 8.7–38, [Bibliography]G–1871–1, for a review of an earlier edition.

11. Review of Persifor Frazer's *Bibliotics,* 73(1 Aug 1901)99–100.

12. Review of Alfred Caldecott's *The Philosophy of Religion in England and America,* 73(15 Aug 1901)139–140.

13. Review of Otto Lummer's *Contributions to Photographic Optics,* Eugene Lommel's *Experimental Physics,* Lassar-Cohn's *An Introduction to Modern Scientific Chemistry,* and Bertram Blount's *Practical Electro–Chemistry,* 73(29 Aug 1901)172–173.

† 14. Review of Michael Maher, S. J., *Psychology: Empirical and Rational,* 73(3 Oct 1901)267–268.

15. Review of Sidney Edward Mezes' *Ethics: Descriptive and Explanatory,* 73(24 Oct 1901)325–326. [CP] 8.157–163, except 158n3 ([Bibliography]G–1901–8).

16. "The National Academy at Philadelphia," an article, signed "M.D.," 73(21 Nov 1901)393–395. This is included in both [Cohen] and [Haskell]. See [CP] 7.162–163, [Bibliography]G–1901–7, which are from a draft of this report in Widener IV.

17. Notice of Arthur H. Wall's *Concise French Grammar*, 73(28 Nov 1901)415.

18. Review of Frank J. Addyman's *Practical X-Ray Work*, 73(12 Dec 1901)462.

1902

1. Review of John Beattie Crozier's *History of Intellectual Development on the Lines of Modern Evolution*, Vol. 3, 74(23 Jan 1902)78–79.

2. Review of Ernest Cushing Richardson's *Classification, Theoretical and Practical*, 74(27 Feb 1902)178–179.

† 3. Review of René Vallery-Radot's *The Life of Pasteur*, 2 vols., 74(6 March 1902)192–194.

4. Review of Franklin Henry Giddings' *Inductive Sociology*, 74(3 April 1902)273–274.

5. "The National Academy of Sciences," an article, 74(24 April 1902) 322–324.

6. Review of Edward R. Emerson's *The Story of the Vine*, 74(29 May 1902)433–434.

7. Notice of Delta's *Charades*, 75(10 July 1902)31.

8. Review of Harold H. Joachim's *A Study of the Ethics of Spinoza*, 75(10 July 1902)36–37.

9. Review of *Studies in Physiological Chemistry* (edited by R. H. Chittenden); Albert B. Prescott and Otis C. Johnson's *Qualitative Chemical Analysis*; Victor von Richter's *Organic Chemistry*, 2 vols.; and Harry C. Jones's *The Elements of Physical Chemistry*, 75(24 July 1902)79.

10. Review of Josiah Royce's *The World and the Individual*, Vol. 2, 75(31 July 1902) 94–96. [CP] 8.117 (in part), except 117n10 and 117n12, 8.120 (in part), and 8.126–130 are from the published review. See [Bibliography]G–c.1902–4 for selections from alternative drafts printed with the above. Cf. [Bibliography]N–1900–15 for the review of Vol. 1.

11. Notice of the *Annales* of the Paris International Congress of 1900, the report of the fifth section on the history of science, 75(7 Aug 1902) 115.

12. Review of T. E. Thorpe's *Essays in Historical Chemistry*, 75(21 Aug 1902)153–154.

† 13. Review of Friedrich Paulsen's *Immanuel Kant: His Life and Doctrine*, 75(11 Sept 1902)209–211.
"Accordingly Kant's great engine and distinction is accurate analysis. But absolute completeness of logical analysis is no less unattainable [than] is omniscience. Carry it as far as you please, and something will always remain unanalyzed." From a ms. review of this book in Widener IV.

† 14. Review of Herbert Austin Aikins' *The Principles of Logic*, 75(18 Sept 1902)229–230.

15. Review of Paul Drude's *The Theory of Optics*, 75(2 Oct 1902)273.

16. Review of E. Seton Valentine and F. L. Tomlinson's *Travels in Space* and Frederic Walker's *Aerial Navigation*, 75(23 Oct 1902)329–330.

17. Review of J. B. Baillie's *The Origin and Significance of Hegel's Logic*, 75(13 Nov 1902)390.

18. Review of Andrew Russell Forsyth's *Theory of Differential Equations*, Vol. 4, 75(27 Nov 1902)430.

19. Review of George H. Ellwanger's *The Pleasures of the Table*, 75(18 Dec 1902)485–486.

20. Review of Alice Morse Earle's *Sundials and Roses of Yesterday*, 75(25 Dec 1902)506–507.

1903

1. Review of Thomas Smith's *Euclid: His Life and System*, 76(29 Jan 1903)99–100.

2. Notice of *The Physical Papers of Henry Augustus Rowland*, 76(5 March 1903)194.

3. Untitled statement, 76(19 March 1903)226. This is a reply to a letter by J. S. Ames, *The Nation* 76(19 March 1903)226, criticizing Peirce's notice of item 2 above. That this is by Peirce is evident from the following remark inserted between Ames's letter and the untitled reply: "[We have received from our contributor the following statement concerning this matter. — ED. NATION.]"

4. Notice of Fiske's *Cosmic Philosophy*, 4 vols., with an introduction by Royce, 76(2 April 1903)269.

5. "The National Academy Meeting," an article, 76(30 April 1903)349–351.

6. Notice of J. W. Mellor's *Higher Mathematics for Students of Chemistry and Physics*, 76(21 May 1903)418.

7. Review of John Grier Hibben's *Hegel's Logic*, 76(21 May 1903)419–420.

8. Notice of E. T. Whittaker's *A Course of Modern Analysis*, 76(28 May 1903)436.

9. Review of *Personal Idealism*, 76(4 June 1903)462–463.

10. Review of James Mark Baldwin's *Dictionary of Philosophy and Psychology*, Vol. 2, 76(11 June 1903)482. [CP] 8.164–166 and 167 (in part) are from this review. See [CP] 8.167 (in part) and 168–170, [Bibliography]G–c.1903–5, from an alternative draft.

11. Notice of Kant's *Prolegomena to any Future Metaphysics* (edited in English by Paul Carus), 76(18 June 1903)497–498.

12. Review of Norman Smith's *Studies in the Cartesian Philosophy*, 77(16 July 1903)57–58.

13. Review of J. I. D. Hinds's *Inorganic Chemistry*, 77(23 July 1903)81–82.

† 14. Review of Agnes M. Clerke's *Problems in Astrophysics*, 77(30 July 1903)98–99.

15. Review of A. A. Michelson's *Light Waves and their Uses* and J. A. Fleming's *Waves and Ripples in Water, Air, and Aether*, 77(13 Aug 1903) 141.

16. Notice of Alfred I. Cohn's *Tests and Reagents*, 77(3 Sept 1903)189. Identification based on Harvard mss.

17. Notice of C. Krauch's *Testing of Chemical Reagents for Purity*, 77(10 Sept 1903)208. Identification based on Harvard mss.

18. Notice of F. A. C. Perrine's *Conductors for Electrical Distribution*, 77(10 Sept 1903)208. Identification based on Harvard mss.

19. Untitled note on Sir Norman Lockyer, 77(17 Sept 1903)229.

20. "British and American Science," an article, 77(1 Oct 1903)263–264. Cf. Peirce's untitled note (item above) and a letter signed "H. T.," *The Nation* 77(1 Oct 1903) 265, commenting on this note.

21. Review of V. Welby's *What is Meaning?* and Bertrand Russell's *The Principles of Mathematics*, Vol. 1, 77(15 Oct 1903)308–309. [CP] 8.171–175.

22. Untitled statement, 77(22 Oct 1903)320. This is a reply to a letter by James McMahon entitled "Practical Application of the Theory of Functions," *The Nation* 77(22 Oct 1903)320, commenting on [Bibliography]N–1903–20 above.

23. "Francis Ellingwood Abbot," a letter signed "C.S.P.," 77(5 Nov 1903)360.

1904

† 1. Review of J. J. Fahie's *Galileo*, 78(11 Feb 1904)113–115.

2. Notice of Frederick J. E. Woodbridge's *The Philosophy of Hobbes in Extracts and Notes collected from his Writings*, 78(17 March 1904)211. Identification based on Harvard mss.

3. Review of Frederick A. Halsey's *The Metric Fallacy* and Samuel S. Dale's *The Metric Failure in the Textile Industry* (bound together), 78(17 March 1904)215–216.

4. Review of Simon Newcomb's *The Reminiscences of an Astronomer*, 78(24 March 1904)237.

5. Review of M. E. Boole's *Lectures on the Logic of Arithmetic* and Joseph Bowden's *Elements of the Theory of Integers*, 78(14 April 1904) 298.

6. "The National Academy Meeting," an article, 78(28 April 1904)328–330.

† 7. Review of L. Lévy-Bruhl's *The Philosophy of Auguste Comte*, 78(28 April 1904)335–336.

8. Notice of A. Clement Jones's *Notes on Analytical Geometry: An Appendix*, 78(19 May 1904)393.

9. Notice of John Hall Ryder's *Electric Traction*, 78(26 May 1904)411. Identification based on Harvard mss.

10. Notice of Hawkins' and Wallis' *The Dynamo*, 78(26 May 1904)411. Identification based on Harvard mss.

† 11. Review of William Turner's *History of Philosophy*, 79(7 July 1904)15–16.

† 12. Review of Robert A. Duff's *Spinoza's Political and Ethical Philosophy*, 79(21 July 1904)63.

13. Review of T. Clifford Allbutt's *Notes on the Composition of Scientific Papers*, 79(28 July 1904)84–85.

14. Notice of Roberdeau Buchanan's *The Mathematical Theory of Eclipses*, 79(25 Aug 1904)162.

† 15. Review of *The Collected Mathematical Papers of James Joseph Sylvester*, Vol. 1, 79(8 Sept 1904)203–204.

16. Review of Ch. Renouvier's *Les Derniers Entretiens* and John Dewey's *Studies in Logical Theory*, 79(15 Sept 1904)219–220. [CP] 8.188–190 are the review of Dewey's *Studies in Logical Theory*.

17. Review of Josiah Royce's *Outlines of Psychology*, 79(29 Sept 1904)264–265.

† 18. Review of George Malcolm Stratton's *Experimental Psychology and its Bearing upon Culture*, 79(17 Nov 1904)402–403.

19. Notices of J. Clark Murray's *Introduction to Psychology* and Florian Cajori's *Introduction to the Modern Theory of Equations*, 79(17 Nov 1904)396. Probably by Peirce; identification based on Harvard mss.

20. "The National Academy in New York," an article, 79(1 Dec 1904) 432–434.

21. Notice of J. C. Olsen's *Text-book of Quantitative Chemical Analysis*, 79(8 Dec 1904)460.

1905

1. Review of M. E. Boole's *The Preparation of the Child for Science*, 80(5 Jan 1905)18–19.

† 2. Review of Josiah Royce's *Herbert Spencer*, 80(26 Jan 1905)71–72.

† 3. Review of the Hon. R. J. Strutt's *The Becquerel Rays and the Properties of Radium*, 80(2 Feb 1905)100.

4. Review of Arthur Schuster's *An Introduction to the Theory of Optics*, 80(9 March 1905)198–199.

5. Review of R. Mullineux Walmsley's *Modern Practical Electricity*, 80(16 March 1905)218–219.

6. Notice of Gaston Laurent's *Les Grands Écrivains Scientifiques*, 80(23 March 1905)231.

7. Review of Alex. Findlay's *The Phase Rule and its Application*, 80(30 March 1905)255–256.

8. "The National Academy of Sciences," an article, 80(27 April 1905) 327–328.

9. Review of Robert Flint's *Philosophy as Scientia Scientiarum* and C. S. Peirce's *A Syllabus of Certain Topics of Logic*, 80(4 May 1905) 360–361. Identified in [Cohen]. Cf. [Bibliography]G–1903–2b.

10. Notice of J. Garcin's *N-Rays*, 80(11 May 1905)374.

11. Notice of Mendeléeff's *Principles of Chemistry*, 80(1 June 1905) 438.

12. Review of Robert Brandon Arnold's *Scientific Fact and Metaphysical Reality*, 80(1 June 1905)444–445.

† 13. Notice of Santayana's *The Life of Reason*, Vols. 1 and 2, 80(8 June 1905)461.

14. Notice of Ida Freund's *The Study of Chemical Composition*, 80(22 June 1905)503.

15. Review of Andrew Carnegie's *James Watt*, 80(29 June 1905) 527–528.

16. Notice of Gertrude Bacon's *Balloons, Airships, and Flying Machines*, 81(13 July 1905)33.

17. Notice of W. Hampson's *Radium Explained*, 81(13 July 1905)33–34.

† 18. Review of *Sociological Papers* (published by the Sociological Society) and Edward Alsworth Ross's *Foundations of Sociology*, 81(13 July 1905)42–43.

19. Review of Wilhelm Wundt's *Principles of Physiological Psychology*, Vol. 1, 81(20 July 1905)56–57. Also in *New York Evening Post* (21 July 1905)4:1–3. [CP] 8.196–204, except 201n3 ([Bibliography]G–c.1905–9) which is from a draft in Widener.

20. Notice of William James's "La Notion de Conscience," 81(3 Aug 1905)97. Also in *New York Evening Post* (31 July 1905) 4:3–4.

21. Review of Maurice de Fleury's *Nos Enfants au Collège*, 81(7 Sept 1905)205.

22. Review of Sir H. E. Roscoe and C. Schorlemmer's *A Treatise on Chemistry*, Vol. 1, 81(7 Sept 1905)205–206.

† 23. Review of Henry de Varigny's *La Nature et la Vie*, 81(5 Oct 1905)286–287.

24. Note on G. W. Hill's contributions to the theory of the moon, 81(19 Oct 1905)321.

25. Notice of Shields' *Philosophia Ultima*, 81(26 Oct 1905)340.

26. Notice of H. Carton de Wiart's *La Cité Ardente*, 81(9 Nov 1905) 382.

27. "The National Academy of Sciences at New Haven," an article, 81(23 Nov 1905)417–419.

28. Review of Edmund Gosse's *Sir Thomas Browne*, 81(14 Dec 1905) 486–488.

1906

† 1. Review of E. Rutherford's *Radio-Activity*, 82(18 Jan 1906)61.

2. Review of Alfred Russel Wallace's *My Life*, 82(22 Feb 1906)160–161.

† 3. Review of Elizabeth S. Haldane's *Descartes*, 82(22 March 1906) 242–243.

4. "Meeting of the National Academy of Sciences," an article, 82(26 April 1906)341–342.

5. Review of *Congress of Arts and Sciences, Universal Exposition, St. Louis, 1904*, Vol. 1, 82(7 June 1906) 475–476.

6. Review of Jacques Loeb's *The Dynamics of Living Matter* and Gustav Mann's *Chemistry of the Proteids*, 83(5 July 1906)17–18.

7. Review of H. E. Roscoe's *The Life and Experiences of Sir Henry Enfield Roscoe*, 83(12 July 1906)43.

8. Notice of Agnes M. Clerke's *System of the Stars*, 83(26 July 1906) 78. Identification based on Harvard mss.

9. Review of Thomas Marshall's *Aristotle's Theory of Conduct*, 83(13 Sept 1906)226–227.

10. Review of Horace William Brindley Joseph's *An Introduction to Logic*, 83(25 Oct 1906)353–354.

1907

1. Review of *The Scientific Papers of J. Willard Gibbs*, 2 vols., 84(24 Jan 1907)92.

2. Review of Ernest von Meyer's *A History of Chemistry*, 84(21 Feb 1907)181–182. Identification based on Harvard mss.

† 3. Review of James Mark Baldwin's *Functional Logic, or Genetic Theory of Knowledge*, Vol. 1 of *Thought and Things: A Study of the Development and Meaning of Thought; or Genetic Logic*, 84(28 Feb 1907)203–204. Identification based on Harvard mss.

4. Review of *The Collected Mathematical Works of George William Hill*, Vol. IV, 85(17 Oct 1907)355. At 85(31 Oct 1907)396 Peirce replies briefly to a letter from Simon Newcomb criticizing the review. Identification based on Harvard mss.

1908

† 1. Review of James Mark Baldwin's *Experimental Logic, or Genetic Theory of Thought*, Vol. 2 of *Thought and Things: A Study of the Development and Meaning of Thought, or Genetic Logic*, 87(20 Aug 1908) 164–165. Identification based on Harvard mss.

BIBLIOGRAPHY

III. MISCELLANEOUS

1. Archibald, Raymond C.
(a) "Benjamin Peirce's Linear Associative Algebra and C. S. Peirce," *The American Mathematical Monthly* 34(Dec 1927)525–527. This contains a note by Peirce on Jordan's *Traité des Substitutions et des Equations Algébriques*, dated 28 June 1910.
(b) *Semicentennial History of the American Mathematical Society, 1888–1938*, American Mathematical Society, New York, 1938, pp. 6 and 7. This contains information concerning Peirce's contributions to various newspapers.

2. Burks, Arthur W., "Icon, Index, and Symbol," *Philosophy and Phenomenological Research* 9(June 1949)674. This contains a brief description of a manuscript in iconic handwriting at Widener.

3. Calderoni. A draft of a letter to "Signor Calderoni" (probably Mario Calderoni), c.1905, in Widener VB2a. [CP] 8.205–213 are from it.

4. Carus, Paul.
(a) "The Founder of Tychism, His Methods, Philosophy, and Criticisms, In Reply to Mr. Charles S. Peirce," *The Monist* 3(July 1893)571–622. On p. 571 there is part of a letter from Peirce concerning his "Reply to the Necessitarians . . . ," [Bibliography]G–1891–1f.
† (b) "The Nature of Logical and Mathematical Thought," *The Monist* 20(Jan 1910)33–75. On p. 45 there is a fragment on non-Aristotelian logic from a letter "on sundry topics of modern logic" from Peirce to Francis C. Russell. There is a comment on this in a letter from Peirce to Carus, quoted in Paul Carus, "Non-Aristotelian Logic," *ibid.*, p. 158.
(c) Two letters in Widener VB2a. One of these letters bears no date but was probably written c.1910. [CP] 8.214–238 except 214n1 and 225n10 are from it. The other letter is dated 19 July 1910. [CP] 8.214n1 contains a quotation from it.

5. Dewey, John. Two letters in Widener VB2a. One of the letters is dated 9 June 1904. [CP] 8.239–242 are from it. The other letter is c.1905. [CP] 8.243–244 are from it. Part of the c.1905 letter is printed in [Bibliography] M–16a, pp. 215–216.

6. Eisele, Carolyn.
(a) "The *Liber Abaci* through the Eyes of Charles S. Peirce," *Scripta Mathematica* 17(Sept–Dec 1951)236–259. This contains a letter dated 1901 May 18 concerning Leonardo Fibonacci's *Liber Abaci* (from the Plimpton Collection at Columbia University), pp. 242–254 and 256–257; and a letter of 1903 (from the David Eugene Smith Library at Columbia University), pp. 254–255 and 258. See p. 255 for a reference to a card by Peirce in the David Eugene Smith Library.
(b) "The Scientist-Philosopher C. S. Peirce at the Smithsonian," *Journal of the History of Ideas* 18(Oct 1957)537–547. This contains correspondence between Samuel P. Langley and Peirce and material on related

Peirce mss. See [Bibliography]M-21a for another reference to Peirce-Langley correspondence.

(c) "The Charles S. Peirce-Simon Newcomb Correspondence," *Proceedings of the American Philosophical Society* 101(Oct 1957)409–433. Besides the correspondence this contains material on related Peirce mss.

7. Fisch, Max H.

(a) Reviews of W. H. Werkmeister's *A History of Philosophical Ideas in America* and of Philip P. Wiener's *Evolution and the Founders of Pragmatism, American Literature* 22(May 1950)185–189. This contains quotations concerning the Metaphysical Club at Cambridge from Peirce's unpublished papers.

(b) "General Introduction," *Classic American Philosophers* (edited by Max H. Fisch, et al.), Appleton-Century-Crofts, Inc., New York, 1951, pp. 1–39. This contains a quote from a letter to D. C. Gilman, p. 10, and references (including quotations) to mss., pp. 16–17, 24, 26, 29, and 32–33.

† (c) [Fisch]. This contains quotations from and references to Peirce mss., pp. 414, 415, 417, 440, and 443–444.

† (d) [Fisch-Cope]. This contains many references to and quotations from correspondence and mss. The following appendices also contain source materials: (II), Peirce to Gilman concerning the Johns Hopkins physics department, 13 Jan 1878, pp. 365–368; (III), Peirce's courses at Johns Hopkins University, pp. 369–370 (it is not clear from [JHUC] that Peirce taught Mill's Logic in 1880 as is indicated here on p. 369, and it seems to the present editor that the intention in [JHUC] is to state that Marquand taught this course); (IV), titles of papers read at the Metaphysical Club at Johns Hopkins University, pp. 371–374.

8. Garrison, Wendell Phillips. *Letters and Memorials of Wendell Phillips Garrison*, Houghton Mifflin, Boston and New York, 1909. This contains a letter to Garrison of 29 May 1905, p. 156; cf. p. 140.

9. Gilman, Daniel C. Jackson I. Cope, "William James' Correspondence with Daniel Coit Gilman, 1877–1881," *Journal of the History of Ideas* 12(Oct 1951)609–627. This contains a letter from Peirce to Gilman, dated 13 Sept 1877, pp. 615–616. See [Bibliography]M-7b and M-7d for other references to correspondence with Gilman.

10. Goudge, Thomas A., *The Thought of C. S. Peirce*, University of Toronto Press, 1950. Peirce's entry in the Harvard class book of 1859 (at the time of his graduation) is reprinted at pp. 347–349. The information contained here differs from that of Peirce's biography in the class book, *Harvard College, Records of the Class of 1859*, Cambridge, 1896, pp. 49–50 (cf. pp. 9, 74, 76, and 77).

Further biographical data, probably supplied by Peirce, are to be found in *American Men of Science*, 1906, p. 248, and 1910, p. 364, and in *The National Cyclopaedia of American Biography*, Vol. 8, 1900, p. 409.

Additional biographical information is given in Paul Weiss, "Charles Sanders Peirce," *Dictionary of American Biography*, Vol. 14, Charles Scribner's Sons, New York, 1937, pp. 398–403.

11. Harris, William T. A letter of 30 Nov 1868 in the Hoose Library of Philosophy, University of Southern California. [CP] 8.245–248. Cf. [Bibliography]G–1868–1a.

12. Huntington, Edward V., "Sets of Independent Postulates for the Algebra of Logic," *Transactions of the American Mathematical Society* 5(1904)288–309. On pp. 300–302 Huntington gives a proof of a distributive principle of which he says: "This demonstration is borrowed, almost verbatim, from a letter of Mr. C. S. Peirce's, dated December 24, 1903 . . ." (p. 300n*). There is also a quotation from a letter from Peirce, dated 14 Feb 1904, concerning this proof, p. 300n*. This quotation is reprinted at [CP] 3.200n* (p. 128); cf. 3.384n1 concerning this proof.

13. James, Henry. A letter to William James's son, Henry, dated 21 Sept 1910, is given in part in [Perry] II, 286–287.

14. James, William.
(a) [Perry]. This contains excerpts from 28 letters to William James: Vol. I: 536–538; Vol. II: 222–224, 407n5, 413–440. Cf. [CP] 8.249n1.
(b) Correspondence, 1897–1909, in the William James Collection, Houghton Library. [CP] 6.478n*, 8.117n10, and 8.249–315 are from it. Cf. [CP] 7.44n17 and 8.39n1.

15. Ladd-Franklin, Christine.
(a) A letter, dated 29 Aug 1891, in Widener VB2a. [CP] 8.316–318 are from it.
† (b) "Charles S. Peirce at the Johns Hopkins," *The Journal of Philosophy, Psychology and Scientific Methods* 13(21 Dec 1916)715–722. This contains four letters to Christine Ladd-Franklin, written in 1900 and later.

16. Royce, Josiah.
(a) James Harry Cotton, *Royce on the Human Self*, Harvard University Press, Cambridge, 1954. This contains part of the correspondence listed under [Bibliography]M–5 and parts of letters to Josiah Royce, pp. 300–301.
(b) Two letters in Widener VB2a. One of these letters is dated 27 May 1902. Quotations from it are at [CP] 8.117n10, 8.117n12, and 8.122n19. The other letter is dated 28 May 1902. A quotation from it is at [CP] 8.122n19.
(c) Josiah Royce and Fergus Kernan, "Charles Sanders Peirce," *The Journal of Philosophy, Psychology, and Scientific Methods* 13(21 Dec 1916)701–709. This contains information about the Harvard mss.

17. Russell, Francis C. A letter dated 14 July 1905 in Widener VB2a. A quotation from it is at [CP] 8.138n4. [Bibliography]M–4b contains a reference to another letter to Russell. See also [CP] 4.85n*.

18. Schiller, F. C. S. Two letters in Widener VB2. [CP] 8.319–320 are from an undated letter. [CP] 8.321–326 are from a letter of 10 Sept 1906.

19. Stokes, G. G. *Memoir and Scientific Correspondence of the Late Sir George Gabriel Stokes* (edited by Joseph Larmor), University Press,

Cambridge, 1907, 2 vols. In Vol. 2, pp. 309–313, there is a letter to Stokes, dated 14 Jan 1886 and Stokes's replies of 19 May and 17 June 1886.

20. Welby, Victoria (Lady).

† (a) *Charles S. Peirce's Letters to Lady Welby* (edited by Irwin C. Lieb), Whitlock's, Inc., New Haven, 1953. This contains 22 letters which are dated from 7 June 1903 to 25 July 1911, pp. 1–48. Photostat copies of these letters, including the deleted existential graphs of the letter of 31 Jan, 24 Feb, 14 March, 1909, are on deposit in the Yale University Library. See also Appendix B, pp. 51–55, on Peirce's classification of signs, and in this connection see Paul Weiss and Arthur W. Burks, "Peirce's Sixty-Six Signs," *The Journal of Philosophy* 42(5 July 1945) 383–388, which contains names of kinds of signs derived from the Harvard mss.

See *Other Dimensions: A Selection from the Later Correspondence of Victoria Lady Welby* (edited by Mrs. Henry Cust), Jonathan Cape, London, 1931, which contains some of Lady Welby's side of the Peirce-Welby correspondence as well as some of the correspondence in the book by Lieb cited above, pp. 144–150, 154–158, 161–164, 296–314. Part of the correspondence published in Lieb's book is also to be found in C. K. Ogden and I. A. Richards, *The Meaning of Meaning*, Harcourt, Brace and Company, New York, 1930, pp. 279–290.

* (b) Photostat copies of two letters in the Yale University Library. One of these letters, on signs and the categories, is dated 12 Oct 1904. [CP] 8.327–341 are from it. The other letter is dated 31 Jan, 24 Feb, and 14 March 1909. [CP] 8.342n15 contains a brief quotation from it. These letters are published in full in Lieb's book, (a) above.

A draft of a letter, on the classification of signs, in Widener IB3a, dated 24, 25, 28 Dec 1908. [CP] 8.342–379, except 368n23, are from it.

21. Wiener, Philip P.

† (a) "The Peirce-Langley Correspondence and Peirce's Manuscript on Hume and the Laws of Nature," *Proceedings of the American Philosophical Society* 91(5 April 1947)201–228. See [Bibliography]G–1901–2.

† (b) *Evolution and the Founders of Pragmatism*, Harvard University Press, Cambridge, 1949. This contains quotations from an unpublished letter on pragmatism to the editor of *The Sun*, pp. 20–21; and quotations from and references to correspondence and mss., pp. 21, 72–75, 81–82, 86, 95, 221–222, 252, and 260–261.

(c) *Values in a Universe of Chance*, to be published in 1958 by Doubleday & Company, Inc., New York, and by Stanford University Press, Stanford University. This is to contain some previously unpublished selections from the Peirce mss.

22. Woods, Frederick A. A letter, written during Oct and Nov 1913 in Widener VB2a. [CP] 8.380–388, except 380n4, are from it. See also [Bibliography]G–1905–1c for a quotation from this letter.

CROSS-REFERENCE INDEX

This index enables the reader to pass directly from any paragraph of *Collected Papers* I–VIII to the place or places in the chronologically-arranged bibliography where the paragraph is listed. In those cases where several items of different dates have been grouped together in the bibliography under one date, the dates appropriate to the particular items, not including revisions, are given in parentheses. Hence, the present index serves the auxiliary purpose of enabling a reader to determine the date assigned to a paragraph of *Collected Papers* I–VIII without further effort. It should be noted that sometimes a footnote and the paragraph to which it is attached have different bibliography references, e.g., [CP] 3.200 and 3.200n*.

BIBLIOGRAPHY

VOLUME I

BIBLIOGRAPHY

VOLUME II

Paragraph Number	Bibliography Item	Paragraph Number	Bibliography Item
1–202	G–c.1902–2	445–460	G–1893–5
203–218	G–1901–6 (1902)	461–516	G–1867–1b;
219–226	G–1903–2b		G–1893–6
227–229	G–c.1897–3	517–531	G–1883–7c; G–1893–5
230–232	G–1910–3	532–535	G–1893–5
233–272	G–1903–2c (c.1903)	536–547	G–1901–6 (1902)
273	G–1901–6 (1902)	548	G–1901–6
274–277	G–1903–2d (c.1902)	549	G–1901–6 (1902)
278–280	G–c.1895–1	550	G–1876–1
281	G–1893–5 (c.1895)	551–592	G–1901–6 (1902)
282	G–c.1893–3	593–600	G–1901–6
283–284	G–1903–2d (c.1902)	601–602	G–1901–6 (1902)
285	G–1893–5 (c.1895)	603–604	G–1901–6
286–291	G–c.1893–3	605–608	G–1901–6 (1902)
292–294	G–1903–2d (c.1902)	609–611	G–1901–6
295–296	G–c.1893–3	612–617	G–1901–6 (1902)
297–302	G–1893–5 (c.1895)	618	G–1901–6
303–304	G–1901–6 (1902)	619–644	G–1877–5f (1878);
305–306	G–1901–6		G–1893–6
307–308	G–1901–6 (1902)	645–660	G–1877–5c (1878);
309–331	G–1903–2d (c.1902)		G–1893–5;
332–356	G–c.1895–1		G–1893–6
357–390	G–1901–6 (1902)	661–668	G–1910–2
391–426	G–1867–1e;	669–693	G–1877–5d (1878);
	G–1893–5;		G–1893–6
	G–1893–6	694–754	G–1883–7b;
427–430	G–1893–7		G–1893–6
431–433	G–1901–6	755–772	G-c.1905–1
	(not by Peirce)	757n1	G–c.1902–1
434	G–1901–6	773–791	G–1901–6 (1902)
435–444	G–c.1893–3	792–807	G–1866–2b
444n1	G–c.1897–3		

BIBLIOGRAPHY

VOLUME III

Paragraph Number	Bibliography Item	Paragraph Number	Bibliography Item
1–19	G–1867–1a	359–403	G–1885–3
20–44	G–1867–1d	396n† (p. 230)	G–1889–3 (1891)
45–149	G–1870–1	403A–403M	G–1885–3 (c.1885)
45n*	G–1903–2a	404–424	G–1892–1b
150–151	G–1875–2	425–455	G–1896–6a
152–153	G–1877–4	456–552	G–1896–6b (1897)
154–251	G–1880–8	553–562	G–1898–2
154n1	G–1903–2	563–570	G–1900–1
200n* (p. 128)	M–12 (1904)	571–608	G–1903–2c (c.1903)
252–288	G–1881–7	609–615	G–1901–6
289–305	G–1881–10	616–643	G–1901–6 (1902)
306–322	G–1882–1	644–645	G–1901–6
323	G–1882–3		(not by Peirce)
324–327	G–1882–8	646–648	G–1883–1
328–358	G–1883–7d; G–1893–5		

VOLUME IV

Paragraph Number	Bibliography Item	Paragraph Number	Bibliography Item
1–5	G–1898–1	530–572	G–1905–1c (1906)
6–11	G–1905–1h (c.1906)	534n1	G–1905–1h (c.1906)
12–20	G–c.1880–1		
21–152	G–1893–5	553n1 (p. 441)	G–1905–1h (c.1906)
118n1	G–1889–3		
153–169	G–c.1897–4	553n2	G–1905–1e (c.1906)
170–226	G–1897–1		
187n1	G–1892–1b	561n1	G–1905–1e (c.1906)
227–323	G–c.1902–2 (1902)		
324–330	G–c.1904–1	564n1	G–1905–1f (c.1906)
331–340	G–c.1905–3		
341–346	G–1905–6	573–584	G–1906–2
347–349	G–1901–6 (1902)	585–593	G–1908–1a
350–371	G–c.1903–3	594–642	G–1908–1b
372–393	G–1901–6 (1902)	643–646	G–1908–1c (1909)
394–417	G–1903–2b	647–681	G–1908–1e (c.1909)
418–509	G–c.1903–2		
510–529	G–1903–2a		

327

BIBLIOGRAPHY

VOLUME V

Paragraph Number	Bibliography Item	Paragraph Number	Bibliography Item
1–4	G–1901–6 (1902)	402n3	G–1905–1b (1906)
5–10	G–c.1907–1b	411–437	G–1905–1a
	(c.1905)	438–463	G–1905–1b
11–13	G–c.1907–1c	448n1	G–1905–1d
	(c.1906)	464–496	G–c.1907–1c
13n1	G–1889–3 (c.1902)		(c.1906)
14–212	G–1903–1	497–501	G–c.1905–7
213–263	G–1868–2a;	502–537	G–c.1905–8
	G–1893–6	538–545	G–c.1902–3
264–317	G–1868–2b;	546–548	G–c.1908–1
	G–1893–6	549–554	G–1905–1d (1906)
318–357	G–1868–2c (1869);	555–564	G–c.1906–1
	G–1893–6	565–573	G–1901–6 (1902)
358–387	G–1877–5a;	574–589	G–1898–1
	G–1893–5;	590–604	G–1903–2a
	G–1893–6	605–606	G–1901–6
358n*	G–1909–1	607–609	G–1901–6 (1902)
388–410	G–1877–5b (1878);	610–614	G–1906–1
	G–1893–5;		
	G–1893–6		

VOLUME VI

Paragraph Number	Bibliography Item	Paragraph Number	Bibliography Item
1–5	G–1898–1	349–352	G–c.1902–2
6	G–c.1903–4	353–383	G–1901–6 (1902)
7–34	G–1891–1a	384	G–1901–6
35–65	G–1891–1b (1892)	385–394	G–1901–6 (1902)
66–87	G–1898–1	395–427	G–1877–5e
88–97	G–1903–2a		(1878); G–1893–6
98–101	G–1901–6 (1902)	428–434	G–1893–1
102–163	G–1891–1c (1892)	435–448	G–1893–3
164	G–1889–3	449–451	G–c.1895–2
165–168	G–1889–3 (1903)	452–485	G–1908–2
169–173	G–1901–6 (1902)	478n*	M–14b (1908)
174–176	G–1905–1e (1906)	486–491	G–c.1910–1
177–184	G–c.1911–1	492–493	G–c.1896–1
185–237	G–1898–1	494–521	G–c.1906–2
238–271	G–1891–1d (1892)	522–547	G–1901–2b
241n1	G–1889–3		(c.1901)
	(1890–91)	548–556	G–1887–1
272–277	G–c.1893–2	557–587	G–c.1905–2
278–286	G–1893–5	588–618	G–1891–1f (1893)
287–317	G–1891–1e (1893)	619–624	G–1868–1a
318–348	G–1908–1e	625–630	G–1868–1b
	(c.1909)		

328

BIBLIOGRAPHY

VOLUME VII

BIBLIOGRAPHY

VOLUME VIII

Paragraph Number	Bibliography Item	Paragraph Number	Bibliography Item
1–6	G–1867–2	171–175	N–1903–21
7–38	G–1871–1	176	G–1903–2a
39–54	G–c.1885–3	176n3	G–1902–6
55–71	N–1891–1	177–185	G–undated–8
72–90	G–c.1891–1	186–187	G–c.1903–6
91–96	N–1892–2	188–190	N–1904–16
93n2	G–undated–6	191–195	G–c.1904–3
97–99	G–undated–7	196–204	N–1905–19
100–107	N–1900–15	201n3	G–c.1905–9
108–116	G–c.1900–2	205–213	M–3 (c.1905)
117(part)–120(part),		214–238	M–4c (c.1910)
121–125	G–c.1902–4	214n1	M–4c (1910)
117n12	M–16b (1902)	225n10	G–1904–4
122n19	M–16b (1902)	239–242	M–5 (1904)
117(part), 120(part),		243–244	M–5 (c.1905)
126–130	N–1902–10	245–248	M–11 (1868)
117n10 (in part)	M–14b (1902)	249–315	M–14b (1897–1909)
117n10 (in part)	M–16b (1902)	316–318	M–15a (1891)
131	G–c.1902–4	319–320	M–18 (undated)
132–152	G–1901–1	321–326	M–18 (1906)
136n3	G–1901–1 (c.1900)	327–341	M–20b (1904)
138n4	M–17 (1905)	342–379	M–20b (1908)
153–156	G–1901–1 (c.1900)	342n15	M–20b (1909)
157–163	N–1901–15	368n23	G–undated–16
158n3	G–1901–8	380–388	M–22 (1913)
164–167 (part)	N–1903–10	380n4	G–undated–17
167 (part)–170	G–c.1903–5		

330

INDEX OF PROPER NAMES*

* The numbers refer to paragraphs, not to pages.

INDEX OF PROPER NAMES

INDEX OF PROPER NAMES

INDEX OF SUBJECTS*

* The numbers refer to paragraphs, not to pages.

334

INDEX OF SUBJECTS

of events 319f
of genus of argument 2
Determine, of signs 177ff, 191, 319, 361
Determinism 309
Diagram
    and signs 335, 358, 360
    in deduction 209
    see also Icon
Dialectic 39, 52, 54, 110, 149
Dialecticism 138
Dicent 337f, 341
Dictionary 164, 169
Dilemma 48, 244
Dimness, of idea 329
Direct, in mind 354
Discovery 136
    see also Abduction
Distance, measurement of 95, 112
Distinctions
    between sciences 297
    dyadic 240
    moral 47
    out of mind 20
Distributive 363f
Doubt
    and belief 45, 270
    idle 191
    settlement of 101
    see also Belief, Surprise
Dream
    and reality 12, 30, 43, 126, 191
    and signs 315
Dualism 123, 145
    Cartesian 30, 58
    cognitive 106
Duality, of consciousness 290
Duns Scotus and realism 18ff
Dynamics 187, 197f, 202

Education 175
Educationalism 138f
Effect
    and cause 187
    of sign 191, 314
    on conduct 262
    practical 43, 119, 201n3
    psychological 326
Effort
    and mind 346
    in secondness 266, 330

Ego 103, 113, 144, 290
    in secondness 266, 330
    see also Mind, Self
Egoism 49
Ejaculative sign 369
Elements
    brute 110, 272
    chemical 239
    humanistic 258
    hypothetical 93n2
    mental 80
    psychical, of percepts 144
Emotion 270
    see also Feelings
Empiricism 37
    English 21
Encyclopaedia 164, 378
    Britannica 342
End
    in the universe 44
    of inquiry 104
    the 256
    ultimate 52
Entelism 138
Entia non sunt multiplicanda praeter necessitatem 20n6
Entity
    consciousness as an 279, 285, 287, 293
    hypostatized 193
Error 2, 149, 282, 379
    and truth 12, 41
    in general belief 16
Esthetics, *see* Aesthetics
Ether 122n19, 168, 275
Ethics 46, 135, 139ff, 158f, 166f, 202
    and logic 242, 255
    of the evil eye 53
Euclid's geometry 92f
Events, determination of 319f
Evidence 224, 251
    and pragmatism 259
Evil, problem of 263
Evolution
    and natural history 239
    of natural ideas 97, 99
    of the world 317f
Evolutionism 58, 138f
Exertion, in molition 303f
Existence 12, 16, 18f, 22, 29f, 33f, 110, 208, 262, 330
    and thought 283
    extending 136n3

INDEX OF SUBJECTS

339

INDEX OF SUBJECTS

INDEX OF SUBJECTS

342

INDEX OF SUBJECTS

INDEX OF SUBJECTS

INDEX OF SUBJECTS

INDEX OF SUBJECTS

INDEX OF SUBJECTS

INDEX OF SUBJECTS

and universality 18
in consciousness 290
of inquiry 102
of proposition 41
of sign 181, 352
see also Index
Subsequent, and previous 330
Substances, in metaphysics 92
Substantive 183
Succession
and numbers 221
and time 114
infinite 225
Suggestion, and inference 63, 66f, 71
see also Association
Suggestive, in trichotomies of signs 371
Summum bonum 133, 138n4
Superstition 22, 171
Supply and demand
law of 38
ratio of 6
Surprise 270
and signs 315
see also Inquiry
Surprising
element in experience 346
state of things 229
Suspicion 270
Swedenborgianism 58
Syllogism 68
in kinds of reasoning 209
Symbol 119
and pragmatism 323
and sciences 342
and signs 335, 337, 341, 368
and thirdness 268
purport of 208f
see also Sign
Sympathetic, in trichotomies of signs 370
Symptom 313
of disease, and signs 119, 185, 335
Syncategorematics, implied 20
Synderesis 162
Synechism 244, 252, 257
System
in mechanics 187
of signs 179, 181

Tendency
agnostic 168
and sign 361, 367

in evolution 317
of universe 44
Term
and signs 337
general 26, 41, 356
in unconscious inference 67
logical 11, 20
technical 162, 169, 319
Terminology 162, 169, 191, 301
Tertium quid 129, 131, 168, 274
Theism 138n4, 262
Theology, and philosophy 109
Theorem
in geometry 92
of pragmatism 191
Theory
and fact 113, 148
and religion 202
Darwinian 133
in abduction 209
in philosophy 108
physical 148
pure 158
recommendation of a 223
Thereness, brute 195
Thinking 191, 199
and pragmaticism 206
and reality 13
Hegel's grades of 213
purpose of 211
see also Reasoning
Third *and* Thirdness 268, 328, 330ff
see also Argument, Law, Thought
This 18
Thomists 291
Thought 80, 85, 88, 90, 103, 144, 191, 275, 283
actualization of 250
and designations 368n23
and matter 168
and pragmatism 261
and reality 12f, 14, 16f, 18, 25, 29f, 40, 153, 284
and sign 332, 339, 343
and the categories 256
classification of 213
compulsions of 101
development of 45
economy of 43
end of 272
function of 201n3
Hegel's stages of 45, 174, 267f, 329

350

INDEX OF SUBJECTS

351

INDEX OF SUBJECTS

COLLECTED PAPERS OF CHARLES SANDERS PEIRCE

Eight Volumes in Four

Volumes I and II, edited by Charles Hartshorne and Paul Weiss
PRINCIPLES OF PHILOSOPHY
  I. General Historical Orientation
  II. The Classification of the Sciences
  III. Phenomenology
  IV. The Normative Sciences

ELEMENTS OF LOGIC
  I. General and Historical Survey of Logic
  II. Speculative Grammar
  III. Critical Logic

Volumes III and IV, edited by Charles Hartshorne and Paul Weiss
EXACT LOGIC (Published Papers)
THE SIMPLEST MATHEMATICS
  I. Logic and Mathematics
  II. Existential Graphs
  III. The Amazing Mazes

Volumes V and VI, edited by Charles Hartshorne and Paul Weiss
PRAGMATISM AND PRAGMATICISM
  I. Lectures on Pragmatism
  II. Published Papers
  III. Unpublished Papers

SCIENTIFIC METAPHYSICS
  I. Ontology and Cosmology
  II. Religion

Volumes VII and VIII, edited by Arthur W. Burks
SCIENCE AND PHILOSOPHY
  I. Experimental Science
  II. Scientific Method
  III. Philosophy of Mind

REVIEWS, CORRESPONDENCE, AND BIBLIOGRAPHY
  I. Reviews
  II. Correspondence
  III. Bibliography